Student's Solutions Manual to Accompany

ALGEBRA & TRIGONOMETRY

SECOND EDITION

1¼1700

David Cohen
Department of Mathematics
University of California-Los Angeles

Prepared by
Ross Rueger
Department of Mathematics
College of the Sequoias

West Publishing Company
St. Paul   New York   Los Angeles   San Francisco

COPYRIGHT © 1989 by WEST PUBLISHING CO.
50 W. Kellogg Boulevard
P.O. Box 64526
St. Paul, MN 55164-1003

Printed in the United States of America
96 95 94 93 92 91 90 89   8 7 6 5 4 3 2 1 0
ISBN 0-314-52473-8

CONTENTS

PREFACE   vii

CHAPTER 1   FUNDAMENTAL CONCEPTS

1.1   Notation and Language   1
1.2   Properties of the Real Numbers   5
1.3   Sets of Real Numbers   7
1.4   Absolute Value   10
1.5   Integer Exponents. Scientific Notation   14
1.6   Nth Roots   18
1.7   Rational Exponents   22
1.8   Polynomials   25
1.9   Factoring   32
1.10 Fractional Expressions   36
1.11 The Complex Number System   44
       Chapter 1 Review Exercises   50

CHAPTER 2   EQUATIONS AND INEQUALITIES

2.1   Linear Equations   61
2.2   Quadratic Equations   69
2.3   Applications   78
2.4   Other Types of Equations   88
2.5   Inequalities. More About Absolute Value   99
2.6   More On Inequalities   108
       Chapter 2 Review Exercises   126

CHAPTER 3 COORDINATES AND GRAPHS

3.1	Rectangular Coordinates	151
3.2	Graphs and Symmetry	162
3.3	Slope	187
3.4	Equations of Lines	197
	Chapter 3 Review Exercises	218

CHAPTER 4 FUNCTIONS

4.1	The Definition of a Function	233
4.2	The Graph of a Function	245
4.3	Techniques in Graphing	264
4.4	Methods of Combining Functions	284
4.5	Inverse Functions	298
4.6	Variation	314
	Chapter 4 Review Exercises	320

CHAPTER 5 POLYNOMIAL FUNCTIONS AND RATIONAL FUNCTIONS

5.1	Linear and Quadratic Functions	335
5.2	Applied Functions: Setting Up Equations	346
5.3	Maximum and Minimum Problems	365
5.4	Polynomial Functions	378
5.5	Graphs of Rational Functions	388
	Chapter 5 Review Exercises	407

CHAPTER 6 EXPONENTIAL AND LOGARITHMIC FUNCTIONS

6.1	Exponential Functions	421
6.2	The Exponential Function $y = e^x$	428
6.3	Logarithmic Functions	437
6.4	Properties of Logarithms	446
6.5	Applications	457
	Chapter 6 Review Exercises	466

CHAPTER 7 TRIGONOMETRIC FUNCTIONS OF ANGLES

7.1	Trigonometric Functions of Acute Angles	479
7.2	Right Triangle Applications	487
7.3	Trigonometric Functions of General Angles	495
7.4	Algebra and the Trigonometric Functions	503
	Chapter 7 Review Exercises	510

CHAPTER 8 TRIGONOMETRIC FUNCTIONS OF REAL NUMBERS

8.1	Radian Measure	525
8.2	Trigonometric Functions of Real Numbers	530
8.3	The Addition Formulas	535
8.4	Further Identities	541
8.5	Graphs of the Sine and Cosine Functions	560
8.6	Graphs of the Tangent and the Reciprocal Functions	573
8.7	Trigonometric Equations	587
8.8	The Inverse Trigonometric Functions	592
	Chapter 8 Review Exercises	601

CHAPTER 9 ADDITIONAL TOPICS IN TRIGONOMETRY

9.1	The Law of Sines and the Law of Cosines	621
9.2	Vectors in the Plane, Part 1: A Geometric Approach	631
9.3	Vectors in the Plane, Part 2: An Algebraic Approach	643
9.4	Introduction to Polar Coordinates	647
9.5	Trigonometric Form for Complex Numbers	655
	Chapter 9 Review Exercises	667

CHAPTER 10 SYSTEMS OF EQUATIONS

10.1	Systems of Two Linear Equations in Two Unknowns	681
10.2	Gaussian Elimination	699
10.3	Matrices	719
10.4	The Inverse of a Square Matrix	729
10.5	Determinants and Cramer's Rule	739
10.6	Nonlinear Systems of Equations	752
10.7	Systems of Inequalities: Linear Programming	760
	Chapter 10 Review Exercises	779

CHAPTER 11 ROOTS OF POLYNOMIAL EQUATIONS

11.1	More on Division of Polynomials	815
11.2	Roots of Polynomial Equations: The Remainder Theorem and the Factor Theorem	818
11.3	The Fundamental Theorem of Algebra	824
11.4	Rational and Irrational Roots	827
11.5	Conjugate Roots and Descartes's Rule of Signs	837
	Chapter 11 Review Exercises	843

CHAPTER 12 THE CONIC SECTIONS

12.1	The Parabola	855
12.2	The Ellipse	865
12.3	The Hyperbola	875
	Chapter 12 Review Exercises	889

CHAPTER 13 ADDITIONAL TOPICS IN ALGEBRA

13.1	Mathematical Induction	901
13.2	The Binomial Theorem	909
13.3	Introduction to Sequences and Series	914
13.4	Arithmetic Sequences and Series	920
13.5	Geometric Sequences and Series	926
13.6	Permutations and Combinations	930
13.7	Introduction to Probability	933
	Chapter 13 Review Exercises	936

PREFACE

This solutions manual contains complete solutions to all odd exercises of David Cohen's <u>Algebra and Trigonometry</u>. I have attempted to format solutions for readability and accuracy, and apologize to you for any errors that you may encounter.

Please use this manual with some degree of caution. Be sure that you have attempted a solution, and re-attempted it, before you look it up in this manual. Mathematics can only be learned by **doing**, and not by observing. As you use this manual, do not just read the solution but work it along with the manual, using my solution to check your work. If you use this manual in that fashion, then it should be helpful to you in your learning. Solutions have been written in the same format as the textbook, however your instructor may prefer an alternate method.

I would like to thank a number of people for their assistance in preparing this manual. Thanks go to David Cohen, Peter Marshall, Mark Jacobsen, and Maralene Bates of West Educational Publishing. Special thanks to Susan Gerstein for her meticulous error-checking of my work. Most especially, I would like to thank Diana Schnelback who dedicated three months of her life to type this manuscript. I am eternally grateful to her. As always, I thank my parents for providing my education and my lovely wife Barbara for putting up with me!

This book is dedicated in memory of Bill Olstad.

Ross Rueger
March, 1989

CHAPTER 1
FUNDAMENTAL CONCEPTS

1.1 Notation and Language

1. $x^5 y^2$

3. $(x + 1)^3$

5. (a) $4x$
   (b) $3(x^2 + 1)$ or $3x^2 + 3$

7. (a) $3a + 2b$
   (b) $3a^2 + 2b^2$

9. (a) $(2a + 1)^3 (2b + 1)^2$
   (b) $(2a + 1)^3 (2b + 1)^2$ Note that $1 + 2a = 2a + 1$ and that $1 + 2b = 2b + 1$

11. $x + 3y = 4 + 3(6) = 22$

13. $a^2 + b^2 = 3^2 + 4^2 = 9 + 16 = 25$

15. $x^2 - 4y^2 = 10^2 - 4(4)^2 = 100 - 64 = 36$

17. $x^2 - x + 1 = 5^2 - 5 + 1 = 25 - 5 + 1 = 21$

19. $2x^3 - 3y^2 = 2(3)^3 - 3(2)^2 = 54 - 12 = 42$

21. $1 \div a^2 + b^2 = (1 \div 1^2) + 1^2 = 1 + 1 = 2$

23. $\dfrac{1}{a^2} + \dfrac{1}{b^2} - \dfrac{1}{a^2 + b^2}$
$$= \frac{1}{(1/2)^2} + \frac{1}{(1/2)^2} - \frac{1}{(1/2)^2 + (1/2)^2}$$
$$= \frac{1}{1/4} + \frac{1}{1/4} - \frac{1}{(1/4) + (1/4)}$$
$$= 4 + 4 - \frac{1}{1/2}$$
$$= 8 - 2$$
$$= 6$$

25. (a) $x^{y^z} = 2^{2^3} = 2^8 = 256$
(b) $x^{y^z} = 2^{3^2} = 2^9 = 512$
(c) $x^{y^z} = 3^{2^2} = 3^4 = 81$

27. $(2^3)^4 = 8^4 = 4{,}096$ while $2^{3^4} = 2^{81}$, which is much larger (2 followed by 24 zeros!)

29. $x + 2$ ($2 + x$ is also correct)

31. $4(a + b^2)$

33. $x^2 + y^2$

35. $x + 2x^2$

37. $\dfrac{x + y + z}{3}$

39. $\dfrac{x^2 + y^2 + z^2}{3}$

41. $2xy - 1$

43. area: $\pi(3y)^2 = 9\pi y^2$
circumference: $2\pi(3y) = 6\pi y$

45. $V = \dfrac{4}{3}(\pi r^3) = \dfrac{4}{3}\pi(3x)^3 = \dfrac{4}{3}\pi(27x^3) = 4\pi(9x^3) = 36\pi x^3$
The required formula, therefore, is $V = 36\pi x^3$.

47. (a) $V = \pi r^2 h = \pi r^2 (r) = \pi r^3$. The required formula, therefore, is $V = \pi r^3$.
     (b) $V = \pi (4)^3 = 64\pi$ cm^3

49. 10.8 cm^3

51. 86.8 cm^3

53. (a) Since the height of the cylinder is 2r, its volume is given by $\pi r^2(2r)$. That is, the volume of the cylinder is $2\pi r^3$. Thus, we have:
$$\frac{\text{volume cylinder}}{\text{volume sphere}} = \frac{2\pi r^3}{(4/3)\pi r^3} = \frac{2}{(4/3)} = \frac{3}{2}$$

     (b) $$\frac{\text{area cylinder}}{\text{area sphere}} = \frac{2\pi r^2 + 2\pi r(2r)}{4\pi r^2} = \frac{6\pi r^2}{4\pi r^2} = \frac{3}{2}$$

55. (a) Denote the width by w. Then the length is 2w and the height is 6w. So the volume V is given by $V = w(2w)(6w) = 12w^3$. Thus, the required formula is $V = 12w^3$.

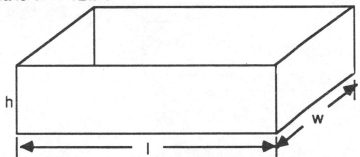

     (b) The front face and the back face each have an area of lh. The two side faces each have an area of wh , and the top and bottom faces   each have an area of lw. So, the total area S is given by:
     $S = 2lh + 2wh + 2lw$.
     Now from part (a) we have $l = 2w$ and $h = 6w$. Thus, our equation for S becomes:
     $S = 2(2w)(6w) + 2w(6w) + 2(2w)w$
        $= 24w^2 + 12w^2 + 4w^2$
        $= 40w^2$
     The required formula is, therefore, $S = 40w^2$.

57. (a) 1.12

(b) $\dfrac{\text{volume}}{\text{area}} = \dfrac{\pi r^2 h}{2\pi r^2 + 2\pi rh} = \dfrac{\pi r^3}{4\pi r^2} = \dfrac{r}{4} = \dfrac{4.48}{4} = 1.12$

59. (a) $\dfrac{1000}{19 - \dfrac{12}{1 - \dfrac{1}{x}}} = \dfrac{1000}{19 - \dfrac{12}{1 - \dfrac{1}{3}}}$

$= \dfrac{1000}{19 - \dfrac{12}{2/3}}$

$= \dfrac{1000}{19 - 18}$

$= \dfrac{1000}{1}$

$= 1000$

(b) $\dfrac{1}{1 + \dfrac{1}{1 + \dfrac{1}{1 + \dfrac{1}{x}}}} = \dfrac{1}{1 + \dfrac{1}{1 + \dfrac{1}{1 + \dfrac{1}{2}}}}$

$= \dfrac{1}{1 + \dfrac{1}{1 + \dfrac{1}{3/2}}}$

$= \dfrac{1}{1 + \dfrac{1}{1 + \dfrac{2}{3}}}$

$= \dfrac{1}{1 + \dfrac{1}{5/3}}$

$= \dfrac{1}{1 + 3/5}$

$= \dfrac{1}{8/5}$

$= \dfrac{5}{8}$

1.2 Properties of the Real Numbers

1. 832

3. 4410

5. (a) $A^2 + 2AB + B^2$
    (b) $A^2 - B^2$
    (c) $A^2 - 2AB + B^2$

7. (a) $x^2 + 4xy + 4y^2$
    (b) $x^2 - 4y^2$
    (c) $x^2 - 4xy + 4y^2$

9. (a) $A(x^2 - x + 1) = Ax^2 - Ax + A$

    (b) $(x + 1)(x^2 - x + 1) = (x + 1)x^2 + (x + 1)(-x) + (x + 1)(1)$
    $$= x^3 + x^2 - x^2 - x + x + 1$$
    $$= x^3 + 1$$

11. commutative property of addition

13. additive inverse property

15. associative property of addition

17. associative property of multiplication

19. identity property for addition

21. closure property with respect to addition

23. distributive property

25. $1 + 2(-3)(4) = 1 - 24 = -23$

27. $4 - (-3 + 5) = 4 - (2) = 2$

29. $-\left((-1)^4\right) = -\left((-1)(-1)(-1)(-1)\right) = -(1) = -1$

31. $1 - \{1 - [-(-1 - 1)]\} = 1 - \{1 - [-(-2)]\} = 1 - \{1 - [2]\} = 1 - (-1) = 2$

33. $\dfrac{7}{5} + \dfrac{2}{3} = \dfrac{21 + 10}{15} = \dfrac{31}{15}$

35. $\dfrac{7}{x} - \dfrac{12}{x} = \dfrac{7 - 12}{x} = -\dfrac{5}{x}$

37. $\dfrac{x^2 + y^2}{x + y} - \dfrac{x^2 - y^2}{x + y}$ $= \dfrac{(x^2 + y^2) - (x^2 - y^2)}{x + y}$

$= \dfrac{x^2 + y^2 - x^2 + y^2}{x + y}$

$= \dfrac{2y^2}{x + y}$

39. $\dfrac{7}{12} \cdot \left(-\dfrac{7}{3}\right) = -\dfrac{49}{36}$

41. $\dfrac{2}{5} \div \dfrac{7}{3} = \dfrac{2}{5} \cdot \dfrac{3}{7} = \dfrac{6}{35}$

43. $1 \div \left(\dfrac{2}{3} + 1\right) = 1 \div \left(\dfrac{2}{3} + \dfrac{3}{3}\right) = 1 \div \left(\dfrac{5}{3}\right) = 1 \cdot \dfrac{3}{5} = \dfrac{3}{5}$

45. (a) $\dfrac{\dfrac{4}{3} + \dfrac{1}{2}}{\dfrac{11}{6} + \dfrac{5}{4}} = \dfrac{12\left(\dfrac{4}{3} + \dfrac{1}{2}\right)}{12\left(\dfrac{11}{6} + \dfrac{5}{4}\right)} = \dfrac{16 + 6}{12 + 15} = \dfrac{22}{37}$

    (b) -1 (according to the rule $\dfrac{a - b}{b - a} = -1$)

47. -1 (according to the rule $\dfrac{a - b}{b - a} = -1$)

49. $\dfrac{12}{12} \cdot \dfrac{\dfrac{1}{2} - \dfrac{1}{3} + \dfrac{1}{4}}{\dfrac{1}{2} + \dfrac{1}{3} - \dfrac{1}{4}} = \dfrac{12\left(\dfrac{1}{2} - \dfrac{1}{3} + \dfrac{1}{4}\right)}{12\left(\dfrac{1}{2} + \dfrac{1}{3} - \dfrac{1}{4}\right)} = \dfrac{6 - 4 + 3}{6 + 4 - 3} = \dfrac{5}{7}$

51. $(-2)^2 - 8(-2) - 4 = 4 + 16 - 4 = 16$

53. $8(-1/2)^3 - 4(-1/2)^2 - 4(-1/2) = 8(-1/8) - 4(1/4) + 2 = -1 - 1 + 2 = 0$

55. $1 - (-1) - (-1)^2 - (-1)^3 - (-1)^4 = 1 + 1 - 1 + 1 - 1 = 1$

57. $d^2 = [-1 - (-2)]^2 + [6 - (-6)]^2$
    $= (-1 + 2)^2 + (6 + 6)^2$
    $= 1^2 + 12^2$
    $= 145$

59. $\dfrac{a}{c} = \dfrac{b}{d} \Leftrightarrow ad = cd \Leftrightarrow ad = bc \Leftrightarrow \dfrac{a}{b} = \dfrac{c}{d}$

61. $\dfrac{a-b}{b} = \dfrac{c-d}{d} \qquad \Leftrightarrow \qquad (a-b)d = b(c-d)$

    $\Leftrightarrow \qquad ad - bd = bc - bd$

    $\Leftrightarrow \qquad ad = bc$

    $\Leftrightarrow \qquad \dfrac{a}{b} = \dfrac{c}{d}$

63. $y = -1.6$ (to two significant digits)

65. (a)

x	1	1.250	1.500	1.750	2.000	2.250
y	0	.2880	.3704	.3848	.3750	.3567

   (b) $x = 1.750$
   (c) $y = .3849$

1.3 Sets of Real Numbers

1.   (a) nat., int., rat.
     (b) int., rat.

3.   (a) rat.
     (b) irr.

5.   (a) nat., int., rat.
     (b) rat.

7.   (a) rat.
     (b) rat.

9.   irr.

11. nat., int., rat

13. (a) $\dfrac{54}{10} = \dfrac{27}{5}$

   (b) Let $x = 5.\overline{4}$ Then $10x = 54.\overline{4}$ and $10x - x = 49$. Thus $9x = 49$, and consequently $x = \dfrac{49}{9}$.

15. (a) $\dfrac{99}{100}$

   (b) Let $x = 0.\overline{9}$ Then $10x = 9.\overline{9}$, and $10x - x = 9$. Thus $9x = 9$, and consequently $x = 1$.

17. (a) $\dfrac{17}{10}$

   (b) Let $x = 1.\overline{7}$ Then $10x = 17.\overline{7}$, and $10x - x = 16$. Thus $9x = 16$, and consequently $x = \dfrac{16}{9}$.

19.

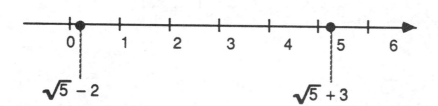

21.

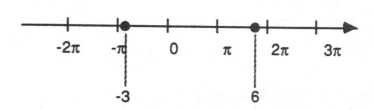

23. false

25. true

27. false

29. (a)

(b)

31. (a)

(b)

33.

35.

37. Let $x = 0.\overline{19}$ Then $100x - x = 19.\overline{19} - 0.\overline{19} = 19$.

Thus $99x = 19$ and $x = \dfrac{19}{99}$.

39. Let $x = 0.3\overline{12}$ Then $1000x - 10x = 312.\overline{12} - 3.\overline{12} = 309$

Thus $990x = 309$ and $x = \dfrac{309}{990}$, which reduces to $\dfrac{103}{330}$.

41. (a) The common value to six decimal places is 3.863703
    (b) The common value to six decimal places is 3.162277
    (c) The common value to six decimal places is 1.847759
    (d) The common value to six decimal places is 1.414213

1.4 Absolute Value

1. $|3| = 3$

3. $|-6| = 6$

5. $|-1 + 3| = |2| = 2$

7. $\left|-\dfrac{4}{5}\right| - \dfrac{4}{5} = \dfrac{4}{5} - \dfrac{4}{5} = 0$

9. $|-6 + 2| - |4| = |-4| - |4| = 4 - 4 = 0$

11. $\big| |-8| + |-9| \big| = |8 + 9| = |17| = 17$

13. $\left|\dfrac{27 - 5}{5 - 27}\right| = \left|\dfrac{22}{-22}\right| = |-1| = 1$

15. $|7\,(-8)| - |7|\,|-8| = |-56| - 7(8) = 56 - 56 = 0$

17. $|a - b|^2 = |-2 - 3|^2 = |-5|^2 = (5)^2 = 25$

19. $|c| - |b| - |a| = |-4| - |3| - |-2| = 4 - 3 - 2 = -1$

21. $\begin{aligned}|a + b|^2 - |b + c|^2 &= |-2 + 3|^2 - |3 + (-4)|^2 \\ &= |1|^2 - |-1|^2 \\ &= (1)^2 - (1)^2 \\ &= 1 - 1 \\ &= 0\end{aligned}$

23. $\begin{aligned}\dfrac{a + b + |a - b|}{2} &= \dfrac{-2 + 3 + |-2 - 3|}{2} \\[2mm] &= \dfrac{1 + |-5|}{2} \\[2mm] &= \dfrac{1 + 5}{2} \\[2mm] &= \dfrac{6}{2} \\[2mm] &= 3\end{aligned}$

25. $\left| \sqrt{2} - 1 \right| - 1 = (\sqrt{2} - 1) - 1$ since $\sqrt{2} > 1$
$$= \sqrt{2} - 2$$

27. If $x \geq 3$, then $\left| x - 3 \right| = x - 3$

29. $\left| t^2 + 1 \right| = t^2 + 1$, since $t^2 + 1 > 0$

31. $\left| -\sqrt{3} - 4 \right| = -(-\sqrt{3} - 4)$ since $-\sqrt{3} - 4 < 0$
$$= \sqrt{3} + 4$$

33. If $x < 3$, then $x - 3 < 0$ and $x - 4 < 0$. Thus:
$$\left| x - 3 \right| + \left| x - 4 \right| = -(x - 3) + -(x - 4)$$
$$= -x + 3 - x + 4$$
$$= -2x + 7$$

35. If $3 < x < 4$, then $x - 3 < 0$ and $x - 4 < 0$. Thus:
$$\left| x - 3 \right| + \left| x - 4 \right| = (x - 3) + -(x - 4)$$
$$= x - 3 - x + 4$$
$$= 1$$

37. If $-\dfrac{5}{2} < x < -\dfrac{3}{2}$, then $x + 1 < 0$ and $x + 3 > 0$. Thus:
$$\left| x + 1 \right| + 4 \left| x + 3 \right| = -(x + 1) + 4(x + 3)$$
$$= -x - 1 + 4x + 12$$
$$= 3x + 11$$

39. $\left| x - 4 \right| = 8$

41. $\left| x - 1 \right| = \dfrac{1}{2}$

43. $\left| x - 1 \right| \geq \dfrac{1}{2}$

45. $\left| y - (-4) \right| < 1$, or $\left| y + 4 \right| < 1$

47. $\left| y - 0 \right| < 3$, or $\left| y \right| < 3$

49. $\left| x^2 - a^2 \right| < M$

51.

53.

55.

57.

59.

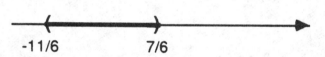

61.

63. (a)

(b)

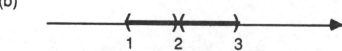

(c) The interval in (b) does not include 2.

65. (a) min (6,1) = 1

$$\min (6,1) = \frac{6 + 1 - |6 - 1|}{2} = \frac{7 - 5}{2} = \frac{2}{2} = 1$$

(b) min $(1,-6) = -6$

$\qquad$ min $(1,-6) = \dfrac{1 + (-6) - |1 - (-6)|}{2}$

$\qquad\qquad\qquad = \dfrac{-5 - |1 + 6|}{2}$

$\qquad\qquad\qquad = \dfrac{-5 - 7}{2}$

$\qquad\qquad\qquad = \dfrac{-12}{12}$

$\qquad\qquad\qquad = -6$

(c) min $(-6,-6) = -6$

$\qquad$ min $(-6,-6) = \dfrac{-6 + (-6) - |-6 - (-6)|}{2}$

$\qquad\qquad\qquad = \dfrac{-12 - |-6 + 6|}{2}$

$\qquad\qquad\qquad = \dfrac{-12}{2}$

$\qquad\qquad\qquad = -6$

67. $|a + b + c| = |a + (b + c)|$

$\qquad\qquad\quad \leq |a| + |b + c| \quad$ by the triangle inequality

$\qquad\qquad\quad \leq |a| + |b| + |c| \quad$ by the triangle inequality

69. <u>case 1</u>: $a = b$

Then max $(a,b) = a$ and $\dfrac{a + b + |a - b|}{2} = \dfrac{a + a + |a - a|}{2}$

$\qquad\qquad\qquad\qquad\qquad\qquad\qquad\qquad\quad = \dfrac{2a}{2}$

$\qquad\qquad\qquad\qquad\qquad\qquad\qquad\qquad\quad = a, \text{ which checks.}$

<u>case 2</u>: $a > b$

Then max $(a,b) = a$ and:

$\dfrac{a + b + |a - b|}{2} = \dfrac{a + b + a - b}{2} \quad$ since $a - b > 0$

$\qquad\qquad\qquad\quad = \dfrac{2a}{2}$

$\qquad\qquad\qquad\quad = a, \text{ which checks.}$

case 3: $a < b$
Then max $(a,b) = b$ and:

$$\frac{a+b+|a-b|}{2} = \frac{a+b+-(a-b)}{2} \quad \text{since } a-b < 0$$

$$= \frac{a+b-a+b}{2}$$

$$= \frac{2b}{2}$$

$$= b, \text{ which checks.}$$

71. (a) Property 1(b)
     (b) $a + b \le |a| + |b|$
     (c) $(-a) + (-b) \le |a| + |b|$, so $-(a+b) \le |a| + |b|$
     (d) Since $a + b \le |a| + |b|$ and $-(a+b) \le |a| + |b|$, then
          $|a+b| \le |a| + |b|$ since $|a+b|$ is either $a+b$ or $-(a+b)$

1.5 Integer Exponents, Scientific Notation

1. $2(-2)^3 - (-2) + 4 = 2(-8) + 2 + 4 = -10$

3. $\dfrac{1 - 2\left(-\dfrac{1}{2}\right)^2}{1 + 2\left(-\dfrac{1}{2}\right)^3} = \dfrac{1 - 2\left(\dfrac{1}{4}\right)}{1 + 2\left(-\dfrac{1}{8}\right)} = \dfrac{1 - \dfrac{1}{2}}{1 - \dfrac{1}{4}} = \dfrac{\dfrac{1}{2}}{\dfrac{3}{4}} = \dfrac{2}{3}$

5. $\dfrac{2^2 + 2^3 - 2^2}{2^2 + 3^2 - 3^2} = \dfrac{8}{4} = 2$

7. $(x + y)^2$

9. $(x + y)^2 + 3$

11. $\left(\dfrac{1}{2}(x^2 - 2y^3)\right)^2$

13. $|x - 1|^3$

15. (a) $a^3 a^{12} = a^{3+12} = a^{15}$
     (b) $(a + 1)^3 (a + 1)^{12} = (a + 1)^{15}$

(c) $(a + 1)^{12} (a + 1)^3 = (a + 1)^{15}$

17. (a) $yy^2y^8 = y^{1+2+8} = y^{11}$
(b) $(y + 1)(y + 1)^2(y + 1)^8 = (y + 1)^{11}$
(c) $\left((y + 1)(y + 1)^8\right)^2 = \left((y + 1)^9\right)^2 = (y + 1)^{18}$

19. (a) $\dfrac{(x^2 + 3)^{10}}{(x^2 + 3)^9} = (x^2 + 3)^{10-9} = x^2 + 3$

(b) $\dfrac{(x^2 + 3)^9}{(x^2 + 3)^{10}} = (x^2 + 3)^{9-10} = (x^2 + 3)^{-1} = \dfrac{1}{x^2 + 3}$

(c) $\dfrac{12^{10}}{12^9} = 12^{10-9} = 12$

21. (a) $\dfrac{t^{15}}{t^9} = t^{15-9} = t^6$

(b) $\dfrac{t^9}{t^{15}} = t^{9-15} = t^{-6} = \dfrac{1}{t^6}$

(c) $\dfrac{(t^2 + 3)^{15}}{(t^2 + 3)^9} = (t^2 + 3)^{15-9} = (t^2 + 3)^6$

23. (a) $\dfrac{x^6y^{15}}{x^2y^{20}} = \dfrac{x^{6-2}}{y^{20-15}} = \dfrac{x^4}{y^5}$

(b) $\dfrac{x^2y^{20}}{x^6y^{15}} = \dfrac{y^{20-15}}{x^{6-2}} = \dfrac{y^5}{x^4}$

(c) $\left(\dfrac{x^2y^{20}}{x^6y^{15}}\right)^2 = \left(\dfrac{y^{20-15}}{x^{6-2}}\right)^2 = \left(\dfrac{y^5}{x^4}\right)^2 = \dfrac{y^{10}}{x^8}$

25. (a) $4(x^3)^2 = 4x^6$

(b) $(4x^3)^2 = 4^2x^6 = 16x^6$

(c) $\dfrac{(4x^2)^3}{(4x^3)^2} = \dfrac{4^3x^6}{4^2x^6} = 4^{3-2} = 4$

27. $64^0 = 1$

29. $\left(\dfrac{1}{25}\right)^0 = 1$

31. $10^{-1} + 10^{-2} = \dfrac{1}{10} + \dfrac{1}{100} = \dfrac{10}{100} + \dfrac{1}{100} = \dfrac{11}{100}$

33. $(5^{-1})^{-1} = 5^1 = 5$

35. 1

37. $(a^2bc^0)^{-3} = \dfrac{1}{(a^2b)^3} = \dfrac{1}{a^6b^3}$

39. $(a^{-2}b^{-1}c^3)^{-2} = a^4b^2c^{-6} = \dfrac{a^4b^2}{c^6}$

41. $\left(\dfrac{x^3y^{-2}z}{xy^2z^{-3}}\right)^{-3} = \dfrac{x^{-9}y^6z^{-3}}{x^{-3}y^{-6}z^9} = \dfrac{y^{6-(-6)}}{x^{-3+9}z^{9+3}} = \dfrac{y^{12}}{x^6z^{12}}$

43. $\left(\dfrac{x^4y^{-8}z^2}{xy^2z^{-6}}\right)^{-2} = \dfrac{x^{-8}y^{16}z^{-4}}{x^{-2}y^{-4}z^{12}} = \dfrac{y^{16+4}}{x^{-2+8}z^{12+4}} = \dfrac{y^{20}}{x^6z^{16}}$

45. $\left(\dfrac{a^{-2}b^{-3}c^{-4}}{a^2b^3c^4}\right)^2 = \dfrac{a^{-4}b^{-6}c^{-8}}{a^4b^6c^8} = \dfrac{1}{a^{4+4}b^{6+6}c^{8+8}} = \dfrac{1}{a^8b^{12}c^{16}}$

47. $\dfrac{x^2}{y^{-3}} \div \dfrac{x^2}{y^3} = \dfrac{x^2}{y^{-3}} \cdot \dfrac{y^3}{x^2} = \dfrac{x^2y^3}{x^2y^{-3}} = y^6$

49. $\dfrac{2^8 \cdot 3^{15}}{9 \cdot 3^{10} \cdot 12} = \dfrac{2^8 \cdot 3^{15}}{3^2 \cdot 3^{10} \cdot 2^2 \cdot 3}$

$= (3^{15-13})(2^{8-2})$

$= (3^2)(2^6)$

$= 576$

51. $$\frac{24^5}{32 \cdot 12^4} = \frac{(2^3 \cdot 3)^5}{(2^5)(2^2 \cdot 3)^4}$$

$$= \frac{2^{15} \cdot 3^5}{2^5 \cdot 2^8 \cdot 3^4}$$

$$= (2^{15-13})(3^{5-4})$$

$$= (4)(3)$$

$$= 12$$

53. 9.29×10^7

55. 6.68×10^4

57. 2.5×10^{19}

59. (a) 8.668×10^1
(b) 1.0604772×10^4
(c) 8.9424×10^4

61. (a) 1×10^{-9}
(b) 1×10^{-18}
(c) 1×10^{-24}

63. $$\frac{a^{3x+y}}{a^{2x}a^{x+y}} = \frac{a^{3x+y}}{a^{3x+y}} = 1$$

65. $$\frac{(x^{5n+1})^n}{(x^n)^{5n}} \cdot \frac{1}{x^{n-2}} = \frac{x^{5n^2+n}}{x^{5n^2}} \cdot \frac{1}{x^{n-2}} = \frac{x^{5n^2+n}}{x^{5n^2+n-2}} = \frac{1}{x^{-2}} = x^2$$

67. 9^{10}

69. $$\frac{1 \text{ sec}}{2.9979 \times 10^{10} \text{ cm}} \cdot \frac{1 \text{ min}}{60 \text{ sec}} \cdot \frac{160930 \text{ cm}}{1 \text{ mi}} \cdot (92.9 \times 10^6 \text{ mi}) = 8 \text{ min}$$

71. Raising both sides of the equation $p = b^x$ to the power of y yields $p^y = b^{xy}$. Similarly, raising both sides of $q = b^y$ to the power of x yields $q^x = b^{xy}$. Now we use these results to substitute for p^y and q^x in the equation $b^2 = (p^y q^x)^z$ to obtain:

   $b^2 = (b^{xy}b^{xy})^z$ or $b^2 = b^{2xyz}$

From this last equation we conclude (by equating exponents) that:
   $2 = 2xyz$,   or $xyz = 1$, as required.

1.6 Nth Roots

1.   false

3.   true

5.   true

7.   true

9.   true

11. (a) $\sqrt[3]{-64} = -4$

    (b) $\sqrt[4]{-64}$ is undefined

13. (a) $\sqrt[3]{\dfrac{8}{125}} = \dfrac{2}{5}$

    (b) $\sqrt[3]{-\dfrac{8}{125}} = -\dfrac{2}{5}$

15. (a) $\sqrt{-16}$ is undefined

    (b) $\sqrt[4]{-16}$ is undefined

17. (a) $\sqrt[4]{\dfrac{256}{81}} = \dfrac{4}{3}$

    (b) $\sqrt[3]{-\dfrac{27}{125}} = -\dfrac{3}{5}$

19. (a) $\sqrt[5]{-32} = -2$

    (b) $-\sqrt[5]{-32} = -(-2) = 2$

21. (a) $\sqrt{18} = \sqrt{9}\,\sqrt{2} = 3\sqrt{2}$

    (b) $\sqrt[3]{54} = \sqrt[3]{27}\,\sqrt[3]{2} = 3\sqrt[3]{2}$

23. (a) $\sqrt{98} = \sqrt{49}\sqrt{2} = 7\sqrt{2}$

    (b) $\sqrt[5]{-64} = \sqrt[5]{-32}\sqrt[5]{2} = -2\sqrt[5]{2}$

25. (a) $\sqrt{\dfrac{25}{4}} = \dfrac{5}{2}$

    (b) $\sqrt[4]{\dfrac{16}{625}} = \dfrac{2}{5}$

27. (a) $\sqrt{2} + \sqrt{8} = \sqrt{2} + \sqrt{4}\sqrt{2} = \sqrt{2} + 2\sqrt{2} = 3\sqrt{2}$

    (b) $\sqrt[3]{2} + \sqrt[3]{16} = \sqrt[3]{2} + \sqrt[3]{8}\sqrt[3]{2} = \sqrt[3]{2} + 2\sqrt[3]{2} = 3\sqrt[3]{2}$

29. (a) $4\sqrt{50} - 3\sqrt{128} = 4\sqrt{25}\sqrt{2} - 3\sqrt{64}\sqrt{2} = 20\sqrt{2} - 24\sqrt{2} = -4\sqrt{2}$

    (b) $\sqrt[4]{32} + \sqrt[4]{162} = \sqrt[4]{16}\sqrt[4]{2} + \sqrt[4]{81}\sqrt[4]{2} = 2\sqrt[4]{2} + 3\sqrt[4]{2} = 5\sqrt[4]{2}$

31. (a) 0.3 [because $(0.3)^2 = 0.09$]
    (b) 0.2 [because $(0.2)^3 = 0.008$]

33. $4\sqrt{24} - 8\sqrt{54} + 2\sqrt{6} = 4\sqrt{4}\sqrt{6} - 8\sqrt{9}\sqrt{6} + 2\sqrt{6}$
$$= 8\sqrt{6} - 24\sqrt{6} + 2\sqrt{6}$$
$$= -14\sqrt{6}$$

35. $\sqrt{\sqrt{64}} = \sqrt{8} = \sqrt{4}\sqrt{2} = 2\sqrt{2}$

37. (a) $\sqrt{36x^2} = 6x$
    (b) $\sqrt{36y^2} = -6y$, since $y < 0$

39. (a) $\sqrt{ab^2}\sqrt{a^2b} = \sqrt{a^3b^3} = ab\sqrt{ab}$

    (b) $\sqrt{ab^3}\sqrt{a^3b} = \sqrt{a^4b^4} = a^2b^2$

41. $\sqrt{72a^3b^4c^5} = \sqrt{36a^2b^4c^4}\sqrt{2ac} = 6ab^2c^2\sqrt{2ac}$

43. $\sqrt[4]{16a^4b^5} = \sqrt[4]{16a^4b^4} \cdot \sqrt[4]{b} = 2ab\sqrt[4]{b}$

45. $\sqrt{18a^3b^2} = \sqrt{9a^2b^2}\sqrt{2a} = 3ab\sqrt{2a}$

47. $\sqrt[3]{\dfrac{16a^{12}b^2}{c^9}} = \dfrac{\sqrt[3]{8a^{12}}\sqrt[3]{2b^2}}{\sqrt[3]{c^9}} = \dfrac{2a^4\sqrt[3]{2b^2}}{c^3}$

49. $\sqrt[6]{\dfrac{5a^7}{a^{-5}b^6}} = \sqrt[6]{\dfrac{5a^{12}}{b^6}} = \dfrac{\sqrt[6]{5}\sqrt[6]{a^{12}}}{\sqrt[6]{b^6}} = \dfrac{a^2\sqrt[6]{5}}{b}$

51. $\dfrac{4}{\sqrt{7}} \cdot \dfrac{\sqrt{7}}{\sqrt{7}} = \dfrac{4\sqrt{7}}{7}$

53. $\dfrac{1}{\sqrt{8}} \cdot \dfrac{\sqrt{2}}{\sqrt{2}} = \dfrac{\sqrt{2}}{\sqrt{16}} = \dfrac{\sqrt{2}}{4}$

55. $\dfrac{1}{1+\sqrt{5}} \cdot \dfrac{1-\sqrt{5}}{1-\sqrt{5}} = \dfrac{1-\sqrt{5}}{1-5} = \dfrac{1-\sqrt{5}}{-4}$ or $\dfrac{\sqrt{5}-1}{4}$

57. $\dfrac{1+\sqrt{3}}{1-\sqrt{3}} \cdot \dfrac{1+\sqrt{3}}{1+\sqrt{3}} = \dfrac{1+\sqrt{3}+\sqrt{3}+3}{1-3} = \dfrac{4+2\sqrt{3}}{-2} = -2-\sqrt{3}$

59. $\dfrac{1}{\sqrt{5}} + 4\sqrt{45} = \dfrac{1}{\sqrt{5}} \cdot \dfrac{\sqrt{5}}{\sqrt{5}} + 4\sqrt{9}\sqrt{5}$

$= \dfrac{\sqrt{5}}{5} + 12\sqrt{5}$

$= \dfrac{\sqrt{5}}{5} + \dfrac{60\sqrt{5}}{5}$

$= \dfrac{61\sqrt{5}}{5}$

61. $\dfrac{1}{\sqrt[3]{25}} \cdot \dfrac{\sqrt[3]{5}}{\sqrt[3]{5}} = \dfrac{\sqrt[3]{5}}{\sqrt[3]{125}} = \dfrac{\sqrt[3]{5}}{5}$

63. $\dfrac{3}{\sqrt[4]{3}} \cdot \dfrac{\sqrt[4]{3^3}}{\sqrt[4]{3^3}} = \dfrac{3\sqrt[4]{27}}{3} = \sqrt[4]{27}$

65. $\dfrac{1}{\sqrt[4]{2ab^5}} \cdot \dfrac{\sqrt[4]{8a^3b^3}}{\sqrt[4]{8a^3b^3}} = \dfrac{\sqrt[4]{8a^3b^3}}{\sqrt[4]{16a^4b^8}} = \dfrac{\sqrt[4]{8a^3b^3}}{2ab^2}$

67. $\dfrac{\sqrt{x} - \sqrt{5}}{x - 5} \cdot \dfrac{\sqrt{x} + \sqrt{5}}{\sqrt{x} + \sqrt{5}} = \dfrac{x - 5}{(x - 5)(\sqrt{x} + \sqrt{5})} = \dfrac{1}{\sqrt{x} + \sqrt{5}}$

69. $\dfrac{\sqrt{2 + h} - \sqrt{2}}{h} \cdot \dfrac{\sqrt{2 + h} + \sqrt{2}}{\sqrt{2 + h} + \sqrt{2}}$

$\qquad\qquad = \dfrac{2 + h - 2}{h(\sqrt{2 + h} + \sqrt{2})}$

$\qquad\qquad = \dfrac{h}{h(\sqrt{2 + h} + \sqrt{2})}$

$\qquad\qquad = \dfrac{1}{\sqrt{2 + h} + \sqrt{2}}$

71. (a) To six decimal places, both values are 1.645751.

(b) $(\sqrt{7} - 1)^2 = (\sqrt{7})^2 - 2\sqrt{7} + 1 = 8 - 2\sqrt{7}$, as required.

73. First rationalize the denominator in $\dfrac{\sqrt{a}}{\sqrt{a} + \sqrt{b}}$:

$\qquad \dfrac{\sqrt{a}}{\sqrt{a} + \sqrt{b}} \cdot \dfrac{\sqrt{a} - \sqrt{b}}{\sqrt{a} - \sqrt{b}} = \dfrac{a - \sqrt{ab}}{a - b}$

Next rationalize the denominator in $\dfrac{\sqrt{b}}{\sqrt{a} - \sqrt{b}}$:

$\qquad \dfrac{\sqrt{b}}{\sqrt{a} - \sqrt{b}} \cdot \dfrac{\sqrt{a} + \sqrt{b}}{\sqrt{a} + \sqrt{b}} = \dfrac{\sqrt{ab} + b}{a - b}$

Thus, we have:

$\qquad \dfrac{\sqrt{a}}{\sqrt{a} + \sqrt{b}} \cdot \dfrac{\sqrt{b}}{\sqrt{a} - \sqrt{b}} \quad = \dfrac{a - \sqrt{ab}}{a - b} + \dfrac{\sqrt{ab} + b}{a - b}$

$\qquad\qquad\qquad\qquad\qquad = \dfrac{a - \sqrt{ab} + \sqrt{ab} + b}{a - b}$

$\qquad\qquad\qquad\qquad\qquad = \dfrac{a + b}{a - b}$

75. $\dfrac{1}{1 + \sqrt{2} + \sqrt{3}} \cdot \dfrac{(1 + \sqrt{2}) - \sqrt{3}}{(1 + \sqrt{2}) - \sqrt{3}} \quad = \dfrac{(1 + \sqrt{2}) - \sqrt{3}}{(1 + \sqrt{2})^2 - (\sqrt{3})^2}$

$\qquad\qquad\qquad\qquad\qquad\qquad = \dfrac{1 + \sqrt{2} - \sqrt{3}}{1 + 2\sqrt{2} + 2 - 3}$

$$= \frac{1 + \sqrt{2} - \sqrt{3}}{2\sqrt{2}} \cdot \frac{\sqrt{2}}{\sqrt{2}}$$

$$= \frac{\sqrt{2} + 2 - \sqrt{6}}{4}$$

1.7 Rational Exponents

1. $16^{1/2} = \sqrt{16} = 4$

3. $\left(\frac{1}{36}\right)^{1/2} = \sqrt{\frac{1}{36}} = \frac{1}{6}$

5. $(-16)^{1/2} = \sqrt{-16}$, which is undefined.

7. $625^{1/4} = \sqrt[4]{625} = 5$

9. $8^{1/3} = \sqrt[3]{8} = 2$

11. $8^{2/3} = \left(\sqrt[3]{8}\right)^2 = (2)^2 = 4$

13. $(-32)^{1/5} = \sqrt[5]{-32} = -2$

15. $(-1000)^{1/3} = \sqrt[3]{-1000} = -10$

17. $49^{-1/2} = (\sqrt{49})^{-1} = 7^{-1} = \frac{1}{7}$

19. $(-49)^{-1/2} = (\sqrt{-49})^{-1}$, which is undefined.

21. $(36)^{-3/2} = (\sqrt{36})^{-3} = 6^{-3} = \frac{1}{6^3} = \frac{1}{216}$

23. $125^{2/3} = \left(\sqrt[3]{125}\right)^2 = (5)^2 = 25$

25. $(-1)^{3/5} = \left(\sqrt[5]{-1}\right)^3 = (-1)^3 = -1$

27. $32^{4/5} - 32^{-4/5} = \left(\sqrt[5]{32}\right)^4 - \left(\sqrt[5]{32}\right)^{-4}$

$\qquad\qquad\qquad = 2^4 - 2^{-4}$

$\qquad\qquad\qquad = 16 - \dfrac{1}{16}$

$\qquad\qquad\qquad = \dfrac{255}{16}$

29. $\left(\dfrac{9}{16}\right)^{-5/2} - \left(\dfrac{1000}{27}\right)^{4/3} = \left(\dfrac{16}{9}\right)^{-5/2} - \left(\dfrac{1000}{27}\right)^{4/3}$

$\qquad\qquad\qquad\qquad = \left(\sqrt{\dfrac{16}{9}}\right)^5 - \left(\sqrt[3]{\dfrac{1000}{27}}\right)^4$

$\qquad\qquad\qquad\qquad = \left(\dfrac{4}{3}\right)^5 - \left(\dfrac{10}{3}\right)^4$

$\qquad\qquad\qquad\qquad = \dfrac{1024}{243} - \dfrac{10000}{81}$

$\qquad\qquad\qquad\qquad = -\dfrac{28976}{243}$

31. $(2a^{1/3})(3a^{1/4}) = 6a^{7/12}$, since $\dfrac{1}{3} + \dfrac{1}{4} = \dfrac{4}{12} + \dfrac{3}{12} = \dfrac{7}{12}$

33. $\sqrt[4]{\dfrac{64a^{2/3}}{a^{1/3}}} = \sqrt[4]{64a^{1/3}}$

$\qquad\qquad\quad = (16 \cdot 4a^{1/3})^{1/4}$

$\qquad\qquad\quad = 2(4a^{1/3})^{1/4}$

$\qquad\qquad\quad = 2(4^{1/4})a^{1/12}$, or $2^{3/2}a^{1/12}$

35. $\dfrac{(x^2 + 1)^{3/4}}{(x^2 + 1)^{-1/4}} = (x^2 + 1)^{4/4} = x^2 + 1$

37. (a) $\sqrt{3}\,\sqrt[3]{6} = 3^{1/2}\,6^{1/3} = 2^{1/3}\,3^{5/6}$

    (b) $3^{1/2}\,6^{1/3} = 3^{3/6}\,6^{2/6} = \sqrt[6]{3^3 6^2} = \sqrt[6]{972}$

39. (a) $\sqrt[3]{6}\,\sqrt[4]{2} = 6^{1/3}\,2^{1/4} = 2^{7/12}\,3^{1/3}$

    (b) $6^{1/3}\,2^{1/4} = 6^{4/12}\,2^{3/12} = \sqrt[12]{6^4 2^3} = \sqrt[12]{10368}$

41. (a) $\sqrt[3]{x^2}\,\sqrt[5]{y^4} = x^{2/3}\,y^{4/5}$

(b) $x^{2/3}\,y^{4/5} = x^{10/15}\,y^{12/15} = \sqrt[15]{x^{10}y^{12}}$

43. (a) $\sqrt[4]{x^a}\,\sqrt[3]{x^b}\,\sqrt{x^{a/6}} = x^{a/4}\,x^{b/3}\,x^{a/12}$
$$= x^{3a/12}\,x^{4b/12}\,x^{a/12}$$
$$= x^{(4a+4b)/12}$$
$$= x^{(a+b)/3}$$

(b) $x^{(a+b)/3} = \sqrt[3]{x^{a+b}}$

45. $\sqrt[3]{(x+1)^2} = (x+1)^{2/3}$

47. $\left(\sqrt[5]{x+y}\right)^2 = (x+y)^{2/5}$

49. $\sqrt[3]{\sqrt{x}} + \sqrt{\sqrt[3]{x}} = (x^{1/2})^{1/3} + (x^{1/3})^{1/2} = x^{1/6} + x^{1/6} = 2x^{1/6}$

51. $\sqrt{\sqrt[3]{x}\,\sqrt[4]{y}} = (x^{1/2}\,y^{1/4})^{1/2} = x^{1/6}\,y^{1/8}$

53. $9^{10/9} \approx 11.5$; $10^{9/10} \approx 7.9$. Thus $9^{10/9}$ is larger.

55.

n	2	5	10	100	10^3	10^4	10^5	10^6
$n^{1/n}$	1.4142	1.3797	1.2589	1.0471	1.0069	1.0009	1.0001	1.0000

57. (a) $2^{2/3}$ is less than 2; $2^{3/2}$ is greater than 2. Thus, $2^{3/2}$ is the larger number.

(b) $5^{1/2} = \sqrt{5}$; $5^{-2} = \dfrac{1}{25}$; thus $5^{1/2}$ is the larger number.

(c) $2^{1/2}$ is larger. (One way to see this is to raise both numbers to the sixth power)

(d) $(1/2)^{1/3}$ is larger. (One way to see this is to raise both numbers to the sixth power.)

(e) $10^{1/10}$ is larger than 1, but $(1/10)^{10}$ is much less than 1. Thus $10^{1/10}$ is the larger number.

59. (a) $2^{1/2} = \sqrt{2}$, which is irrational.

(b) $(\sqrt{2})^2 = 2$, which is rational.

61. $(-0.5)^{1/3} \approx -.7937$ while $(-0.4)^{1/3} \approx -.7368$, so $(-0.5)^{1/3}$ is smaller. Without a calculator, we only need to see that -0.5 is smaller, and since both numbers are raised to the same exponent, then $(-0.5)^{1/3}$ is smaller.

63.

$$\frac{a-b}{a+b} \sqrt{\frac{a+b}{a-b}} = \frac{a-b}{a+b} \cdot \frac{(a+b)^{1/2}}{(a-b)^{1/2}}$$

$$= \frac{a-b}{(a-b)^{1/2}} \cdot \frac{(a+b)^{1/2}}{a+b}$$

$$= \frac{(a-b)^{1/2}}{(a+b)^{1/2}}$$

$$= \left(\frac{a-b}{a+b}\right)^{1/2}, \text{ as required.}$$

1.8 Polynomials

1. (a) all real numbers, or $(-\infty, \infty)$

(b) non-negative real numbers, or $[0, \infty)$

3. (a) all real numbers, or $(-\infty, \infty)$

(b) all real numbers, or $(-\infty, \infty)$

5. (a) non-negative real numbers, or $[0, \infty)$

(b) positive real numbers except 1, or $(0,1) \cup (1, \infty)$

7. (a) degree: 3
coefficients: 4, -2, -6, -1

   (b) degree: 2
   coefficients: a, b, c

9. (a) degree: 1
    coefficients; 6

    (b) degree: 3
    coefficients: -1, 1, 6

11. $(12x^2 - 4x + 2) + (8x^2 + 6x - 1) = 20x^2 + 2x + 1$

13. $(x^2 - x - 1) - (x^2 + x + 1) = x^2 - x - 1 - x^2 - x - 1 = -2x - 2$

15. $(2x^2 - 4x - 4) - (6x^2 + 5) - (8x - 1) = 2x^2 - 4x - 4 - 6x^2 - 5 - 8x + 1$
     $$= -4x^2 - 12x - 8$$

17. $(2x^2 - 6x - 1) + (5x^2 - 5x - 1) - (3x^2 + 8x + 12)$
     $$= 2x^2 - 6x - 1 + 5x^2 - 5x - 1 - 3x^2 - 8x - 12$$
     $$= 4x^2 - 19x - 14$$

19. $(ax^2 + bx + c) - (2ax^2 - 3bx + c) = ax^2 + bx + c - 2ax^2 + 3bx - c = -ax^2 + 4bx$

21. $2x(x^2 - 4x - 5) = 2x^3 - 8x^2 - 10x$

23. $(x - 1)(x - 2) = x^2 - 3x + 2$

25. $(2x + 4)(x + 1) = 2x^2 + 6x + 4$

27. $(x^2 + 3x)(x^2 + x) = x^4 + 4x^3 + 3x^2$

29. $(2xy - 3)(2xy - 1) = 4x^2y^2 - 8xy + 3$

31. $\left(x + \dfrac{1}{x}\right)\left(x + \dfrac{1}{x}\right) = x^2 + 1 + 1 + \dfrac{1}{x^2} = x^2 + 2 + \dfrac{1}{x^2}$

33. $\left(\sqrt{a+b} + 1\right)\left(\sqrt{a+b} + 3\right)$ $= \left(\sqrt{a+b}\right)^2 + 4\sqrt{a+b} + 3$
     $$= a + b + 4\sqrt{a+b} + 3$$

35. $(x^{1/2} - 1)(x^{1/2} - 2) = (x^{1/2})^2 - 3x^{1/2} + 2 = x - 3x^{1/2} + 2$

37. $(y + 2)(y^2 - 3y - 5)$ = $y(y^2 - 3y - 5) + 2(y^2 - 3y - 5)$
    = $y^3 - 3y^2 - 5y + 2y^2 - 6y - 10$
    = $y^3 - y^2 - 11y - 10$

39. $(x - 2y + z)(x + 2y - z)$ = $\left(x - (2y - z)\right)\left(x + (2y - z)\right)$
    = $x^2 - (2y - z)^2$
    = $x^2 - (4y^2 - 4yz + z^2)$
    = $x^2 - 4y^2 + 4yz - z^2$

41. (a) $x^2 - y^2$
    (b) $(x^2)^2 - 5^2 = x^4 - 25$

43. (a) $A^2 - 16$
    (b) $(a + b)^2 - 4^2 = a^2 + 2ab + b^2 - 16$

45. (a) $x^2 - 16x + 64$
    (b) $(2x^2)^2 - 2(10x^2) + 25 = 4x^4 - 20x^2 + 25$

47. (a) $\left(\sqrt{x}\right)^2 + 2\sqrt{xy} + \left(\sqrt{y}\right)^2 = x + 2\sqrt{xy} + y$

    (b) $\left(\sqrt{x + y}\right)^2 - 2\sqrt{x + y}\,\sqrt{x} + \left(\sqrt{x}\right)^2$ = $x + y - 2\sqrt{x(x + y)} + x$
    = $2x + y - 2\sqrt{x^2 + xy}$

49. (a) $(a + 1)^3 = a^3 + 3a^2(1) + 3a(1)^2 + 1^3 = a^3 + 3a^2 + 3a + 1$

    (b) $(3x^2 - 2a^2)^3$ = $(3x^2)^3 + 3(3x^2)^2(-2a^2) + 3(3x^2)(-2a^2)^2 + (-2a^2)^3$
    = $27x^6 - 54x^4a^2 + 36x^2a^4 - 8a^6$

51. (a) $x^3 + 1^3 = x^3 + 1$
    (b) $x^3 + 2^3 = x^3 + 8$

53. (a)

$$
\begin{array}{r}
x + 7 \\
x - 1 \enclose{longdiv}{x^2 + 6x - 1} \\
\underline{x^2 - x} \\
7x - 1 \\
\underline{7x - 7} \\
6
\end{array}
$$

quotient: $x + 7$
remainder: 6

(b)

$$\begin{array}{r} x^2 + x + 7 \\ x - 1 \overline{\smash{\big)}\ x^3 + 0x^2 + 6x - 1} \\ \underline{x^3 - x^2} \\ x^2 + 6x \\ \underline{x^2 - x} \\ 7x - 1 \\ \underline{7x - 7} \\ 6 \end{array}$$

quotient: $x^2 + x + 7$
remainder: 6

(c)

$$\begin{array}{r} 1 \\ x^2 - 1 \overline{\smash{\big)}\ x^2 + 6x - 1} \\ \underline{x^2 - 1} \\ 6x \end{array}$$

quotient: 1
remainder: $6x$

55.

$$\begin{array}{r} x^2 + 0x - 3 \\ 2x + 4 \overline{\smash{\big)}\ 2x^3 + 4x^2 - 6x + 2} \\ \underline{2x^3 + 4x^2} \\ 0x^2 - 6x \\ \underline{0x^2 + 0x} \\ -6x + 2 \\ \underline{-6x - 12} \\ 14 \end{array}$$

quotient: $x^2 - 3$
remainder: 14

57.

$$
\begin{array}{r}
x^5 + 2x^4 + 4x^3 + 8x^2 + 16x + 32 \\
x - 2 \enclose{longdiv}{x^6 + 0x^5 + 0x^4 + 0x^3 + 0x^2 + 0x - 64} \\
\underline{x^6 - 2x^5} \\
2x^5 + 0x^4 \\
\underline{2x^5 - 4x^4} \\
4x^4 + 0x^3 \\
\underline{4x^4 - 8x^3} \\
8x^3 + 0x^2 \\
\underline{8x^3 - 16x^2} \\
16x^2 + 0x \\
\underline{16x^2 - 32x} \\
32x - 64 \\
\underline{32x - 64} \\
0
\end{array}
$$

quotient: $x^5 + 2x^4 + 4x^3 + 8x^2 + 16x + 32$
remainder: 0

59.

$$
\begin{array}{r}
a \\
x + c \enclose{longdiv}{ax + b} \\
\underline{ax + ac} \\
b - ac
\end{array}
$$

quotient: a
remainder : b - ac

61. (a)

x	$\dfrac{x^2 - 16}{x - 4}$
3.9	7.9
3.99	7.99
3.999	7.999
3.9999	7.9999
3.99999	7.99999

x	$\dfrac{x^2 - 16}{x - 4}$
4.1	8.1
4.01	8.01
4.001	8.001
4.0001	8.0001
4.00001	8.00001

(b) As x approaches 4, the value of the expression $\dfrac{x^2 - 16}{x - 4}$ approaches 8.

63. The first of the three products can be computed as follows:

$$(b - c) \, [(b + c) - a] = b^2 - c^2 - a(b - c) = b^2 - c^2 - ab + ac$$

Similarly, the two other products are found to be:

$$(c - a) \, (c + a - b) = c^2 - a^2 - bc + ab$$

and

$$(a - b) \, (a + b - c) = a^2 - b^2 - ac + bc$$

The sum of the three products, then, is:

$$b^2 - c^2 - ab + ac + c^2 - a^2 - bc + ab + a^2 - b^2 - ac + bc$$
$$= (a^2 - a^2) + (b^2 - b^2) + (c^2 - c^2) + (ab - ab) + (ac - ac) + (bc - bc)$$
$$= 0,$$

as required.

65. $[(x^2 + 8) - 4x] \, [(x^2 + 8) + 4x] = (x^2 + 8)^2 - (4x)^2$
$$= x^4 + 16x^2 + 64 - 16x^2$$
$$= x^4 + 64, \text{ as required.}$$

67. (a)

$$\begin{array}{r}
ax + (b + ar) \\
x - r \enclose{longdiv}{ax^2 + bx + c} \\
\underline{ax^2 - arx} \\
(b + ar)x + c \\
\underline{(b + ar)x - r(b + ar)} \\
c + r(b + ar)
\end{array}$$

The remainder is $c + r(b + ar) = ar^2 + br + c$

(b)

$$\begin{array}{r}
ax^2 + (b + ra)x + (c + br + ar^2) \\
x - r \enclose{longdiv}{ax^3 + bx^2 + cx + d} \\
\underline{ax^3 - rax^2} \\
(b + ra)x^2 + cx \\
\underline{(b + ra)x^2 - r(b + ra)x} \\
(c + br + ar^2)x + d \\
\underline{(c + br + ar^2)x - r(c + br + ar^2)} \\
d + r(c + br + ar^2)
\end{array}$$

The remainder is $d + r(c + br + ar^2) = ar^3 + br^2 + cr + d$

(c) $ar^4 + br^3 + cr^2 + dr + e$

69. (a)

n	1	2	3	4	5	6
$\dfrac{n^2}{n+1}$	$\dfrac{1}{2}$	$\dfrac{4}{3}$	$\dfrac{9}{4}$	$\dfrac{16}{5}$	$\dfrac{25}{6}$	$\dfrac{36}{7}$

(b)

$$
n + 1 \enclose{longdiv}{
\begin{array}{l}
\underline{n - 1} \\
n^2 + 0n + 0 \\
\underline{n^2 + n} \\
 -n + 0 \\
 \underline{-n - 1} \\
 1
\end{array}}
$$

Since the remainder is always 1, then $\dfrac{n^2}{n + 1}$ can never be a natural number.

1.9 Factoring

1. (a) $x^2 - 64 = (x + 8)(x - 8)$

(b) $7x^4 + 14x^2 = 7x^2(x^2 + 2)$

(c) $121z - z^3 = z(121 - z^2) = z(11 + z)(11 - z)$

(d) $a^2b^2 - c^2 = (ab + c)(ab - c)$

3. (a) $x^2 + 2x - 3 = (x + 3)(x - 1)$

(b) $x^2 - 2x - 3 = (x - 3)(x + 1)$

(c) $x^2 - 2x + 3$ is irreducible

(d) $-x^2 + 2x + 3 = (-x + 3)(x + 1)$ or $-(x - 3)(x + 1)$

5. (a) $x^3 + 1 = (x + 1)(x^2 - x + 1)$

(b) $x^3 + 216 = (x + 6)(x^2 - 6x + 36)$

(c) $1000 - 8x^6 = 8(125 - x^6)$
$= 8[5^3 - (x^2)^3]$
$= 8(5 - x^2)(25 + 5x^2 + x^4)$

(d) $64a^3x^3 - 125 = (4ax)^3 - 5^3 = (4ax - 5)(16a^2x^2 + 20ax + 25)$

7. $2x - 2x^3 = 2x(1 - x^2) = 2x(1 - x)(1 + x)$

9. $100x^3 - x^5 = x^3(100 - x^2) = x^3(10 - x)(10 + x)$

11. $2x^4 + 3x^3 - 9x^2 = x^2(2x^2 + 3x - 9) = x^2(2x - 3)(x + 3)$

13. $4x^3 - 20x^2 + 25x = x(4x^2 - 20x + 25) = x(2x - 5)^2$

15. $x^2z^2 + xzt + xyz + yt = xz(xz + t) + y(xz + t) = (xz + t)(xz + y)$

17. $a^2t^2 + b^2t^2 - cb^2 - ca^2 = t^2(a^2 + b^2) - c(b^2 + a^2) = (a^2 + b^2)(t^2 - c)$

19. $x^3 - 13x^2 - 90x = x(x^2 - 13x - 90) = x(x - 18)(x + 5)$

21. $4x^2 - 29xy - 24y^2 = (4x + 3y)(x - 8y)$

23. $x^2 + 2x + 16$ is irreducible

25. $1 - (x + y)^2 = \left(1 + (x + y)\right)\left(1 - (x + y)\right) = (1 + x + y)(1 - x - y)$

27. $x^8 - 1 = (x^4 - 1)(x^4 + 1)$
$$= (x^2 - 1)(x^2 + 1)(x^4 + 1)$$
$$= (x - 1)(x + 1)(x^2 + 1)(x^4 + 1)$$

29. $x^3 + 3x^2 + 3x + 1 = (x^3 + 1) + (3x^2 + 3x)$
$$= (x + 1)(x^2 - x + 1) + 3x(x + 1)$$
$$= (x + 1)(x^2 - x + 1 + 3x)$$
$$= (x + 1)(x^2 + 2x + 1)$$
$$= (x + 1)(x + 1)^2$$
$$= (x + 1)^3$$

31. $27x^3 + 108x^2 + 144x + 64 = (27x^3 + 64) + 36x(3x + 4)$
$$= (3x + 4)(9x^2 - 12x + 16) + 36x(3x + 4)$$
$$= (3x + 4)(9x^2 - 12x + 16 + 36x)$$
$$= (3x + 4)(9x^2 + 24x + 16)$$
$$= (3x + 4)(3x + 4)^2$$
$$= (3x + 4)^3$$

33. $64a^6 - b^6 = (8a^3 - b^3)(8a^3 + b^3)$
$$= (2a - b)(4a^2 + 2ab + b^2)(2a + b)(4a^2 - 2ab + b^2)$$

35. $x^4 - 25x^2 + 144 = (x^2 - 9)(x^2 - 16) = (x - 3)(x + 3)(x - 4)(x + 4)$

37. $x^2 + 16y^2$ is irriducible

39. $x^3 - 2x^2 - 255x = x(x^2 + 2x - 255) = x(x + 17)(x - 15)$

41. $x^3 + a^3 + x + a = (x + a)(x^2 - xa + a^2) + (x + a) \cdot 1$
$$= (x + a)(x^2 - xa + a^2 + 1)$$

43. $x^2 - a^2 + y^2 - 2xy = (x^2 - 2xy + y^2) - a^2$
$$= (x - y)^2 - a^2$$
$$= (x - y - a)(x - y + a)$$

45. $21x^3 + 82x^2 - 39x = x(21x^2 + 82x - 39) = x(7x - 3)(3x + 13)$

47. $12xy + 25 - 4x^2 - 9y^2 = 5^2 - (4x^2 - 12xy + 9y^2)$
$$= 5^2 - (2x - 3y)^2$$
$$= [5 - (2x - 3y)][5 + (2x - 3y)]$$
$$= (5 - 2x + 3y)(5 + 2x - 3y)$$

49. (a) $100^2 - 99^2 = (100 + 99)(100 - 99) = (199)(1) = 199$

  (b) $8^3 - 6^3 = (8 - 6)(8^2 + 8 \cdot 6 + 6^2)$
$$= 2(64 + 48 + 36)$$
$$= 2(148)$$
$$= 296$$

  (c) $1000^2 - 999^2 = (1000 + 999)(1000 - 999) = (1999)(1) = 1999$

51. $ax^2 + (1 + ab)xy + by^2 = ax^2 + xy + abxy + by^2$
$$= x(ax + y) + by(ax + y)$$
$$= (ax + y)(x + by)$$

53. $(5a^2 - 11a + 10)^2 - (4a^2 - 15a + 6)^2$
$$= \big((5a^2-11a+10) - (4a^2-15a+6)\big)\big((5a^2-11a+10) + (4a^2-15a+6)\big)$$
$$= (a^2 + 4a + 4)(9a^2 - 26a + 16)$$
$$= (a + 2)^2(9a - 8)(a - 2)$$

55. $(x + 1)^{1/2} - (x + 1)^{3/2}$
$$= (x + 1)^{1/2}\big(1 - (x + 1)^{2/2}\big)$$
$$= (x + 1)^{1/2}(1 - x - 1)$$
$$= (x + 1)^{1/2}(- x)$$
$$= -x(x + 1)^{1/2}$$

57. $(x + 1)^{-1/2} - (x + 1)^{-3/2} = (x + 1)^{-3/2}\big((x + 1)^1 - 1\big)$

$$= (x + 1)^{-3/2}(x)$$

$$= x(x + 1)^{-3/2} \quad \text{or} \quad \frac{x}{(x + 1)^{3/2}}$$

59. $x^2(x - 2)^{-4} + x(x - 2)^{-3} = x(x - 2)^{-4}\big(x + (x - 2)^1\big)$

$$= x(x - 2)^{-4}(2x - 2)$$

$$= 2x(x - 1)(x - 2)^{-4} \quad \text{or} \quad \frac{2x(x - 1)}{(x - 2)^4}$$

61. $(x + y)^2 + (x + z)^2 - (z + t)^2 - (y + t)^2$

$$= \big((x + y)^2 - (y + t)^2\big) + \big((x + z)^2 - (z + t)^2\big)$$

$$= \big(x + y - (y+t)\big)\big(x + y + (y+t)\big) + \big(x + z - (z+t)\big)\big(x + z + (z+t)\big)$$

$$= (x - t)(x + 2y + t) + (x - t)(x + 2z + t)$$

$$= (x - t)(x + 2y + t + x + 2z + t)$$

$$= (x - t)(2x + 2y + 2z + 2t)$$

$$= 2(x - t)(x + y + z + t)$$

63. $(b - c)^3 + (c - a)^3 + (a - b)^3$

$$= b^3 - 3b^2c + 3bc^2 - c^3 + c^3 - 3c^2a + 3ca^2 - a^3 + a^3 - 3a^2b + 3ab^2 - b^3$$

$$= -3b^2c + 3bc^2 - 3c^2a + 3ca^2 - 3a^2b + 3ab^2$$

$$= (3bc^2 - 3c^2a) + (3ca^2 - 3b^2c) + (3ab^2 - 3a^2b)$$

$$= 3c^2(b - a) + 3c(a^2 - b^2) + 3ab(b - a)$$

$$= 3c^2(b - a) - 3c(b^2 - a^2) + 3ab(b - a)$$

$$= 3(b - a)[c^2 - c(b + a) + ab]$$

$$= 3(b - a)[c^2 - cb - ca + ab]$$

$$= 3(b - a)[c(c - b) - a(c - b)]$$

$$= 3(b - a)[(c - b)(c - a)]$$

$$= 3(b - a)(c - a)(c - b)$$

65. (a) $x^4 - 6x^2 + 9 = (x^2 - 3)^2$

(b) $x^4 - 15x^2 + 9 = x^4 - 15x^2 + 9x^2 - 9x^2 + 9$

$$= (x^4 - 6x^2 + 9) - 9x^2$$

$$= (x^2 - 3)^2 - (3x)^2$$

$$= (x^2 - 3 - 3x)(x^2 - 3 + 3x)$$

$$= (x^2 - 3x - 3)(x^2 + 3x - 3)$$

1.10 Fractional Expressions

1. $\dfrac{x^2 - 9}{x + 3} = \dfrac{(x - 3)(x + 3)}{x + 3} = x - 3$

3. $\dfrac{x + 2}{x^4 - 16} = \dfrac{x + 2}{(x^2 - 4)(x^2 + 4)}$

    $= \dfrac{x + 2}{(x - 2)(x + 2)(x^2 + 4)}$

    $= \dfrac{1}{(x - 2)(x^2 + 4)}$

5. $\dfrac{x^2 + 2x + 4}{x^3 - 8} = \dfrac{x^2 + 2x + 4}{(x - 2)(x^2 + 2x + 4)} = \dfrac{1}{x - 2}$

7. $\dfrac{9ab - 12b^2}{6a^2 - 8ab} = \dfrac{3b(3a - 4b)}{2a(3a - 4b)} = \dfrac{3b}{2a}$

9. $\dfrac{a^3 + a^2 + a + 1}{a^2 - 1} = \dfrac{a^2(a + 1) + (a + 1)}{(a - 1)(a + 1)}$

    $= \dfrac{(a + 1)(a^2 + 1)}{(a - 1)(a + 1)}$

    $= \dfrac{a^2 + 1}{a - 1}$

11. $\dfrac{x^3 - y^3}{(x - y)^3} = \dfrac{(x - y)(x^2 + xy + y^2)}{(x - y)^3} = \dfrac{x^2 + xy + y^2}{(x - y)^2}$

13. $\dfrac{2}{x - 2} \cdot \dfrac{x^2 - 4}{x + 2} = \dfrac{2(x - 2)(x + 2)}{(x - 2)(x + 2)} = 2$

15. $\dfrac{x^2 - x - 2}{x^2 + x - 12} \cdot \dfrac{x^2 - 3x}{x^2 - 4x + 4} = \dfrac{(x - 2)(x + 1)}{(x + 4)(x - 3)} \cdot \dfrac{x(x - 3)}{(x - 2)^2}$

    $= \dfrac{x(x + 1)}{(x + 4)(x - 2)}$

    $= \dfrac{x^2 + x}{(x + 4)(x - 2)}$

17. $\dfrac{x^3 + y^3}{x^2 - 4xy + 3y^2} \div \dfrac{(x + y)^3}{x^2 - 2xy - 3y^2}$

$= \dfrac{(x + y)(x^2 - xy + y^2)}{(x - 3y)(x - y)} \cdot \dfrac{(x + y)(x - 3y)}{(x + y)^3}$

$= \dfrac{x^2 - xy + y^2}{(x - y)(x + y)}$

19. $\dfrac{x^2 + xy - 2y^2}{x^2 - 5xy + 4y^2} \cdot \dfrac{x^2 - 7xy + 12y^2}{x^2 + 5xy + 6y^2}$

$= \dfrac{(x + 2y)(x - y)}{(x - 4y)(x - y)} \cdot \dfrac{(x - 4y)(x - 3y)}{(x + 3y)(x + 2y)}$

$= \dfrac{x - 3y}{x + 3y}$

21. $\dfrac{4}{x} - \dfrac{2}{x^2} = \dfrac{4x}{x^2} - \dfrac{2}{x^2} = \dfrac{4x - 2}{x^2}$

23. $\dfrac{6}{a} - \dfrac{a}{6} = \dfrac{36}{6a} - \dfrac{a^2}{6a} = \dfrac{36 - a^2}{6a}$

25. $\dfrac{1}{x + 3} + \dfrac{3}{x + 2}$

$= \dfrac{x + 2}{(x + 3)(x + 2)} + \dfrac{3(x + 3)}{(x + 3)(x + 2)}$

$= \dfrac{x + 2 + 3(x + 3)}{(x + 3)(x + 2)}$

$= \dfrac{4x + 11}{(x + 3)(x + 2)}$

27. $\dfrac{3x}{x - 2} - \dfrac{6}{x^2 - 4}$

$= \dfrac{3x}{x - 2} - \dfrac{6}{(x - 2)(x + 2)}$

$= \dfrac{3x(x + 2) - 6}{(x - 2)(x + 2)}$

$= \dfrac{3x^2 + 6x - 6}{(x - 2)(x + 2)}$

29. $\dfrac{a}{x - 1} + \dfrac{2ax}{(x - 1)^2} + \dfrac{3ax^2}{(x - 1)^3}$

$= \dfrac{a(x - 1)^2 + 2ax(x - 1) + 3ax^2}{(x - 1)^3}$

$= \dfrac{ax^2 - 2ax + a + 2ax^2 - 2ax + 3ax^2}{(x - 1)^3}$

$= \dfrac{6ax^2 - 4ax + a}{(x - 1)^3}$

31. $\dfrac{x}{x^2 - 9} + \dfrac{x - 1}{x^2 - 5x + 6}$

$\qquad = \dfrac{x}{(x - 3)(x + 3)} + \dfrac{x - 1}{(x - 3)(x - 2)}$

$\qquad = \dfrac{x(x - 2) + (x - 1)(x + 3)}{(x - 3)(x + 3)(x - 2)}$

$\qquad = \dfrac{x^2 - 2x + x^2 + 2x - 3}{(x - 3)(x + 3)(x - 2)}$

$\qquad = \dfrac{2x^2 - 3}{(x - 3)(x + 3)(x - 2)}$

33. $\dfrac{4}{x - 5} - \dfrac{4}{5 - x} = \dfrac{4}{x - 5} + \dfrac{4}{x - 5} = \dfrac{8}{x - 5}$

35. $\dfrac{a^2 + b^2}{a^2 - b^2} + \dfrac{a}{a + b} + \dfrac{b}{b - a}$

$\qquad = \dfrac{a^2 + b^2}{(a - b)(a + b)} + \dfrac{a}{a + b} - \dfrac{b}{a - b}$

$\qquad = \dfrac{a^2 + b^2 + a(a - b) - b(a + b)}{(a - b)(a + b)}$

$\qquad = \dfrac{a^2 + b^2 + a^2 - ab - ab - b^2}{(a - b)(a + b)}$

$\qquad = \dfrac{2a^2 - 2ab}{(a - b)(a + b)}$

$\qquad = \dfrac{2a(a - b)}{(a - b)(a + b)}$

$\qquad = \dfrac{2a}{a + b}$

37. $\dfrac{1}{x^2 + x - 20} - \dfrac{1}{x^2 - 8x + 16}$

$\qquad = \dfrac{1}{(x + 5)(x - 4)} - \dfrac{1}{(x - 4)^2}$

$\qquad = \dfrac{x - 4 - (x + 5)}{(x + 5)(x - 4)^2}$

$\qquad = \dfrac{-9}{(x + 5)(x - 4)^2}$

39. $\dfrac{2q + p}{2p^2 - 9pq - 5q^2} - \dfrac{p + q}{p^2 - 5pq}$

$\qquad = \dfrac{2q + p}{(2p + q)(p - 5q)} - \dfrac{p + q}{p(p - 5q)}$

$\qquad = \dfrac{(2q + p)p - (p + q)(2p + q)}{p(2p + q)(p - 5q)}$

$\qquad = \dfrac{2pq + p^2 - 2p^2 - 3pq - q^2}{p(2p + q)(p - 5q)}$

$\qquad = \dfrac{-p^2 - pq - q^2}{p(2p + q)(p - 5q)}$

41. $\dfrac{x}{(x-y)(x-z)} + \dfrac{y}{(y-z)(y-x)} + \dfrac{z}{(z-x)(z-y)}$

$= \dfrac{x}{(x-y)(x-z)} - \dfrac{y}{(y-z)(x-y)} + \dfrac{z}{(x-z)(y-z)}$

$= \dfrac{x(y-z) - y(x-z) + z(x-y)}{(x-y)(x-z)(y-z)}$

$= \dfrac{xy - xz - xy + yz + xz - yz}{(x-y)(x-z)(y-z)}$

$= \dfrac{0}{(x-y)(x-z)(y-z)}$

$= 0$

43. $\dfrac{y+z}{x^2 - xy - xz + yz} - \dfrac{x+z}{xy - xz - y^2 + yz} + \dfrac{x+y}{xy - yz - xz + z^2}$

$= \dfrac{y+z}{x(x-y) - z(x-y)} - \dfrac{x+z}{x(y-z) - y(y-z)} + \dfrac{x+y}{y(x-z) - z(x-z)}$

$= \dfrac{y+z}{(x-y)(x-z)} - \dfrac{x+z}{(y-z)(x-y)} - \dfrac{x+y}{(x-z)(y-z)}$

$= \dfrac{(y+z)(y-z) - (x+z)(x-z) + (x+y)(x-y)}{(x-y)(x-z)(y-z)}$

$= \dfrac{y^2 - z^2 - x^2 + z^2 + x^2 - y^2}{(x-y)(x-z)(y-z)}$

$= \dfrac{0}{(x-y)(x-z)(y-z)}$

$= 0$

45. $\dfrac{x^2 + x - a - 1}{a^2 - x^2} + \dfrac{x+1}{x+a} \div \dfrac{x-a}{x-1}$

$= \dfrac{x^2 + x - a - 1}{a^2 - x^2} + \dfrac{x+1}{x+a} \bullet \dfrac{x-1}{x-a}$

$= \dfrac{x^2 + x - a - 1}{-(x^2 - a^2)} + \dfrac{x^2 - 1}{x^2 - a^2}$

$= \dfrac{-x^2 - x + a + 1 + x^2 - 1}{x^2 - a^2}$

$= \dfrac{-x + a}{(x+a)(x-a)}$

$= \dfrac{-(x-a)}{(x+a)(x-a)}$

$= \dfrac{-1}{x+a}$

47. $\dfrac{x^2 - 2ax + a^2}{px + q} \bullet \left(\dfrac{p}{x - a} + \dfrac{ap + q}{(x - a)^2} \right)$

$$= \dfrac{(x - a)^2}{px + q} \bullet \dfrac{p(x - a) + ap + q}{(x - a)^2}$$

$$= \dfrac{1}{px + q} \bullet \dfrac{px - pa + ap + q}{1}$$

$$= \dfrac{px + q}{px + q}$$

$$= 1$$

49. $\dfrac{1 + \dfrac{4}{x}}{\dfrac{3}{x} - 2} = \dfrac{x}{x} \bullet \dfrac{1 + \dfrac{4}{x}}{\dfrac{3}{x} - 2} = \dfrac{x + 4}{3 - 2x}$

51. $\dfrac{a - \dfrac{1}{a}}{1 + \dfrac{1}{a}} = \dfrac{a}{a} \bullet \dfrac{a - \dfrac{1}{a}}{1 + \dfrac{1}{a}}$

$$= \dfrac{a^2 - 1}{a + 1}$$

$$= \dfrac{(a - 1)(a + 1)}{a + 1}$$

$$= a - 1$$

53. $\dfrac{\dfrac{1}{2 + h} - \dfrac{1}{2}}{h}$

$$= \dfrac{2(2 + h)}{2(2 + h)} \bullet \dfrac{\dfrac{1}{2 + h} - \dfrac{1}{2}}{h}$$

$$= \dfrac{2 - (2 + h)}{2h(2 + h)}$$

$$= \dfrac{-h}{2h(2 + h)}$$

$$= \dfrac{-1}{2(2 + h)}$$

55. $\dfrac{\dfrac{a}{x^2} + \dfrac{x}{a^2}}{a^2 - ax + x^2}$

$$= \dfrac{x^2 a^2}{x^2 a^2} \bullet \dfrac{\dfrac{a}{x^2} + \dfrac{x}{a^2}}{a^2 - ax + x^2}$$

$$= \dfrac{a^3 + x^3}{x^2 a^2 (a^2 - ax + x^2)}$$

$$= \dfrac{(a + x)(a^2 - ax + x^2)}{x^2 a^2 (a^2 - ax + x^2)}$$

$$= \frac{a + x}{x^2 a^2}$$

57. $\dfrac{x + y}{2(x^2 + y^2)} - \dfrac{1}{2(x + y)} + \dfrac{x - y}{x^2 - y^2} - \dfrac{x^3 - y^3}{x^4 - y^4}$

$$= \frac{x + y}{2(x^2 + y^2)} - \frac{1}{2(x + y)} + \frac{1}{x + y} - \frac{(x - y)(x^2 + xy + y^2)}{(x - y)(x + y)(x^2 + y^2)}$$

$$= \frac{x + y}{2(x^2 + y^2)} - \frac{1}{2(x + y)} + \frac{1}{x + y} - \frac{x^2 + xy + y^2}{(x + y)(x^2 + y^2)}$$

$$= \frac{(x + y)(x + y) - (x^2 + y^2) + 2(x^2 + y^2) - 2(x^2 + xy + y^2)}{2(x^2 + y^2)(x + y)}$$

$$= \frac{x^2 + 2xy + y^2 - x^2 - y^2 + 2x^2 + 2y^2 - 2x^2 - 2xy - 2y^2}{2(x^2 + y^2)(x + y)}$$

$$= \frac{0}{2(x^2 + y^2)(x + y)}$$

$$= 0$$

59. $\dfrac{\dfrac{a + b}{a - b} + \dfrac{a - b}{a + b}}{\dfrac{a - b}{a + b} - \dfrac{a + b}{a - b}} \cdot \dfrac{ab^3 - a^3 b}{a^2 + b^2}$

$$= \frac{(a - b)(a + b)}{(a - b)(a + b)} \cdot \frac{\dfrac{a + b}{a - b} + \dfrac{a - b}{a + b}}{\dfrac{a - b}{a + b} - \dfrac{a + b}{a - b}} \cdot \frac{ab(b^2 - a^2)}{a^2 + b^2}$$

$$= \frac{(a + b)^2 + (a - b)^2}{(a - b)^2 - (a + b)^2} \cdot \frac{ab(b - a)(b + a)}{a^2 + b^2}$$

$$= \frac{2a^2 + 2b^2}{-4ab} \cdot \frac{ab(b - a)(b + a)}{a^2 + b^2}$$

$$= \frac{2(a^2 + b^2)}{-4} \cdot \frac{(b - a)(b + a)}{a^2 + b^2}$$

$$= \frac{(b - a)(b + a)}{-2}$$

$$= \frac{b^2 - a^2}{-2}$$

$$= \frac{a^2 - b^2}{2}$$

61. $\dfrac{ap + q}{ax - bx - a^2 + ab} + \dfrac{bp + q}{bx - ax - b^2 + ab}$

$= \dfrac{ap + q}{x(a - b) - a(a - b)} + \dfrac{bp + q}{x(b - a) - b(b - a)}$

$= \dfrac{ap + q}{(a - b)(x - a)} + \dfrac{bp + q}{(b - a)(x - b)}$

$= \dfrac{ap + q}{(a - b)(x - a)} - \dfrac{bp + q}{(a - b)(x - b)}$

$= \dfrac{(ap + q)(x - b) - (bp + q)(x - a)}{(a - b)(x - a)(x - b)}$

$= \dfrac{apx + qx - abp - bq - bpx - qx + apb + aq}{(a - b)(x - a)(x - b)}$

$= \dfrac{apx - bq - bpx + aq}{(a - b)(x - a)(x - b)}$

$= \dfrac{a(px + q) - b(px + q)}{(a - b)(x - a)(x - b)}$

$= \dfrac{(px + q)(a - b)}{(a - b)(x - a)(x - b)}$

$= \dfrac{px + q}{(x - a)(x - b)}$

63. $\dfrac{\dfrac{1}{a} - \dfrac{a - x}{a^2 + x^2}}{\dfrac{1}{x} - \dfrac{x - a}{x^2 + a^2}} + \dfrac{\dfrac{1}{a} - \dfrac{a + x}{a^2 + x^2}}{\dfrac{1}{x} - \dfrac{x + a}{x^2 + a^2}}$

$= \dfrac{ax(a^2 + x^2)}{ax(a^2 + x^2)} \bullet \dfrac{\dfrac{1}{a} - \dfrac{a - x}{a^2 + x^2}}{\dfrac{1}{x} - \dfrac{x - a}{x^2 + a^2}} + \dfrac{ax(a^2 + x^2)}{ax(a^2 + x^2)} \bullet \dfrac{\dfrac{1}{a} - \dfrac{a + x}{a^2 + x^2}}{\dfrac{1}{x} - \dfrac{x + a}{x^2 + a^2}}$

$= \dfrac{x(a^2 + x^2) - (a - x)ax}{a(a^2 + x^2) - (x - a)ax} + \dfrac{x(a^2 + x^2) - (a + x)ax}{a(a^2 + x^2) - (x + a)ax}$

$= \dfrac{a^2x + x^3 - a^2x + ax^2}{a^3 + ax^2 - ax^2 + a^2x} + \dfrac{a^2x + x^3 - a^2x - ax^2}{a^3 + ax^2 - ax^2 - a^2x}$

$= \dfrac{x^3 + ax^2}{a^3 + a^2x} + \dfrac{x^3 - ax^2}{a^3 - a^2x}$

$= \dfrac{x^2(x + a)}{a^2(a + x)} + \dfrac{x^2(x - a)}{a^2(a - x)}$

$= \dfrac{x^2}{a^2} + \dfrac{x^2}{a^2} (-1)$

$= 0$

65. $\dfrac{x^2 - qr}{(p - q)(p - r)} + \dfrac{x^2 - rp}{(q - r)(q - p)} + \dfrac{x^2 - pq}{(r - p)(r - q)}$

$= \dfrac{x^2 - qr}{(p - q)(p - r)} - \dfrac{x^2 - rp}{(q - r)(p - q)} + \dfrac{x^2 - pq}{(p - r)(q - r)}$

$= \dfrac{(x^2 - qr)(q - r) - (x^2 - rp)(p - r) + (x^2 - pq)(p - q)}{(p - q)(p - r)(q - r)}$

$= \dfrac{qx^2 - q^2r - rx^2 + qr^2 - px^2 + p^2r + rx^2 - pr^2 + px^2 - p^2q - qx^2 + pq^2}{(p - q)(p - r)(q - r)}$

$= \dfrac{-q^2r + qr^2 + p^2r - pr^2 - p^2q + pq^2}{(p - q)(p - r)(q - r)}$

$= \dfrac{(p^2r - q^2r) - (pr^2 - qr^2) - (p^2q - pq^2)}{(p - q)(p - r)(q - r)}$

$= \dfrac{r(p - q)(p + q) - r^2(p - q) - pq(p - q)}{(p - q)(p - r)(q - r)}$

$= \dfrac{(p - q)\left(r(p + q) - r^2 - pq\right)}{(p - q)(p - r)(q - r)}$

$= \dfrac{rp + rq - r^2 - pq}{(p - r)(q - r)}$

$= \dfrac{p(r - q) + r(q - r)}{(p - r)(q - r)}$

$= \dfrac{-p(q - r) + r(q - r)}{(p - r)(q - r)}$

$= \dfrac{(q - r)(-p + r)}{(p - r)(q - r)}$

$= \dfrac{-p + r}{p - r}$

$= -1$

67. (a) The sum and the product both equal 1/42

(b) After adding the three fractions and combining the many like terms appearing in the resulting numerator, we obtain:

$\dfrac{b - c}{1 + bc} + \dfrac{c - a}{1 + ca} + \dfrac{a - b}{1 + ab}$

$= \dfrac{ab^2 - ac^2 + bc^2 - a^2b + a^2c - b^2c}{(1 + bc)(1 + ca)(1 + ab)}$

$= \dfrac{(ab^2 - b^2c) + (a^2c - ac^2) + (bc^2 - a^2b)}{(1 + bc)(1 + ca)(1 + ab)}$

$= \dfrac{b^2(a - c) + ac(a - c) + b(c^2 - a^2)}{(1 + bc)(1 + ca)(1 + ab)}$

$$= \frac{b^2(a - c) + ac(a - c) - b(a - c)(a + c)}{(1 + bc)(1 + ca)(1 + ab)}$$

$$= \frac{(a - c)\left(b^2 + ac - b(a + c)\right)}{(1 + bc)(1 + ca)(1 + ab)}$$

$$= \frac{(a - c)\left(b^2 + ac - ab - bc\right)}{(1 + bc)(1 + ca)(1 + ab)}$$

$$= \frac{(a - c)\left(c(a - b) - b(a - b)\right)}{(1 + bc)(1 + ca)(1 + ab)}$$

$$= \frac{(a - c)\left((a - b)(c - b)\right)}{(1 + bc)(1 + ca)(1 + ab)}$$

$$= \frac{(c - a)(a - b)(b - c)}{(1 + bc)(1 + ca)(1 + ab)}$$

$$= \frac{b - c}{1 + bc} \bullet \frac{c - a}{1 + ca} \bullet \frac{a - b}{1 + ab}, \text{ as required.}$$

69. For convenience, let $z = x - y$. Then $-z = y - x$, and we have:

$$(1 + a^z)^{-1} + (1 + a^{-z})^{-1} = \frac{1}{1 + a^z} + \frac{1}{1 + \frac{1}{a^z}}$$

$$= \frac{1}{1 + a^z} + \frac{a^z}{a^z} \bullet \frac{1}{1 + \frac{1}{a^z}}$$

$$= \frac{1}{1 + a^z} + \frac{a^z}{a^z + 1}$$

$$= \frac{1 + a^z}{1 + a^z}$$

$$= 1$$

1.11 The Complex Number System

1.

i^2	i^3	i^4	i^5	i^6	i^7	i^8
−1	−i	1	i	−1	−i	1

3. (a) real: 4
        imaginary: 5

    (b) real: 4
        imaginary: -5

    (c) real: $\frac{1}{2}$
        imaginary: -1

    (d) real: 0
        imaginary: 16

5. Equating the real parts gives 2c = 8, and therefore c = 4.
    Similarly, equating the imaginary parts yields d = -3.

7. (a) (5 - 6i) + (9 + 2i) = (5 + 9) + (-6 + 2)i = 14 - 4i
    (b) (5 - 6i) - (9 + 2i) = (5 - 9) + (-6 - 2)i = -4 - 8i

9. (a) $(3 - 4i)(5 + i) = 15 - 17i - 4i^2 = 19 - 17i$

    (b) (5 + i)(3 - 4i) = 19 - 17i , from part (a)

    (c) $\dfrac{3 - 4i}{5 + i} \cdot \dfrac{5 - i}{5 - i}$ $= \dfrac{15 - 23i + 4i^2}{25 - i^2}$

        $= \dfrac{11 - 23i}{26}$

        $= \dfrac{11}{26} - \dfrac{23}{26} i$

    (d) $\dfrac{5 + i}{3 - 4i} \cdot \dfrac{3 + 4i}{3 + 4i}$ $= \dfrac{15 + 23i + 4i^2}{9 - 16i^2}$

        $= \dfrac{11 + 23i}{25}$

        $= \dfrac{11}{25} + \dfrac{23}{25} i$

11. (a) z + w = (2 + 3i) + (9 - 4i) = 11 - i

    (b) $\bar{z}$ + w = (2 - 3i) + (9 - 4i) = 11 - 7i

    (c) z + $\bar{z}$ = (2 + 3i) + (2 - 3i) = 4

13. $(z + w) + w_1 = \big((2 + 3i) + (9 - 4i)\big) + (-7 - i)$
$$= (11 - i) + (-7 - i)$$
$$= 4 - 2i$$

15. $zw = (2 + 3i)(9 - 4i) = 18 + 19i - 12i^2 = 30 + 19i$

17. $z\overline{z} = (2 + 3i)(2 - 3i) = 4 - 9i^2 = 13$

19. $ww_1 = (9 - 4i)(-7 - i) = -63 + 19i + 4i^2 = -67 + 19i$, so
$z(ww_1) = (2 + 3i)(-67 + 19i) = -134 - 163i + 57i^2 = -191 - 163i$

21. $w + w_1 = (9 - 4i)(-7 - i) = 2 - 5i$, so
$z(w + w_1) = (2 + 3i)(2 - 5i) = 4 - 4i - 15i^2 = 19 - 4i$

23. $z^2 = (2 + 3i)(2 + 3i) = 4 + 12i + 9i^2 = -5 + 12i$, and
$w^2 = (9 - 4i)(9 - 4i) = 81 - 72i + 16i^2 = 65 - 72i$, so
$z^2 - w^2 = (-5 + 12i) - (65 - 72i) = -70 + 84i$

25. $zw = 30 + 19i$ (from # 15), so $(zw)^2 = (30 + 19i)(30 + 19i)$
$$= 900 + 1140i + 361i^2$$
$$= 539 + 1140i$$

27. $z^2 = -5 + 12i$ (from # 23), so
$z^3 = z \bullet z^2 = (2 + 3i)(-5 + 12i) = -10 + 9i + 36i^2 = -46 + 9i$

29. $\dfrac{z}{w} = \dfrac{2 + 3i}{9 - 4i} \bullet \dfrac{9 + 4i}{9 + 4i}$

$$= \dfrac{18 + 35i + 12i^2}{81 - 16i^2}$$

$$= \dfrac{6 + 35i}{97}$$

$$= \dfrac{6}{97} + \dfrac{35}{97}i$$

31. By first calculating $\overline{z}$ and $\overline{w}$, we have:

$\dfrac{2 - 3i}{9 + 4i} \bullet \dfrac{9 - 4i}{9 - 4i} \quad = \dfrac{18 - 35i + 12i^2}{81 - 16i^2}$

$$= \dfrac{6 - 35i}{97}$$

$$= \dfrac{6}{97} - \dfrac{35}{97}i$$

33. By first calculating $\bar{z}$, we have:

$$\frac{2+3i}{2-3i} \cdot \frac{2+3i}{2+3i} = \frac{4+12i+9i^2}{4-9i^2}$$

$$= \frac{-5+12i}{13}$$

$$= -\frac{5}{13} + \frac{12}{13}i$$

35. $w - \bar{w} = (9-4i) - (9+4i) = -8i,$ so the fraction becomes $\frac{-8i}{2i} = -4$

37. $\dfrac{i}{5+i} \cdot \dfrac{5-i}{5-i} = \dfrac{5i-i^2}{25-i^2}$

$$= \frac{1+5i}{26}$$

$$= \frac{1}{26} + \frac{5}{26}i$$

39. $\dfrac{1}{i} \cdot \dfrac{i}{i} = \dfrac{i}{i^2} = \dfrac{i}{-1} = -i$

41. $\sqrt{-49} + \sqrt{-9} + \sqrt{-4} = 7i + 3i + 2i = 12i$

43. $\sqrt{-20} - 3\sqrt{-45} + \sqrt{-80} = \sqrt{4}\sqrt{-5} - 3\sqrt{9}\sqrt{-5} + \sqrt{16}\sqrt{-5}$

$$= 2\sqrt{5}i - 9\sqrt{5}i + 4\sqrt{5}i$$

$$= -3\sqrt{5}i$$

45. $1 + \sqrt{-36}\sqrt{-36} = 1 + (6i)(6i) = 1 + 36i^2 = -35$

47. $3\sqrt{-128} - 4\sqrt{-18} = 3\sqrt{-64}\sqrt{2} - 4\sqrt{-9}\sqrt{2}$

$$= 3(8i)\sqrt{2} - 4(3i)\sqrt{2}$$

$$= 24\sqrt{2}i - 12\sqrt{2}i$$

$$= 12\sqrt{2}i$$

49. (a) $z + w = (a+bi) + (c+di) = (a+c) + (b+d)i$

   (b) $z - w = (a+bi) - (c+di) = (a-c) + (b-d)i$

   (c) $zw = (a+bi)(c+di)$
   $$= ac + bci + adi + bdi^2$$
   $$= (ac-bd) + (bc+ad)i$$

(d) $\dfrac{z}{w} = \dfrac{a + bi}{c + di} \cdot \dfrac{c - di}{c - di}$

$\phantom{(d) \dfrac{z}{w}} = \dfrac{ac + bci - adi - bdi^2}{c^2 - d^2i^2}$

$\phantom{(d) \dfrac{z}{w}} = \dfrac{ac + bd}{c^2 + d^2} + \dfrac{bc - ad}{c^2 + d^2}\,i$

51. (a) $z^3 = \left(\dfrac{-1 + i\sqrt{3}}{2}\right)^3$ $\qquad\qquad$ $w^3 = \left(\dfrac{-1 - i\sqrt{3}}{2}\right)^3$

$ = \dfrac{(-1 + i\sqrt{3})^3}{8}$ $\qquad\qquad = \dfrac{(-1 - i\sqrt{3})^3}{8}$

$ = \dfrac{(-1 + i\sqrt{3})(-1 + i\sqrt{3})^2}{8}$ $\qquad = \dfrac{(-1 - i\sqrt{3})(-1 - i\sqrt{3})^2}{8}$

$ = \dfrac{(-1 + i\sqrt{3})(1 - 2i\sqrt{3} + 3i^2)}{8}$ $\qquad = \dfrac{(-1 - i\sqrt{3})(1 + 2i\sqrt{3} + 3i^2)}{8}$

$ = \dfrac{(-1 + i\sqrt{3})(-2 - 2i\sqrt{3})}{8}$ $\qquad = \dfrac{(-1 - i\sqrt{3})(-2 + 2i\sqrt{3})}{8}$

$ = \dfrac{2 - 2i\sqrt{3} + 2i\sqrt{3} - 6i^2}{8}$ $\qquad = \dfrac{2 + 2i\sqrt{3} - 2i\sqrt{3} - 6i^2}{8}$

$ = \dfrac{8}{8}$ $\qquad\qquad\qquad\qquad = \dfrac{8}{8}$

$ = 1$ $\qquad\qquad\qquad\qquad\qquad = 1$

(b) $zw = \left(\dfrac{-1 + i\sqrt{3}}{2}\right)\left(\dfrac{-1 - i\sqrt{3}}{2}\right) = \dfrac{1 - i\sqrt{3} + i\sqrt{3} - 3i^2}{4} = \dfrac{4}{4} = 1$

(c) $w^2 = \left(\dfrac{-1 - i\sqrt{3}}{2}\right)^2$ $\qquad\qquad$ $z^2 = \left(\dfrac{-1 + i\sqrt{3}}{2}\right)^2$

$ = \dfrac{1 + 2i\sqrt{3} + 3i^2}{4}$ $\qquad\qquad = \dfrac{1 - 2i\sqrt{3} + 3i^2}{4}$

$ = \dfrac{-2 + 2i\sqrt{3}}{4}$ $\qquad\qquad\qquad = \dfrac{-2 - 2i\sqrt{3}}{4}$

$ = \dfrac{-1 + i\sqrt{3}}{2}$ $\qquad\qquad\qquad = \dfrac{-1 - i\sqrt{3}}{2}$

$ = z$ $\qquad\qquad\qquad\qquad\qquad = w$

(d) $(1 - z + z^2)(1 + z - z^2)$

$ = (1 - z + w)(1 + z - w)$

$ = \left(\dfrac{2}{2} - \dfrac{-1 + i\sqrt{3}}{2} + \dfrac{-1 - i\sqrt{3}}{2}\right)\left(\dfrac{2}{2} + \dfrac{-1 + i\sqrt{3}}{2} - \dfrac{-1 - i\sqrt{3}}{2}\right)$

$$= \left(\frac{2 - 2i\sqrt{3}}{2}\right)\left(\frac{2 + 2i\sqrt{3}}{2}\right)$$
$$= (1 - i\sqrt{3})(1 + i\sqrt{3})$$
$$= 1 - 3i^2$$
$$= 4$$

53. (a) Let $z = a + bi$, then $0 + z = (0 + 0i) + (a + bi) = a + bi = z$, and
$$z + 0 = (a + bi) + (0 + 0i) = a + bi = z.$$

(b) $0 \cdot z = (0 + 0i)(a + bi) = 0 + 0i = 0$, and
$z \cdot 0 = (a + bi)(0 + 0i) = 0.$

55. (a) $z + w = (a + bi) + (c + di) = (a + c) + (b + d)i$
$w + z = (c + di) + (a + bi) = (c + a) + (b + d)i = z + w$

(b) $zw = (a + bi)(c + di)$
$\quad\quad = ac + bci + adi + bdi^2$
$\quad\quad = (ac - bd) + (bc + ad)i$
$wz = (c + di)(a + bi)$
$\quad\quad = ac + adi + bci + bdi^2$
$\quad\quad = (ac - bd) + (bc + ad)i$
$\quad\quad = zw$

57. $\dfrac{a + bi}{a - bi} + \dfrac{a - bi}{a + bi}$

$\quad\quad = \dfrac{a + bi}{a - bi} \cdot \dfrac{a + bi}{a + bi} + \dfrac{a - bi}{a + bi} \cdot \dfrac{a - bi}{a - bi}$

$\quad\quad = \dfrac{(a + bi)^2}{a^2 + b^2} + \dfrac{(a - bi)^2}{a^2 + b^2}$

$\quad\quad = \dfrac{a^2 + 2abi - b^2 + a^2 - 2abi - b^2}{a^2 + b^2}$

$\quad\quad = \dfrac{2a^2 - 2b^2}{a^2 + b^2}$

Thus the real part is $\dfrac{2a^2 - 2b^2}{a^2 + b^2}$, and the imaginary part is 0.

59. $\dfrac{(a + bi)^2}{a - bi} - \dfrac{(a - bi)^2}{a + bi}$

$\quad = \dfrac{(a + bi)^3 - (a - bi)^3}{(a - bi)(a + bi)}$

$\quad = \dfrac{(a^3 + 3a^2bi + 3ab^2i^2 + b^3i^3) - (a^3 - 3a^2bi + 3ab^2i^2 - b^3i^3)}{a^2 - b^2i^2}$

$$= \frac{(a^3 - 3ab^2) + (3a^2b - b^3)i - (a^3 - 3ab^2) + (3a^2b - b^3)i}{a^2 + b^2}$$

$$= \frac{(6a^2b - 2b^3)}{a^2 + b^2} \, i$$

Thus the real part is 0.

Chapter 1 Review Exercises

1. $a^2 - 16b^2 \;=\; a^2 - (4b)^2 \;=\; (a - 4b)(a + 4b)$

3. $8 - (a + 1)^3 \;=\; \big(2 - (a + 1)\big)\big(4 + 2(a + 1) + (a + 1)^2\big)$

$$= (1 - a)(4 + 2a + 2 + a^2 + 2a + 1)$$
$$= (1 - a)(7 + 4a + a^2)$$

5. $a^2x^3 + 2ax^2b + b^2x \;=\; x(a^2x^2 + 2abx + b^2)$

$$= x(ax + b)^2$$

7. $8x^2 + 6x + 1 \;=\; (4x + 1)(2x + 1)$

9. $a^4x^4 - x^8a^8 \;=\; a^4x^4(1 - x^4a^4)$

$$= a^4x^4(1 - x^2a^2)(1 + x^2a^2)$$
$$= a^4x^4(1 - xa)(1 + xa)(1 + x^2a^2)$$

11. $8 + 12a + 6a^2 + a^3 \;=\; (8 + a^3) + (12a + 6a^2)$

$$= (2 + a)(4 - 2a + a^2) + 6a(2 + a)$$
$$= (2 + a)(4 - 2a + a^2 + 6a)$$
$$= (2 + a)(4 + 4a + a^2)$$
$$= (2 + a)(2 + a)^2$$
$$= (2 + a)^3$$

13. $4x^2y^2z^3 - 3xyz^3 - z^3 \;=\; z^3(4x^2y^2 - 3xy - 1)$

$$= z^3(4xy + 1)(xy - 1)$$

15. $1 - x^6 \;=\; (1^3)^2 - (x^3)^2$

$$= (1 - x^3)(1 + x^3)$$
$$= (1 - x)(1 + x + x^2)(1 + x)(1 - x + x^2)$$

17. $a^2x^2 + 2abx + b^2 - 4a^2b^2x^2 = (ax + b)^2 - (2abx)^2$
$= (ax + b - 2abx)(ax + b + 2abx)$

19. $a^2 - b^2 + ac - bc + a^2b - b^2a = (a - b)(a + b) + c(a - b) + ab(a - b)$
$= (a - b)(a + b + c + ab)$

21. $4^{3/2} = (\sqrt{4})^3 = 2^3 = 8$

23. $\left((3025)^{1/2}\right)^0 = 1$

25. $8^{-4/3} = \left(\sqrt[3]{8}\right)^{-4} = 2^{-4} = \dfrac{1}{2^4} = \dfrac{1}{16}$

27. $(-243)^{-2/5} = \left(\sqrt[5]{-243}\right)^{-2} = (-3)^{-2} = \dfrac{1}{(-3)^2} = \dfrac{1}{9}$

29. $(a^2b^6c^8)^{1/2} = a^{2/2}b^{6/2}c^{8/2} = ab^3c^4$

31. $\sqrt{a^3b^5}\,\sqrt{4ab^3} = \sqrt{4a^4b^8} = 2a^2b^4$

33. $\sqrt[3]{16} - \sqrt[3]{-54} = \sqrt[3]{8}\,\sqrt[3]{2} - \sqrt[3]{-27}\,\sqrt[3]{2}$
$= 2\sqrt[3]{2} - (-3)\sqrt[3]{2}$
$= 5\sqrt[3]{2}$

35. $\sqrt{24a^2b^3} + ba\sqrt{54b} = \sqrt{4a^2b^2}\,\sqrt{6b} + ba\sqrt{9}\,\sqrt{6b}$
$= 2ab\sqrt{6b} + 3ab\sqrt{6b}$
$= 5ab\sqrt{6b}$

37. $\sqrt{t^2} = |t|$

39. $\sqrt[4]{16x^4} = |2x| = 2|x|$

41. (a) $\sqrt[3]{x}\,\sqrt[4]{x^3} = x^{1/3}\,x^{3/4} = x^{4/12}\,x^{9/12} = x^{13/12}$

(b) $x^{13/12} = \sqrt[12]{x^{13}} = x\sqrt[12]{x}$

43. (a) $\sqrt{\sqrt[3]{t}\,\sqrt[5]{t^4}}$ $= (t^{1/3}\, t^{4/5})^{1/2}$

$= (t^{5/15}\, t^{12/15})^{1/2}$

$= (t^{17/15})^{1/2}$

$= t^{17/30}$

(b) $t^{17/30} = \sqrt[30]{t^{17}}$

45. $\dfrac{6}{\sqrt{3}} \cdot \dfrac{\sqrt{3}}{\sqrt{3}} = \dfrac{6\sqrt{3}}{3} = 2\sqrt{3}$

47. $\dfrac{1}{\sqrt{6} - \sqrt{3}} \cdot \dfrac{\sqrt{6} + \sqrt{3}}{\sqrt{6} + \sqrt{3}} = \dfrac{\sqrt{6} + \sqrt{3}}{6 - 3} = \dfrac{\sqrt{6} + \sqrt{3}}{3}$

49. $\dfrac{\sqrt{a^2 + x^2} + \sqrt{a^2 - x^2}}{\sqrt{a^2 + x^2} - \sqrt{a^2 - x^2}} \cdot \dfrac{\sqrt{a^2 + x^2} + \sqrt{a^2 - x^2}}{\sqrt{a^2 + x^2} + \sqrt{a^2 - x^2}}$

$= \dfrac{(a^2 + x^2) + 2\sqrt{a^4 - x^4} + (a^2 - x^2)}{(a^2 + x^2) - (a^2 - x^2)}$

$= \dfrac{2a^2 + 2\sqrt{a^4 - x^4}}{2x^2}$

$= \dfrac{a^2 + \sqrt{a^4 - x^4}}{x^2}$

51. $\dfrac{1}{\sqrt{2} + \sqrt{3} + \sqrt{5}} \cdot \dfrac{\sqrt{2} + \sqrt{3} - \sqrt{5}}{\sqrt{2} + \sqrt{3} - \sqrt{5}}$

$= \dfrac{\sqrt{2} + \sqrt{3} - \sqrt{5}}{(\sqrt{2} + \sqrt{3})^2 - 5}$

$= \dfrac{\sqrt{2} + \sqrt{3} - \sqrt{5}}{2 + 2\sqrt{6} + 3 - 5}$

$= \dfrac{\sqrt{2} + \sqrt{3} - \sqrt{5}}{2\sqrt{6}} \cdot \dfrac{\sqrt{6}}{\sqrt{6}}$

$= \dfrac{\sqrt{12} + \sqrt{18} - \sqrt{30}}{2(6)}$

$= \dfrac{2\sqrt{3} + 3\sqrt{2} - \sqrt{30}}{12}$

53. $\dfrac{\sqrt{t} - a}{t - a^2} \cdot \dfrac{\sqrt{t} + a}{\sqrt{t} + a} = \dfrac{t - a^2}{(t - a^2)(\sqrt{t} + a)} = \dfrac{1}{\sqrt{t} + a}$

55. $\dfrac{\sqrt[3]{x} - 2}{x - 8}$ $= \dfrac{x^{1/3} - 2}{(x^{1/3})^3 - 2^3}$

$= \dfrac{x^{1/3} - 2}{(x^{1/3} - 2)(x^{2/3} + 2x^{1/3} + 4)}$

$= \dfrac{1}{\sqrt[3]{x^2} + 2\sqrt[3]{x} + 4}$

57. $(3x + 1)^2 = (3x)^2 + 2(3x)(1) + (1)^2$
$= 9x^2 + 6x + 1$

59. $(3x^2 + y^2)^2 = (3x^2)^2 + 2(3x^2)(y^2) + (y^2)^2$
$= 9x^4 + 6x^2y^2 + y^4$

61. $(2a + 3)^3 = (2a)^3 + 3(2a)^2(3) + 3(2a)(3^2) + 3^3$
$= 8a^3 + 36a^2 + 54a + 27$

63. $(1 - 3a)(1 + 3a + 9a^2) = 1^3 - (3a)^3 = 1 - 27a^3$

65. $(x^{1/2} - y^{1/2})(x^{1/2} + y^{1/2}) = (x^{1/2})^2 - (y^{1/2})^2 = x - y$

67. $(x^{1/3} + y^{1/3})^3 = (x^{1/3})^3 + 3(x^{1/3})^2(y^{1/3}) + 3(x^{1/3})(y^{1/3})^2 + (y^{1/3})^3$
$= x + 3x^{2/3}y^{1/3} + 3x^{1/3}y^{2/3} + y$

69. $(x^2 - 3x + 1)^2 = \left(x^2 - (3x - 1)\right)^2$
$= x^4 - 2x^2(3x - 1) + (3x - 1)^2$
$= x^4 - 6x^3 + 2x^2 + 9x^2 - 6x + 1$
$= x^4 - 6x^3 + 11x^2 - 6x + 1$

71. $(3 - 2i)(3 + 2i) + (1 + 3i)^2 = 9 - 4i^2 + 1 + 6i + 9i^2$
$= 9 + 4 + 1 + 6i - 9$
$= 5 + 6i$

73. $(1 + i\sqrt{2})(1 - i\sqrt{2}) + (\sqrt{2} + i)(\sqrt{2} - i) = 1 - 2i^2 + 2 - i^2$
$= 1 + 2 + 2 + 1$
$= 6$

75. $\dfrac{3 - i\sqrt{3}}{3 + i\sqrt{3}} \cdot \dfrac{3 - i\sqrt{3}}{3 - i\sqrt{3}}$

$= \dfrac{9 - 6i\sqrt{3} - 3}{9 + 3}$

$= \dfrac{6 - 6i\sqrt{3}}{12}$

$= \dfrac{1 - i\sqrt{3}}{2}$

$= \dfrac{1}{2} - \dfrac{\sqrt{3}}{2} i$

77. $-\sqrt{-2}\,\sqrt{-9} + \sqrt{-8} - \sqrt{-72} = -(i\sqrt{2})(3i) + 2i\sqrt{2} - 6i\sqrt{2}$

$= 3\sqrt{2} - 4i\sqrt{2}$

$= 3\sqrt{2} - 4\sqrt{2}\,i$

79. Let $z = a + bi$, so $\bar{z} = a - bi$. Then

$\dfrac{z + \bar{z}}{2} = \dfrac{a + bi + a - bi}{2} = \dfrac{2a}{2} = a = \text{Re}(z)$

81. (a) $|6 + 2i| = \sqrt{6^2 + 2^2} = \sqrt{36 + 4} = \sqrt{40} = 2\sqrt{10}$

$|6 - 2i| = \sqrt{6^2 + (-2)^2} = \sqrt{36 + 4} = \sqrt{40} = 2\sqrt{10}$

(b) $|-3| = |-3 + 0i| = \sqrt{(-3)^2 + 0^2} = \sqrt{9} = 3$

(c) Let $z = a + bi$, so $\bar{z} = a - bi$. Then

$z\bar{z} = (a + bi)(a - bi) = a^2 - b^2 i^2 = a^2 + b^2$, and

$|z|^2 = \left(\sqrt{a^2 + b^2}\right)^2 = a^2 + b^2$

Thus $z\bar{z} = |z|^2$

83. distributive property (used twice), associative property of addition

85. distributive property

87. $|x - 6| = 2$

89. $|a - b| = 3$

91. $|x - 0| > 10$, so $|x| > 10$

93. $|\sqrt{6} - 2| = \sqrt{6} - 2$, since $\sqrt{6} - 2 > 0$

95. $\left| x^4 + x^2 + 1 \right| = x^4 + x^2 + 1$, since $x^4 + x^2 + 1 > 0$

97. (a) If $x < 2$, then $x - 2 < 0$ and $x - 3 < 0$, so:

$$\left| x - 2 \right| + \left| x - 3 \right| = -(x - 2) - (x - 3)$$
$$= -2x + 5$$

(b) If $2 < x < 3$, then $x - 2 > 0$ and $x - 3 < 0$, so:

$$\left| x - 2 \right| + \left| x - 3 \right| = x - 2 - (x - 3)$$
$$= x - 2 - x + 3$$
$$= 1$$

(c) If $x > 3$, then $x - 2 > 0$ and $x - 3 > 0$, so:

$$\left| x - 2 \right| + \left| x - 3 \right| = x - 2 + x - 3$$
$$= 2x - 5$$

99. (a) true
(b) true
(c) true

(d) true (since $0.\overline{9} = 1$!)

101.

103.

105. 1.4×10^{-3}

107. 1.2001×10^{1}

109. $1 - 2\big(3 - 4(1 - 5)\big) = 1 - 2\big(3 - 4(-4)\big) = 1 - 2(19) = -37$

111. $1 + 3(x^2 - 5x - 4) - \big(1 - (15x - 3x^2)\big)$
$= 1 + 3x^2 - 15x - 12 - (1 - 15x + 3x^2)$
$= 3x^2 - 15x - 11 - 1 + 15x - 3x^2$
$= -12$

113. $(x - 1)(x + 1)(x + 2) = (x^2 - 1)(x + 2)$

113. $(x - 1)(x + 1)(x + 2) = (x^2 - 1)(x + 2)$
$$= x^3 - x + 2x^2 - 2$$
$$= x^3 + 2x^2 - x - 2$$

115. $x^2 + 4 - (x - 1)(x - 2) = x^2 + 4 - (x^2 - 3x + 2)$
$$= x^2 + 4 - x^2 + 3x - 2$$
$$= 3x + 2$$

117.

$$\begin{array}{r} x^2 - x \\ x - 1 \overline{\smash{\big)}\ x^3 - 2x^2 + x + 4} \\ \underline{x^3 - x^2} \\ -x^2 + x \\ \underline{-x^2 + x} \\ 0 + 4 \end{array}$$

quotient: $x^2 - x$
remainder: 4

119.

$$\begin{array}{r} x^2 - 2 \\ x^2 + 1 \overline{\smash{\big)}\ x^4 - x^2 + 1} \\ \underline{x^4 + x^2} \\ -2x^2 + 1 \\ \underline{-2x^2 - 2} \\ 3 \end{array}$$

quotient: $x^2 - 2$
remainder: 3

121.

3   9

123.

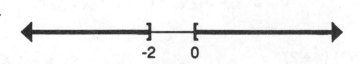

-2   0

125. (a)

(b)

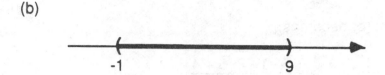

127. Let $x = 12.\overline{71}$, so $100x = 1271.\overline{71}$. Then $100x - x = 1259$

$$99x = 1259$$

$$x = \frac{1259}{99}$$

129.

x	$1 + \dfrac{x}{2}$	$\sqrt{1+x}$
0.1	1.05	1.048808
0.01	1.005	1.004987
0.001	1.0005	1.000499

131. (a) 0.447214 (to six decimal places)

(b) 0.447214 (to six decimal places)

(c) $\dfrac{\sqrt{3} - \sqrt{5}}{\sqrt{2} + \sqrt{7 - 3\sqrt{5}}} \cdot \dfrac{\sqrt{2} - \sqrt{7 - 3\sqrt{5}}}{\sqrt{2} - \sqrt{7 - 3\sqrt{5}}}$

$$= \frac{\sqrt{6 - 2\sqrt{5}} - \sqrt{(3 - \sqrt{5})(7 - 3\sqrt{5})}}{2 - (7 - 3\sqrt{5})}$$

$$= \frac{\sqrt{6 - 2\sqrt{5}} - \sqrt{21 - 16\sqrt{5} + 15}}{-5 + 3\sqrt{5}}$$

$$= \frac{\sqrt{6 - 2\sqrt{5}} - \sqrt{36 - 16\sqrt{5}}}{-5 + 3\sqrt{5}}$$

$$= \frac{\sqrt{6 - 2\sqrt{5}} - 2\sqrt{9 - 4\sqrt{5}}}{-5 + 3\sqrt{5}}$$

(d) $(\sqrt{5} - 1)^2 = 5 - 2\sqrt{5} + 1 = 6 - 2\sqrt{5}$, so $\sqrt{5} - 1 = \sqrt{6 - 2\sqrt{5}}$. Also

$(\sqrt{5} - 2)^2 = 5 - 4\sqrt{5} + 4 = 9 - 4\sqrt{5}$, so $\sqrt{5} - 2 = \sqrt{9 - 4\sqrt{5}}$

(e) The expression from (c) becomes:

$$\frac{\sqrt{5} - 1 - 2(\sqrt{5} - 2)}{-5 + 3\sqrt{5}} = \frac{\sqrt{5} - 1 - 2\sqrt{5} + 4}{-5 + 3\sqrt{5}}$$

$$= \frac{3 - \sqrt{5}}{-5 + 3\sqrt{5}} \cdot \frac{-5 - 3\sqrt{5}}{-5 - 3\sqrt{5}}$$

$$= \frac{-15 - 4\sqrt{5} + 15}{25 - 45}$$

$$= \frac{-4\sqrt{5}}{-20}$$

$$= \frac{\sqrt{5}}{5} , \text{ as required.}$$

133. $\dfrac{1}{a - bi} - \dfrac{1}{a + bi} = \dfrac{(a + bi) - (a - bi)}{(a - bi)(a + bi)}$

$$= \frac{2bi}{a^2 - b^2 i^2}$$

$$= \frac{2bi}{a^2 + b^2}$$

135. $\dfrac{a + bi}{a - bi} - \dfrac{a - bi}{a + bi} = \dfrac{(a + bi)^2 - (a - bi)^2}{(a - bi)(a + bi)}$

$$= \frac{a^2 + 2abi - b^2 - a^2 + 2abi + b^2}{a^2 + b^2}$$

$$= \frac{4abi}{a^2 + b^2}$$

137. The LCM is $(a - b)(a - c)(b - c)$. We first build each fraction:

$$\frac{bc(x - a)^2}{(a - b)(a - c)} \cdot \frac{b - c}{b - c} = \frac{(b^2 c - bc^2)(x - a)^2}{(a - b)(a - c)(b - c)}$$

$$\frac{ca(x - b)^2}{(b - c)(b - a)} \cdot \frac{-1 (a - c)}{-1 (a - c)} = \frac{(ac^2 - a^2 c)(x - b)^2}{(a - b)(a - c)(b - c)}$$

$$\frac{ab(x - c)^2}{(c - a)(c - b)} \cdot \frac{(-1)(-1)(a - b)}{(-1)(-1)(a - b)} = \frac{(a^2 b - ab^2)(x - c)^2}{(a - b)(a - c)(b - c)}$$

Adding the fractions, multiplying out all numerators, and grouping terms results in the fraction:

$$\frac{[a^2(b-c) + b^2(c-a) + c^2(a-b)]x^2}{(a-b)(a-c)(b-c)} = \frac{(b-c)(a-b)(a-c)x^2}{(a-b)(a-c)(b-c)} = x^2$$

So the fractions add to x^2 !

CHAPTER 2
EQUATIONS AND INEQUALITIES

2.1 Linear Equations

1. $2x - 3 = -5$
   $2x = -2$
   $x = -1$

3. $8x - 4 = 20$
   $8x = 24$
   $x = 3$

5. $1 - y = 12$
   $-y = 11$
   $y = -11$

7. $2m - 1 + 3m + 5 = 6m - 8$
   $5m + 4 = 6m - 8$
   $-m = -12$
   $m = 12$

9. $(x + 2)(x + 1) = x^2 + 11$

$x^2 + 3x + 2 = x^2 + 11$

$3x + 2 = 11$

$3x = 9$

$x = 3$

11. $4(y - 1) + 5(y - 3) = 2(y + 1) - 28$

$4y - 4 + 5y - 15 = 2y + 2 - 28$

$9y - 19 = 2y - 26$

$7y = -7$

$y = -1$

13. $1 - (x - 2)^2 = -x^2 + 5x + 3$

$1 - (x^2 - 4x + 4) = -x^2 + 5x + 3$

$1 - x^2 + 4x - 4 = -x^2 + 5x + 3$

$4x - 3 = 5x + 3$

$-x = 6$

$x = -6$

15. $(x - 1)^2 - (x^2 - 1) = 16$

$x^2 - 2x + 1 - x^2 + 1 = 16$

$-2x + 2 = 16$

$-2x = 14$

$x = -7$

17. $\dfrac{x}{3} + \dfrac{2x}{5} = \dfrac{-11}{5}$

$15\left(\dfrac{x}{3}\right) + 15\left(\dfrac{2x}{5}\right) = 15\left(\dfrac{-11}{5}\right)$

$5x + 6x = -33$

$11x = -33$

$x = -3$

19. $1 - \dfrac{y}{3} = 6$

$3(1) - 3\left(\dfrac{y}{3}\right) = 3(6)$

$3 - y = 18$

$-y = 15$

$y = -15$

21.
$$3 - \frac{x - 1}{4} = \frac{x}{9}$$
$$36\left(3 - \frac{x - 1}{4}\right) = 36\left(\frac{x}{9}\right)$$
$$108 - 9(x - 1) = 4x$$
$$108 - 9x + 9 = 4x$$
$$-13x = -117$$
$$x = \frac{-117}{-13}$$
$$x = 9$$

23.
$$\frac{x - 1}{4} + \frac{2x + 3}{-1} = 0$$
$$4\left(\frac{x - 1}{4} + \frac{2x + 3}{-1}\right) = 4(0)$$
$$x - 1 - 4(2x + 3) = 0$$
$$x - 1 - 8x - 12 = 0$$
$$-7x = 13$$
$$x = -\frac{13}{7}$$

25.
$$\frac{1}{x - 3} - \frac{2}{x + 3} = \frac{1}{x^2 - 9}$$
$$\frac{(x - 3)(x + 3)}{x - 3} - \frac{2(x - 3)(x + 3)}{x + 3} = \frac{(x - 3)(x + 3)}{(x - 3)(x + 3)}$$
$$x + 3 - 2(x - 3) = 1$$
$$x + 3 - 2x + 6 = 1$$
$$-x = -8$$
$$x = 8$$

Check: Replacing x by 8 in the original equation yields:
$$\frac{1}{5} - \frac{2}{11} = \frac{1}{55}$$
$$\frac{11}{55} - \frac{10}{55} = \frac{1}{55} \text{, which is true.}$$

27.
$$\frac{1}{x - 5} + \frac{1}{x + 5} = \frac{2x}{x^2 - 25}$$
$$\frac{(x - 5)(x + 5)}{x - 5} + \frac{(x - 5)(x + 5)}{x + 5} = \frac{2x(x - 5)(x + 5)}{(x - 5)(x + 5)}$$
$$x + 5 + x - 5 = 2x$$
$$2x = 2x$$

This last equation is an identity; it is satisfied by all real numbers. However, in the original equation, note that x cannot take on the values ±5, since that leads to denominators that are zero. Thus the original equation is satisfied by all real numbers except 5 and -5.

29.
$$\frac{4}{x + 2} + \frac{1}{x - 2} = \frac{4}{x^2 - 4}$$

$$\frac{4(x - 2)(x + 2)}{x + 2} + \frac{(x - 2)(x + 2)}{x - 2} = \frac{4(x - 2)(x + 2)}{(x - 2)(x + 2)}$$

$$4(x - 2) + (x + 2) = 4$$
$$4x - 8 + x + 2 = 4$$
$$5x = 10$$
$$x = 2$$

This shows that <u>if</u> the original equation has a solution, it must be $x = 2$. However, the value $x = 2$ does not check in the original equation (it produces zeros in two of the denominators). Consequently, the original equation has no solutions.

31.
$$\frac{2(x + 1)}{x - 1} - 3 = \frac{5x - 1}{x - 1}$$

$$2(x + 1) - 3(x - 1) = 5x - 1$$
$$2x + 2 - 3x + 3 = 5x - 1$$
$$-x + 5 = 5x - 1$$
$$-6x = -6$$
$$x = 1$$

This shows that if the original equation has a solution, it must be $x = 1$. However, the value $x = 1$ does not satisfy the original equation, since it yields zeros in the denominators. Consequently, the original equation has no solution.

33.
$$\frac{1}{x} = \frac{4}{x} - 1$$
$$1 = 4 - x \quad \text{(multiplying by x)}$$
$$x = 3$$

<u>Check:</u>
$$\frac{1}{3} = \frac{4}{3} - 1$$
$$\frac{1}{3} = \frac{4}{3} - \frac{3}{3} \quad , \text{which is true.}$$

35. $|x - 5| = 1$
If $x - 5 \geq 0$, the equation becomes:
$$x - 5 = 1$$
$$x = 6$$

If x - 5 < 0, the equation becomes:
$$-(x - 5) = 1$$
$$-x + 5 = 1$$
$$-x = -4$$
$$x = 4$$

The solutions of the original equation are x = 6 and x = 4.

37. $|6x - 5| = 25$

If $6x - 5 \geq 0$, the equation becomes:
$$6x - 5 = 25$$
$$6x = 30$$
$$x = 5$$

If $6x - 5 < 0$, the equation becomes:
$$-(6x - 5) = 25$$
$$-6x + 5 = 25$$
$$-6x = 20$$
$$x = -\frac{10}{3}$$

The solutions of the original equation are 5 and $-\frac{10}{3}$.

39.
$$4.50 - 9.11x = 1.72$$
$$-9.11x = -2.78$$
$$x \approx 0.31$$

41.
$$3ax - 2b = b + 3$$
$$3ax = 3b + 3$$
$$ax = b + 1$$
$$x = \frac{b + 1}{a}$$

43.
$$ax + b = bx + a$$
$$ax - bx = a - b$$
$$x(a - b) = a - b$$
$$x = \frac{a - b}{a - b}$$
$$x = 1$$

45. $\frac{1}{x} = a + b$
$$1 = x(a + b)$$
$$x = \frac{1}{a + b}$$

47.
$$(x + b)(x + c) - a(a + b) = (x - a)(x + a) + bc$$
$$x^2 + bx + cx + bc - a^2 - ab = x^2 - a^2 + bc$$
$$bx + cx - ab = 0$$
$$x(b + c) = ab$$
$$x = \frac{ab}{b + c}$$

49.
$$(a - x)^2 = x^2 + b^2$$
$$a^2 - 2ax + x^2 = x^2 + b^2$$
$$a^2 - 2ax = b^2$$
$$-2ax = b^2 - a^2$$
$$x = \frac{b^2 - a^2}{-2a}$$
$$x = \frac{a^2 - b^2}{2a}$$

51.
$$\frac{|x - 3|}{2} + \frac{|x - 3|}{3} = \frac{-5x}{3}$$
$$3|x - 3| + 2|x - 3| = -10x \quad \text{(multiplying by 6)}$$
$$5|x - 3| = -10x$$

Now there are two cases to consider:

If $x - 3 \geq 0$:	If $x - 3 < 0$:
$5(x - 3) = -10x$	$5[-(x - 3)] = -10x$
$5x - 15 = -10x$	$-5x + 15 = -10x$
$15x = 15$	$5x = -15$
$x = 1$	$x = -3$

Upon checking in the original equation, we find that -3 is a solution, but 1 is not.

53.
$$a^2(a - x) = b^2(b + x) - 2abx$$
$$a^3 - a^2x = b^3 + b^2x - 2abx$$
$$a^3 - b^3 = a^2x + b^2x - 2abx$$
$$a^3 - b^3 = x(a^2 + b^2 - 2ab)$$
$$a^3 - b^3 = x(a - b)^2$$
$$x = \frac{(a - b)(a^2 + ab + b^2)}{(a - b)^2}$$
$$x = \frac{a^2 + ab + b^2}{a - b}$$

55.

$$\frac{a - x}{a - b} - 2 = \frac{c - x}{b - c}$$

$$(a - x)(b - c) - 2(a - b)(b - c) = (c - x)(a - b)$$

$$ab - bx - ac + cx - 2ab + 2b^2 + 2ac - 2bc = ac - ax - bc + bx$$

$$-ab - bx + ac + cx + 2b^2 - 2bc = ac - ax - bc + bx$$

$$ax - 2bx + cx = ab - 2b^2 + bc$$

$$x(a - 2b + c) = b(a - 2b + c)$$

$$x = b$$

57.

$$\frac{x - a}{x - b} = \frac{b - x}{a - x}$$

$$(x - a)(a - x) = (b - x)(x - b)$$

$$ax - a^2 - x^2 + ax = bx - x^2 - b^2 + bx$$

$$2ax - a^2 = 2bx - b^2$$

$$2ax - 2bx = a^2 - b^2$$

$$2x(a - b) = a^2 - b^2$$

$$x = \frac{a^2 - b^2}{2(a - b)}$$

$$x = \frac{(a - b)(a + b)}{2(a - b)}$$

$$x = \frac{a + b}{2}$$

59.

$$d = \frac{r}{1 + rt}$$

$$d(1 + rt) = r$$

$$d + drt = r$$

$$drt - r = -d$$

$$r(dt - 1) = -d$$

$$r = \frac{-d}{dt - 1}$$

$$r = \frac{d}{1 - dt}$$

61.

$$S = 2\pi r^2 + 2\pi rh$$

$$S - 2\pi r^2 = 2\pi rh$$

$$\frac{S - 2\pi r^2}{2\pi r} = h \quad \text{or} \quad h = \frac{S - 2\pi r^2}{2\pi r}$$

63.

$$S = \frac{rl - a}{r - 1}$$

$$S(r - 1) = rl - a$$

$$Sr - S = rl - a$$

$$Sr - rl = S - a$$

$$r(S - l) = S - a$$

$$r = \frac{S - a}{S - l}$$

65. Replacing x by $\dfrac{ab}{a + b}$ yields:

$$\frac{1}{\dfrac{ab}{a + b}} = \frac{1}{a} + \frac{1}{b}$$

$$\frac{a + b}{ab} = \frac{1}{a} + \frac{1}{b}$$

$$\frac{a}{ab} + \frac{b}{ab} = \frac{1}{a} + \frac{1}{b}$$

$$\frac{1}{b} + \frac{1}{a} = \frac{1}{a} + \frac{1}{b} \quad , \text{which is true.}$$

67. $\dfrac{1}{x - p} - \dfrac{1}{x - q} = \dfrac{p - q}{x^2 - pq}$

Rather than clearing the equation of fractions directly, we show an alternate approach. First, add the two fractions on the left-hand side of the equation:

$$\frac{(x - q) - (x - p)}{(x - p)(x - q)} = \frac{p - q}{x^2 - pq}$$

$$\frac{-q + p}{(x - p)(x - q)} = \frac{p - q}{x^2 - pq}$$

Now divide both sides by $p - q$ (assuming $p \neq q$) to obtain:

$$\frac{1}{(x - p)(x - q)} = \frac{1}{x^2 - pq}$$

$$x^2 - px - qx + pq = x^2 - pq$$

$$- x (p + q) = -2pq$$

$$x = \frac{2pq}{p + q}$$

2.2 Quadratic Equations

1. $2(-3)^2 - 6(-3) - 36 = 0$
    $18 + 18 - 36 = 0$, which is true.
    So $x = -3$ is a solution.

3. $4(-1/4)^2 - 1 = 0$
    $4(1/16) - 1 = 0$
    $\dfrac{1}{4} - 1 = 0$, which is false.
    So $x = -1/4$ is not a solution.

5. $(-1 - \sqrt{7})^2 - 2(-1 - \sqrt{7}) - 6 = 0$
    $1 + 2\sqrt{7} + 7 + 2 + 2\sqrt{7} - 6 = 0$
    $4\sqrt{7} + 4 = 0$, which is false.
    So $x = -1 - \sqrt{7}$ is not a solution.

7. $x^2 - 5x - 6 = 0$
    $(x - 6)(x + 1) = 0$
    $x = 6$ or $x = -1$

9. $x^2 - 100 = 0$
    $(x - 10)(x + 10) = 0$
    $x = \pm 10$

11. $25x^2 - 60x + 36 = 0$
    $(5x - 6)^2 = 0$
    $5x - 6 = 0$
    $x = 6/5$ (double root)

13. $10z^2 - 13z - 3 = 0$
    $(5z + 1)(2z - 3) = 0$
    $z = -1/5$ or $z = 3/2$

15. $(x + 1)^2 - 4 = 0$
    $(x + 1)^2 - 2^2 = 0$
    $(x + 1 - 2)(x + 1 + 2) = 0$
    $(x - 1)(x + 3) = 0$
    $x = 1$ or $x = -3$

17.
$$x(2x - 13) = -6$$
$$2x^2 - 13x + 6 = 0$$
$$(2x - 1)(x - 6) = 0$$
$$x = 1/2 \text{ or } x = 6$$

19.
$$x(x + 1) = 156$$
$$x^2 + x - 156 = 0$$
$$(x + 13)(x - 12) = 0$$
$$x = -13 \text{ or } x = 12$$

21.
$$x^2 - 49 = 0$$
$$x^2 = 49$$
$$x = \pm 7$$

23.
$$\frac{1}{4} - x^2 = 0$$
$$x^2 = 1/4$$
$$x = \pm 1/2$$

25.
$$3x^2 - 192 = 0$$
$$x^2 - 64 = 0$$
$$x^2 = 64$$
$$x = \pm 8$$

27.   (a)
$$x^2 + 10x + 9 = 0$$
$$x^2 + 10x = -9$$
$$x^2 + 10x + 25 = 16$$
$$(x + 5)^2 = 16$$
$$x + 5 = \pm 4$$
$$x = -5 + 4 = -1 \text{ or } x = -5 - 4 = -9$$

(b) $a = 1, b = 10, c = 9$
$$x = \frac{-10 \pm \sqrt{100 - 36}}{2} = \frac{-10 \pm \sqrt{64}}{2} = \frac{-10 \pm 8}{2}$$
$$x = \frac{-10 + 8}{2} = \frac{-2}{2} = -1 \text{ or } x = \frac{-10 - 8}{2} = \frac{-18}{2} = -9$$

29.   (a)
$$x^2 - x - 5 = 0$$
$$x^2 - x = 5$$
$$x^2 - x + \frac{1}{4} = \frac{21}{4}$$
$$\left(x - \frac{1}{2}\right)^2 = \frac{21}{4}$$

$$x - \frac{1}{2} = \pm \sqrt{\frac{21}{4}}$$

$$x - \frac{1}{2} = \pm \frac{\sqrt{21}}{2}$$

$$x = \frac{1 \pm \sqrt{21}}{2}$$

(b) $a = 1, b = -1, c = -5$

$$x = \frac{1 \pm \sqrt{1 - 4(1)(-5)}}{2(1)} = \frac{1 \pm \sqrt{21}}{2}$$

31. (a) $$2x^2 + 3x - 4 = 0$$

$$x^2 + \frac{3}{2}x = 2$$

$$x^2 + \frac{3}{2}x + \frac{9}{16} = \frac{41}{16}$$

$$\left(x + \frac{3}{4}\right)^2 = \frac{41}{16}$$

$$x + \frac{3}{4} = \pm \frac{\sqrt{41}}{4}$$

$$x = \frac{-3 \pm \sqrt{41}}{4}$$

(b) $a = 2, b = 3, c = -4$

$$x = \frac{-3 \pm \sqrt{9 - 4(2)(-4)}}{2(2)} = \frac{-3 \pm \sqrt{41}}{4}$$

33. (a) $$12x^2 + 32x + 5 = 0$$

$$x^2 + \frac{8}{3}x = -\frac{5}{12}$$

$$x^2 + \frac{8}{3}x + \frac{16}{9} = \frac{49}{36}$$

$$\left(x + \frac{4}{3}\right)^2 = \frac{49}{36}$$

$$x + \frac{4}{3} = \pm \frac{7}{6}$$

$$x = -\frac{4}{3} + \frac{7}{6} = -\frac{1}{6} \quad \text{or} \quad x = -\frac{4}{3} - \frac{7}{6} = -\frac{5}{2}$$

(b) $a = 12, b = 32, c = 5$

$$x = \frac{-32 \pm \sqrt{(32)^2 - 4(12)(5)}}{2(12)}$$

$$= \frac{-32 \pm \sqrt{784}}{24}$$

$$= \frac{-32 \pm 28}{24}$$

$x = -1/6$ or $x = -5/2$

35.   (a)
$$2x^2 = x + 5$$
$$2x^2 - x - 5 = 0$$
$$x^2 - \frac{1}{2}x = \frac{5}{2}$$
$$x^2 - \frac{1}{2}x + \frac{1}{16} = \frac{41}{16}$$
$$\left(x - \frac{1}{4}\right)^2 = \frac{41}{16}$$
$$x - \frac{1}{4} = \pm\frac{\sqrt{41}}{4}$$
$$x = \frac{1 \pm \sqrt{41}}{4}$$

(b) $a = 2, b = -1, c = -5$

$$x = \frac{1 \pm \sqrt{1 - 4(2)(-5)}}{2(2)} = \frac{1 \pm \sqrt{41}}{4}$$

37.   (a)
$$-6x^2 + 12x = -1$$
$$-6x^2 + 12x + 1 = 0$$
$$x^2 - 2x = \frac{1}{6}$$
$$x^2 - 2x + 1 = \frac{7}{6}$$
$$(x - 1)^2 = \frac{7}{6}$$
$$x - 1 = \pm\frac{\sqrt{7}}{\sqrt{6}}$$
$$x - 1 = \pm\frac{\sqrt{42}}{6}$$
$$x = 1 \pm \frac{\sqrt{42}}{6} \quad \text{or} \quad x = \frac{6 \pm \sqrt{42}}{6}$$

(b) $a = -6, b = 12, c = 1$

$$x = \frac{-12 \pm \sqrt{144 - 4(-6)(1)}}{2(-6)}$$

$$= \frac{-12 \pm \sqrt{168}}{-12}$$

$$= \frac{-12 \pm \sqrt{(4)(42)}}{-12}$$

$$= \frac{-12 \pm 2\sqrt{42}}{-12}$$

$$x = \frac{-6 \pm \sqrt{42}}{-12} \quad \text{or} \quad x = \frac{6 \pm \sqrt{42}}{6}$$

39. $x^2 + 3x + 2.249 = 0$
Using the quadratic formula, we have:

$$x = \frac{-3 \pm \sqrt{9 - 4(1)(2.249)}}{2(1)}$$

$$x \approx -1.47 \text{ or } x \approx -1.53$$

41. $a = 1, b = -12, c = 16$
We compute the discriminant:

$$b^2 - 4ac = 144 - 4(1)(16) = 80 > 0$$

The equation has two real roots.

43. $a = 4, b = -5, c = -\frac{1}{2}$
We compute the discriminant:

$$b^2 - 4ac = 25 - 4(4)\left(-\frac{1}{2}\right) = 33 > 0$$

The equation has two real roots.

45. $a = 1, b = \sqrt{3}, c = \frac{3}{4}$
We compute the discriminant:

$$b^2 - 4ac = 3 - 4(1)\left(\frac{3}{4}\right) = 0$$

The equation has one real root.

47. $a = 1, b = -\sqrt{5}, c = 1$
We compute the discriminant:

$$b^2 - 4ac = 5 - 4(1)(1) = 1 > 0$$

The equation has two real roots.

49.
$$b^2 - 4ac = 0$$
$$144 - 4(1)(k) = 0$$
$$4k = 144$$
$$k = 36$$

51.
$$b^2 - 4ac = 0$$
$$k^2 - 4(1)(5) = 0$$
$$k = \pm\sqrt{20} = \pm 2\sqrt{5}$$

53. $\dfrac{3}{x+5} + \dfrac{4}{x} = 2$

Multiplying through by the least common denominator $x(x+5)$ gives us:
$$3x + 4(x+5) = 2x(x+5)$$
$$7x + 20 = 2x^2 + 10x$$
$$-2x^2 - 3x + 20 = 0$$
$$2x^2 + 3x - 20 = 0$$
$$(2x - 5)(x + 4) = 0$$
$$x = 5/2 \quad \text{or} \quad x = -4$$

Both of these values check in the original equation.

55. $1 - x - \dfrac{2}{6x+1} = 0$

Multiplying through by the least common denominator $6x + 1$ gives us:
$$-6x^2 + 5x - 1 = 0$$
$$6x^2 - 5x + 1 = 0$$
$$(3x - 1)(2x - 1) = 0$$
$$x = 1/3 \quad \text{or} \quad x = 1/2$$

Both values check in the original equation.

57. $\dfrac{3x^2 - 6x - 3}{(x+1)(x-2)(x-3)} + \dfrac{5 - 2x}{x^2 - 5x + 6} = 0$

$\dfrac{3x^2 - 6x - 3}{(x+1)(x-2)(x-3)} + \dfrac{5 - 2x}{(x-3)(x-2)} = 0$

Multiplying through by the least common denominator $(x+1)(x-2)(x-3)$ gives us:
$$3x^2 - 6x - 3 + (5 - 2x)(x + 1) = 0$$
$$3x^2 - 6x - 3 - 2x^2 + 3x + 5 = 0$$
$$x^2 - 3x + 2 = 0$$
$$(x - 2)(x - 1) = 0$$
$$x = 2 \quad \text{or} \quad x = 1$$

Of these two values, only $x = 1$ checks in the original equation.

59.
$$\frac{2x}{x^2 - 1} - \frac{1}{x + 3} = 0$$

$$\frac{2x}{(x - 1)(x + 1)} - \frac{1}{(x - 3)} = 0$$

Multiplying through by the least common denominator $(x - 1)(x + 1)(x - 3)$ gives us:

$$2x(x + 3) - (x - 1)(x + 1) = 0$$
$$2x^2 + 6x - x^2 + 1 = 0$$
$$x^2 + 6x + 1 = 0$$
$$x = \frac{-6 \pm \sqrt{36 - 4}}{2}$$
$$= \frac{-6 \pm 4\sqrt{2}}{2}$$
$$x = -3 \pm 2\sqrt{2}$$

Both values check in the original equation.

61.
$$(ax + b)^2 - (bx + a)^2 = 0$$
$$[ax + b - (bx + a)][(ax + b) + (bx + a)] = 0$$
$$(ax - bx + b - a)(ax + bx + b + a) = 0$$
$$x(a - b) = a - b \quad \text{or} \quad x(a + b) = -(a + b)$$
$$x = \frac{a - b}{a - b} = 1 \quad \text{or} \quad x = \frac{-(a + b)}{a + b} = -1$$

$$x = 1 \quad \text{or} \quad x = -1$$

63.   If the roots are A and B, then:
$$x^2 + Ax + B = (x - A)(x - B)$$
$$x^2 + Ax + B = x^2 - (A + B)x + AB$$
So $-(A + B) = A \quad$ and $\quad AB = B$
$$-A - B = A \qquad B(A - 1) = 0$$
$$2A + B = 0 \qquad\qquad B = 0 \text{ or } A = 1$$
If $B = 0$, then $A = 0$
If $A = 1$, then $B = -2$
So the values of A and B are:
$$A = 0 \text{ and } B = 0$$
$$A = 1 \text{ and } B = -2$$

65.   Let $\alpha = \dfrac{-b + \sqrt{b^2 - 4ac}}{2a}$ and $\beta = \dfrac{-b - \sqrt{b^2 - 4ac}}{2a}$

(a) $\alpha + \beta = \dfrac{-2b}{2a} = \dfrac{-b}{a}$

(b) $\alpha\beta = \dfrac{b^2 - (b^2 - 4ac)}{4a^2}$

$= \dfrac{b^2 - b^2 + 4ac}{4a^2}$

$= \dfrac{4ac}{4a^2}$

$= \dfrac{c}{a}$

(c) $\alpha^2 + \beta^2 = (\alpha + \beta)^2 - 2\alpha\beta$

$= \left(\dfrac{-b}{a}\right)^2 - 2\left(\dfrac{c}{a}\right)$

$= \dfrac{b^2}{a^2} - \dfrac{2ac}{a^2}$

$= \dfrac{b^2 - 2ac}{a^2}$

(d) $\dfrac{1}{\alpha^2} + \dfrac{1}{\beta^2} = \dfrac{\alpha^2 + \beta^2}{\alpha^2\beta^2}$

$= \dfrac{\alpha^2 + \beta^2}{(\alpha\beta)^2}$

$= \dfrac{\dfrac{b^2 - 2ac}{a^2}}{\left(\dfrac{c}{a}\right)^2}$

$= \dfrac{b^2 - 2ac}{c^2}$

67. (a)   Let r be one root and $3r$ be another. Then:

$r^2 + pr + q = 0 \qquad$ and $\qquad (3r)^2 + p(3r) + q = 0$

$\qquad\qquad\qquad\qquad\qquad\qquad\qquad 9r^2 + 3pr + q = 0$

Thus $r^2 + pr = 9r^2 + 3pr$, so:

$\qquad 8r^2 = -2pr$

$\quad 8r^2 + 2pr = 0$

$\quad 2r(4r + p) = 0$

$\qquad\qquad r = 0 \quad$ or $\quad r = \dfrac{-p}{4}$

Now $r = 0$ implies $q = 0$, which is impossible. So $r = \frac{-p}{4}$, and:

$$\left(-\frac{p}{4}\right)^2 + p\left(-\frac{p}{4}\right) + q = 0$$

$$\frac{p^2}{16} - \frac{p^2}{4} + q = 0$$

$$\frac{-3p^2}{16} + q = 0$$

$$-3p^2 + 16q = 0$$

$$16q = 3p^2$$

$$\frac{p^2}{q} = \frac{16}{3}$$

(b) Let r be one root and nr be another. Then:

$$r^2 + pr + q = 0 \quad \text{and} \quad (nr)^2 + p(nr) + q = 0$$

$$n^2r^2 + npr + q = 0$$

Thus $r^2 + pr = n^2r^2 + npr$, so $pr(1 - n) = (n^2 - 1)r^2$
Now $r \neq 0$, so we can divide each side by r to get:

$$p(1 - n) = (n^2 - 1)\,r$$

$$r = \frac{p(1 - n)}{n^2 - 1}$$

$$r = \frac{-p}{n + 1}$$

Thus $\left(\frac{-p}{n + 1}\right)^2 + p\left(\frac{-p}{n + 1}\right) + q = 0$

$$\frac{p^2}{(n + 1)^2} - \frac{p^2}{n + 1} + q = 0$$

Multiplying each side of the equation by $(n + 1)^2$ yields:

$$p^2 - (n + 1)p^2 + (n + 1)^2 q = 0$$

$$(n + 1)^2 q = np^2$$

$$\frac{p^2}{q} = \frac{(n + 1)^2}{n}$$

69. $ab(a + b)x^2 - (a^2 + b^2)x - 2(a + b) = 0$
The equation can be solved by means of the quadratic formula. Alternately,
we have the following solution by factoring:

$$\left(abx - (a + b)\right)\left((a + b)x + 2\right) = 0$$

$abx = a + b \quad \text{or} \quad (a + b)x + 2 = 0$

$x = \dfrac{a + b}{ab} \quad \text{or} \quad x = \dfrac{-2}{a + b}$

The two solutions are, therefore, $\dfrac{a + b}{ab}$ and $\dfrac{-2}{a + b}$

2.3 Applications

1.   Denote the two numbers by x and 7 - x.   Since the difference is 17, we have:

$$x - (7 - x) = 17$$
$$2x = 24$$
$$x = 12$$

Then 7 - x = 7 - 12 = -5
The two numbers are 12 and -5.

3.   Denoting the two numbers by x and 17 - x, we have:

$$x(17 - x) = 52$$
$$x^2 - 17x + 52 = 0$$
$$(x - 13)(x - 4) = 0$$
$$x = 13 \text{ or } x = 4$$

If x = 13, then 17 - x = 4.   Similarly, if x = 4, then 17 - x = 13. So in either case, we find the two numbers are 13 and 4.

5.   Let x denote the number. Then we have:

$$x + 2x = 63$$
$$3x = 63$$
$$x = 21$$

The number is 21.

7.   Let x denote the positive number. Then:

$$x(x + 4) = 96$$
$$x^2 + 4x - 96 = 0$$
$$(x + 12)(x - 8) = 0$$
$$x = -12 \text{ or } x = 8$$

Since x is supposed to be positive, we discard the first solution. The required positive number is 8.

9.   Letting x denote the required number, we have:

$$\frac{3 + x}{7 + x} = \frac{2}{3}$$
$$9 + 3x = 14 + 2x$$
$$x = 14 - 9$$
$$x = 5$$

The required number is 5.

11. Call the numbers x and y. Then we have $x - y = \frac{1}{3}(x + y)$. Solving this for x in terms of y yields $x = 2y$. Since the sum of the squares is 180, we have:

$$(2y)^2 + y^2 = 180$$
$$5y^2 = 180$$
$$y^2 = 36$$
$$y = \pm 6$$

Since y is supposed to be positive, we have $y = 6$ and $x = 2(6) = 12$. The two numbers are 12 and 6.

13. Letting x denote the required score, we have:

$$\frac{70 + 77 + 75 + x}{4} = 75$$
$$222 + x = 300$$
$$x = 300 - 222$$
$$x = 78$$

The required score is 78.

15. Letting x denote the fourth number, we have:

$$\frac{1}{4}(80 + 22 + 62 + x) = 52$$
$$164 + x = 208$$
$$x = 208 - 164$$
$$x = 44$$

The fourth number is 44.

17. Let x denote the length of the hypotenuse. Then the lenths of the other two sides are $x - 8$ and $x - 1$, and we have:

$$(x - 1)^2 + (x - 8)^2 = x^2$$
$$x^2 - 18x + 65 = 0$$
$$(x - 13)(x - 5) = 0$$
$$x = 13 \quad \text{or} \quad x = 5$$

If $x = 13$, the other two sides are $13 - 8 = 5$, and $13 - 1 = 12$. The second solution $x = 5$ must be discarded, for in that case $x - 8$ is negative. The required lengths are 5 cm, 12 cm, 13 cm.

19. Letting x denote the length of a side in the original square, we have:

$$(x + 2)^2 = x^2 + 14$$
$$4x = 10$$
$$x = 5/2$$

The length of a side in the original square is 2.5 cm.

21. If x and y are the dimensions of the rectangle, we have:

$$2x + 2y = 104$$
$$x + y = 52$$

$$y = 52 - x$$

Then, since the area is 640 cm^2, we have:

$$x(52 - x) = 640$$
$$-x^2 + 52x = 640$$
$$x^2 - 52x + 640 = 0$$
$$(x - 20)(x - 32) = 0$$
$$x = 20 \ \text{ or } \ x = 32$$

Now if $x = 20$, then $y = 52 - 20 = 32$. Similarly, if $x = 32$, then $y = 52 - 32 = 20$. So in either case, the shorter side is 20 cm.

23. If the shortest side is 2 in., that leaves 10 in. for the other two sides. Call those sides x and $10 - x$. Then:

$$2^2 + x^2 = (10 - x)^2$$
$$4 + x^2 = 100 - 20x + x^2$$
$$20x = 96$$
$$x = \frac{96}{20}$$
$$x = 4.8$$

The other two sides of the triangle are 4.8 in. and $10 - 4.8 = 5.2$ in.

25. Let x denote the length of the base. Then the legs each have length 3x and we have:

$$x + 3x + 3x = 70$$
$$7x = 70$$
$$x = 10$$

The three sides are 10 cm, 30 cm, and 30 cm.

27. Letting t represent the number of years until the total interest is $5840, we have:

$$(4000)(0.07)t + (5000)(0.09)t = 5840$$
$$280t + 450t = 5840$$
$$730t = 5840$$
$$t = \frac{5840}{730}$$
$$t = 8$$

Thus it will take 8 years until the interest is $5840.

29. Let t be the number of years until the balance in the account reaches $21,000. Then we have:

$$10,000 + (10,000)(0.11)t = 21,000$$
$$10,000 + 1100t = 21,000$$
$$100 + 11t = 210$$
$$11t = 110$$
$$t = 10$$

It will take 10 years for the balance to reach $21,000.

31. Let i be the overall interest rate on the entire investment of $11,500. Then we have:

$$(11,500)(i)(1) = (7500)(0.075)(1) + (4000)(0.05)(1)$$
$$11500i = 762.5$$
$$i = \frac{762.5}{11500}$$
$$i \approx 0.06630$$

To convert this value to a percent, we move the decimal two places to the right. Then by rounding off to the nearest tenth of one percent, we obtain $i \approx 6.6\%$, as required.

33. Let the interest rate for the $8000 account be r %. Then the rate for the $9000 account is (r + 1) %. Since the $9000 account earns $165 more than the $8000 account each year, we have:

$$(8000)\left(\frac{r}{100}\right) + 165 = (9000)\left(\frac{r+1}{100}\right)$$
$$80r + 165 = 90r + 90$$
$$-10r = -75$$
$$r = 7.5$$

Thus, the interest rate on the $8000 account is 7.5%, and the rate on the $9000 account is 8.5%.

35. Let x be the number of cc of the 10% solution, and let 200 - x be the number of cc of the 35% solution:

type of solution	cc	% acid	total acid (cc)
10% solution	x	10 %	0.10 (x)
35% solution	200 - x	35 %	0.35 (200 - x)
mixture	200	25 %	0.25 (200)

Since the total acid in the mixture comes from that in the two given solutions, we have:

$$0.10(x) + 0.35(200 - x) = 0.25(200)$$
$$10x + 35(200 - x) = 25(200)$$
$$10x + 7000 - 35x = 5000$$
$$-25x = -2000$$
$$x = 80$$

Then 200 - x = 200 - 80 = 120. Consequently, the student should use 80 cc of the 10% solution and 120 cc of the 35% solution.

37. Let x denote the required number of pounds of the first type of coffee:

type of coffee	pounds	cost/pound	total cost
first type	x	$5.20	5.20 (x)
second type	5	$5.80	5.80 (5)
blend	x + 5	$5.35	5.35 (x + 5)

Looking at the total cost column in our table, we obtain the equation:

$$5.2(x) + 5.8(5) = 5.35(x + 5)$$
$$520x + 580(5) = 535(x + 5)$$
$$520x + 2900 = 535x + 2675$$
$$-15x = -225$$
$$x = 15$$

Thus, 15 pounds of the first type of coffee are required.

39. Let x denote the required number of tons of the second ore:

type of ore	tons	% iron	total iron (tons)
first type	16	20 %	.20 (16)
second type	x	35 %	.35 (x)
blend	16 + x	25 %	.25 (16 + x)

By considering the total iron, we have:

$$2(16) + .35(x) = .25(16 + x)$$
$$20(16) + 35x = 25(16 + x)$$
$$320 + 35x = 400 + 25x$$
$$10x = 80$$
$$x = 8$$

Thus, 8 tons of the second ore are required.

41. Denoting the lengths of the two shorter sides by x and x - 7, we have:

$$\frac{1}{2}x(x - 7) = 60$$
$$x^2 - 7x - 120 = 0$$
$$(x - 15)(x + 8) = 0$$

$$x = 15 \quad \text{or} \quad x = -8$$

We discard the negative root here since x represents a length. Thus, $x = 15$ and $x - 7 = 8$. Therefore, the hypotenuse is:

$$\sqrt{15^2 + 8^2} = \sqrt{289} = 17 \text{ cm.}$$

43. The area of the square and the rectangle are $(1 - x)^2$ and $(1)(x)$, respectively. Therefore:

$$(1 - x)^2 = x$$
$$x^2 - 3x + 1 = 0$$
$$x = \frac{3 \pm \sqrt{9 - 4}}{2}$$
$$= \frac{3 \pm \sqrt{5}}{2}$$

We choose the negative root here, since the quantity $1 - x$ is supposed to be positive. Therefore $x = \dfrac{3 - \sqrt{5}}{2}$.

45.
$$\frac{AC}{AB} = \frac{AB}{BC}$$
$$AC \bullet BC = (AB)^2 = 1^2 = 1$$
$$AC \bullet (AC - 1) = 1$$
$$(AC)^2 - AC - 1 = 0$$
$$AC = \frac{1 \pm \sqrt{1 - 4(-1)}}{2} = \frac{1 \pm \sqrt{5}}{2}$$

We choose the positive root here since $AC > 0$. The required ratio is, therefore:

$$\frac{AC}{AB} = \frac{AC}{1} = \frac{1 + \sqrt{5}}{2}$$

47. (a) When the ball lands, $h = 0$. Therefore:

$$-16t^2 + 96t = 0$$
$$-16t (t - 6) = 0$$
$$t = 0 \text{ or } t = 6$$

The value $t = 0$ gives the time when the ball is first thrown.
Consequently, the ball lands after 6 seconds.

(b) With $h = 80$, the equation becomes:

$$80 = -16t^2 + 96t$$
$$16t^2 - 96t + 80 = 0$$
$$t^2 - 6t + 5 = 0$$
$$(t - 5)(t - 1) = 0$$
$$t = 5 \text{ or } t = 1$$

At $t = 1$ second, the ball is 80 ft. high and rising. At $t = 5$ seconds, the ball is 80 ft. high and falling.

49. After t minutes, the distance covered by Emily and Ernie are t/9 and t/11, respectively. Emily will lap Ernie when her distance exceeds Ernie's by 1/4 mile. In that case we have:

$$\frac{t}{9} = \frac{t}{11} + \frac{1}{4}$$
$$44t = 36t + 99$$
$$8t = 99$$
$$t = \frac{99}{8}$$

It will take $12\frac{3}{8}$ minutes for Emily to lap Ernie on the track.   (This is about 12 minutes and 22 seconds.)

51. Let r and r - 5 denote the speeds of the eastbound and westbound trains, respectively. Then when t = 6 hours, the total distance traveled by the two trains is 630 mi, and we have:

$$r(6) + (r - 5)6 = 630$$
$$6r + 6r - 30 = 630$$
$$12r = 660$$
$$r = 55$$

Thus, the speed of the eastbound train is 55 mph.

53. Let r and r + 50 represent the speeds of the slower and faster planes, respectively. Then when t = 2 , the total distance covered is 1500, and we have:

$$r(2) + (r + 50)2 = 1500$$
$$4r = 1400$$
$$r = 350$$

The speed of the slower plane is 350 mph.

55. Let D be the distance that the boat can travel out to sea, and let t be the time for that part of the trip. Then the time for the return trip is 2 - t. For the trip out to sea we have:

$$D = 20t$$

and for the trip back:

$$D = 12 (2 - t)$$

Solving the first equation for t yields $t = \frac{D}{20}$ and then substitutung in the second equation:

$$D = 12\left(2 - \frac{D}{20}\right)$$

$$D = 24 - \frac{3D}{5}$$

$$5D = 120 - 3D$$

$$8D = 120$$

$$D = 15$$

Thus, the boat can travel 15 miles out to sea before heading back.

57. Let x represent the additional amount that must be invested. Then the total of the two deposits and one investment (in dollars) is 2650 + 3300 + x , or 5950 + x. Since the overall return on this investment is to be 10%, we have:

$$0.1(5950 + x) = 0.081(2650) + 0.092(3300) + 0.115x$$
$$595 + 0.1x = 214.65 + 303.60 + 0.115x$$
$$-0.015x = -76.75$$
$$x \approx 5116.67$$

The additional investment at 11.5% should be $5117.

59. Let Linda's initial rate be r. When Larry has covered 2 miles, the elapsed time is $\frac{2}{1/15}$ = 30 minutes. In that 30 minutes Linda has walked a distance of r(30). At 1:15 (75 minutes past noon), the distances covered by Larry and Linda are equal, and consequently:

Larry's total distance	=	Linda's distance in first 30 min.	+	Linda's distance in next 45 min.
$\left(\frac{1}{15}\right)(75)$	=	30r	+	(2r) (45)

Thus:

$$5 = 30r + 90r$$
$$5 = 120r$$
$$r = \frac{5}{120}$$
$$r = \frac{1}{24}$$

So Linda's initial rate was $\frac{1}{24}$ mi/min.

61. Let D denote the distance from town A to town B. Then the time to go from town A to town B is $\frac{D}{v_1}$, and the time for the return trip is $\frac{D}{v_2}$. Thus, we have:

$$\text{average speed} = \frac{\text{total distance}}{\text{total time}}$$

$$= \frac{2D}{\dfrac{D}{v_1} + \dfrac{D}{v_2}}$$

$$= \frac{2}{\dfrac{1}{v_1} + \dfrac{1}{v_2}}$$

$$= \frac{2v_1 v_2}{v_1 + v_2}$$

63. Let t denote the required number of years. Then:

$$d\left(\frac{r}{100}\right)t + D\left(\frac{R}{100}\right)t = d + D$$
$$drt + DRt = 100(d + D)$$
$$t(dr + DR) = 100(d + D)$$
$$t = \frac{100(d + D)}{dr + DR}$$

65. Let x denote the length of the hypotenuse. Then, since the perimeter is a, and the length of the shortest side is b, the length of the third side is a - b - x. By the Pythagorean Theorem, now we have:

$$x^2 = (a - b - x)^2 + b^2$$
$$x^2 = (a - b)^2 - 2(a - b)x + x^2 + b^2$$
$$2(a - b)x = a^2 - 2ab + 2b^2$$
$$x = \frac{a^2 - 2ab + 2b^2}{2(a - b)} \text{ inches}$$

67. Denoting the length of a side of the original square by x, we have:

$$(ax)^2 = x^2 + b^2$$
$$a^2 x^2 - x^2 = b^2$$
$$x^2(a^2 - 1) = b^2$$
$$x^2 = \frac{b^2}{a^2 - 1}$$
$$x = \frac{b}{\sqrt{a^2 - 1}}$$

The length of each side in the original square is $\dfrac{b}{\sqrt{a^2 - 1}}$ units. This

quantity can also be written as $\dfrac{b\sqrt{a^2 - 1}}{a^2 - 1}$ units.

69. Let x and 16 - x denote the lengths of the two pieces. Therefore, the two circumferences are x and 16 - x, respectively. We can find the corresponding radii by writing the formula $C = 2\pi r$ as $r = \dfrac{C}{2\pi}$. Thus the corresponding radii are $\dfrac{x}{2\pi}$ and $\dfrac{16 - x}{2\pi}$, respectively. Now if the sum of the two areas is 12 cm^2, we have:

$$\pi \left(\frac{x}{2\pi}\right)^2 + \pi \left(\frac{16 - x}{2\pi}\right)^2 = 12$$

$$\frac{x^2}{4\pi} + \frac{256 - 32x + x^2}{4\pi} = 12$$

$$2x^2 - 32x + 256 = 48\pi$$

$$x^2 - 16x + 128 = 24\pi$$

$$x^2 - 16x + (128 - 24\pi) = 0$$

Applying the quadratic formula with a = 1, b = -16, and c = 128 - 24π yields:

$$x = \frac{16 \pm \sqrt{256 - 4(128 - 24\pi)}}{2}$$

$$= \frac{16 \pm \sqrt{96\pi - 256}}{2}$$

$$= \frac{16 \pm 4\sqrt{6\pi - 16}}{2}$$

$$= 8 \pm 2\sqrt{6\pi - 16}$$

Both roots here yield positive values for x. First consider the positive sign. Then $x = 8 + 2\sqrt{6\pi - 16}$ and consequently $16 - x = 8 - 2\sqrt{6\pi - 16}$ (which is the same as the value obtained for x using the negative root). Similarly, if we begin with $x = 8 - 2\sqrt{6\pi - 16}$, we find that 16 - x is $8 + 2\sqrt{6\pi - 16}$. So in either case, the lengths are:

$$8 + 2\sqrt{6\pi - 16} \quad \text{and} \quad 8 - 2\sqrt{6\pi - 16}$$

The smaller of these two numbers is $8 - 2\sqrt{6\pi - 16}$. Using a calculator now and rounding off to two decimal places, we find the required length to be 4.62 cm.

71.   Call the side x, thus we have the following figure:

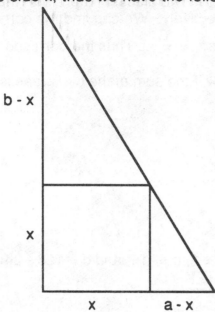

By similar triangles: $\dfrac{x}{a - x} = \dfrac{b - x}{x}$

$$x^2 = ab - bx - ax + x^2$$
$$0 = ab - (a + b)x$$
$$(a + b)x = ab$$
$$x = \dfrac{ab}{a + b}$$

2.4   Other Types of Equations

1. $3x^2 - 48x = 0$
$3x(x - 16) = 0$
$\qquad 3x = 0$ or $x - 16 = 0$
$\qquad\quad x = 0$ or $\qquad x = 16$
Solutions: 0,16

3. $\qquad\qquad t^3 - 125 = 0$
$(t - 5)(t^2 + 5t + 25) = 0$
Setting the first factor equal to zero yields t = 5. Setting the second factor equal to zero yields a quadratic equation with no real roots.
Solution: 5

5. $7x^4 - 28x^2 = 0$
         $7x^2(x^2 - 4) = 0$
      $7x^2(x - 2)(x + 2) = 0$
                  $x = 0$ or $x = 2$ or $x = -2$
      Solutions: 0, ± 2

7. $225(x - 1) - x^2(x - 1) = 0$
            $(x - 1)(225 - x^2) = 0$
      $(x - 1)(15 - x)(15 + x) = 0$
                  $x - 1 = 0$ or $15 - x = 0$ or $15 + x = 0$
                     $x = 1$ $x = 15$ $x = -15$
      Solutions: 1, ± 15

9. $4y^3 - 20y^2 + 25y = 0$
      $y(4y^2 - 20y + 25) = 0$
                  $y = 0$ or $4y^2 - 20y + 25 = 0$
                                  $(2y - 5)^2 = 0$
                                  $2y - 5 = 0$
                                  $2y = 5$
                                  $y = 5/2$
      Solutions: 0, 5/2 (5/2 is a double root)

11. $t^4 + 2t^3 - 3t^2 = 0$
      $t^2(t^2 + 2t - 3) = 0$
      $t(t + 3)(t - 1) = 0$
                  $t^2 = 0$ or $t + 3 = 0$ or $t - 1 = 0$
                  $t = 0$ $t = -3$ $t = 1$
      Solutions: 0, -3, 1

13. $6x - 23x^2 - 4x^3 = 0$
      $-x(4x^2 + 23x - 6) = 0$
                  $-x = 0$ or $4x - 1 = 0$ or $x + 6 = 0$
                   $x = 0$ $x = 1/4$ $x = -6$
      Solutions: 0, 1/4, -6

15. $x^4 - x^2 - 6 = 0$
      $(x^2 - 3)(x^2 + 2) = 0$
                  $x^2 - 3 = 0$ or $x^2 + 2 = 0$
                   $x = \pm\sqrt{3}$ $x^2 + 2 \neq 0$ for real values of x
      Solutions: $\pm\sqrt{3}$

17.
$$y^4 + 4y^2 - 5 = 0$$
$$(y^2 - 1)(y^2 + 5) = 0$$
$$(y - 1)(y + 1)(y^2 + 5) = 0$$

$y - 1 = 0$ or $y + 1 = 0$ or $y^2 + 5 = 0$

$y = 1$ $y = -1$ $y^2 + 5 \neq 0$ for real values of y

Solutions: ± 1

19.
$$9t^4 - 3t^2 - 2 = 0$$
$$(3t^2 - 2)(3t^2 + 1) = 0$$

$3t^2 - 2 = 0$ or $3t^2 + 1 = 0$

$t = \pm\sqrt{2/3}$ $3t^2 + 1 \neq 0$ for real values of t

$= \pm\sqrt{6}/3$

Solutions: $\dfrac{\pm\sqrt{6}}{3}$

21.
$$x^6 - 10x^4 + 24x^2 = 0$$
$$x^2(x^4 - 10x^2 + 24) = 0$$
$$x^2(x^2 - 6)(x^2 - 4) = 0$$
$$x^2(x^2 - 6)(x - 2)(x + 2) = 0$$

$x^2 = 0$ or $x^2 - 6 = 0$ or $x - 2 = 0$ or $x + 2 = 0$

$x = 0$ $x = \pm\sqrt{6}$ $x = 2$ $x = -2$

Solutions: $0, \pm\sqrt{6}, \pm 2$

23. $x^4 + x^2 - 1 = 0$

Letting $x^2 = t$ and $x^4 = t^2$ yields:

$$t^2 + t - 1 = 0$$

$$t = \frac{-1 \pm \sqrt{1 - 4(-1)}}{2} = \frac{-1 \pm \sqrt{5}}{2}$$

Since t must be non-negative (because $t = x^2$) we choose the value:

$$t = \frac{-1 + \sqrt{5}}{2}$$

Therefore:

$$x^2 = \frac{-1 + \sqrt{5}}{2}$$

$$x = \pm\sqrt{\frac{-1 + \sqrt{5}}{2}}$$

Solutions: $\pm\sqrt{\dfrac{-1 + \sqrt{5}}{2}}$

25. $x^4 + 3x^2 - 2 = 0$

Letting $x^2 = t$ and $x^4 = t^2$ we obtain $t^2 + 3t - 2 = 0$. By means of the quadratic formula, we find that the roots of this last equation are:

$$t = \frac{-3 \pm \sqrt{17}}{2}$$

We want the plus sign on the right-hand side here, since $t \geq 0$. Thus we have:

$$x = \pm \sqrt{t} = \pm \sqrt{\frac{-3 + \sqrt{17}}{2}}$$

Solutions: $\pm \sqrt{\dfrac{-3 + \sqrt{17}}{2}}$

27. $x^6 + 7x^3 = 8$

Letting $x^3 = t$ and $x^6 = t^2$, we find that the equation becomes:

$$t^2 + 7t - 8 = 0$$
$$(t + 8)(t - 1) = 0$$

$$t = -8 \quad \text{or} \quad t = 1$$
$$x^3 = -8 \qquad x^3 = 1$$
$$x = -2 \qquad x = 1$$

Solutions: -2, 1

29. $t^{-2} - 7t^{-1} + 12 = 0$

Let $t^{-1} = x$ and $t^{-2} = x^2$. Then the equation becomes:

$$x^2 - 7x + 12 = 0$$
$$(x - 3)(x - 4) = 0$$

$$x = 3 \quad \text{or} \quad x = 4$$
$$t^{-1} = 3 \qquad t^{-1} = 4$$
$$t = 1/3 \qquad t = 1/4$$

Solutions: 1/3, 1/4

31. $12y^{-2} - 23y^{-1} = -5$

Letting $y^{-1} = t$ and $y^{-2} = t^2$, we have the equation:

$$12t^2 - 23t + 5 = 0$$
$$(3t - 5)(4t - 1) = 0$$

$$t = 5/3 \quad \text{or} \quad t = 1/4$$
$$y^{-1} = 5/3 \qquad y^{-1} = 1/4$$

Solutions: 3/5, 4

33. $4x^{-4} - 33x^{-2} - 27 = 0$

Letting $x^{-2} = t$ and $x^{-4} = t^2$, we have the equation:

$$4t^2 - 33t - 27 = 0$$
$$(4t + 3)(t - 9) = 0$$

$t = -3/4$	or $t = 9$
$x^{-2} = -3/4$	$x^{-2} = 9$
$x^2 = -4/3$	$x^{-2} = 9$
no real sol.	$x^2 = 1/9$
	$x = \pm 1/3$

Solutions: $\pm 1/3$

35. $t^{2/3} = 9$

Raising both sides of the given equation to the power 3/2 yields:

$$t = \pm 9^{3/2} = \pm \left(\sqrt{9}\right)^3 = \pm 27$$

Upon checking, we find $t = \pm 27$ both satisfy the original equation.
Solutions: ± 27

37. $x^4 = 81$

$$x = \pm \sqrt[4]{81} = \pm 3$$

Solutions: ± 3

39. $(y - 1)^3 = 7$

$$y - 1 = \sqrt[3]{7}$$
$$y = 1 + \sqrt[3]{7}$$

Solution: $1 + \sqrt[3]{7}$

41. $(t + 1)^5 = -243$

$$t + 1 = \sqrt[5]{-243}$$
$$t + 1 = -3$$
$$t = -4$$

Solution: -4

43. $9x^{4/3} - 10x^{2/3} + 1 = 0$

Letting $x^{2/3} = t$ and $x^{4/3} = t^2$, the equation becomes:

$$9t^2 - 10t + 1 = 0$$
$$(t - 1)(9t - 1) = 0$$

$t = 1$	or $t = 1/9$
$x^{2/3} = 1$	$x^{2/3} = 1/9$
$\left(\sqrt[3]{x}\right)^2 = 1$	$\left(\sqrt[3]{x}\right)^2 = 1/9$

$$\sqrt[3]{x} = \pm 1 \qquad\qquad \sqrt[3]{x} = \pm 1/3$$
$$x = \pm 1 \qquad\qquad x = (\pm 1/3)^3$$
$$= \pm 1/27$$

Solutions: $\pm 1, \pm 1/27$

45. $\sqrt{1 - 3x} = 2$

Squaring both sides yields:
$$1 - 3x = 4$$
$$-3x = 3$$
$$x = -1$$

Check: $\sqrt{1 - 3(-1)} = \sqrt{4} = 2$, which is true.

Solution: -1

47. $\sqrt{x^4 - 13x^2 + 37} = 1$

After squaring both sides we obtain:
$$x^4 - 13x^2 + 36 = 0$$
$$(x^2 - 4)(x^2 - 9) = 0$$
$$(x - 2)(x + 2)(x - 3)(x + 3) = 0$$
$$x = \pm 2 \text{ or } x = \pm 3$$

Upon checking, we find that all four of these numbers satisfy the original equation.

Solutions: $\pm 2, \pm 3$

49. $\sqrt{1 - 2x} + \sqrt{x + 5} = 4$
$$\left(\sqrt{1 - 2x}\right)^2 = \left(4 - \sqrt{x + 5}\right)^2$$
$$1 - 2x = 16 - 8\sqrt{x + 5} + x + 5$$
$$8\sqrt{x + 5} = 3x + 20$$

After squaring both sides again, and then simplifying, we obtain:
$$9x^2 + 56x + 80 = 0$$
$$(x + 4)(9x + 20) = 0$$
$$x = -4 \text{ or } x = -20/9$$

Upon checking, we find that both of these values satisfy the original equation.

Solutions: -4, -20/9

51. $\sqrt{3 + 2t} + \sqrt{-1 + 4t} = 1$
$$\left(\sqrt{3 + 2t}\right)^2 = \left(1 - \sqrt{-1 + 4t}\right)^2$$
$$3 + 2t = 1 - 2\sqrt{-1 + 4t} - 1 + 4t$$
$$2\sqrt{-1 + 4t} = 2t - 3$$

After squaring both sides again, and then simplifying, we obtain:
$$4t^2 - 28t + 13 = 0$$
$$(2t - 1)(2t - 13) = 0$$
$$t = 1/2 \text{ or } t = 13/2$$

Upon checking, however, we find that neither of these values satisfies the original equation. So there is no solution to the equation.

53. $\sqrt{2y-3} - \sqrt{3y+3} + \sqrt{3y-2} = 0$

$$\left(\sqrt{2y-3} - \sqrt{3y+3}\right)^2 = \left(-\sqrt{3y-2}\right)^2$$

$2y-3 - 2\sqrt{2y-3}\sqrt{3y+3} + 3y+3 = 3y-2$

$2y+2 = 2\sqrt{2y-3}\sqrt{3y+3}$

$y+1 = \sqrt{2y-3}\sqrt{3y+3}$

After squaring this last equation and then simplifying, we obtain:

$$y^2 - y - 2 = 0$$
$$(y-2)(y+1) = 0$$
$$y = 2 \text{ or } y = -1$$

Upon checking, we find that only $y = 2$ satisfies the original equation.
Solution: 2

55. $\sqrt{2x+1} + \sqrt{x+4} = 1$

$$\left(\sqrt{2x+1}\right)^2 = \left(1 - \sqrt{x+4}\right)^2$$

$2x+1 = 1 - 2\sqrt{x+4} + x + 4$

$x - 4 = -2\sqrt{x+4}$

After squaring this last equation and then simplifying, we obtain:

$$x^2 - 12x = 0$$
$$x(x-12) = 0$$
$$x = 0 \text{ or } x = 12$$

Upon checking, we find that neither of these values satisfies the original equation.
So there is no solution to the equation.

57.   Letting $x^2 = t$ and $x^4 = t^2$, we have:

$$t^2 - 2t - 4 = 0$$

$$t = \frac{2 \pm \sqrt{20}}{2}$$

$$= \frac{2 \pm 2\sqrt{5}}{2}$$

$$= 1 \pm \sqrt{5}$$

We want the positive value for t here, because $t = x^2$. Thus:

$$x^2 = 1 + \sqrt{5}$$

$$x = \pm\sqrt{1 + \sqrt{5}}$$

Using a calculator now and rounding off to two decimal places, we find these values of x to be ± 1.80.
Solutions: ± 1.80

59. $2x\sqrt{x^2 + 4} + 2x\sqrt{x^2 + 1} = 3$

$$2x\sqrt{x^2 + 4} = 3 - 2x\sqrt{x^2 + 1}$$

$$4x^2(x^2 + 4) = 9 - 12x\sqrt{x^2 + 1} + 4x^2(x^2 + 1)$$

$$12x^2 - 9 = -12x\sqrt{x^2 + 1}$$

$$4x^2 - 3 = -4x\sqrt{x^2 + 1}$$

$$16x^4 - 24x^2 + 9 = 16x^4 + 16x^2$$

$$-40x^2 = -9$$

$$x = \pm\sqrt{\frac{9}{40}}$$

$$= \frac{\pm 3}{2\sqrt{10}}$$

$$= \pm\frac{3\sqrt{10}}{20}$$

Solution: 0.47

61.
$$\sqrt{\sqrt{x} + \sqrt{a}} + \sqrt{\sqrt{x} - \sqrt{a}} = \sqrt{2\sqrt{x} + 2\sqrt{b}}$$

$$\left(\sqrt{\sqrt{x} + \sqrt{a}} + \sqrt{\sqrt{x} - \sqrt{a}}\right)^2 = \left(\sqrt{2\sqrt{x} + 2\sqrt{b}}\right)^2$$

$$\sqrt{x} + \sqrt{a} + 2\sqrt{\sqrt{x} + \sqrt{a}}\sqrt{\sqrt{x} - \sqrt{a}} + \sqrt{x} - \sqrt{a} = 2\sqrt{x} + 2\sqrt{b}$$

$$\sqrt{\sqrt{x} + \sqrt{a}}\sqrt{\sqrt{x} - \sqrt{a}} = \sqrt{b}$$

Squaring both sides of this last equation yields:

$$\left(\sqrt{x} + \sqrt{a}\right)\left(\sqrt{x} - \sqrt{a}\right) = b$$

$$x - a = b$$

$$x = a + b$$

Upon checking, we find that this value of x satisfies the original equation. (Note: the following fact is useful in carrying out the check. Two non-negative quantities are equal if and only if their squares are equal.)
Solution: a + b

63. $\dfrac{\sqrt{x} - a}{\sqrt{x}} - \dfrac{\sqrt{x} + a}{\sqrt{x} - b} = 0$ (a, b > 0)

Let $t = \sqrt{x}$. Then the given equation can be written as:

$$\frac{t - a}{t} = \frac{t + a}{t - b}$$

$$t^2 + at = t^2 - at - bt + ab$$

$$2at + bt = ab$$

$$t(2a + b) = ab$$

$$t = \frac{ab}{2a + b}$$

Thus, $x = t^2 = \dfrac{a^2b^2}{(2a + b)^2}$

Thus, $x = t^2 = \dfrac{a^2b^2}{(2a + b)^2}$

Upon checking, we find that this value of x satisfies the original equation.

Solution: $\dfrac{a^2b^2}{(2a + b)^2}$

65. $\sqrt{x^2 - x - 1} - \dfrac{2}{\sqrt{x^2 - x - 1}} = 1$

Let $t = x^2 - x - 1$. Then the given equation becomes:

$$\sqrt{t} - \dfrac{2}{\sqrt{t}} = 1 \qquad (1)$$

$$t - 2 = \sqrt{t} \quad \text{(multiplying by } \sqrt{t}\text{)}$$

$$t^2 - 4t + 4 = t \qquad \text{(squaring)}$$

$$t^2 - 5t + 4 = 0$$

$$(t - 4)(t - 1) = 0$$

$$t = 4 \text{ or } t = 1$$

Upon checking, we find that t = 4 satisfies Equation (1), but t = 1 does not. With t = 4 we have:

$$x^2 - x - 1 = 4$$

$$x^2 - x - 5 = 0$$

and after applying the quadratic formula:

$$x = \dfrac{1 \pm \sqrt{21}}{2}$$

Solutions: $\dfrac{1 \pm \sqrt{21}}{2}$

67. $\sqrt{\dfrac{x - a}{x}} + 4\sqrt{\dfrac{x}{x - a}} = 5 \quad (a \neq 0)$

With $t = \dfrac{x - a}{x}$ the given equation becomes:

$$\sqrt{t} + \dfrac{4}{\sqrt{t}} = 5$$

$$t + 4 = 5\sqrt{t} \qquad \text{(multiplying by } \sqrt{t}\text{)}$$

After squaring and rearranging terms, we obtain:

$$t^2 - 17t + 16 = 0$$

$$(t - 1)(t - 16) = 0$$

$$t = 1 \text{ or } t = 16$$

After checking, we find that both of these values satisfy the equation

$$\sqrt{t} + \dfrac{4}{\sqrt{t}} = 5$$

$$1 = \frac{x - a}{x}$$

$$x = x - a$$

$$0 = -a$$

But since $a \neq 0$, we discard this case.

If $t = 16$, we have:

$$16 = \frac{x - a}{x}$$

$$16x = x - a$$

$$x = -a/15$$

Solution: $\frac{-a}{15}$

69. $2\sqrt{\frac{x}{a}} + 3\sqrt{\frac{a}{x}} = \frac{b}{a} + \frac{6a}{b}$

Let $t = \frac{x}{a}$, so the given equation becomes:

$$2\sqrt{t} + \frac{3}{\sqrt{t}} = \frac{b^2 + 6a^2}{ab}$$

$$2t + 3 = \frac{b^2 + 6a^2}{ab}\sqrt{t} \qquad \text{(multiplying by } \sqrt{t}\text{)}$$

Squaring each side yields:

$$4t^2 + 12t + 9 = \frac{(b^2 + 6a^2)^2}{a^2b^2} t$$

Multiplying through by a^2b^2 and collecting terms, we have:

$4a^2b^2t^2 - (b^4 + 36a^4)t + 9a^2b^2 = 0$

Which (conveniently) factors as:

$$(4a^2t - b^2)(b^2t - 9a^2) = 0$$

$$4a^2t = b^2 \quad \text{or} \quad b^2t = 9a^2$$

$$t = \frac{b^2}{4a^2} \quad \text{or} \quad t = \frac{9a^2}{b^2}$$

Since $t = \frac{x}{a}$, we have:

$$\frac{x}{a} = \frac{b^2}{4a^2} \quad \text{or} \quad \frac{x}{a} = \frac{9a^2}{b^2}$$

$$x = \frac{b^2}{4a} \quad \text{or} \quad x = \frac{9a^3}{b^2}$$

Solutions: $\frac{b^2}{4a}, \frac{9a^3}{b^2}$

71. $\sqrt{8 + 2t} + \sqrt{5 + t} = \sqrt{15 + 3t}$
We could begin by squaring both sides of the given equation. However, the following preliminary simplification saves some steps (and avoids the introduction of an extraneous root later):

$$\sqrt{8 + 2t} + \sqrt{5 + t} = \sqrt{3(5 + t)}$$
$$\sqrt{8 + 2t} = \sqrt{3}\sqrt{5 + t} - \sqrt{5 + t}$$
$$\sqrt{8 + 2t} = (\sqrt{3} - 1)(\sqrt{5 + t})$$

Now we square both sides to obtain:

$$8 + 2t = (\sqrt{3} - 1)^2 (5 + t)$$
$$8 + 2t = (4 - 2\sqrt{3})(5 + t)$$
$$8 + 2t = 20 - 10\sqrt{3} + (4 - 2\sqrt{3})t$$
$$(2 - 4 + 2\sqrt{3})t = 12 - 10\sqrt{3}$$
$$t = \frac{12 - 10\sqrt{3}}{-2 + 2\sqrt{3}}$$
$$= \frac{6 - 5\sqrt{3}}{-1 + \sqrt{3}}$$
$$= \frac{\sqrt{3} - 9}{2} \quad \text{(after rationalizing)}$$

After a lengthy check, we find that this value satisfies the original equation.

Solution: $\dfrac{\sqrt{3} - 9}{2}$

73. $\sqrt{x^2 + x} + \dfrac{1}{\sqrt{x^2 + x}} = \dfrac{5}{2}$

Letting $x^2 + x = t$, the given equation becomes:

$$\sqrt{t} + \frac{1}{\sqrt{t}} = \frac{5}{2}$$
$$2t + 2 = 5\sqrt{t} \quad \text{(multiplying by } 2\sqrt{t}\text{)}$$
$$4t^2 + 8t + 4 = 25t \quad \text{(squaring)}$$
$$4t^2 - 17t + 4 = 0$$
$$(4t - 1)(t - 4) = 0$$
$$t = 1/4 \text{ or } t = 4$$

(Both of these values for t check in the equation $\sqrt{t} + \dfrac{1}{\sqrt{t}} = \dfrac{5}{2}$.)

If t = 1/4, we have:

$$x^2 + x = 1/4$$
$$x = \frac{-1 \pm \sqrt{2}}{2} \quad \text{(quadratic formula)}$$

If t = 4 we have:

$$x^2 + x = 4$$

$$x = \frac{-1 \pm \sqrt{17}}{2} \quad \text{(quadratic formula)}$$

Now by using a calculator and rounding off to two decimal places, we obtain the following four approximations:

$$\frac{-1 + \sqrt{2}}{2} \approx 0.21 \qquad \frac{-1 + \sqrt{17}}{2} \approx 1.56$$

$$\frac{-1 - \sqrt{2}}{2} \approx -1.21 \qquad \frac{-1 - \sqrt{17}}{2} \approx -2.56$$

Solutions: 0.21, -1.21, 1.56, -2.56

75. $\sqrt[m]{(a + x)^2} + 2\sqrt[m]{(a - x)^2} = 3\sqrt[m]{a^2 - x^2}$

If we rewrite using rational exponents as:

$$(a + x)^{2/m} + 2(a - x)^{2/m} = 3(a + x)^{1/m}(a - x)^{1/m}$$

$$(a + x)^{2/m} - 3(a + x)^{1/m}(a - x)^{1/m} + 2(a - x)^{2/m} = 0$$

$$\left((a + x)^{1/m} - 2(a - x)^{1/m}\right)\left((a + x)^{1/m} - (a - x)^{1/m}\right) = 0$$

$$(a + x)^{1/m} = 2(a - x)^{1/m} \qquad \text{or} \qquad (a + x)^{1/m} = (a - x)^{1/m}$$

$$a + x = 2^m(a - x) \qquad\qquad\qquad a + x = a - x$$

$$a + x = 2^m a - 2^m x \qquad\qquad\qquad 2x = 0$$

$$(2^m + 1)x = a(2^m - 1) \qquad\qquad\qquad x = 0$$

$$x = \frac{a(2^m - 1)}{2^m + 1}$$

Solutions: $0, \dfrac{a(2^m - 1)}{2^m + 1}$

2.5 Inequalities. More About Absolute Value

1. (a)

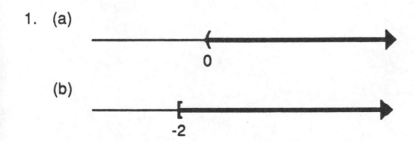

(b)

3. (a)

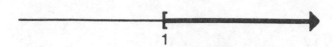

   (b)

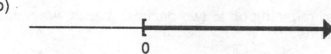

5.

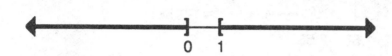

7. $x + 5 < 4$
    $x < -1$

   Solution set: $(-\infty, -1)$

9. $1 - 3x \leq 0$
    $-3x \leq -1$
    $x \geq 1/3$

   Solution set: $[\frac{1}{3}, \infty)$

11. $4x - 3 > 33$
     $4x > 36$
     $x > 9$

   Solution set: $(9, \infty)$

13. $\frac{3}{2}x + 4 \geq -1$
     $3x + 8 \geq -2$
     $3x \geq -10$
     $x \geq -\frac{10}{3}$

   Solution set: $[-\frac{10}{3}, \infty)$

15. $3x - 1 < 1 + x$
     $2x < 2$
     $x < 1$

   Solution set: $(-\infty, 1)$

17.　$2(t - 1) - 3(t + 1) \leq -5$

$\qquad 2t - 2 - 3t - 3 \leq -5$

$\qquad\qquad\qquad -t \leq 0$

$\qquad\qquad\qquad\ \ t \geq 0$

Solution set: $[0, \infty)$

19.　$t - 4[1 - (t - 1)] > 7 + 10t$

$\qquad t - 4 + 4(t - 1) > 7 + 10t$

$\qquad\qquad\quad 5t - 8 > 7 + 10t$

$\qquad\qquad\qquad -5t > 15$

$\qquad\qquad\qquad\ \ t < -3$

Solution set: $(-\infty, -3)$

21.　$(t + 4)(t - 4) \geq t(t + 3) - 1$

$\qquad\quad t^2 - 16 \geq t^2 + 3t - 1$

$\qquad\qquad -16 \geq 3t - 1$

$\qquad\qquad -3t \geq 15$

$\qquad\qquad\ \ t \leq -5$

Solution set: $(-\infty, -5]$

23.　$\dfrac{3x}{5} - \dfrac{x - 1}{3} < 1$

$\qquad 9x - 5(x - 1) < 15$

$\qquad\qquad 4x + 5 < 15$

$\qquad\qquad\quad 4x < 10$

$\qquad\qquad\quad\ x < 5/2$

Solution set: $(-\infty, \dfrac{5}{2})$

25.　$\dfrac{x - 1}{4} - \dfrac{2x + 3}{5} \leq x$

$\qquad 5(x - 1) - 4(2x + 3) \leq 20x$

$\qquad\quad 5x - 5 - 8x - 12 \leq 20x$

$\qquad\qquad\qquad -23x \leq 17$

$\qquad\qquad\qquad\quad x \geq -17/23$

Solution set: $[-\dfrac{17}{23}, \infty)$

27. $3\left(\dfrac{x}{2} + 1\right) - 2\left(\dfrac{x}{3} - 1\right) \geq 12$

$$\dfrac{3x}{2} + 3 - \dfrac{2x}{3} + 2 \geq 12$$

$$\dfrac{3x}{2} - \dfrac{2x}{3} \geq 7$$

$$9x - 4x \geq 42$$

$$5x \geq 42$$

$$x \geq 42/5$$

Solution set: $[\dfrac{42}{5}, \infty)$

29. $-2 \leq x - 6 \leq 0$

$4 \leq x \leq 6$

Solution set: $[4,6]$

31. $-6 < \dfrac{x + 4}{3} < -2$

$-18 < x + 4 < -6$

$-22 < x < -10$

Solution set: $(-22,-10)$

33. $-1 \leq \dfrac{1 - 4t}{3} \leq 1$

$-3 \leq 1 - 4t \leq 3$

$-4 \leq -4t \leq 2$

$1 \geq t \geq -\dfrac{1}{2}$

Or equivalently: $-\dfrac{1}{2} \leq t \leq 1$

Solution set: $[-\dfrac{1}{2}, 1]$

35. $.99 < \dfrac{x}{2} - 1 < .999$

$1.98 < x - 2 < 1.998$

$3.98 < x < 3.998$

Solution set: $(3.98, 3.998)$

37. $1.86 < 4.11x - 0.15 < 1.95$

$2.01 < 4.11x < 2.1$

$0.49 < x < 0.51$

Solution set: $(0.49, 0.51)$

39. Let x be the amount to be invested at 7%. Then 6000 - x will be invested at
     9%. Since the total dividends are to be at least $500, we have:

$$(x)(7\%) + (6000 - x)(9\%) \geq 500$$
$$.07x + .09(6000 - x) \geq 500$$
$$7x + 9(6000 - x) \geq 50000$$
$$7x + 54000 - 9x \geq 50000$$
$$-2x \geq -4000$$
$$x \leq 2000$$

At most $2000 can be invested at 7%.

41.
$$-25 \leq C \leq 475$$
$$-25 \leq \frac{5F - 160}{9} \leq 475$$
$$-225 \leq 5F - 160 \leq 4275$$
$$-65 \leq 5F \leq 4435$$
$$-13° \leq F \leq 887° \quad \text{or} \quad [-13°, 887°]$$

43.
$$50 \geq v \geq 40$$
$$50 \geq -32t + 60 \geq 40$$
$$-10 \geq -32t \geq -20$$
$$\frac{10}{32} \leq t \leq \frac{20}{32}$$
$$\frac{5}{16} \leq t \leq \frac{5}{8}$$

The velocity will be in the required range during the time interval
$$\frac{5}{16} \leq t \leq \frac{5}{8}, \text{ or } [\frac{5}{16}, \frac{5}{8}].$$

45. $|x| < 6$
     $-6 < x < 6$
     Solution set: (-6, 6)

47. The numbers whose distances from the origin are at least 2 are the numbers
     in the intervals $(-\infty, -2]$ or $[2, \infty)$.

     Solution set: $(-\infty, -2] \cup [2, \infty)$

49. Every real number satisfies the condition $|x| \geq 0$.

     Solution set: $(-\infty, \infty)$

51. $|x - 4| < 4$
     $-4 < x - 4 < 4$

$$0 < x < 8$$
Solution set: $(0,8)$

53. $|3x + 5| < 17$
$$-17 < 3x + 5 < 17$$
$$-22 < 3x < 12$$
$$-\frac{22}{3} < x < 4$$

Solution set: $(-\frac{22}{3}, 4)$

55. $|4 - 5t| < \frac{1}{10}$
$$-\frac{1}{10} < 4 - 5t < \frac{1}{10}$$
$$-\frac{41}{10} < -5t < -\frac{39}{10}$$
$$\frac{41}{50} > t > \frac{39}{50}$$

Solution set: $(\frac{39}{50}, \frac{41}{50})$

57. $\left|\frac{x - 2}{3}\right| < 4$
$$-4 < \frac{x - 2}{3} < 4$$
$$-12 < x - 2 < 12$$
$$-10 < x < 14$$
Solution set: $(-10, 14)$

59. $\left|\frac{3(x - 2)}{4} + \frac{4(x - 1)}{3}\right| \leq 2$
$$-2 \leq \frac{3(x - 2)}{4} + \frac{4(x - 1)}{3} \leq 2$$
$$-24 \leq 9(x - 2) + 16(x - 1) \leq 24$$
$$-24 \leq 25x - 34 \leq 24$$
$$10 \leq 25x \leq 58$$
$$\frac{10}{25} \leq x \leq \frac{58}{25}$$
$$\frac{2}{5} \leq x \leq \frac{58}{25}$$

Solution set: $[\frac{2}{5}, \frac{58}{25}]$

61. (a) $|(x + h)^2 - x^2| < 3h^2$ $(h > 0)$
     $-3h^2 < 2xh + h^2 < 3h^2$
     $-2h <\quad x \quad< h$
     Solution set: $(-2h, h)$

     (b) $|(x + h)^2 - x^2| < 3h^2$ $(h < 0)$
     $-3h^2 < 2xh + h^2 < 3h^2$
     $-4h^2 <\quad 2xh \quad< 2h^2$
     Now we divide through by the negative quantity $2h$ to obtain
     $-2h > x > h$
     Solution set: $(h, -2h)$

63.

a	b	G.M. $\sqrt{ab}$	A.M. $\dfrac{a+b}{2}$	R.M. $\sqrt{\dfrac{a^2 + b^2}{2}}$	largest	smallest
1	2	1.4142	1.5	1.5811	R.M.	G.M.
1	3	1.7320	2.0	2.2361	R.M.	G.M.
1	4	2.0000	2.5	2.9155	R.M.	G.M.
2	3	2.4495	2.5	2.5495	R.M.	G.M.
3	4	3.4641	3.5	3.5355	R.M.	G.M.
9	10	9.4868	9.5	9.5131	R.M.	G.M.
99	100	99.4987	99.5	99.5012	R.M.	G.M.
999	1000	999.4999	999.5	999.5001	R.M.	G.M.

65. (a)

x	y	$\frac{x}{y} + \frac{y}{x}$	$\frac{x}{y} + \frac{y}{x} \geq 2$
1	1	2.0000	true
2	3	2.1667	true
3	5	2.2667	true
4	7	2.3214	true
5	9	2.3556	true
9	10	2.0111	true
49	50	2.0004	true
99	100	2.0001	true

(b)
$$\sqrt{ab} \leq \frac{a+b}{2}$$

$$\sqrt{\left(\frac{x}{y}\right)\left(\frac{y}{x}\right)} \leq \frac{\frac{x}{y} + \frac{y}{x}}{2} \quad \text{(letting } a = x/y \text{ and } b = y/x\text{)}$$

$$1 \leq \frac{\frac{x}{y} + \frac{y}{x}}{2}$$

$$2 \leq \frac{x}{y} + \frac{y}{x}$$

67. Since $x(y-3) + 3(x-2) = xy - 3x + 3x - 6 = xy - 6$, then:

$$|xy - 6| \leq |x(y-3)| \leq |x||y-3| + 3|x-2|$$

Now $|y-3| < 0.01$ and $|x-2| < 0.1$. Since $|x-2| < 0.1$, then $-0.1 < x - 2 < 0.1$, so $1.9 < x < 2.1$, and thus $|x| < 2.1$. Thus:

$$|xy - 6| < (2.1)(0.01) + 3(0.1)$$
$$= .021 + .3$$
$$= .321, \text{ which proves the desired result.}$$

69. (a) $\sqrt{abcd} = \sqrt{(ab)(cd)} \leq \dfrac{ab + cd}{2}$

    (b) $\left(\sqrt{ab} + \sqrt{cd}\right)^2 = ab + 2\sqrt{abcd} + cd$

$$\leq ab + 2\left(\dfrac{ac + bd}{2}\right) + cd \quad [\text{ from \#69 (a) }]$$
$$= ab + ac + bd + cd$$
$$= (a + c)(b + d)$$

Therefore $\sqrt{ab} + \sqrt{cd} \leq \sqrt{(a + c)(b + d)}$

71. (a) Let l be the length, so $xl = 25$, and $l = \dfrac{25}{x}$. So the perimeter is given by:

$$P = 2x + 2\left(\dfrac{25}{x}\right) = 2x + \dfrac{50}{x}$$

    (b) $\dfrac{2x + \dfrac{50}{x}}{2} \geq \sqrt{2x \cdot \dfrac{50}{x}}$, so $2x + \dfrac{50}{x} \geq 2\sqrt{100} = 20$

    (c) We find where: $\quad 2x + \dfrac{50}{x} = 20$

$$2x^2 + 50 = 20x$$
$$x^2 - 10x + 25 = 0$$
$$(x - 5)^2 = 0$$
$$x = 5$$

Since the length is also 5, the rectangle is a square of dimensions 5ft. by 5ft.

2.6 More on Inequalities

1. $x^2 + x - 6 = (x + 3)(x - 2)$, so the key numbers are -3 and 2.

Interval	Test Number	$x + 3$	$x - 2$	$(x + 3)(x - 2)$
$(-\infty, -3)$	-4	neg.	neg.	pos.
$(-3, 2)$	0	pos.	neg.	neg.
$(2, \infty)$	3	pos.	pos.	pos.

Solution set for $x^2 + x - 6 < 0$: $(-3, 2)$

3. $x^2 - 11x + 18 = (x - 2)(x - 9)$, so the key numbers are 2 and 9.

Interval	Test Number	$x - 2$	$x - 9$	$(x - 2)(x - 9)$
$(-\infty, 2)$	0	neg.	neg.	pos.
$(2, 9)$	3	pos.	neg.	neg.
$(9, \infty)$	10	pos.	pos.	pos.

Solution set for $x^2 - 11x + 18 > 0$: $(-\infty, 2) \cup (9, \infty)$

5. $9x - x^2 \le 20 \iff -x^2 + 9x - 20 \le 0 \iff x^2 - 9x + 20 \ge 0$.

    Thus, the given inequality is equivalent to $x^2 - 9x + 20 \ge 0$, or $(x - 4)(x - 5) \ge 0$; so the key numbers are 4 and 5.

Interval	Test Number	x - 4	x - 5	(x - 4)(x - 5)
$(-\infty, 4)$	0	neg.	neg.	pos.
$(4, 5)$	9/2	pos.	neg.	neg.
$(5, \infty)$	6	pos.	pos.	pos.

The solution set for $x^2 - 9x + 20 \geq 0$ (and consequently for the original inequality also) is: $(-\infty, 4] \cup [5, \infty)$

7. $x^2 - 16 = (x - 4)(x + 4)$, so the key numbers are ±4.

Interval	Test Number	x - 4	x + 4	(x - 4)(x + 4)
$(-\infty, -4)$	-5	neg.	neg.	pos.
$(-4, 4)$	0	neg.	pos.	neg.
$(4, \infty)$	5	pos.	pos.	pos.

Solution set for $x^2 - 16 \geq 0$: $(-\infty, -4] \cup [4, \infty)$.

9. $16x^2 + 24x + 9 = (4x + 3)^2$, so the only key number is -3/4.

Interval	Test Number	4x + 3	$(4x + 3)^2$
$(-\infty, -3/4)$	-1	neg.	pos.
$(-3/4, \infty)$	1	pos.	pos.

The polynomial $16x^2 + 24x + 9$ is positive for all values of x except x = -3/4. The polynomial is zero when x = -3/4. Thus the inequality $16x^2 + 24x + 9 < 0$ (and consequently the original inequality also) has no solution. <u>Alternate Method:</u> The inequality $(4x + 3)^2 < 0$ has no solution, since the square of a real number is never negative.

11. $x^3 + 13x^2 + 42x = x(x^2 + 13x + 42) = x(x + 7)(x + 6)$
      Thus the key numbers are 0, -7, and -6.

Interval	Test Number	x	x + 7	x + 6	x(x + 7)(x + 6)
$(-\infty, -7)$	-8	neg.	neg.	neg.	neg.
$(-7, -6)$	-13/2	neg.	pos.	neg.	pos.
$(-6, 0)$	-1	neg.	pos.	pos.	neg.
$(0, \infty)$	1	pos.	pos.	pos.	pos.

Solution set for $x^3 + 13x^2 + 42x > 0$: $(-7, -6) \cup (0, \infty)$

13. $225x \leq x^3$
                 $225x - x^3 \leq 0$
           $x(15 - x)(15 + x) \leq 0$
      Thus, the key numbers are 0 and ± 15.

Interval	Test Number	x	15 - x	15 + x	x(15 - x)(15 + x)
$(-\infty, -15)$	-16	neg.	pos.	neg.	pos.
$(-15, 0)$	-1	neg.	pos.	pos.	neg.
$(0, 15)$	1	pos.	pos.	pos.	pos.
$(15, \infty)$	16	pos.	neg.	pos.	neg.

From these results we see that the solution set for $x(15 - x)(15 + x) \leq 0$ (and
for the original inequality) is: $[-15, 0] \cup [15, \infty)$

15.   There are no key numbers since the equation $2x^2 + 1 = 0$ has no real
      solutions. So the only interval is $(-\infty, \infty)$, and any number will suffice as a
      test number. With $x = 0$, we have $2(0)^2 + 1 = 2 > 0$. Consequently, the
      polynomial is positive for all values of x, and the solution set is $(-\infty, \infty)$.
      [Note: this answer is obvious from the start; the techniques of this section

aren't really needed.]

17. $12x^3 + 17x^2 + 6x = x(12x^2 + 17x + 6) = x(4x + 3)(3x + 2)$
    Thus, the key numbers are 0, -3/4, and -2/3.

Interval	Test Number	x	4x + 3	3x + 2	x(4x + 3)(3x + 2)
$(-\infty, -3/4)$	-1	neg.	neg.	neg.	neg.
$(-3/4, -2/3)$	-17/24	neg.	pos.	neg.	pos.
$(-2/3, 0)$	-1/3	neg.	pos.	pos.	neg.
$(0, \infty)$	1	pos.	pos.	pos.	pos.

Solution set for $12x^3 + 17x^2 + 6x < 0$: $(-\infty, -3/4) \cup (-2/3, 0)$

19. $x^2 + x - 1 > 0$
    The key numbers are found by solving the equation $x^2 + x - 1 = 0$. Using the quadratic formula we have:
    $$x = \frac{-1 \pm \sqrt{1 - 4(-1)}}{2} = \frac{-1 \pm \sqrt{5}}{2}$$
    For purposes of picking appropriate test-numbers, note that:
    $$\frac{-1 + \sqrt{5}}{2} \approx 0.6 \quad \text{and} \quad \frac{-1 - \sqrt{5}}{2} \approx -1.6$$

Interval	Test Number	x + 1.6	x - 0.6	$x^2 + x - 1$
$(-\infty, \frac{-1-\sqrt{5}}{2})$	-2	neg.	neg.	pos.
$(\frac{-1-\sqrt{5}}{2}, \frac{-1+\sqrt{5}}{2})$	0	pos.	neg.	neg.
$(\frac{-1+\sqrt{5}}{2}, \infty)$	1	pos.	pos.	pos.

Solution set: $(-\infty, \frac{-1 - \sqrt{5}}{2}) \cup (\frac{-1 + \sqrt{5}}{2}, \infty)$

21. The key numbers are found by using the quadratic formula to solve
     $x^2 - 8x + 2 = 0$.
     We have:

$$x = \frac{8 \pm \sqrt{64 - 4(2)}}{2} = \frac{8 \pm \sqrt{56}}{2} = \frac{8 \pm 2\sqrt{14}}{2} = 4 \pm \sqrt{14}$$

For purposes of picking appropriate test-numbers, note that $4 + \sqrt{14} \approx 7.4$
and $4 - \sqrt{14} \approx 0.3$.

Interval	Test Number	x - 7.4	x - 0.3	$x^2 - 8x + 2$
$(-\infty, 4 - \sqrt{14})$	0	neg.	neg.	pos.
$(4 - \sqrt{14}, 4 + \sqrt{14})$	4	neg.	pos.	neg.
$(4 + \sqrt{14}, \infty)$	8	pos.	pos.	pos.

Solution set for $x^2 - 8x + 2 \leq 0$: $[4 - \sqrt{14}, 4 + \sqrt{14}]$

23. The key numbers are -4, -3, and 1.

Interval	Test Number	x - 1	x + 3	x + 4	(x - 1)(x + 3)(x + 4)
$(-\infty, -4)$	-5	neg.	neg.	neg.	neg.
$(-4, -3)$	-7/2	neg.	neg.	pos.	pos.
$(-3, -1)$	0	neg.	pos.	pos.	neg.
$(-1, \infty)$	2	pos.	pos.	pos.	pos.

Solution set of the inequality $(x - 1)(x + 3)(x + 4) \geq 0$: $[-4, -3] \cup [1, \infty)$

25. The key numbers are -4, -5, and -6.

Interval	Test Number	x + 4	x + 5	x + 6	(x + 4)(x + 5)(x + 6)
$(-\infty, -6)$	-7	neg.	neg.	neg.	neg.
(-6, -5)	-11/2	neg.	neg.	pos.	pos.
(-5, -4)	-9/2	neg.	pos.	pos.	neg.
$(-4, \infty)$	0	pos.	pos.	pos.	pos.

Solution set for (x + 4) (x + 5) (x + 6) < 0: $(-\infty, -6) \cup (-5, -4)$

27. The key numbers are ±1/3 and 2.

Interval	Test Number	x - 2	3x + 1	3x - 1	$(x - 2)^2(3x + 1)^3(3x - 1)$
$(-\infty, -1/3)$	-1	neg.	neg.	neg.	pos.
(-1/3, 1/3)	0	neg.	pos.	neg.	neg.
(1/3, 2)	1	neg.	pos.	pos.	pos.
$(2, \infty)$	3	pos.	pos.	pos.	pos.

Solution set for $(x - 2)^2 (3x + 1)^3 (3x - 1) > 0$: $(-\infty, -1/3) \cup (1/3, 2) \cup (2, \infty)$

29.   The key numbers are 3, -1, -1/2, and -2/3.

Interval	Test Number	x - 3	x+1	2x + 1	3x + 2	$(x-3)^2(x+1)^4(2x+1)^4(3x+2)$
$(-\infty, -1)$	-2	neg.	neg.	neg.	neg.	neg.
$(-1, -2/3)$	-3/4	neg.	pos.	neg.	neg.	neg.
$(-2/3, -1/2)$	-7/12	neg.	pos.	neg.	pos.	pos.
$(-1/2, 3)$	0	neg.	pos.	pos.	pos.	pos.
$(3, \infty)$	4	pos.	pos.	pos.	pos.	pos.

The solution set for the inequality $(x - 3)^2 (x + 1)^4 (2x + 1)^4 (3x + 2) \leq 0$ consists of the two intervals $(-\infty, -1]$ and $[-1, -2/3]$. This is equivalent to the single interval $(-\infty, -2/3]$.

31. $x^4 - 9x^2 + 20 \geq 0$
                   $(x^2 - 4)(x^2 - 5) \geq 0$
      $(x - 2)(x + 2)(x - \sqrt{5})(x + \sqrt{5}) \geq 0$
Thus the key numbers are ± 2 and $\pm \sqrt{5}$.

Interval	Test Number	$x - \sqrt{5}$	x - 2	x + 2	$x + \sqrt{5}$	$x^4 - 9x^2 + 20$
$(-\infty, \sqrt{5})$	-3	neg.	neg.	neg.	neg.	pos.
$(-\sqrt{5}, -2)$	-2.1	neg.	neg.	neg.	pos.	neg.
$(-2, 2)$	0	neg.	neg.	pos.	pos.	pos.
$(2, \sqrt{5})$	2.1	neg.	pos.	pos.	pos.	neg.
$(\sqrt{5}, \infty)$	3	pos.	pos.	pos.	pos.	pos.

Solution set for $x^4 - 9x^2 + 20 \geq 0$: $(-\infty, -\sqrt{5}] \cup [-2, 2] \cup [\sqrt{5}, \infty)$

33. One of the key numbers is 4. The others are found by solving the equation $2x^2 - 6x - 1 = 0$. With the quadratic formula, we have:

$$x = \frac{6 \pm \sqrt{36 - 4(2)(-1)}}{2(2)} = \frac{6 \pm \sqrt{44}}{4} = \frac{6 \pm 2\sqrt{11}}{4} = \frac{3 \pm \sqrt{11}}{2}$$

Thus, the key numbers are 4 and $\frac{3 \pm \sqrt{11}}{2}$. For purposes of picking appropriate test numbers, note that $\frac{3 + \sqrt{11}}{2} \approx 3.2$ and that $\frac{3 - \sqrt{11}}{2} \approx -0.2$.

Interval	Test Number	$x - 4$	$x - 3.2$	$x + 0.2$	$(x - 4)(2x^2 - 6x - 1)$
$(-\infty, -0.2)$	-1	neg.	neg.	neg.	neg.
$(-0.2, 3.2)$	0	neg.	neg.	pos.	pos.
$(3.2, 4)$	3.5	neg.	pos.	pos.	neg.
$(4, \infty)$	5	pos.	pos.	pos.	pos.

Solution set for $(x - 4)(2x^2 - 6x - 1) < 0$: $(-\infty, \frac{3 - \sqrt{11}}{2}) \cup (\frac{3 + \sqrt{11}}{2}, 4)$

35.
$$x^3 + 2x^2 - x - 2 > 0$$
$$x^2(x + 2) - (x + 2) > 0$$
$$(x + 2)(x^2 - 1) > 0$$
$$(x + 2)(x + 1)(x - 1) > 0$$

The key numbers are -2 and ± 1.

Interval	Test Number	$x - 1$	$x + 1$	$x + 2$	$(x - 1)(x + 1)(x + 2)$
$(-\infty, -2)$	-3	neg.	neg.	neg.	neg.
$(-2, -1)$	-1.5	neg.	neg.	pos.	pos.
$(-1, 1)$	0	neg.	pos.	pos.	neg.
$(1, \infty)$	2	pos.	pos.	pos.	pos.

Solution set for $(x + 2)(x - 1)(x + 1) > 0$ (and for original inequality):

$(-2, -1) \cup (1, \infty)$

37.   Key numbers: ± 1

Interval	Test Number	$x + 1$	$x - 1$	$\dfrac{x - 1}{x + 1}$
$(-\infty, -1)$	-2	neg.	neg.	pos.
$(-1, 1)$	0	pos.	neg.	neg.
$(1, \infty)$	2	pos.	pos.	pos.

Thus, the quotient is negative on $(-1, 1)$, and it is zero when $x = 1$. So the solution set for $\dfrac{x - 1}{x + 1} \leq 0$ is $(-1, 1]$.

39.   Key numbers: 2 and 3/2

Interval	Test Number	$2 - x$	$3 - 2x$	$\dfrac{2 - x}{3 - 2x}$
$(-\infty, 3/2)$	0	pos.	pos.	pos.
$(3/2, 2)$	$7/4$	pos.	neg.	neg.
$(2, \infty)$	3	neg.	neg.	pos.

Thus, the quotient is positive on $(-\infty, 3/2)$ and $(2, \infty)$. Also, the quotient is zero when $x = 2$. So the solution set for $\dfrac{2 - x}{3 - 2x} \geq 0$ consists of the two intervals: $(-\infty, 3/2) \cup [2, \infty)$.

41. $\dfrac{x^2 - 8x - 9}{x} < 0$

$\dfrac{(x + 1)(x - 9)}{x} < 0$

Thus, the key numbers are -1, 0, and 9.

Interval	Test Number	x - 9	x	x + 1	$\dfrac{(x-9)(x+1)}{x}$
$(-\infty, -1)$	-2	neg.	neg.	neg.	neg.
$(-1, 0)$	-1/2	neg.	neg.	pos.	pos.
$(0, 9)$	1	neg.	pos.	pos.	neg.
$(9, \infty)$	10	pos.	pos.	pos.	pos.

Solution set: $(-\infty, -1) \cup (0, 9)$

43. $\dfrac{2x^3 + 5x^2 - 7x}{3x^2 + 7x + 4} > 0$

$\dfrac{x(2x^2 + 5x - 7)}{(3x + 4)(x + 1)} > 0$

$\dfrac{x(2x + 7)(x - 1)}{(3x + 4)(x + 1)} > 0$

Thus, the key numbers are 0, -7/2, 1, -4/3, and -1.

Interval	Test Number	x - 1	x	x + 1	3x + 4	2x + 7	$\dfrac{x(2x+7)(x-1)}{(3x+4)(x+1)}$
$(-\infty, -7/2)$	-4	neg.	neg.	neg.	neg.	neg.	neg.
$(-7/2, -4/3)$	-2	neg.	neg.	neg.	neg.	pos.	pos.
$(-4/3, -1)$	-7/6	neg.	neg.	neg.	pos.	pos.	neg.
$(-1, 0)$	-1/2	neg.	neg.	pos.	pos.	pos.	pos.
$(0, 1)$	1/2	neg.	pos.	pos.	pos.	pos.	neg.
$(1, \infty)$	2	pos.	pos.	pos.	pos.	pos.	pos.

Solution set: $(-7/2, -4/3) \cup (-1, 0) \cup (1, \infty)$

45.
$$\frac{x + 2}{x + 5} \leq 1$$

$$\frac{x + 2}{x + 5} - \frac{x + 5}{x + 5} \leq 0$$

$$\frac{x + 2 - (x + 5)}{x + 5} \leq 0$$

$$\frac{-3}{x + 5} \leq 0$$

The only key number is x = -5.

Interval	Test Number	x + 5	$\frac{-3}{x + 5}$
$(-\infty, -5)$	-6	neg.	pos.
$(-5, \infty)$	0	pos.	neg.

Solution set for $\frac{x + 2}{x + 5} \leq 1$: $(-5, \infty)$

(Note: The quotient is never zero because the numerator is a non-zero constant.)

47.
$$\frac{1}{x - 2} - \frac{1}{x - 1} \geq \frac{1}{6}$$

$$\frac{1}{x - 2} - \frac{1}{x - 1} - \frac{1}{6} \geq 0$$

$$\frac{6(x - 1) - 6(x - 2) - (x - 2)(x - 1)}{6(x - 2)(x - 1)} \geq 0$$

$$\frac{-x^2 + 3x + 4}{6(x - 2)(x - 1)} \geq 0$$

$$\frac{x^2 - 3x - 4}{6(x - 2)(x - 1)} \leq 0$$

$$\frac{(x - 4)(x + 1)}{6(x - 2)(x - 1)} \leq 0$$

Thus, the key numbers are -1, 1, 2, and 4.

Interval	Test Number	x - 4	x - 2	x - 1	x + 1	$\dfrac{(x - 4)(x + 1)}{6(x - 2)(x - 1)}$
$(-\infty, -1)$	-2	neg.	neg.	neg.	neg.	pos.
$(-1, 1)$	0	neg.	neg.	neg.	pos.	neg.
$(1, 2)$	3/2	neg.	neg.	pos.	pos.	pos.
$(2, 4)$	3	neg.	pos.	pos.	pos.	neg.
$(4, \infty)$	5	pos.	pos.	pos.	pos.	pos.

The initial sequence of steps shows that the original inequality is equivalent to:

$$\frac{(x - 4)(x + 1)}{6(x - 2)(x - 1)} \leq 0$$

This quotient is negative on the intervals (-1, 1) and (2, 4). It is zero when x = -1 and 4. Thus, the required solution set is [-1, 1) $\cup$ (2, 4].

49.

$$\frac{1 + x}{1 - x} - \frac{1 - x}{1 + x} < -1$$

$$\frac{1 + x}{1 - x} - \frac{1 - x}{1 + x} + 1 < 0$$

$$\frac{(1 + x)^2 - (1 - x)^2 + (1 - x^2)}{(1 - x)(1 + x)} < 0$$

$$\frac{-x^2 + 4x + 1}{(1 - x)(1 + x)} < 0$$

The denominator is zero when x = ± 1. Using the quadratic formula, we find the numerator is zero when x = $2 \pm \sqrt{5}$. Thus, the key numbers are ±1 and $2 \pm \sqrt{5}$. For purposes of picking appropriate test numbers, note that $2 + \sqrt{5} \approx 4.2$ and that $2 - \sqrt{5} \approx -0.2$.

Interval	Test Number	$x - 4.2$	$x - 1$	$x + 0.2$	$x + 1$	$\dfrac{-x^2 + 4x + 1}{1 - x^2}$
$(-\infty, -1)$	-2	neg.	neg.	neg.	neg.	pos.
$(-1, -0.2)$	-0.5	neg.	neg.	neg.	pos.	neg.
$(-0.2, 1)$	0	neg.	neg.	pos.	pos.	pos.
$(1, 4.2)$	2	neg.	pos.	pos.	pos.	neg.
$(4.2, \infty)$	5	pos.	pos.	pos.	pos.	pos.

Solution set: $(-1, 2 - \sqrt{5}) \cup (1, 2 + \sqrt{5})$

51.

$$\frac{3 - 2x}{3 + 2x} > \frac{1}{x}$$

$$\frac{3 - 2x}{3 + 2x} - \frac{1}{x} > 0$$

$$\frac{x(3 - 2x) - (3 + 2x)}{x(3 + 2x)} > 0$$

$$\frac{x - 2x^2 - 3}{x(3 + 2x)} > 0$$

$$\frac{2x^2 - x - 3}{x(3 + 2x)} < 0$$

The denominator is zero when $x = 0$ and $x = -3/2$. By using the quadratic formula, we find that there are no real numbers for which the numerator is zero. Thus, 0 and -3/2 are the only key numbers.

Interval	Test Number	$2x + 3$	x	$\dfrac{2x^2 - x + 3}{x(2x + 3)}$
$(-\infty, -3/2)$	-2	neg.	neg.	pos.
$(-3/2, 0)$	-1	pos.	neg.	neg.
$(0, \infty)$	1	pos.	pos.	pos.

The initial steps show that the given inequality is equivalent to:

$$\frac{2x^2 - x - 3}{x(3 + 2x)} < 0$$

The solution set is, therefore, (-3/2,0).

53.
$$1 + \frac{1}{x} \geq \frac{1}{1 + x}$$

$$1 + \frac{1}{x} - \frac{1}{1 + x} \geq 0$$

$$\frac{x(1 + x) + (1 + x) - x}{x(1 + x)} \geq 0$$

$$\frac{x^2 + x + 1}{x(1 + x)} \geq 0$$

The only key numbers are 0 and -1. (By using the quadratic formula, we find that there are no real numbers for which the numerator $x^2 + x + 1$ is zero.)

Interval	Test Number	x + 1	x	$\frac{x^2 + x + 1}{x(x + 1)}$
(-∞, -1)	-2	neg.	neg.	pos.
(-1, 0)	-1/2	pos.	neg.	neg.
(0, ∞)	1	pos.	pos.	pos.

The initial steps show that the given inequality is equivalent to:
$$\frac{x^2 + x + 1}{x(1 + x)} \geq 0$$

The solution set for this is (-∞, -1) ∪ (0, ∞). (There are no x - values for which the quotient is zero.)

55. (a) We solve the inequality:
$$x^2 - 4x - 5 \geq 0$$
$$(x - 5)(x + 1) \geq 0$$
The key numbers here are 5 and -1.

Interval	Test Number	x - 5	x + 1	(x - 5)(x + 1)
(-∞, -1)	-2	neg.	neg.	pos.
(-1, 5)	0	neg.	pos.	neg.
(5, ∞)	6	pos.	pos.	pos.

The solution set for $(x - 5) (x + 1) \geq 0$, therefore, is $(-\infty, -1] \cup [5, \infty)$.

(b)   We solve the inequality $\dfrac{1}{x^2 - 4x - 5} \geq 0$

This will have the same solutions as in (a), except the endpoints $x = -1$ and $x = 5$ are not included. The solution set for this is $(-\infty, -1) \cup (5, \infty)$.

57.   The solutions will be real provided the discriminant $b^2 - 4ac$ is non-negative. Thus, we have:

$$b^2 - 4 \geq 0$$
$$(b - 2)(b + 2) \geq 0$$

The key numbers here are ± 2.

Interval	Test Number	b - 2	b + 2	(b - 2)(b + 2)
$(-\infty, -2)$	-3	neg.	neg.	pos.
$(-2, 2)$	0	neg.	pos.	neg.
$(2, \infty)$	3	pos.	pos.	pos.

Thus, the solution set consists of the two intervals $(-\infty, -2] \cup [2, \infty)$. For values of b in either of these two intervals, the equation $x^2 + bx + 1 = 0$ will have real solutions. [Note: A more efficient way to solve the inequality $b^2 - 4 \geq 0$ is to write it as $b^2 \geq 4$, and then take the square roots of both (nonnegative) sides to obtain $|b| \geq 2$.]

59.   If $x = 1$ is a solution of $\dfrac{2a + x}{x - 2a} < 1$, then we have:

$$\dfrac{2a + 1}{1 - 2a} < 1$$

$$\dfrac{2a + 1}{1 - 2a} - 1 < 0$$

$$\dfrac{2a + 1 - (1 - 2a)}{1 - 2a} < 0$$

$$\dfrac{4a}{1 - 2a} < 0$$

Thus, the key numbers are 0 and 1/2.

Interval	Test Number	a	1 - 2a	$\dfrac{4a}{1-2a}$
$(-\infty, 0)$	-1	neg.	pos.	neg.
$(0, 1/2)$	1/4	pos.	pos.	pos.
$(1/2, \infty)$	1	pos.	neg.	neg.

The allowable values of a are, therefore, those numbers in either of the intervals $(-\infty, 0)$ or $(1/2, \infty)$. In other words $a < 0$ or $a > 1/2$.

61. Using the Pythagorean Theorem, we find the hypotenuse is $\sqrt{x^2 + (1 - x)^2}$, or $\sqrt{2x^2 - 2x + 1}$. If this is less than $\sqrt{17}/5$, then we have:

$$\sqrt{2x^2 - 2x + 1} < \sqrt{17}/5$$
$$\left(5\sqrt{2x^2 - 2x + 1}\right)^2 < \left(\sqrt{17}\right)^2$$
$$50x^2 - 50x + 25 < 17$$
$$50x^2 - 50x + 8 < 0$$
$$25x^2 - 25x + 4 < 0$$
$$(5x - 1)(5x - 4) < 0$$

The key numbers here are 1/5 and 4/5.

Interval	Test Number	5x - 1	5x - 4	(5x - 1)(5x - 4)
$(-\infty, 1/5)$	0	neg.	neg.	pos.
$(1/5, 4/5)$	2/5	pos.	neg.	neg.
$(4/5, \infty)$	1	pos.	pos.	pos.

The solution set is the interval (1/5,4/5). In other words, if $\dfrac{1}{5} < x < \dfrac{4}{5}$, then the hypotenuse will be less than $\sqrt{17}/5$.

63. For the cylinder, we have:

$$\frac{V}{S} = \frac{\pi r^2 h}{2\pi r^2 + 2\pi rh} = \frac{\pi r^2}{2\pi r^2 + 2\pi r} = \frac{r}{2r + 2}$$

The condition $\frac{V}{S} < \frac{1}{3}$ then becomes:

$$\frac{r}{2r + 2} < \frac{1}{3}$$

Since r is positive here, we can multiply through by the positive quantity $3(2r + 2)$. This yields:

$$3r < 2r + 2$$
$$r < 2$$

So $0 < r < 2$.

65. (a)

x	$x^2 + 1000$	$2x^2 + x$	$\dfrac{x^2 + 1000}{2x^2 + x}$
1	1001	3	333.67
2	1004	10	100.4
5	1025	55	18.64
10	1100	210	5.24
100	11,000	20,100	0.55
200	41,000	80,200	0.51
10,000	100,001,000	200,010,000	0.50

(b)

$$\frac{x^2 + 1000}{2x^2 + x} < \frac{1}{2}$$

$$\frac{x^2 + 1000}{x(2x + 1)} - \frac{1}{2} < 0$$

$$\frac{2(x^2 + 1000) - x(2x + 1)}{2x(2x + 1)} < 0$$

$$\frac{-x + 2000}{2x(2x + 1)} < 0$$

Thus, the key numbers are 2000, 0, and -1/2.

Interval	Test Number	$2x + 1$	x	$-x + 2000$	$\dfrac{-x + 2000}{2x(2x + 1)}$
$(-\infty, -1/2)$	-1	neg.	neg.	pos.	pos.
$(-1/2, 0)$	$-1/4$	pos.	neg.	pos.	neg.
$(0, 2000)$	1	pos.	pos.	pos.	pos.
$(2000, \infty)$	2001	pos.	pos.	neg.	neg.

The solution set for $\dfrac{x^2 + 1000}{2x^2 + x} < \dfrac{1}{2}$ is, therefore, $(-1/2, 0) \cup (2000, \infty)$.

(c) The inequality holds when $n > 2000$, and the smallest natural number fulfilling this condition is 2001.

<u>Answer</u>: $n = 2001$

<u>Check</u>: $n = 2000$ $\dfrac{2000^2 + 1000}{2(2000^2) + 2000} = \dfrac{1}{2}$

$n = 2001$ $\dfrac{2001^2 + 1000}{2(2001^2) + 2001} = 0.499....... < \dfrac{1}{2}$

67. $(x - a)^2 - (x - b)^2 > \dfrac{(a - b)^2}{4}$

We multiply this out to get:

$x^2 - 2ax + a^2 - x^2 + 2bx - b^2 > \dfrac{(a - b)^2}{4}$

$(2b - 2a)x + (a^2 - b^2) > \dfrac{(a - b)^2}{4}$

$8(b - a)x + 4(a + b)(a - b) > (a - b)^2$

Since $a > b$, then $a - b > 0$, so we can divide by $a - b$ and preserve the inequality. Thus:

$-8x + 4(a + b) > a - b$

$-8x + 4a + 4b > a - b$

$-8x > -3a - 5b$

$x < \dfrac{3a + 5b}{8}$

So the solution is $\left(-\infty, \dfrac{3a + 5b}{8}\right)$.

An alternate approach to dividing by $a - b$ is:

$8(b - a)x + 4(a + b)(a - b) - (a - b)^2 > 0$

$$(a - b)\big(-8x + 4(a + b) - (a - b)\big) > 0$$
$$(a - b)(-8x + 4a + 4b - a + b) > 0$$
$$(a - b)(-8x + 3a + 5b) > 0$$

Since $a - b > 0$, then:

$$-8x + 3a + 5b > 0$$
$$-8x > -3a - 5b$$
$$x < \frac{3a + 5b}{8}$$

The two approaches yield the same solution.

Chapter 2 Review Exercises

1.   T

3.   F   (For instance: $x = 5$)

5.   F   (For instance: $x = 1/4$)

7.   T

9.   F   (For instance: $x = 0$, $y = -1$)

11. F   (For instance: $a = -5$, $b = 1$)

13. $5 - 9x = 2$
$$-9x = -3$$
$$x = 1/3$$

15. $(t - 4)(t + 3) = (t + 5)^2$
$$t^2 - t - 12 = t^2 + 10t + 25$$
$$-11t = 37$$
$$t = -37/11$$

17. $\dfrac{2t - 1}{t + 2} = 5$
$$2t - 1 = 5t + 10$$
$$-3t = 11$$
$$t = -11/3 \qquad \text{(it checks)}$$

19. $\dfrac{2}{x+4} - \dfrac{1}{x-4} = \dfrac{-7}{x^2-16}$

$2(x-4) - (x+4) = -7$ [multiplying by $(x+4)(x-4)$]

$2x - 8 - x - 4 = -7$

$x = 5$ [It checks in the original equation.]

21. $\dfrac{2y-5}{4y+1} = \dfrac{y-1}{2y+5}$

$4y^2 - 25 = 4y^2 - 3y - 1$

$3y = 24$

$y = 8$ [This checks.]

23. $|y+4| = 2$

$|y-(-4)| = 2$

Thus, y is two units from -4; that is, $y = -6$ or $y = -2$.

25. $|3x-1| = 2$

$3x - 1 = 2$ or $-(3x-1) = 2$

$3x = 3$ $-3x + 1 = 2$

$x = 1$ $-3x = 1$

$x = -1/3$

Solutions: 1 and -1/3

27. $12x^2 + 2x - 2 = 0$

$6x^2 + x - 1 = 0$

$(3x-1)(2x+1) = 0$

$x = 1/3$ or $x = -1/2$

29. $\dfrac{1}{2}x^2 + x - 12 = 0$

$x^2 + 2x - 24 = 0$

$(x+6)(x-4) = 0$

$x = -6$ or $x = 4$

31. $\dfrac{1}{1-x} + \dfrac{4}{2-x} = \dfrac{11}{6}$

$6(2-x) + 4(6)(1-x) = 11(1-x)(2-x)$

$12 - 6x + 24 - 24x = 22 - 33x + 11x^2$

$-11x^2 + 3x + 14 = 0$

$11x^2 - 3x - 14 = 0$

$(11x-14)(x+1) = 0$

$x = 14/11$ or $x = -1$ (both answers check)

33.
$$\frac{x}{5 - x} = \frac{-2}{11 - x}$$
$$11x - x^2 = -10 + 2x$$
$$-x^2 + 9x + 10 = 0$$
$$x^2 - 9x - 10 = 0$$
$$(x - 10)(x + 1) = 0$$
$$x = 10 \quad \text{or} \quad x = -1 \quad \text{(both answers check)}$$

35.
$$\frac{1}{3x - 7} - \frac{2}{5x - 5} - \frac{3}{3x + 1} = 0$$
$$(5x - 5)(3x + 1) - 2(3x - 7)(3x + 1) - 3(3x - 7)(5x - 5) = 0$$
$$15x^2 - 10x - 5 - 18x^2 + 36x + 14 - 45x^2 + 150x - 105 = 0$$
$$-48x^2 + 176x - 96 = 0$$
$$6x^2 - 22x + 12 = 0$$
$$3x^2 - 11x + 6 = 0$$
$$(3x - 2)(x - 3) = 0$$
$$x = 2/3 \quad \text{or} \quad x = 3$$
$$\text{(both answers check)}$$

37. $x^2 + 4x - 1 = 0$

$$x = \frac{-4 \pm \sqrt{16 - 4(-1)}}{2}$$
$$= \frac{-4 \pm \sqrt{20}}{2}$$
$$= \frac{-4 \pm 2\sqrt{5}}{2}$$
$$= -2 \pm \sqrt{5}$$

39. $t^2 + t - \frac{1}{2} = 0$

$$2t^2 + 2t - 1 = 0$$
$$t = \frac{-2 \pm \sqrt{4 - 4(2)(-1)}}{2(2)}$$
$$= \frac{-2 \pm \sqrt{12}}{4}$$
$$= \frac{-2 \pm 2\sqrt{3}}{4}$$
$$= \frac{-1 \pm \sqrt{3}}{2}$$

41. $y^4 = 9$
     $y^2 = \pm 3$
     $y^2 = 3$ or $y^2 = -3$ (which has no real solution)
     $y = \pm \sqrt{3}$
     Solutions: $y = \pm \sqrt{3}$

43. $x^4 - 7x^2 + 12 = 0$
     $(x^2 - 4)(x^2 - 3) = 0$
     $\qquad\qquad x^2 = 4$ or $x^2 = 3$
     $\qquad\qquad x = \pm 2$ or $x = \pm \sqrt{3}$

45. $x^5 - 2x^3 - 2x = 0$
     $x(x^4 - 2x^2 - 2) = 0$
     $$x = 0 \text{ or } x^2 = \frac{2 \pm \sqrt{4 - 4(-2)}}{2}$$
     $$= \frac{2 \pm \sqrt{12}}{2}$$
     $$= \frac{2 \pm 2\sqrt{3}}{2}$$
     $$= 1 \pm \sqrt{3}$$

     Note that $1 - \sqrt{3}$ is negative, so no real solutions are obtained from
     $x^2 = 1 - \sqrt{3}$. Consequently, $x^2 = 1 + \sqrt{3}$ and $x = \pm \sqrt{1 + \sqrt{3}}$.
     Solutions: $0, \pm \sqrt{1 + \sqrt{3}}$

47. $1 + 14x^{-1} + 48x^{-2} = 0$
     $\qquad x^2 + 14x + 48 = 0$ (multiplying by x^2)
     $\qquad (x + 6)(x + 8) = 0$
     $\qquad\qquad x = -6$ or $x = -8$ (both values check)

49. $4x^{4/3} - 13x^{2/3} + 9 = 0$
     Let $t = x^{2/3}$ and $t^2 = x^{4/3}$ so that the equation becomes:
     $\qquad 4t^2 - 13t + 9 = 0$
     Thus, $t = \dfrac{13 \pm \sqrt{169 - 4(4)(9)}}{2(4)} = \dfrac{13 \pm \sqrt{25}}{8} = \dfrac{13 \pm 5}{8}$
     The two values for t are 9/4 and 1. With $t = 9/4$ we have:
     $\qquad x^{2/3} = 9/4$
     $\qquad x^{1/3} = \pm 3/2$
     $\qquad x = \pm 27/8$

With $t = 1$ we have:
$$x^{2/3} = 1$$
$$x^{1/3} = \pm 1$$
$$x = \pm 1$$
Solutions: $\pm 27/8,\ \pm 1$

51. $x^{1/2} - 13x^{1/4} + 36 = 0$
Let $t = x^{1/4}$ and $t^2 = x^{1/2}$. Then:
$$t^2 - 13t + 36 = 0$$
$$(t - 9)(t - 4) = 0$$
$$t = 9 \quad \text{or} \quad t = 4$$
If $t = 9$, then $x^{1/4} = 9$ and $x = 9^4 = 6561$.
If $t = 4$, then $x^{1/4} = 4$ and $x = 4^4 = 256$.
Solutions: 6561, 256

53. $\sqrt{4 - 3x} = 5$
$$4 - 3x = 25$$
$$-3x = 21$$
$$x = -7$$
This value checks in the original equation.
Solution: -7

55.
$$\sqrt{4x + 3} = \sqrt{11 - 8x} - 1$$
$$4x + 3 = 11 - 8x - 2\sqrt{11 - 8x} + 1$$
$$12x - 9 = -2\sqrt{11 - 8x}$$
$$144x^2 - 216x + 81 = 44 - 32x$$
$$144x^2 - 184x + 37 = 0$$
$$(4x - 1)(36x - 37) = 0$$
$$x = 1/4 \quad \text{or} \quad x = 37/36 \text{ (which does not check)}$$
Solution: 1/4

57. $\sqrt{5 - 2x} - \sqrt{2 - x} - \sqrt{3 - x} = 0$
$$\sqrt{5 - 2x} = \sqrt{2 - x} + \sqrt{3 - x}$$
$$5 - 2x = 2 - x + 2\sqrt{2 - x}\ \sqrt{3 - x} + 3 - x$$
$$0 = 2\sqrt{2 - x}\ \sqrt{3 - x}$$
Thus $\sqrt{2 - x} = 0$ and consequently $x = 2$, or $\sqrt{3 - x} = 0$ and consequently $x = 3$. The value $x = 2$ checks in the original equation. But (considering only the real number system) the value $x = 3$ does not check.
Solution: 2

59. $\sqrt{x + 48} - \sqrt{x} = 4$

$\sqrt{x + 48} = \sqrt{x} + 4$

$x + 48 = x + 8\sqrt{x} + 16$

$32 = 8\sqrt{x}$

$4 = \sqrt{x}$

$16 = x$ (which checks)

Solution: 16

61. $\dfrac{2}{\sqrt{x^2 - 36}} + \dfrac{1}{\sqrt{x + 6}} - \dfrac{1}{\sqrt{x - 6}} = 0$

$2 + \sqrt{x - 6} - \sqrt{x + 6} = 0$ (multiplying by $\sqrt{x + 6}$ $\sqrt{x - 6}$)

$2 + \sqrt{x - 6} = \sqrt{x + 6}$

$4 + 4\sqrt{x - 6} + x - 6 = x + 6$

$4\sqrt{x - 6} = 8$

$\sqrt{x - 6} = 2$

$x - 6 = 4$

$x = 10$ (which checks)

Solution: 10

63. $\sqrt{x + 7} - \sqrt{x + 2} = \sqrt{x - 1} - \sqrt{x - 2}$

$x + 7 - 2\sqrt{x + 7}\ \sqrt{x + 2} + x + 2 = x - 1 - 2\sqrt{x - 1}\ \sqrt{x - 2} + x - 2$

$-2\sqrt{x + 7}\ \sqrt{x + 2} + 9 = -2\sqrt{x - 1}\ \sqrt{x - 2} - 3$

$-2\sqrt{x + 7}\ \sqrt{x + 2} = -2\sqrt{x - 1}\ \sqrt{x - 2} - 12$

$\sqrt{x + 7}\ \sqrt{x + 2} = \sqrt{x - 1}\ \sqrt{x - 2} + 6$

$(x + 7)(x + 2) = (x - 1)(x - 2) + 12\sqrt{x - 1}\ \sqrt{x - 2} + 36$

$x^2 + 9x + 14 = x^2 - 3x + 2 + 12\sqrt{x - 1}\ \sqrt{x - 2} + 36$

$12x - 24 = 12\sqrt{x - 1}\ \sqrt{x - 2}$

$x - 2 = \sqrt{x - 1}\ \sqrt{x - 2}$

$x^2 - 4x + 4 = x^2 - 3x + 2$

$-x = -2$

$x = 2$ (which checks)

Solution: 2

65. $\dfrac{ax + b}{cx + d} = e$

$ax + b = cex + de$

$ax - cex = de - b$

$x(a - ce) = de - b$

$x = \dfrac{de - b}{a - ce}$

67.
$$(a^2 + b^2)x = a^3 + b^3 + abx$$
$$(a^2 + b^2)x - abx = a^3 + b^3$$
$$x(a^2 - ab + b^2) = a^3 + b^3$$
$$x = \frac{a^3 + b^3}{a^2 - ab + b^2}$$
$$x = \frac{(a + b)(a^2 - ab + b^2)}{a^2 - ab + b^2}$$
$$x = a + b$$

69.
$$\frac{x}{a} + \frac{a}{x} = 2$$
$$x^2 + a^2 = 2ax$$
$$x^2 - 2ax + a^2 = 0$$
$$(x - a)^2 = 0$$
$$x = a \quad \text{(double root)}$$

(This value checks in the original equation; the form of that equation requires that a be nonzero.)

71.
$$4x^2y^2 - 4xy = -1 \quad (y \neq 0)$$
$$4x^2y^2 - 4xy + 1 = 0$$
$$(2xy - 1)^2 = 0$$
$$2xy - 1 = 0$$
$$x = \frac{1}{2y} \quad \text{(double root)}$$

73. $x + \dfrac{1}{a} - \dfrac{1}{b} = \dfrac{2}{a^2x} + \dfrac{2}{abx}$

Multiplying through by a^2bx yields:
$$a^2bx^2 + abx - a^2x = 2b + 2a$$
$$a^2bx^2 + (ab - a^2)x - 2(b + a) = 0$$
Applying the quadratic equation:

$$x = \frac{-(ab - a^2) \pm \sqrt{(ab - a^2)^2 - 4(a^2b)[-2(b + a)]}}{2(a^2b)}$$

$$= \frac{-ab + a^2 \pm \sqrt{a^4 + 6a^3b + 9a^2b^2}}{2a^2b} \quad \text{(simplifying)}$$

$$= \frac{-ab + a^2 \pm \sqrt{(a^2 + 3ab)^2}}{2a^2b}$$

$$= \frac{-ab + a^2 \pm (a^2 + 3ab)}{2a^2b}$$

Using the Plus Sign

$$x = \frac{-ab + a^2 + a^2 + 3ab}{2a^2b}$$

$$= \frac{2a^2 + 2ab}{2a^2b}$$

$$= \frac{2a(a + b)}{2a^2b}$$

$$= \frac{a + b}{ab}$$

Using the Minus Sign

$$x = \frac{-ab + a^2 - a^2 - 3ab}{2a^2b}$$

$$= \frac{-4ab}{2a^2b}$$

$$= \frac{-2}{a}$$

Both of these values satisfy the original equation.

75. $\dfrac{1}{x + a + b} = \dfrac{1}{x} + \dfrac{1}{a} + \dfrac{1}{b}$

$$abx = ab(x + a + b) + bx(x + a + b) + ax(x + a + b)$$
$$abx = abx + a^2b + ab^2 + bx^2 + abx + b^2x + ax^2 + a^2x + abx$$
$$0 = (a + b)x^2 + (a^2 + 2ab + b^2)x + (a^2b + ab^2)$$
$$0 = (a + b)x^2 + (a + b)^2x + ab(a + b)$$
$$0 = x^2 + (a + b)x + ab$$
$$0 = (x + a)(x + b)$$
$$x = -a \quad \text{or} \quad x = -b \quad \text{(both values check)}$$

77. $\dfrac{a^2 - b^2}{x} - \dfrac{2(a^2 + b^2)}{\sqrt{x}} = b^2 - a^2$

Letting $t = \dfrac{1}{\sqrt{x}}$ and $t^2 = \dfrac{1}{x}$, we have:

$$(a^2 - b^2)t^2 - 2(a^2 + b^2)t + (a^2 - b^2) = 0$$
$$\big((a - b)t - (a + b)\big)\big((a + b)t - (a - b)\big) = 0$$

Setting each factor equal to zero, we have:

$(a - b)t - (a + b) = 0$ or $(a + b)t - (a - b) = 0$

$$t = \frac{a + b}{a - b} \qquad\qquad t = \frac{a - b}{a + b}$$

$$\frac{1}{\sqrt{x}} = \frac{a + b}{a - b} \qquad\qquad \frac{1}{\sqrt{x}} = \frac{a - b}{a + b}$$

$$\sqrt{x} = \frac{a - b}{a + b} \qquad\qquad \sqrt{x} = \frac{a + b}{a - b}$$

$$x = \left(\frac{a - b}{a + b}\right)^2 \qquad\qquad x = \left(\frac{a + b}{a - b}\right)^2$$

Both of these values check in the original equation.

79. $4(1 + x) - 3(2x - 1) \geq 1$

$\quad\quad\quad 4 + 4x - 6x + 3 \geq 1$

$\quad\quad\quad\quad\quad\quad\quad -2x \geq -6$

$\quad\quad\quad\quad\quad\quad\quad\quad x \leq 3$

Solution set: $(-\infty, 3]$

81. $-1 < \dfrac{1 - 2(1 + x)}{3} < 1$

$\quad -3 < \quad 1 - 2 - 2x \quad < 3$

$\quad -2 < \quad\quad -2x \quad\quad < 4$

$\quad\ \ 1 > \quad\quad\ x \quad\quad\ > -2$

Solution set: $(-2, 1)$

83. $\dfrac{3}{5} < \dfrac{3 - 2x}{-4} < \dfrac{4}{5}$

$\quad -12 > 15 - 10x > -16 \quad\quad$ (multiplying by -20)

$\quad -27 > \quad -10x \quad\ > -31$

$\quad \dfrac{27}{10} < \quad\quad x \quad\quad < \dfrac{31}{10}$

Solution set: $\left(\dfrac{27}{10}, \dfrac{31}{10} \right)$

85. $|x| \leq \dfrac{1}{2}$ is equivalent to $-\dfrac{1}{2} \leq x \leq \dfrac{1}{2}$

Solution set: $\left[-\dfrac{1}{2}, \dfrac{1}{2} \right]$

87. $\quad |x + 4| < \dfrac{1}{10}$

$\quad -\dfrac{1}{10} < x + 4 < \dfrac{1}{10}$

$\quad -\dfrac{41}{10} < \quad x \quad < -\dfrac{39}{10}$

Solution set: $\left(-\dfrac{41}{10}, -\dfrac{39}{10} \right)$

89. $\quad\quad\quad |2x - 1| \geq 5$

$\quad 2x - 1 \geq 5 \quad$ or $\quad -(2x - 1) \geq 5$

$\quad\quad 2x \geq 6 \quad\quad\quad\quad 2x - 1 \leq -5$

$\quad\quad\ x \geq 3 \quad\quad\quad\quad\quad 2x \leq -4$

$\quad\quad\ x \leq -2$

Solution set: $(-\infty, -2] \cup [3, \infty)$

91. $x^2 + 3x - 40 < 0$
$(x - 5)(x + 8) < 0$
Key numbers: 5, -8

Interval	Test Number	x + 8	x - 5	(x + 8)(x - 5)
$(-\infty, -8)$	-9	neg.	neg.	pos.
$(-8, 5)$	0	pos.	neg.	neg.
$(5, \infty)$	6	pos.	pos.	pos.

Solution set: (-8, 5)

93. $x^2 - 6x - 1 < 0$
The key numbers are found by using the quadratic formula to solve $x^2 - 6x - 1 = 0$. The result is $x = 3 \pm \sqrt{10}$. For purposes of picking appropriate test numbers, note that $3 + \sqrt{10} \approx 6.2$ and that $3 - \sqrt{10} \approx -0.2$.

Interval	Test Number	x - 6.2	x + 0.2	$x^2 - 6x - 1$
$(-\infty, 3 - \sqrt{10})$	-1	neg.	neg.	pos.
$(3 - \sqrt{10}, 3 + \sqrt{10})$	0	neg.	pos.	neg.
$(3 + \sqrt{10}, \infty)$	7	pos.	pos.	pos.

Solution set: $(3 - \sqrt{10}, 3 + \sqrt{10})$

95. $(x - 4)^2(x + 8)^3 \geq 0$
     Key numbers: 4, -8

Interval	Test Number	x + 8	x - 4	$(x - 4)^2(x + 8)^3$
$(-\infty, -8)$	-9	neg.	neg.	neg.
$(-8, 4)$	0	pos.	neg.	pos.
$(4, \infty)$	5	pos.	pos.	pos.

Solution set: $[-8, 4] \cup [4, \infty)$, which simplifies to $[-8, \infty)$

97. $x^4 - 34x^2 + 225 < 0$
                 $(x^2 - 9)(x^2 - 25) < 0$
     $(x - 3)(x + 3)(x - 5)(x + 5) < 0$
     Key numbers: $\pm 3, \pm 5$

Interval	Test Number	x - 5	x - 3	x + 3	x + 5	$(x^2 - 9)(x^2 - 25)$
$(-\infty, -5)$	-6	neg.	neg.	neg.	neg.	pos.
$(-5, -3)$	-4	neg.	neg.	neg.	pos.	neg.
$(-3, 3)$	0	neg.	neg.	pos.	pos.	pos.
$(3, 5)$	4	neg.	pos.	pos.	pos.	neg.
$(5, \infty)$	6	pos.	pos.	pos.	pos.	pos.

Solution set: $(-5, -3) \cup (3, 5)$

99. $\dfrac{(x-7)^2}{(x+2)^3} \geq 0$

Key numbers: 7, -2

Interval	Test Number	x + 2	x - 7	$\dfrac{(x-7)^2}{(x+2)^3}$
$(-\infty, -2)$	-3	neg.	neg.	neg.
$(-2, 7)$	0	pos.	neg.	pos.
$(7, \infty)$	8	pos.	pos.	pos.

Solution set: $(-2, 7] \cup [7, \infty)$. This is equivalent to the single interval $(-2, \infty)$

101. $\dfrac{x^2 - 10x + 9}{x^3 + 1} \leq 0$

$\dfrac{(x-1)(x-9)}{(x+1)(x^2 - x + 1)} \leq 0$

Key numbers: ± 1, 9

Interval	Test Number	x - 9	x - 1	x + 1	$\dfrac{(x-1)(x-9)}{x^3 + 1}$
$(-\infty, -1)$	-2	neg.	neg.	neg.	neg.
$(-1, 1)$	0	neg.	neg.	pos.	pos.
$(1, 9)$	2	neg.	pos.	pos.	neg.
$(9, \infty)$	10	pos.	pos.	pos.	pos.

Solution set: $(-\infty, -1) \cup [1, 9]$

103.
$$\frac{1 - 2x}{1 + 2x} \le \frac{1}{2}$$

$$\frac{1 - 2x}{1 + 2x} - \frac{1}{2} \le 0$$

$$\frac{2(1 - 2x) - (1 + 2x)}{2(1 + 2x)} \le 0$$

$$\frac{-6x + 1}{2(1 + 2x)} \le 0$$

Key numbers: 1/6, -1/2

Interval	Test Number	$2x + 1$	$-6x + 1$	$\dfrac{-6x + 1}{2(2x + 1)}$
$(-\infty, -1/2)$	-1	neg.	pos.	neg.
$(-1/2, 1/6)$	0	pos.	pos.	pos.
$(1/6, \infty)$	1	pos.	neg.	neg.

Solution set: $(-\infty, -1/2) \cup [1/6, \infty)$

105.
$$\frac{1}{x} + \frac{1}{x + 1} + \frac{1}{x + 2} \ge 0$$

$$\frac{(x + 1)(x + 2) + x(x + 2) + x(x + 1)}{x(x + 1)(x + 2)} \ge 0$$

$$\frac{3x^2 + 6x + 2}{x(x + 1)(x + 2)} \ge 0$$

Three of the key numbers are 0, -1, and -2. The other two are found by using the quadratic formula to solve $3x^2 + 6x + 2 = 0$. The roots are found to be $\frac{-3 \pm \sqrt{3}}{3}$. For purposes of picking appropriate test numbers, note that $\frac{-3 + \sqrt{3}}{3} \approx -0.4$ and that $\frac{-3 - \sqrt{3}}{3} \approx -1.6$.

Interval	Test Number	x	x + 0.4	x + 1	x + 1.6	x + 2	$\dfrac{3x^2 + 6x + 2}{x(x + 1)(x + 2)}$
$(-\infty, -2)$	-3	neg.	neg.	neg.	neg.	neg.	neg.
$(-2, -1.6)$	-1.8	neg.	neg.	neg.	neg.	pos.	pos.
$(-1.6, -1)$	-1.5	neg.	neg.	neg.	pos.	pos.	neg.
$(-1, -0.4)$	-0.5	neg.	neg.	pos.	pos.	pos.	pos.
$(-0.4, 0)$	-0.1	neg.	pos.	pos.	pos.	pos.	neg.
$(0, \infty)$	2	pos.	pos.	pos.	pos.	pos.	pos.

Solution set: $\left(-2, \dfrac{-3 - \sqrt{3}}{3}\right] \cup \left(-1, \dfrac{-3 + \sqrt{3}}{3}\right] \cup (0, \infty)$

107. $\sqrt{x} - \dfrac{5}{\sqrt{x}} \leq 4$

$\dfrac{x - 5 - 4\sqrt{x}}{\sqrt{x}} \leq 0$

Looking at the denominator, we see that one key number is $x = 0$. The others, if any, are found by solving the equation:

$x - 5 - 4\sqrt{x} = 0$

Writing this as $x - 5 = 4\sqrt{x}$, and then squaring both sides, we have:

$x^2 - 10x + 25 = 16x$

$x^2 - 26x + 25 = 0$

$(x - 25)(x - 1) = 0$

$x = 25$ or $x = 1$

The value $x = 25$ satisfies the equation $x - 5 - 4\sqrt{x} = 0$, but $x = 1$ is an extraneous root. Thus, our key numbers are 0 and 25.

Interval	Test Number	$\sqrt{x}$	$x - 5 - 4\sqrt{x}$	$\dfrac{x - 5 - 4\sqrt{x}}{\sqrt{x}}$
$(-\infty, 0)$	-1		undefined	
$(0, 25)$	1	pos.	neg.	neg.
$(25, \infty)$	36	pos.	pos.	pos.

Solution set: $(0, 25\,]$

109. $x^2 + x + k^2 = 0$

discriminant $= b^2 - 4ac = 1 - 4k^2$

We solve for when this discriminant is non-negative:

$$1 - 4k^2 \geq 0$$
$$(1 - 2k)(1 + 2k) \geq 0$$

The key numbers here are $k = \pm\, 1/2$.

Interval	Test Number	$1 + 2k$	$1 - 2k$	$1 - 4k^2$
$(-\infty, -1/2)$	-1	neg.	pos.	neg.
$(-1/2, 1/2)$	0	pos.	pos.	pos.
$(1/2, \infty)$	1	pos.	neg.	neg.

Thus the original equation will have real solutions when $-1/2 \leq k \leq 1/2$.

111. $x^2 + (k + 1)x + 2k = 0$

discriminant $= (k + 1)^2 - 4(2k)$

Thus we have:

$$k^2 + 2k + 1 - 8k \geq 0$$
$$k^2 - 6k + 1 \geq 0$$

The key numbers are:

$$k = \frac{6 \pm \sqrt{36 - 4}}{2} = \frac{6 \pm \sqrt{32}}{2} = \frac{6 \pm 4\sqrt{2}}{2} = 3 \pm 2\sqrt{2}$$

For purposes of picking appropriate test numbers, note that $3 + 2\sqrt{2} \approx 5.8$ and that $3 - 2\sqrt{2} \approx 0.2$.

Interval	Test Number	k - 5.8	k - 0.2	$k^2 - 6k + 1$
$(-\infty, 3 - 2\sqrt{2})$	0	neg.	neg.	pos.
$(3 - 2\sqrt{2}, 3 + 2\sqrt{2})$	3	neg.	pos.	neg.
$(3 + 2\sqrt{2}, \infty)$	7	pos.	pos.	pos.

Thus the original equation will have real solutions when either $k \le 3 - 2\sqrt{2}$ or $k \ge 3 + 2\sqrt{2}$.

113. Let x and 280 - x denote the required number of pounds of Kona and Columbian beans, respectively. We organize the data in a chart:

type of coffee	pounds	cost/pound	total cost
Kona	x	$6.00	6 (x)
Columbian	280 - x	$5.00	5 (280 - x)
Blend	280	$5.60	5.6 (280)

$$6x + 5(280 - x) = 5.6(280)$$
$$6x + 1400 - 5x = 1568$$
$$x = 168$$
$$280 - x = 112$$

Thus, 168 pounds of Kona beans and 112 pounds of Columbian beans are required.

115. Let x and 11 - x denote the units digit and tens digit, respectively. Then we have:

$$\text{original number} + 27 = \text{new number}$$
$$10(11 - x) + x + 27 = 10x + (11 - x)$$
$$110 - 10x + x + 27 = 10x + 11 - x$$
$$-18x = -126$$
$$x = 7$$
$$11 - x = 4$$

The original number, therefore, is 47.

117. In the three hours from 6 a.m. to 9 a.m., the train from Los Angeles covers a distance of (50)(3) = 150 miles. Now let t = 0 correspond to 9 a.m. Then in t hours the train from Los Angeles has covered a total distance of 150 + 50t, while the train from San Francisco has traveled 40t miles. When the trains pass one another, the total distances must add up to 450 miles. Thus we have:

$$(150 + 50t) + 40t = 450$$
$$90t = 300$$
$$t = 3\frac{1}{3} \text{ hours}$$
$$t = 3 \text{ hours and 20 minutes}$$

So the trains meet 3 hours and 20 minutes after 9 a.m. That is 12:20 p.m.

119. We first re-draw the figure:

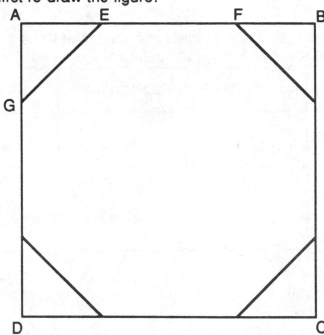

$$AE + EF + FB = 1 \quad \text{(given)}$$
$$EF + 2AE = 1 \quad (AE = FB)$$
$$AE = \frac{1 - EF}{2}$$

By the Pythagorean Theorem we have:

$$(AG)^2 + (AE)^2 = (GE)^2$$
$$(AE)^2 + (AE)^2 = (EF)^2 \quad \text{(because AG = AE and EF = GE)}$$
$$2(AE)^2 = (EF)^2$$
$$2\left(\frac{1 - EF}{2}\right)^2 = EF^2 \quad \text{(substituting for AE)}$$

Now, for convenience, let EF = x. Then we have:

$$2\left(\frac{1 - 2x + x^2}{4}\right) = x^2$$

$$1 - 2x + x^2 = 2x^2$$

$$0 = x^2 + 2x - 1$$

The quadratic formula then gives us:

$$x = \frac{-2 \pm \sqrt{4 + 4}}{2} = \frac{-2 \pm \sqrt{8}}{2} = \frac{-2 \pm 2\sqrt{2}}{2} = -1 \pm \sqrt{2}$$

We choose the positive root, since $x > 0$. Thus, $x = EF = -1 + \sqrt{2}$ cm

121. We draw a figure with the side labeled as $\frac{x}{4}$:

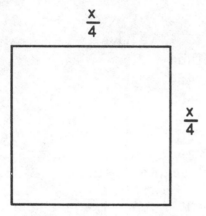

We compute the area and the perimeter:

$$\text{area} = \left(\frac{x}{4}\right)^2 = \frac{x^2}{16}$$

$$\text{perimeter} = x$$

If the area is numerically greater than the perimeter, then we have:

$$\frac{x^2}{16} > x$$

$$x^2 > 16x$$

$$x^2 - 16x > 0$$

$$x(x - 16) > 0$$

The key numbers here are 0 and 4. Since x itself must be positive, we obtain the two intervals (0, 16) and (16, ∞):

Interval	Test Number	x	x - 16	x(x - 16)
(0, 16)	1	pos.	neg.	neg.
(16, ∞)	17	pos.	pos.	pos.

From this, we conclude that the area will be numerically greater than the perimeter when x > 16 cm.

123.   Denoting the integers by x - 1, x, and x + 1, we have:
$$(x - 1)^2 + x^2 + (x + 1)^2 = 1454$$
$$x^2 - 2x + 1 + x^2 + x^2 + 2x + 1 = 1454$$
$$3x^2 = 1452$$
$$x^2 = 484$$
$$x = \sqrt{484}$$
$$x = 22$$

Thus, x - 1 = 21, and x + 1 = 23, and the three integers are 21, 22, and 23.

125.   Let Joan's speed for the first four miles be r mph. Then the time for those four miles is $\frac{4}{r}$. Since her rate for the next six miles is $r + \frac{1}{2}$, her time on that portion is $\frac{6}{r + \frac{1}{2}}$, or $\frac{12}{2r + 1}$, after simplifying. Thus, her time for the race is $\frac{4}{r} + \frac{12}{2r + 1}$ hours.

On the other hand, had she run the entire ten miles at the faster pace, her time would have been $\frac{10}{r + \frac{1}{2}}$, or $\frac{20}{2r + 1}$, after simplifying. Since this time is $\frac{2}{60} = \frac{1}{30}$ of an hour faster than her actual time, we can write:

$$\frac{4}{r} + \frac{12}{2r + 1} - \frac{1}{30} = \frac{20}{2r + 1}$$
$$\frac{4}{r} - \frac{8}{2r + 1} - \frac{1}{30} = 0$$

$$4(30)(2r + 1) - 8(30)r - r(2r + 1) = 0$$
$$120 - 2r^2 - r = 0$$
$$2r^2 + r - 120 = 0$$
$$(2r - 15)(r + 8) = 0$$

We choose the positive value here, since $r > 0$. Thus, Joan's speed for the first four miles is 7.5 mph, and for the last six miles it is 8mph. Her time for the entire race, then, is $\left(\dfrac{4}{7.5} + \dfrac{6}{8}\right)$ hours. This simplifies to 77/60 hours, or 1 hour and 17 minutes.

127. We first draw a figure:

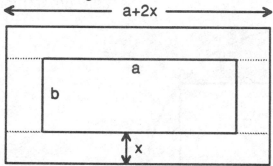

Let x denote the width of the path, as indicated in the figure. To compute the area of the path, we divide it into four rectangular portions, as indicated by the dotted lines in the figure. Then the area of the path is:
$$2[x(a + 2x)] + 2(bx) = 4x^2 + 2ax + 2bx$$
Since the area of the path and the flower garden are equal, we have:
$$4x^2 + 2ax + 2bx = ab$$
$$4x^2 + 2(a + b)x - ab = 0$$
$$x = \frac{-2(a + b) \pm \sqrt{4(a + b)^2 + 16ab}}{8}$$
Choosing the positive root here (since $x > 0$), we have:
$$x = \frac{-2(a + b) + 2\sqrt{(a + b)^2 + 4ab}}{8}$$
$$x = \frac{-(a + b) + \sqrt{a^2 + 6ab + b^2}}{4}$$

129.   First Ball: Second Ball:
   $16t^2 + 40t + 50 = h$ $-16t^2 + 5t + 100 = h$
   Setting h = 0 yields: Setting h = 0 yields:
   $-16t^2 + 40t + 50 = 0$ $-16t^2 + 5t + 100 = 0$
   $8t^2 - 20t - 25 = 0$ $16t^2 - 5t - 100 = 0$

$$t = \frac{20 \pm \sqrt{400 + 32(25)}}{2(8)}$$ $$t = \frac{5 \pm \sqrt{25 + 6400}}{2(16)}$$

$$t = \frac{20 \pm 20\sqrt{3}}{16}$$ $$t = \frac{5 \pm \sqrt{6425}}{32}$$

$$t = \frac{5 \pm 5\sqrt{3}}{4}$$ $$t = \frac{5 \pm 5\sqrt{257}}{32}$$

$$t = \frac{5 + 5\sqrt{3}}{4} \text{ (positive root)}$$ $$t = \frac{5 + 5\sqrt{257}}{32} \text{ (positive root)}$$

$$t \approx 3.4 \text{ sec}$$ $$t \approx 2.7 \text{ sec}$$

Therefore, the second ball (the one thrown from 100 ft) hits the ground first.

131.   We re-draw the figure:

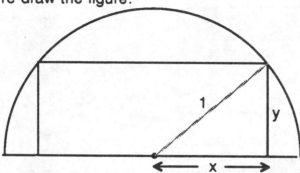

With x and y as indicated in the figure, the area of the rectangle is:

$$\text{area} = 2xy = 2x\sqrt{1 - x^2} \quad \text{(Pythagorean Theorem)}$$

If the area is 1 cm^2, then we have:

$$2x\sqrt{1 - x^2} = 1$$
$$4x^2(1 - x^2) = 1 \quad \text{(squaring)}$$
$$4x^2 - 4x^4 - 1 = 0$$
$$4x^4 - 4x^2 + 1 = 0$$
$$(2x^2 - 1)^2 = 0$$
$$2x^2 - 1 = 0$$
$$x^2 = 1/2$$
$$x = \sqrt{\frac{1}{2}} = \frac{\sqrt{2}}{2}$$

Check: If $x = \frac{\sqrt{2}}{2}$, then:

$$\text{area} = 2x\sqrt{1 - x^2} = \sqrt{2}\sqrt{1 - 1/2} = \sqrt{2}\sqrt{1/2} = \frac{\sqrt{2}}{\sqrt{2}} = 1$$

Answer: $x = \frac{\sqrt{2}}{2}$

133.   Let x be the integer, so x + 1 is the next highest integer. We find where:
$$x^2 + x^3 = N(x + 1)^2, \text{ where N is an integer:}$$
$$x^2(1 + x) = N(x + 1)^2$$
$$\frac{x^2}{x + 1} = N \quad \text{, if } x \neq -1 \text{ (which is guaranteed since x is positive)}$$

But, by exercise #69 of Section 1.8, $\dfrac{x^2}{x + 1}$ cannot be a natural number (positive integer), thus there is no solution to the equation. This proves the desired result.

135.   (a) $\sqrt{a - \sqrt{a + x}} = x$
$$a - \sqrt{a + x} = x^2$$
$$-\sqrt{a + x} = x^2 - a$$
Squaring again, we get:
$$a + x = (x^2 - a)^2$$
$$a + x = x^4 - 2ax^2 + a^2$$
$$0 = x^4 - 2ax^2 - x + a^2 - a$$

(b) Rewriting, we have $a^2 - (2x^2 + 1)a + (x^4 - x) = 0$
Using the quadratic, we have:
$$a = \frac{(2x^2 + 1) \pm \sqrt{(2x^2 + 1)^2 - 4(x^4 - x)}}{2}$$
$$a = \frac{(2x^2 + 1) \pm \sqrt{4x^4 + 4x^2 + 1 - 4x^4 + 4x}}{2}$$
$$a = \frac{(2x^2 + 1) \pm \sqrt{4x^2 + 4x + 1}}{2}$$
$$a = \frac{(2x^2 + 1) \pm (2x + 1)}{2}$$
So:
$$a = \frac{2x^2 + 1 + 2x + 1}{2} = \frac{2x^2 + 2x + 2}{2} = x^2 + x + 1, \quad \text{or}$$
$$a = \frac{2x^2 + 1 - 2x - 1}{2} = \frac{2x^2 - 2x}{2} = x^2 - x \text{ , as desired.}$$

(c) $a = x^2 + x + 1$ or $a = x^2 - x$
$$x^2 + x + (1 - a) = 0 \qquad\qquad x^2 - x - a = 0$$
$$x = \frac{-1 \pm \sqrt{1 - 4(1 - a)}}{2} \qquad x = \frac{1 \pm \sqrt{1 - 4(-a)}}{2}$$
$$x = \frac{-1 \pm \sqrt{4a - 3}}{2} \qquad\qquad x = \frac{1 \pm \sqrt{4a + 1}}{2}$$

(d) We now (painfully) check each solution in our original equation.

(1) $x = \dfrac{-1 - \sqrt{4a - 3}}{2}$

Since $x < 0$, this cannot be a solution.

(2) $x = \dfrac{-1 + \sqrt{4a - 3}}{2}$

$$\sqrt{a - \sqrt{a + \dfrac{-1 + \sqrt{4a - 3}}{2}}} = \dfrac{-1 + \sqrt{4a - 3}}{2}$$

Since $a \geq 1$, both values are positive, so we can square each side to get:

$$a - \sqrt{\dfrac{2a - 1 + \sqrt{4a - 3}}{2}} = \dfrac{1 + 4a - 3 - 2\sqrt{4a - 3}}{4}$$

Multiplying by 4, we have:

$$4a - 2\sqrt{4a - 2 + 2\sqrt{4a - 3}} = 4a - 2 - 2\sqrt{4a - 3}$$
$$-\sqrt{4a - 2 + 2\sqrt{4a - 3}} = -1 - \sqrt{4a - 3}$$

Squaring again (both sides are negative, so this preserves equality):

$$4a - 2 + 2\sqrt{4a - 3} = 1 + 2\sqrt{4a - 3} + 4a - 3$$
$$4a - 2 = 4a - 2$$

It checks!

(3) $x = \dfrac{1 - \sqrt{4a + 1}}{2}$

Since $a \geq 1$, $x < 0$, thus this cannot be a solution.

(4) $x = \dfrac{1 + \sqrt{4a + 1}}{2}$

$$\sqrt{a - \sqrt{a + \dfrac{1 + \sqrt{4a + 1}}{2}}} = \dfrac{1 + \sqrt{4a + 1}}{2}$$

Since $a \geq 1$, both values are positive, so we can square each side to get:

$$a - \sqrt{\dfrac{2a + 1 + \sqrt{4a + 1}}{2}} = \dfrac{1 + 4a + 1 + 2\sqrt{4a + 1}}{4}$$

Multiplying by 4, we have:

$$4a - 2\sqrt{4a + 2 + 2\sqrt{4a + 1}} = 4a + 2 + 2\sqrt{4a + 1}$$
$$-\sqrt{4a + 2 + 2\sqrt{4a + 1}} = 2a + 1 + \sqrt{4a + 1}$$

But the left hand side is non-positive and the right hand side is non-negative, thus:
$$2a + 1 + \sqrt{4a + 1} = 0$$
$$\sqrt{4a + 1} = -2a - 1$$
But $a \geq 1$, and this is impossible.

Thus the only value that checks is $x = \dfrac{-1 + \sqrt{4a - 3}}{2}$

OK, now how many of you *really* checked these values?

CHAPTER 3
COORDINATES AND GRAPHS

3.1   Rectangular Coordinates

1.

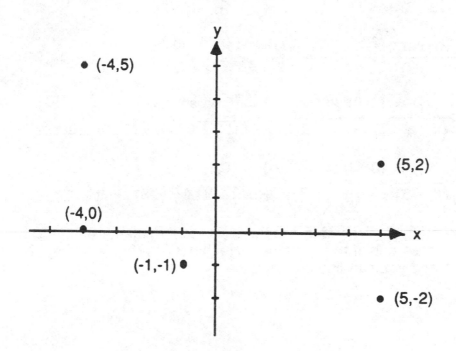

3.   (a)   We draw the figure:

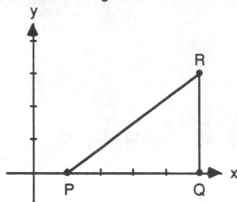

(b)   Since $b = 5 - 1 = 4$ and $h = 3 - 0 = 3$, then
$A = (1/2)\,bh = (1/2)\,(4)\,(3) = 6$

5.   (a)   Here $(x_1,y_1) = (0, 0)$ and $(x_2,y_2) = (-3, 4)$, so by the distance formula:
$d = \sqrt{(-3 - 0)^2 + (4 - 0)^2} = \sqrt{9 + 16} = \sqrt{25} = 5$

(b)   Here $(x_1,y_1) = (2,1)$ and $(x_2,y_2) = (7,13)$, so:
$d = \sqrt{(7 - 2)^2 + (13 - 1)^2} = \sqrt{25 + 144} = \sqrt{169} = 13$

7.   (a)   Here $(x_1,y_1) = (-5,0)$ and $(x_2,y_2) = (5,0)$, so:
$d = \sqrt{\left(5 - (-5)\right)^2 + (0 - 0)^2} = \sqrt{100 + 0} = \sqrt{100} = 10$

(b)   Here $(x_1,y_1) = (0, -8)$ and $(x_2,y_2) = (0,1)$, so:
$d = \sqrt{(0 - 0)^2 + \left(1 - (-8)\right)^2} = \sqrt{0 + 81} = \sqrt{81} = 9$

Note that we really don't need to use the distance formula for either (a) or (b), since in each case one of the coordinates (either x or y) is the same. Draw quick graphs and you can find the distance by inspection:

(a)

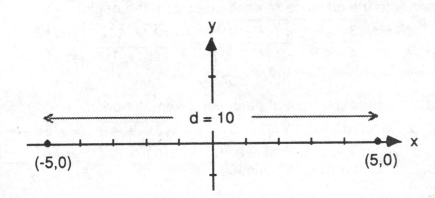

(b)

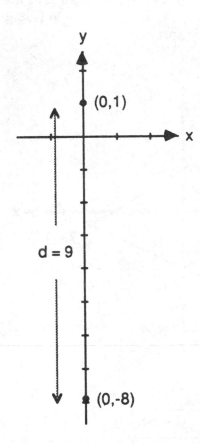

9. Here $(x_1, y_1) = (1, \sqrt{3})$ and $(x_2, y_2) = (-1, -\sqrt{3})$, so:

$$d = \sqrt{(-1 - 1)^2 + (-\sqrt{3} - \sqrt{3})^2} = \sqrt{(-2)^2 + (-2\sqrt{3})^2} = \sqrt{4 + 12} = 4$$

11. (a) We calculate the distance of each point from the origin:

$(3, -2)$: $d = \sqrt{(3 - 0)^2 + (-2 - 0)^2}$ $= \sqrt{9 + 4}$ $= \sqrt{13}$

$(4, 1/2)$: $d = \sqrt{(4 - 0)^2 + (1/2 - 0)^2}$ $= \sqrt{16 + 1/4}$ $= \sqrt{16.25}$

So $(4, 1/2)$ is farther from the origin.

(b) We calculate the distance of each point from the origin:

$(-6, 7)$: $d = \sqrt{(-6 - 0)^2 + (7 - 0)^2}$ $= \sqrt{36 + 49}$ $= \sqrt{85}$

$(9, 0)$: $d = \sqrt{(9 - 0)^2 + (0 - 0)^2}$ $= \sqrt{81 + 0}$ $= \sqrt{81}$

So $(-6, 7)$ is farther from the origin.

13. The hint is a good one. We will graph the triangle and then determine (using $a^2 + b^2 = c^2$) whether the triangle is a right triangle (we are using the <u>converse</u> of the Pythagorean Theorem.)

(a)

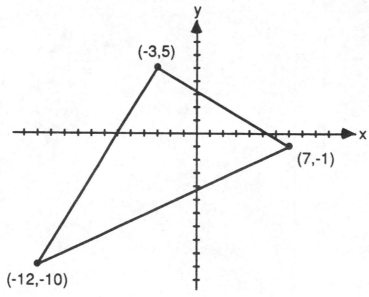

$a = \sqrt{(-3 - 7)^2 + \left(5 - (-1)\right)^2}$ $= \sqrt{100 + 36} = \sqrt{136}$

$b = \sqrt{\left(-12 - (-3)\right)^2 + (-10 - 5)^2}$ $= \sqrt{81 + 225} = \sqrt{306}$

$c = \sqrt{(-12 - 7)^2 + \left(-10 - (-1)\right)^2}$ $= \sqrt{361 + 81} = \sqrt{442}$

We check: $a^2 + b^2 = 136 + 306 = 442 = c^2$

So the triangle is a right triangle.

Note: By graphing the triangle you can get a good guess as to what a, b, and c <u>should</u> be. Don't be afraid to draw the figure, it really helps!

(b)

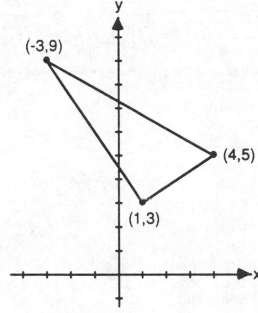

$$a = \sqrt{(-3 - 1)^2 + (9 - 3)^2} \quad = \sqrt{16 + 36} \quad = \sqrt{52}$$
$$b = \sqrt{(4 - 1)^2 + (5 - 3)^2} \quad = \sqrt{9 + 4} \quad\ \ = \sqrt{13}$$
$$c = \sqrt{(-3 - 4)^2 + (9 - 5)^2} \quad = \sqrt{49 + 16} \quad = \sqrt{65}$$

We check: $a^2 + b^2 = 52 + 13 = 65 = c^2$.
So the triangle is a right triangle.

(c)

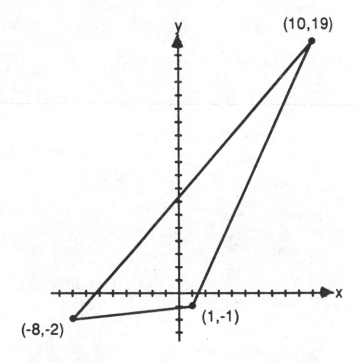

$$a = \sqrt{(-8 - 1)^2 + \left(-2 - (-1)\right)^2} \qquad = \sqrt{81 + 1} \qquad = \sqrt{82}$$

$$b = \sqrt{(10 - 1)^2 + \left(19 - (-1)\right)^2} \qquad = \sqrt{81 + 400} \qquad = \sqrt{481}$$

$$c = \sqrt{\left(10 - (-8)\right)^2 + \left(19 - (-2)\right)^2} \quad = \sqrt{324 + 441} \quad = \sqrt{765}$$

We check: $a^2 + b^2 = 82 + 481 = 563$, which does not equal 765, which is c^2.

So the triangle is not a right triangle.

15. We let $(x_1, y_1) = (1, -4)$, $(x_2, y_2) = (5, 3)$, and $(x_3, y_3) = (13, 17)$, so using the formula from exercise #14 (b) we have:

$$\begin{aligned}
\text{Area} \quad &= (1/2) \left| 1(3) - 5(-4) + 5(17) - 13(3) + 13(-4) - 1(17) \right| \\
&= (1/2) \left| 3 + 20 + 85 - 39 - 52 - 17 \right| \\
&= (1/2) \left| 0 \right| \\
&= 0
\end{aligned}$$

For the area of the triangle to be 0 it must be that these three points do not form a triangle. The only way that could occur is if the three points are collinear, that is, they all lie on the same line.

17. (a) Here $(x_1, y_1) = (3, 2)$ and $(x_2, y_2) = (9, 8)$, so by the midpoint formula:

$$M = \left(\frac{3 + 9}{2}, \frac{2 + 8}{2} \right) = \left(\frac{12}{2}, \frac{10}{2} \right) = (6, 5)$$

   (b) Here $(x_1, y_1) = (-4, 0)$ and $(x_2, y_2) = (5, -3)$, so:

$$M = \left(\frac{-4 + 5}{2}, \frac{0 - 3}{2} \right) = \left(\frac{1}{2}, \frac{-3}{2} \right)$$

   (c) Here $(x_1, y_1) = (3, -6)$ and $(x_2, y_2) = (-1, -2)$, so:

$$M = \left(\frac{3 - 1}{2}, \frac{-6 - 2}{2} \right) = \left(\frac{2}{2}, \frac{-8}{2} \right) = (1, -4)$$

19. Let's call $C(x, y)$. Since B is the midpoint of $\overline{AC}$, then:

$$\frac{-1 + x}{2} = 5 \qquad \text{and} \qquad \frac{2 + y}{2} = -3$$

We solve each of these for x and y:

$$\frac{-1 + x}{2} = 5 \qquad \text{and} \qquad \frac{2 + y}{2} = -3$$

$$\begin{aligned}
-1 + x &= 10 & 2 + y &= -6 \\
x &= 11 & y &= -8
\end{aligned}$$

So the coordinates of C must be $(11, -8)$.

21. (a) We draw the figure:

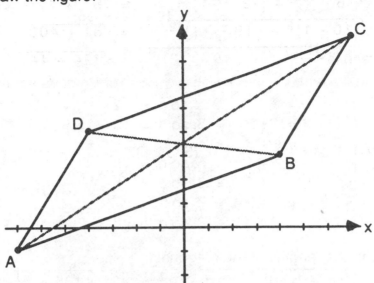

(b) For $\overline{AC}$, let $(x_1,y_1) = (-7,-1)$ and $(x_2,y_2) = (7,8)$, so the midpoint is:

$$M_1 = \left(\frac{-7 + 7}{2}, \frac{-1 + 8}{2}\right) = (0, 7/2)$$

For $\overline{BD}$, let $(x_1,y_1) = (4,3)$ and $(x_2,y_2) = (-4,4)$, so the midpoint is:

$$M_2 = \left(\frac{4 - 4}{2}, \frac{3 + 4}{2}\right) = (0,7/2)$$

(c) It appears that the midpoints of the two diagonals of a parallelogram are the same. Or, stated more clearly, the diagonals of a parallelogram bisect each other.

23. (a) Since $(AB)^2 = 68$, $(BC)^2 = 40$, and $(AC)^2 = 20$, then:
$(AB)^2 + (BC)^2 + (AC)^2 = 128$

(b) Let the midpoints be X, Y, and Z, so:
$$X = M_{AB} = (5,2)$$
$$Y = M_{BC} = (6,4)$$
$$Z = M_{AC} = (2,3)$$
Then the medians are:
$$AY = \sqrt{(6 - 1)^2 + (4 - 1)^2} = \sqrt{25 + 9} = \sqrt{34}$$
$$BZ = \sqrt{(2 - 9)^2 + (3 - 3)^2} = \sqrt{49 + 0} = \sqrt{49} = 7$$
$$CX = \sqrt{(5 - 3)^2 + (2 - 5)^2} = \sqrt{4 + 9} = \sqrt{13}$$

So, the required value is:

$$(AY)^2 + (BZ)^2 + (CX)^2 = 34 + 49 + 13 = 96$$

(c)   This ratio is $\dfrac{128}{96} = \dfrac{4}{3}$

25. $\begin{aligned}
a^2 &= 1^2 + 1^2 &&= 2, && \text{so } a = \sqrt{2} \\
b^2 &= 1^2 + (\sqrt{2})^2 &&= 1 + 2 &&= 3, \text{ so } b = \sqrt{3} \\
c^2 &= 1^2 + (\sqrt{3})^2 &&= 1 + 3 &&= 4, \text{ so } c = 2 \\
d^2 &= 1^2 + 2^2 &&= 1 + 4 &&= 5, \text{ so } d = \sqrt{5} \\
e^2 &= 1^2 + (\sqrt{5})^2 &&= 1 + 5 &&= 6, \text{ so } e = \sqrt{6} \\
f^2 &= 1^2 + (\sqrt{6})^2 &&= 1 + 6 &&= 7, \text{ so } f = \sqrt{7} \\
g^2 &= 1^2 + (\sqrt{7})^2 &&= 1 + 7 &&= 8, \text{ so } g = \sqrt{8} = 2\sqrt{2}
\end{aligned}$

27. Let's first find the lengths of the diagonals:

$$OB = \sqrt{(a + b - 0)^2 + (c - 0)^2} = \sqrt{(a + b)^2 + c^2}$$
$$AC = \sqrt{(b - a)^2 + (c - 0)^2} = \sqrt{(b - a)^2 + c^2}$$

So $\begin{aligned}
S &= OB^2 + AC^2 \\
&= (a + b)^2 + c^2 + (b - a)^2 + c^2 \\
&= a^2 + 2ab + b^2 + b^2 - 2ab + a^2 + 2c^2 \\
&= 2a^2 + 2b^2 + 2c^2
\end{aligned}$

Now we find the lengths of each side:

$$OA = \sqrt{(a - 0)^2 + (0 - 0)^2} = \sqrt{a^2}$$
$$AB = \sqrt{(a + b - a)^2 + (c - 0)^2} = \sqrt{b^2 + c^2}$$
$$BC = \sqrt{(a + b - b)^2 + (c - c)^2} = \sqrt{a^2}$$
$$OC = \sqrt{(b - 0)^2 + (c - 0)^2} = \sqrt{b^2 + c^2}$$

So $\begin{aligned}
S &= OA^2 + AB^2 + BC^2 + OC^2 \\
&= a^2 + b^2 + c^2 + a^2 + b^2 + c^2 \\
&= 2a^2 + 2b^2 + 2c^2
\end{aligned}$

This proves the result.

29. Let's first draw a figure:

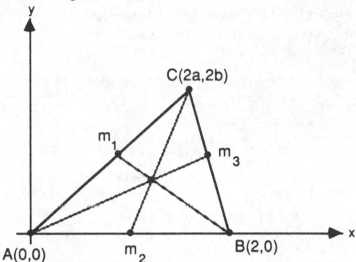

We find the sides of the triangle:

$$AB = \sqrt{(2 - 0)^2 + (0 - 0)^2} = \sqrt{4 + 0} = 2$$
$$BC = \sqrt{(2a - 2)^2 + (2b - 0)^2} = \sqrt{(2a - 2)^2 + 4b^2}$$
$$AC = \sqrt{(2a - 0)^2 + (2b - 0)^2} = \sqrt{4a^2 + 4b^2}$$

So $S_1 = AB^2 + BC^2 + AC^2$

$$= 4 + (2a - 2)^2 + 4b^2 + 4a^2 + 4b^2$$
$$= 4 + 4a^2 - 8a + 4 + 4b^2 + 4a^2 + 4b^2$$
$$= 8a^2 + 8b^2 + 8 - 8a$$

Now we must do the same for the medians. First, we find the midpoints:

$$M_1 = \left(\frac{0 + 2a}{2}, \frac{0 + 2b}{2}\right) = (a, b)$$

$$M_2 = \left(\frac{0 + 2}{2}, \frac{0 + 0}{2}\right) = (1, 0)$$

$$M_3 = \left(\frac{2a + 2}{2}, \frac{2b + 0}{2}\right) = (a + 1, b)$$

Now we compute the distances:

$$AM_3 = \sqrt{(a + 1 - 0)^2 + (b - 0)^2} = \sqrt{(a + 1)^2 + b^2}$$
$$BM_1 = \sqrt{(a - 2)^2 + (b - 0)^2} = \sqrt{(a - 2)^2 + b^2}$$
$$CM_2 = \sqrt{(2a - 1)^2 + (2b - 0)^2} = \sqrt{(2a - 1)^2 + 4b^2}$$

So $S_2 = (AM_3)^2 + (BM_1)^2 + (CM_2)^2$

$$= (a + 1)^2 + b^2 + (a - 2)^2 + b^2 + (2a - 1)^2 + 4b^2$$
$$= a^2 + 2a + 1 + a^2 - 4a + 4 + 4a^2 - 4a + 1 + 6b^2$$
$$= 6a^2 + 6b^2 + 6 - 6a$$

We must show $S_1 = (4/3) S_2$:

$(4/3) \, S_2 = (4/3) \, (6a^2 + 6b^2 + 6 - 6a) = 8a^2 + 8b^2 + 8 - 8a = S_1$

This proves the desired result. Note that although it may appear that we have only proved the result for these three specific vertices, they are arbitrary enough that we have proved the result in general.

31. We first find the distances from P (x,y) to A (-3,-3) and B (5,5):

$$PA = \sqrt{(x - (-3))^2 + \left(y - (-3)\right)^2} = \sqrt{(x + 3)^2 + (y + 3)^2}$$

$$PB = \sqrt{(x - 5)^2 + (y - 5)^2}$$

Now, since P is equidistant from A and B, we have PA = PB:

$$\sqrt{(x + 3)^2 + (y + 3)^2} = \sqrt{(x - 5)^2 + (y - 5)^2}$$

Squaring each side, we get:

$$(x + 3)^2 + (y + 3)^2 = (x - 5)^2 + (y - 5)^2$$
$$x^2 + 6x + 9 + y^2 + 6y + 9 = x^2 - 10x + 25 + y^2 - 10y + 25$$
$$6x + 6y + 18 = -10x - 10y + 50$$
$$16x + 16y = 32$$
$$x + y = 2$$

This proves the desired result.

33. We first find the distances from P (x,y) to A (0,0) and B (4,0):

$$PA = \sqrt{(x - 0)^2 + (y - 0)^2} = \sqrt{x^2 + y^2}$$

$$PB = \sqrt{(x - 4)^2 + (y - 0)^2} = \sqrt{(x - 4)^2 + y^2}$$

Now PA = 2 • PB, so:

$$\sqrt{x^2 + y^2} = 2\sqrt{(x - 4)^2 + y^2}$$

Squaring each side:

$$x^2 + y^2 = 4\left((x - 4)^2 + y^2\right)$$
$$x^2 + y^2 = 4(x^2 - 8x + 16 + y^2)$$
$$x^2 + y^2 = 4x^2 - 32x + 64 + 4y^2$$
$$0 = 3x^2 + 3y^2 - 32x + 64$$

This proves the desired result.

35. (a) Approaching this as in exercise #34 (using the distance formula), we have:

$$6 = \sqrt{(-2 - t)^2 + (3 - 1)^2}$$

Squaring each side, we get:

$$36 = (-2 - t)^2 + 4$$
$$32 = (-2 - t)^2$$

Taking roots:

$$-2 - t = \sqrt{32} \qquad \text{or} \qquad -2 - t = -\sqrt{32}$$
$$t = -2 - 4\sqrt{2} \quad \text{or} \qquad t = -2 + 4\sqrt{2}$$

Thus there are two real solutions for t, $-2 \pm 4\sqrt{2}$.

(b)   As in exercise #35 (a) we have:
$$1 = \sqrt{(-2 - t)^2 + (3 - 1)^2}$$
Squaring each side, we get:
$$1 = (-2 - t)^2 + 4$$
$$-3 = (-2 - t)^2$$
But notice this is impossible, since $(-2 - t)^2 \geq 0$ for all real values of t.
A diagram can help us answer the second question:

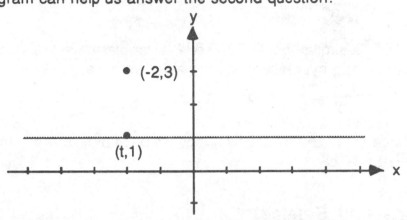

You can see that the closet (t,1) could get is when t = -2, and even
then it is 2 units away from (-2,3). So it would be impossible for (t,1) to
be within 1 unit of (-2,3), regardless of the value of t.

37.   We first find the distances from P (x,y) to A (-1,0), and B (1,0):
$$PA = \sqrt{\left(x - (-1)\right)^2 + (y - 0)^2} = \sqrt{(x + 1)^2 + y^2}$$
$$PB = \sqrt{(x - 1)^2 + (y - 0)^2} = \sqrt{(x - 1)^2 + y^2}$$
Now PA + PB = 4, so:
$$\sqrt{(x + 1)^2 + y^2} + \sqrt{(x - 1)^2 + y^2} = 4$$
$$\sqrt{(x + 1)^2 + y^2} = 4 - \sqrt{(x - 1)^2 + y^2}$$
Squaring each side, we get:
$$(x + 1)^2 + y^2 = 16 - 8\sqrt{(x - 1)^2 + y^2} + (x - 1)^2 + y^2$$
$$x^2 + 2x + 1 = 16 + x^2 - 2x + 1 - 8\sqrt{(x - 1)^2 + y^2}$$
$$4x - 16 = -8\sqrt{(x - 1)^2 + y^2}$$
$$x - 4 = -2\sqrt{(x - 1)^2 + y^2}$$
We square each side again to get:
$$x^2 - 8x + 16 = 4\left((x - 1)^2 + y^2\right)$$
$$x^2 - 8x + 16 = 4\left(x^2 - 2x + 1 + y^2\right)$$
$$x^2 - 8x + 16 = 4x^2 - 8x + 4 + 4y^2$$
$$12 = 3x^2 + 4y^2$$
This proves the desired result.

39. (a) $\angle CAD = \angle DCB$ since they are both complementary to the same angle ($\angle ACB$). Thus $\triangle BAC$ and $\triangle BCD$ are similar, as all angles have the same measure.

    (b)   Comparing hypotenuse to short side, we have:
    $$\frac{a}{y} = \frac{c}{a}, \text{ so } a^2 = cy$$

    (c) $\triangle ACD$ is similar to $\triangle ABC$, since their angles have the same measure. Comparing hypotenuse to long side, we have:
    $$\frac{b}{c - y} = \frac{c}{b}, \text{ so } b^2 = c^2 - cy$$

    (d)   Since $b^2 = c^2 - cy$ and $cy = a^2$, we have $b^2 = c^2 - a^2$, thus $a^2 + b^2 = c^2$

3.2 Graphs and Symmetry

1. $3x + 4y = 12$
     x-intercept: 4
     y-intercept: 3

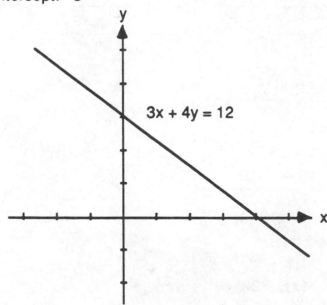

3. $y = 2x - 4$
    x-intercept: 2
    y-intercept: -4

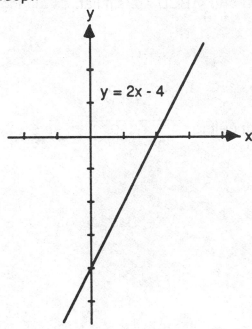

5. $x + y = 1$
    x-intercept: 1
    y-intercept: 1

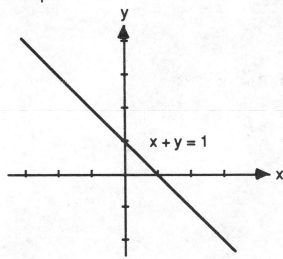

7. $y = x^2 - 5x - 6$
    y-intercept: $x = 0$: $y = 0 - 0 - 6 = -6$
    x-intercepts: $y = 0$: $x^2 - 5x - 6 = 0$
                                $(x - 6)(x + 1) = 0$
                                          $x = -1, 6$

9. $y = x^2 + x - 1$
    y-intercept: $x = 0$: $y = 0 + 0 - 1 = -1$
    x-intercepts: $y = 0$: $x^2 + x - 1 = 0$
$$x = \frac{-1 \pm \sqrt{1 - 4(1)(-1)}}{2} = \frac{-1 \pm \sqrt{5}}{2}$$

11. $\dfrac{x}{2} + \dfrac{y}{3} = 1$

    y-intercept: $x = 0$: $\dfrac{y}{3} = 1$
                                $y = 3$
    x-intercept: $y = 0$: $\dfrac{x}{2} = 1$
                                $x = 2$

13. $3x - 5y = 10$
    y-intercept: $x = 0$: $-5y = 10$
                                $y = -2$
    x-intercept: $y = 0$: $3x = 10$
                                $x = \dfrac{10}{3}$

15. $y = x^3 - 8$
    y-intercept: $x = 0$: $y = 0 - 8 = -8$
    x-intercept: $y = 0$: $x^3 - 8 = 0$
                                $x^3 = 8$
                                  $x = 2$

17. (a)   The graph is symmetric about the x-axis:

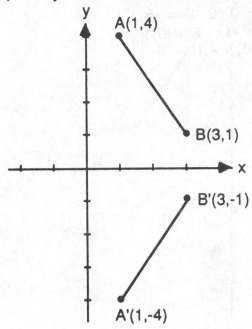

(b)   The graph is symmetric about the y-axis:

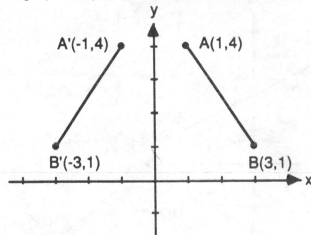

(c)   The graph is symmetric about the origin:

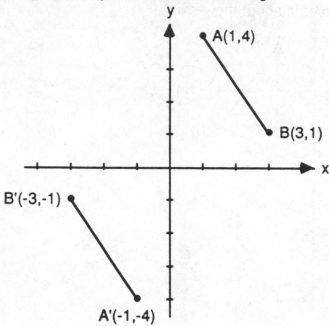

19.   (a)   The graph is symmetric about the x-axis:

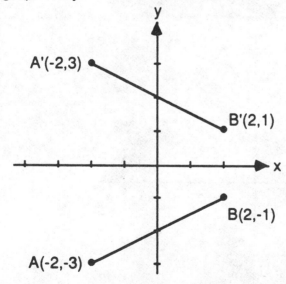

(b)   The graph is symmetric about the y-axis:

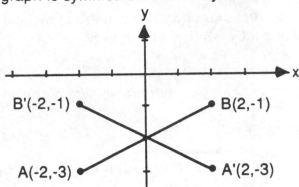

(c)   The graph is symmetric about the origin:

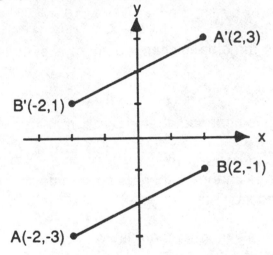

21.   x-axis: Replace y by -y: $3x^2 + (-y) = 16$

$$3x^2 - y = 16$$

Since the equation is changed, there is no symmetry.

y-axis: Replace x by - x: $3(-x)^2 + y = 16$

$$3x^2 + y = 16$$

Since the equation remains unchanged, there is symmetry.

Origin: Replace x by -x <u>and</u> y by -y: $3 (-x)^2 + (-y) = 16$

$$3x^2 - y = 16$$

Since the equation is changed, there is no symmetry.

23.   x-axis: Replace y by -y: $(-y) = x^4 - 3$

$$y = -x^4 + 3$$

Since the equation is changed, there is no symmetry.

y-axis: Replace x by -x: $y = (-x)^4 - 3$

$\qquad y = x^4 - 3$

Since the equation remains unchanged, there is symmetry.

Origin: Replace y by -y and x by -x: $(-y) = (-x)^4 - 3$

$\qquad -y = x^4 - 3$

$\qquad y = -x^4 + 3$

Since the equation is changed, there is no symmetry.

25. x-axis: Replace y by -y: $x^2 + (-y)^2 = 16$

$\qquad x^2 + y^2 = 16$

Since the equation remains unchanged, there is symmetry.

y-axis: Replace x by -x: $(-x)^2 + y^2 = 16$

$\qquad x^2 + y^2 = 16$

Since the equation remains unchanged, there is symmetry.

Origin: Replace y by -y and x by -x: $(-x)^2 + (-y)^2 = 16$

$\qquad x^2 + y^2 = 16$

Since the equation remains unchanged, there is symmetry.

27. x-axis: Replace y by - y: $-y = x^2 + x^3$

$\qquad y = -x^2 - x^3$

Since the equation is changed, there is no symmetry.

y-axis: Replace x by -x: $y = (-x)^2 + (-x)^3$

$\qquad y = x^2 - x^3$

Since the equation is changed, there is no symmetry.

Origin: Replace y by -y and x by -x: $-y = (-x)^2 + (-x)^3$

$\qquad y = -x^2 + x^3$

Since the equation is changed, there is no symmetry.

29. x-axis: Replace y by -y: $x + (-y) = 1$

$\qquad x - y = 1$

Since the equation is changed, there is no symmetry.

y-axis: Replace x by -x: $(-x) + y = 1$

$\qquad -x + y = 1$

Since the equation is changed, there is no symmetry.

Origin: Replace y by -y and x by -x: $(-x) + (-y) = 1$

$\qquad x + y = -1$

Since the equation is changed, there is no symmetry.

31. $y = x^2$
x and y-intercept: 0
symmetry: y-axis
We set up a table of values:

x	1	2	3	4
y	1	4	9	16

Now graph the curve:

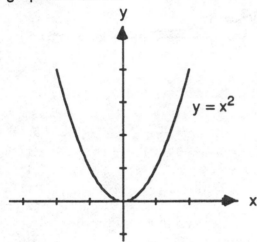

$y = x^2$

33. $y = \dfrac{1}{x}$
x and y-intercepts: none
symmetry: origin
We set up a table of values:

x	1/5	1	2	3
y	5	1	1/2	1/3

Now graph the curve:

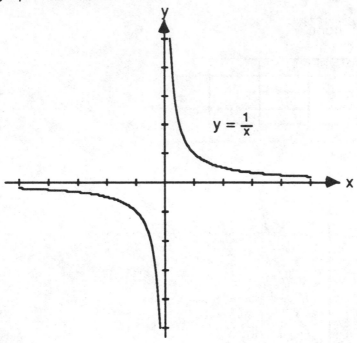

$$y = \frac{1}{x}$$

35. $y = -x^2$
x and y-intercept: 0
symmetry: y-axis
We set up a table of values:

x	1	2	3	4
y	-1	-4	-9	-16

Now graph the curve:

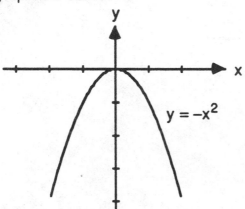

$$y = -x^2$$

37. $y = -\dfrac{1}{x^2}$

x and y-intercepts: none
symmetry: y-axis
We set up a table of values:

x	1/3	1/2	1	2	3
y	-9	-4	-1	-1/4	-1/9

Now graph the curve:

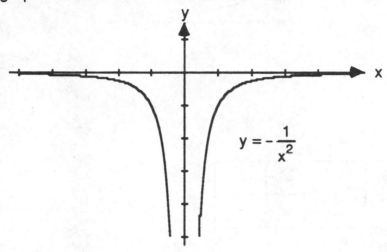

$$y = -\frac{1}{x^2}$$

39. $y = \sqrt{x^2}$

x and y-intercept: 0
symmetry: y-axis
We set up a table of values:

x	1	2	3	4
y	1	2	3	4

Now graph the curve:

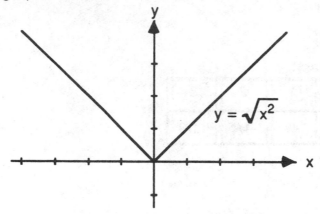

$$y = \sqrt{x^2}$$

41. $y = x^2 - 2x + 1$
     x-intercept: 1
     y-intercept: 1
     symmetry: none
     We set up a table of values:

x	-2	-1	2	3
y	9	4	1	4

Now graph the curve:

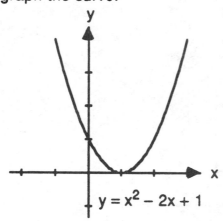

$$y = x^2 - 2x + 1$$

43. $y = 2x - 4$
x-intercept: 2
y-intercept: -4
symmetry: none
We set up a table of values:

x	-2	-1	0	1	2
y	-8	-6	-4	-2	0

Now graph the curve:

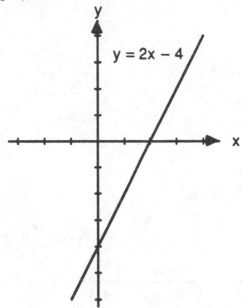

45. $y = 2x^2 + x - 4$

x-intercepts: $\dfrac{-1 \pm \sqrt{33}}{4}$

y-intercept: -4
symmetry: none
We set up a table of values:

x	-3	-2	-1	0	1	2
y	11	2	-3	-1	6	17

Now graph the curve:

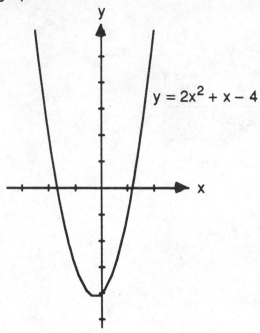

$$y = 2x^2 + x - 4$$

47   (a) $y = 3x - 6$
x-intercept: 2
y-intercept: -6
symmetry: none
We set up a table of values:

x	-3	-2	-1	1	3	4
y	-15	-12	-9	-3	3	6

Now graph the curve:

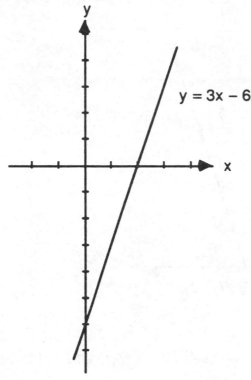

$y = 3x - 6$

(b) $y = |3x - 6|$
      x-intercept: 2
      y-intercept: 6
      symmetry: none
      We set up a table of values:

x	-2	-1	1	3	4
y	12	9	3	3	6

Now graph the curve:

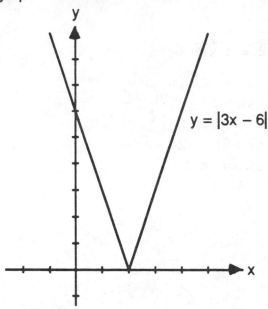

$y = |3x - 6|$

49. $(x - 3)^2 + (y - 1)^2 = 25$

The circle is in standard form, so its center is (3,1) and its radius is $\sqrt{25} = 5$.

x-intercepts: $y = 0$

$$(x - 3)^2 + 1 = 25$$
$$(x - 3)^2 = 24$$
$$x - 3 = \pm\sqrt{24} = \pm 2\sqrt{6}$$
$$x = 3 \pm 2\sqrt{6}$$

y-intercepts: $x = 0$

$$9 + (y - 1)^2 = 25$$
$$(y - 1)^2 = 16$$
$$y - 1 = \pm 4$$
$$y = 1 \pm 4 = 5 \text{ or } -3$$

51. $x^2 + y^2 = \sqrt{2}$

The circle is in standard form, so its center is (0,0) and its radius is

$\sqrt{\sqrt{2}} = \sqrt[4]{2}.$

x-intercepts: $y = 0$

$$x^2 = \sqrt{2}$$
$$x = \pm\sqrt{\sqrt{2}} = \pm\sqrt[4]{2}$$

y-intercepts: $x = 0$

$$y^2 = \sqrt{2}$$

$$y = \pm\sqrt{\sqrt{2}} = \pm\sqrt[4]{2}$$

53. $x^2 + y^2 + 8x - 6y = -24$

We must complete the square:

$$x^2 + 8x + y^2 - 6y = -24$$

$$(x^2 + 8x + 16) + (y^2 - 6y + 9) = -24 + 16 + 9$$

$$(x + 4)^2 + (y - 3)^2 = 1$$

The center is $(-4,3)$ and the radius is $\sqrt{1} = 1$.

x-intercepts: $y = 0$

$$(x + 4)^2 + 9 = 1$$

$$(x + 4)^2 = -8$$

Impossible!

There are no x-intercepts.

y-intercepts: $x = 0$

$$16 + (y - 3)^2 = 1$$

$$(y - 3)^2 = -15$$

Impossible!

There are no y-intercepts.

55. $9x^2 + 54x + 9y^2 - 6y + 64 = 0$

We divide by 9 and complete the square:

$$x^2 + 6x + y^2 - \frac{2}{3}y = -\frac{64}{9}$$

$$(x^2 + 6x + 9) + (y^2 - \frac{2}{3}y + \frac{1}{9}) = -\frac{64}{9} + 9 + \frac{1}{9}$$

$$(x + 3)^2 + (y - 1/3)^2 = 2$$

The center is $(-3, 1/3)$ and the radius is $\sqrt{2}$.

x-intercepts: $y = 0$

$$(x + 3)^2 + \frac{1}{9} = 2$$

$$(x + 3)^2 = \frac{17}{9}$$

$$|x + 3| = \sqrt{\frac{17}{9}} = \frac{\sqrt{17}}{3}$$

$$x + 3 = \pm\frac{\sqrt{17}}{3}$$

$$x = -3 \pm \frac{\sqrt{17}}{3}$$

y-intercepts: $x = 0$

$$9 + (y - 1/3)^2 = 2$$
$$(y - 1/3)^2 = -7$$

Impossible!
There are no y-intercepts.

57. We must find the radius by completing the square:

$$x^2 - 2ax + y^2 - 2by = c^2 - a^2 - b^2$$
$$(x^2 - 2ax + a^2) + (y^2 - 2by + b^2) = c^2 - a^2 - b^2 + a^2 + b^2$$
$$(x - a)^2 + (y - b)^2 = c^2, \text{ so the radius is } c \text{ (recall } c > 0)$$

Then $A = \pi(c)^2 = \pi c^2$ and $C = 2\pi(c) = 2\pi c$.

59. If $\overline{PQ}$ is the diameter, then its midpoint must be the center of the circle:

$$M = \left(\frac{-3 + 2}{2}, \frac{-4 + 8}{2}\right) = \left(-\frac{1}{2}, \frac{4}{2}\right) = (-1/2, 2)$$

Furthermore, the diameter is twice the length of the radius, so we use the distance formula to find:

$$d = \sqrt{(-3 - 2)^2 + (-4 - 8)^2} = \sqrt{25 + 144} = \sqrt{169} = 13$$

Thus the radius is $\frac{1}{2}d = \frac{13}{2}$. Thus the equation of the circle in standard form is:

$$(x + \frac{1}{2})^2 + (y - 2)^2 = \frac{169}{4}$$

61. The circle will have an equation of $(x + 3)^2 + (y - 2)^2 = r^2$. We now find the y-intercepts of the other circle: $x = 0$

$$y^2 - 4 = 0$$
$$(y + 2)(y - 2) = 0$$
$$y = \pm 2$$

So the radius is $2(4) = 8$, and thus the equation is $(x + 3)^2 + (y - 2)^2 = 64$.

63. (a) We set up a table of values:

x	0	1	2	3
y	0	16	64	144

Now graph the curve:

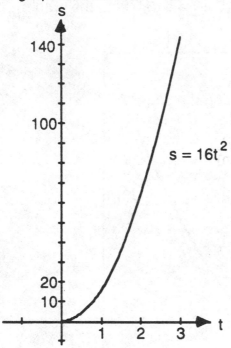

(b)   When $0 \leq t \leq 1$, we have $0 \leq s \leq 16$, from the graph:

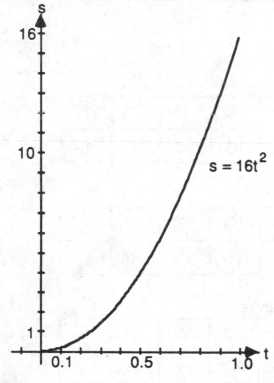

(c)   When $1 \leq t \leq 2$, we have $16 \leq s \leq 64$, from the graph:

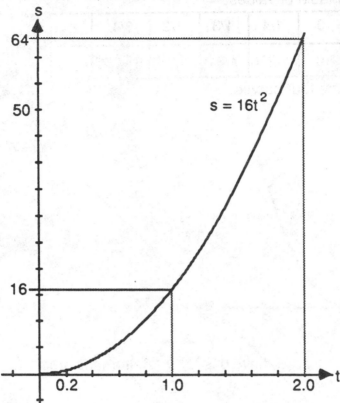

65. (a) $y = x$
We set up a table of values:

x	0	1/4	1/3	1/2	3/4	1
y	0	1/4	1/3	1/2	3/4	1

(b) $y = x^2$
We set up a table of values:

x	0	1/4	1/3	1/2	3/4	1
y	0	1/16	1/9	1/4	9/16	1

(c) $y = x^3$
We set up a table of values:

x	0	1/4	1/3	1/2	3/4	1
y	0	1/64	1/27	1/8	27/64	1

(d) $y = x^4$

We set up a table of values:

x	0	1/4	1/3	1/2	3/4	1
y	0	1/256	1/81	1/16	81/256	1

Now graph the four curves:

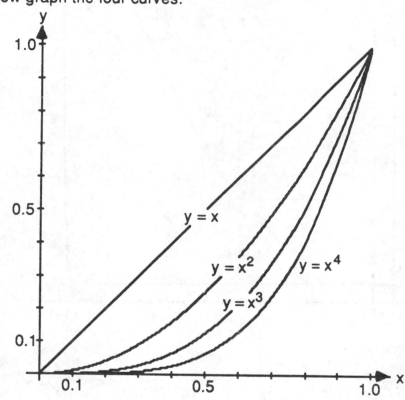

The pattern seems to be as n gets larger on $y = x^n$, the graph flattens out more and more as in the figure. We could guess $y = x^{100}$ would look something like:

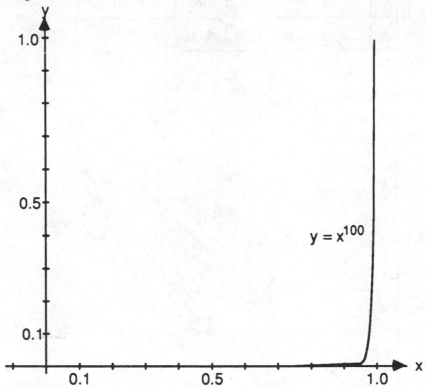

67. We re-draw the graph identifying points we are interested in:

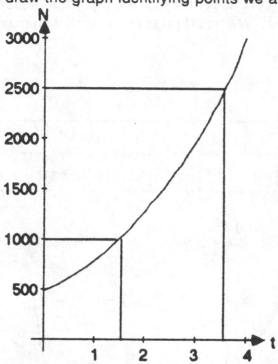

(a)   Tracing up to the curve from t = 0, we get N = 500 bacteria.

(b)   Since (0,500) lies on the curve, we find where (t , 1000) would be on
the curve, since the population would now be double. Tracing down
from N = 1000, we get t = 1.5 hours. So the population will double
in 1.5 hours.

(c)   As in (b), we find where (t , 2500) would be on the curve. Tracing
down from N = 2500, we get t = 3.5 hours.

(d)   Between t = 0 and t = 1, the population has grown from N = 500 to
N = 800, so it has increased by 300 bacteria. Between t = 3 and
t = 4, the population has grown from N = 2000 to N = 3000, so it has
increased by 1000 bacteria. So the population has increased more
rapidly between t = 3 and t = 4.

Note: This is the normal case with population growth. The world's
population has grown as much during the last 35 years as it had from the
beginning of time. The problem here is the shape of the curve (increasing at
greater and greater rates), rather than with the fact that the population is
merely increasing.

69.   x-intercepts: $y = 0$

$$x^3 - 27x = 0$$

$$x(x - 3\sqrt{3})(x + 3\sqrt{3}) = 0$$

$$x = 0, \pm 3\sqrt{3} \approx 0, \pm 5.2$$

y-intercept: 0
symmetry: origin
We set up a table of values:

x	0	0.5	1	1.5	2	2.5	3	3.5	4	4.5	5	5.5	6
y	0	-13.4	-26	-37.1	-46	-51.9	-54	-51.6	-44	-30.4	-10	17.9	54

Now graph the curve:

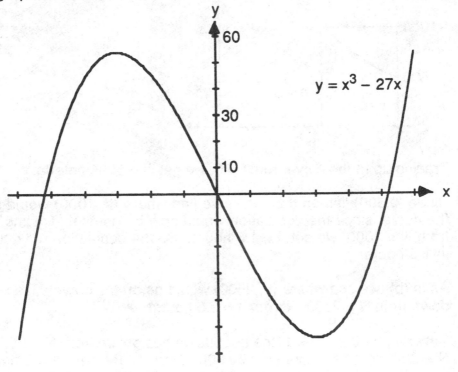

$$y = x^3 - 27x$$

71. Note that if $(x^2 + y^2 - 1)(x^2 + y^2 - 4) = 0$, then either $x^2 + y^2 - 1 = 0$ or $x^2 + y^2 - 4 = 0$, thus $x^2 + y^2 = 1$ or $x^2 + y^2 = 4$. Thus the graph is two circles:

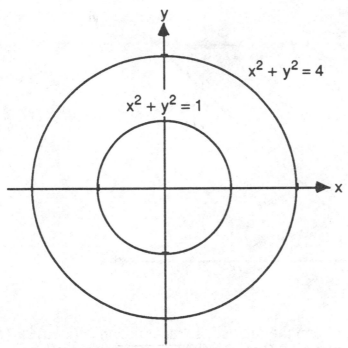

73. $y = x + \dfrac{1}{\sqrt{x + 1}}$

symmetry: none
We set up a table of values:

x	-1	-0.9	-0.8	-0.5	0	1	2	3	4	5	6	7	8
y	none	2.3	1.4	0.9	1	1.7	2.6	3.5	4.4	5.4	6.4	7.4	8.3

Now graph the curve:

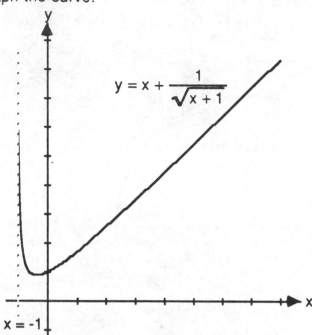

$$y = x + \frac{1}{\sqrt{x+1}}$$

$x = -1$

75. Call the center (a, b) and the radius r, so its equation is $(x - a)^2 + (y - b)^2 = r^2$. Since (2,5), (0,7), and (-6,1) are all points on the circle, we have:
$$(2 - a)^2 + (5 - b)^2 = r^2$$
$$(0 - a)^2 + (7 - b)^2 = r^2$$
$$(-6 - a)^2 + (1 - b)^2 = r^2$$
Setting the first two equations equal, we have:
$$4 - 4a + a^2 + 25 - 10b + b^2 = a^2 + 49 - 14b + b^2$$
$$29 - 4a - 10b = 49 - 14b$$
$$-4a + 4b = 20$$
$$-a + b = 5$$
Similarly, setting the last two equations equal, we have:
$$a^2 + 49 - 14b + b^2 = 36 + 12a + a^2 + 1 - 2b + b^2$$
$$49 - 14b = 37 + 12a - 2b$$
$$-12a - 12b = -12$$
$$a + b = 1$$
Now adding these two equations:
$$-a + b = 5$$
$$\underline{a + b = 1}$$
$$2b = 6$$
$$b = 3$$
Substituting:
$$a + 3 = 1, \text{ so } a = -2$$
Finally, we find r using the first equation:

$$\left(2 - (-2)\right)^2 + (5 - 3)^2 = r^2$$
$$16 + 4 = r^2$$
$$20 = r^2$$

So the equation of the circle is $(x + 2)^2 + (y - 3)^2 = 20$.

3.3 Slope

1. (a) Here $(x_1, y_1) = (-3, 2)$ and $(x_2, y_2) = (1, -6)$, so:

    $$\text{slope} = \frac{-6 - 2}{1 - (-3)} = \frac{-8}{4} = -2$$

   (b) Here $(x_1, y_1) = (2, -5)$ and $(x_2, y_2) = (4, 1)$, so:

    $$\text{slope} = \frac{1 - (-5)}{4 - 2} = \frac{6}{2} = 3$$

   (c) Here $(x_1, y_1) = (-2, 7)$ and $(x_2, y_2) = (1, 0)$, so:

    $$\text{slope} = \frac{0 - 7}{1 - (-2)} = -\frac{7}{3}$$

   (d) Here $(x_1, y_1) = (4, 5)$ and $(x_2, y_2) = (5, 8)$, so:

    $$\text{slope} = \frac{8 - 5}{5 - 4} = \frac{3}{1} = 3$$

3. (a) Here $(x_1, y_1) = (1, 1)$ and $(x_2, y_2) = (-1, -1)$, so:

    $$\text{slope} = \frac{-1 - 1}{-1 - 1} = \frac{-2}{-2} = 1$$

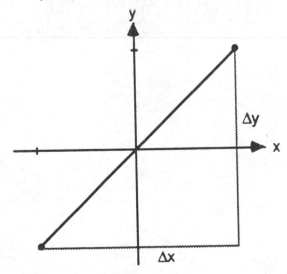

(b)   Here $(x_1, y_1) = (0,5)$ and $(x_2, y_2) = (-8,5)$, so:

slope $= \dfrac{5 - 5}{-8 - 0} = \dfrac{0}{-8} = 0$

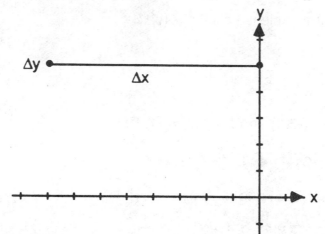

(c)   Here $(x_1, y_1) = (-1,1)$ and $(x_2, y_2) = (1,-1)$, so:

slope $= \dfrac{-1 - 1}{1 - (-1)} = \dfrac{-2}{2} = -1$

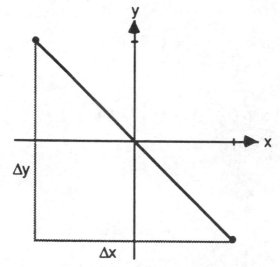

(d)   Here $(x_1, y_1) = (a,b)$ and $(x_2, y_2) = (b,a)$, so:

$$\text{slope} = \frac{a - b}{b - a} = -1$$

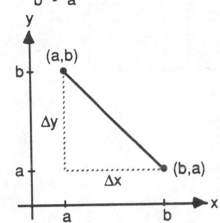

5. m_3 is smallest (since it is negative)
m_2 is next (it appears to be zero)
m_4 is next (it is not as steep as m_1)
m_1 is largest (it is steeper than m_4)

7.   slope of AB $= \dfrac{1/2 - (-2)}{2 - (-8)} = \dfrac{5/2}{10} = \dfrac{1}{4}$

slope of BC $= \dfrac{-1 - 1/2}{11 - 2} = \dfrac{-3/2}{9} = -\dfrac{1}{6}$

Since these slopes are different, the three points cannot be collinear.

9.   slope of AB $= \dfrac{4 - (-5)}{3 - 0} = \dfrac{9}{3} = 3$

slope of BC $= \dfrac{-8 - 4}{-1 - 3} = \dfrac{-12}{-4} = 3$

Since these slopes are equal, the three points are collinear.

11.   (a)   Let $(x_1, y_1) = (3,1)$ and $(x_2, y_2) = (5,3)$, so:
$\Delta x = x_2 - x_1 = 5 - 3 = 2$ and $\Delta y = y_2 - y_1 = 3 - 1 = 2$,
so $m = \dfrac{2}{2} = 1$

(b)   Let $(x_1, y_1) = (5,3)$ and $(x_2, y_2) = (3,1)$, so:
$\Delta x = x_2 - x_1 = 3 - 5 = -2$ and $\Delta y = y_2 - y_1 = 1 - 3 = -2$,
so $m = \dfrac{-2}{-2} = 1$

Notice that regardless of where you start, the slopes are the same.

13. (a) y = 2x - 3
        We draw the chart:

x	-2	-1	0	1	2
y	-7	-5	-3	-1	1

Now graph the curve:

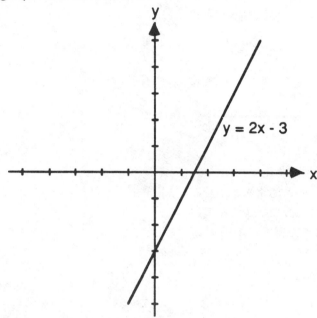

y = 2x - 3

Slope: Use (0,-3) and (2,1)

$$m = \frac{1 - (-3)}{2 - 0} = \frac{4}{2} = 2$$

(b) y = 2x
    We draw the chart:

x	-2	-1	0	1	2
y	-4	-2	0	2	4

Now graph the curve:

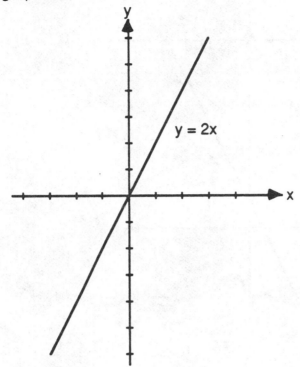

Slope: Use (0,0) and (2,4)

$$m = \frac{4 - 0}{2 - 0} = \frac{4}{2} = 2$$

(c) $y = 2x + 1$
We draw the chart:

x	-2	-1	0	1	2
y	-3	-1	1	3	5

Now graph the curve:

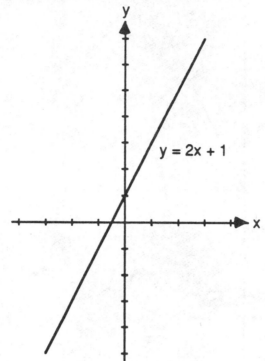

$$y = 2x + 1$$

Slope: Use (0,1) and (2,5)

$$m = \frac{5 - 1}{2 - 0} = \frac{4}{2} = 2$$

15. d = 5t

Set up a table (note that $t \geq 0$):

t	0	1	2
d	0	5	10

Now graph the curve:

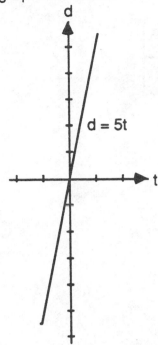

d = 5t

Slope: Use (1,5) and (2,10)

$$\text{slope} = \frac{10 - 5}{2 - 1} = \frac{5}{1} = 5$$

Notice that the slope of the distance line is the speed of the object.

17. Since the velocity will be the slope of the distance line, we compute the slope of each line.

(a)   Let $(x_1, y_1) = (1,4)$ and $(x_2, y_2) = (6,8)$. Then:

$$m = \frac{8 - 4}{6 - 1} = \frac{4}{5}$$

So the velocity is 4/5 ft/sec.

(b)   Let $(x_1, y_1) = (2,4)$ and $(x_2, y_2) = (5,4)$. Then:

$$m = \frac{4 - 4}{5 - 2} = \frac{0}{3} = 0$$

So the velocity is 0 cm/sec.

(c)   Let $(x_1, y_1) = (0,0)$ and $(x_2, y_2) = (2,16)$. Then:

$$m = \frac{16 - 0}{2 - 0} = \frac{16}{2} = 8$$

So the velocity is 8 mph.

19. $C = 0.5x + 500$
Set up a table (note that $x \geq 0$):

x	0	100	200	300	400
C	500	550	600	650	700

Now draw the graph:

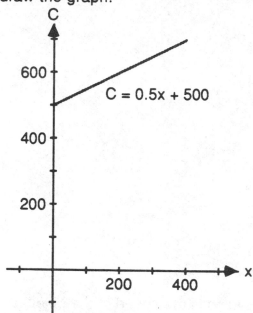

Slope: Use $(0,500)$ and $(400,700)$

$$\text{slope} = \frac{700 - 500}{400 - 0} = \frac{200}{400} = 0.5$$

So the marginal cost is \$0.50/album.

21.   Let $(x_1,y_1) = (x,x^2)$ and $(x_2,y_2) = (x + h, (x + h)^2)$. Then:

$$
\begin{aligned}
\text{slope} &= \frac{(x + h)^2 - x^2}{x + h - x} \\
&= \frac{x^2 + 2xh + h^2 - x^2}{h} \\
&= \frac{2xh + h^2}{h} \\
&= \frac{h(2x + h)}{h} \\
&= 2x + h
\end{aligned}
$$

23. (a) Let $(x_1, y_1) = (x, \sqrt{x})$ and $(x_2, y_2) = (x + h, \sqrt{x + h})$, so:

$$\text{slope} = \frac{\sqrt{x + h} - \sqrt{x}}{x + h - x} = \frac{\sqrt{x + h} - \sqrt{x}}{h}$$

   (b) Using the hint, we have:

$$\text{slope} = \frac{\sqrt{x + h} - \sqrt{x}}{h} \cdot \frac{\sqrt{x + h} + \sqrt{x}}{\sqrt{x + h} + \sqrt{x}}$$

$$= \frac{x + h - x}{h(\sqrt{x + h} + \sqrt{x})}$$

$$= \frac{h}{h(\sqrt{x + h} + \sqrt{x})}$$

$$= \frac{1}{\sqrt{x + h} + \sqrt{x}}$$

25. Let $(x_1, y_1) = (4, 2)$ and $(x_2, y_2) = (4 + h, \sqrt{4 + h})$, so:

$$\text{slope} = \frac{\sqrt{4 + h} - 2}{4 + h - 4} = \frac{\sqrt{4 + h} - 2}{h}$$

We multiply by $\dfrac{\sqrt{4 + h} + 2}{\sqrt{4 + h} + 2}$.

$$\text{slope} = \frac{\sqrt{4 + h} - 2}{h} \cdot \frac{\sqrt{4 + h} + 2}{\sqrt{4 + h} + 2}$$

$$= \frac{4 + h - 4}{h(\sqrt{4 + h} + 2)}$$

$$= \frac{h}{h(\sqrt{4 + h} + 2)}$$

$$= \frac{1}{\sqrt{4 + h} + 2}$$

27. monter means "to climb"

29. We draw the graph:

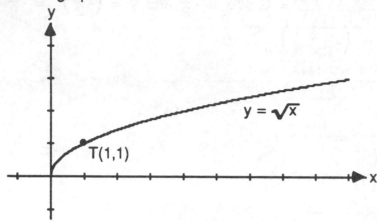

We draw the chart:

x	1.1	1.01	1.001	1.0001	1.00001
y	1.048809	1.004988	1.000500	1.000050	1.000005
Δx	0.1	0.01	0.001	0.0001	0.00001
Δy	0.048809	0.004988	0.0005	0.00005	0.000005
slope	0.48809	0.4988	0.5	0.5	0.5

It appears that as x approaches 1, the slope of the secant lines approach 0.5. So the slope of the tangent line to $y = \sqrt{x}$ at T(1,1) is 0.5.

31. Let the coordinate of P be (x, x^3). Since the slope of the line passing through P and (1,1) is $\frac{3}{4}$, we have:

$$\frac{x^3 - 1}{x - 1} = \frac{3}{4}$$

$$\frac{(x - 1)(x^2 + x + 1)}{x - 1} = \frac{3}{4}$$

$$x^2 + x + 1 = \frac{3}{4}$$

$$4x^2 + 4x + 4 = 3$$

$$4x^2 + 4x + 1 = 0$$

$$(2x + 1)^2 = 0$$

$$2x + 1 = 0, \text{ so } x = -\frac{1}{2} \text{ and } y = \left(-\frac{1}{2}\right)^3 = -\frac{1}{8}$$

Thus the point P is $\left(-\frac{1}{2}, -\frac{1}{8}\right)$.

33. Let the coordinates of P be $(x, 1/x)$. Since the slope of the line through P and $(2, 1/2)$ is $-\frac{1}{16}$, we have:

$$\frac{\frac{1}{x} - \frac{1}{2}}{x - 2} = \frac{-1}{16}$$

Multiply the left side by $\frac{2x}{2x}$:

$$\frac{2 - x}{2x(x - 2)} = \frac{-1}{16}$$

$$\frac{-1}{2x} = \frac{-1}{16}$$

$$2x = 16$$

$$x = 8$$

So the point P is $(8, 1/8)$.

3.4 Equations of Lines

1. (a) Here $(x_1, y_1) = (-2, 1)$ and $m = -5$, so by the point-slope formula:

$$y - 1 = -5[x - (-2)]$$
$$y - 1 = -5(x + 2)$$
$$y - 1 = -5x - 10$$
$$y = -5x - 9$$

(b) Here $(x_1, y_1) = (4, -4)$ and $m = 4$, so by the point-slope formula:

$$y - (-4) = 4(x - 4)$$
$$y + 4 = 4x - 16$$
$$y = 4x - 20$$

(c) Here $(x_1, y_1) = (-6, -2/3)$ and $m = 1/3$, so by the point-slope formula:

$$y - (-2/3) = (1/3)[x - (-6)]$$
$$y + 2/3 = (1/3)(x + 6)$$
$$y + 2/3 = 1/3x + 2$$
$$y = 1/3x + 4/3$$

(d)   Here $(x_1,y_1) = (0,1)$ and $m = -1$, so by the point-slope formula:
$$y - 1 = -1 (x - 0)$$
$$y - 1 = -x$$
$$y = -x + 1$$

Note in (d) that, since the given point is the y-intercept, we could have immediately written $y = -x + 1$ using the slope-intercept formula.

3.   (a)   First we find the slope: $m = \dfrac{-6 - 8}{-3 - 4} = \dfrac{-14}{-7} = 2$

Using $(x_1,y_1) = (4,8)$ in the point-slope formula, we have:
$$y - 8 = 2 (x - 4)$$
$$y - 8 = 2x - 8$$
$$y = 2x$$

(b)   First we find the slope: $m = \dfrac{-10 - 0}{3 - (-2)} = \dfrac{-10}{5} = -2$

Using $(x_1,y_1) = (-2,0)$ in the point-slope formula, we have:
$$y - 0 = -2 [x - (-2)]$$
$$y = -2 (x + 2)$$
$$y = -2x - 4$$

(c)   First we find the slope: $m = \dfrac{-1 - (-2)}{4 - (-3)} = \dfrac{1}{7}$

Using $(x_1,y_1) = (4,-1)$ in the point-slope formula, we have:
$$y - (-1) = 1/7 (x - 4)$$
$$y + 1 = 1/7\, x - 4/7$$
$$y = 1/7\, x - 11/7$$

5.   Since vertical lines have the form x = constant, and (-3,4) is on the line, then the equation is x = -3.

7.   Since horizontal lines have the form y = constant, and (-3,4) is on the line, then the equation is y = 4.

9.   The y-axis is vertical, so its equation must have the form x = constant. Since (0,0) is on the y-axis, the equation is x = 0.

11.   (a)   Using the slope-intercept formula with m = -4 and b = 7, we have
$$y = -4x + 7.$$

(b)   Using the slope-intercept formula with m = 2 and $b = \dfrac{3}{2}$, we have
$$y = 2x + \dfrac{3}{2}.$$

(c)   Using the slope-intercept formula with $m = -\frac{4}{3}$ and $b = 14$, we have

$$y = -\frac{4}{3}x + 14.$$

13. $y = -7x + 4$
This is already in slope-intercept form, so its slope is -7 and its y-intercept is 4.

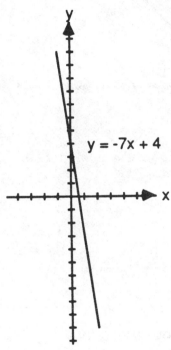

15. $x - y - 1 = 0$

We first put the line into slope-intercept form by solving for y:

$$x - y - 1 = 0$$
$$-y = -x + 1$$
$$y = x - 1$$

Its slope is 1, and the y-intercept is -1.

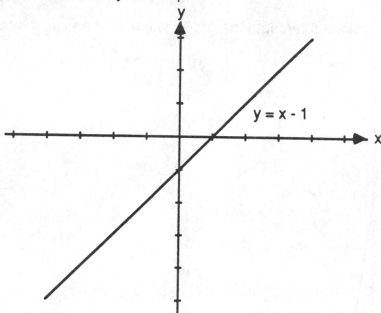

17. $\frac{x}{2} + \frac{y}{3} = 1$

We first put the line into slope-intercept form by solving for y:

$$\frac{x}{2} + \frac{y}{3} = 1$$
$$\frac{y}{3} = -\frac{x}{2} + 1$$
$$y = -\frac{3}{2}x + 3$$

Its slope is $-\frac{3}{2}$, and the y-intercept is 3.

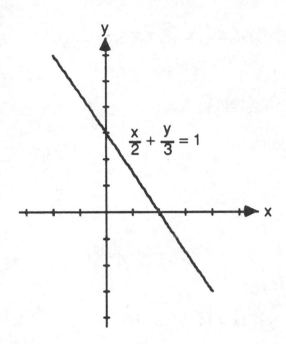

$$\frac{x}{2} + \frac{y}{3} = 1$$

19. $y - 4 = \frac{1}{2}(x - 2)$

This line is in point-slope form where the slope is $\frac{1}{2}$ and the point is (2,4). We
find the y-intercept by substituting $x = 0$:

$$y - 4 = \frac{1}{2}(-2)$$
$$y - 4 = -1$$
$$y = 3$$

So the y-intercept is 3.

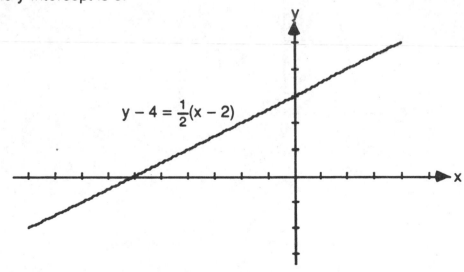

$$y - 4 = \frac{1}{2}(x - 2)$$

An alternate approach is to solve for y: $y - 4 = \frac{1}{2}x - 1$

$$y = \frac{1}{2}x + 3$$

This has a slope of $\frac{1}{2}$ and a y-intercept of 3.

21. (a)   We use the point-slope formula:

$$y - (-1) = 4\,[\,x - (-3)\,]$$
$$y + 1 = 4\,(x + 3)$$
$$y + 1 = 4x + 12$$
$$y = 4x + 11$$

We draw the graph:

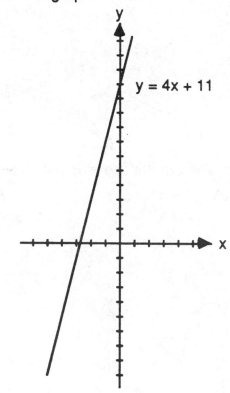

(b) We use the point-slope formula:

$$y - 0 = 1/2 \ (x - 5/2)$$
$$y = 1/2x - 5/4$$

We draw the graph:

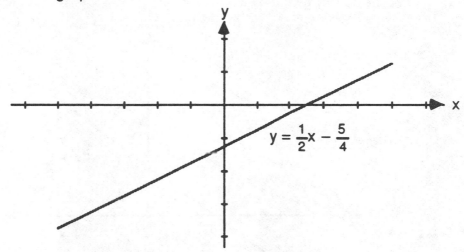

$$y = \frac{1}{2}x - \frac{5}{4}$$

(c) We find the slope between the points (6,0) and (0,5):

$$m = \frac{5 - 0}{0 - 6} = -\frac{5}{6}$$

Since 5 is the y-intercept, then by the slope-intercept formula:

$$y = -5/6 \ x + 5.$$

We draw the graph:

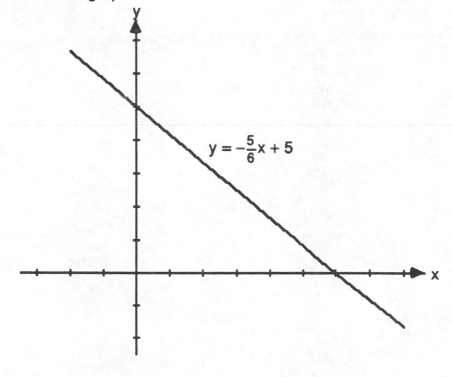

$$y = -\frac{5}{6}x + 5$$

(d)   We use the point-slope formula with the point (-2,0):
$$y - 0 = 3/4 [x - (-2)]$$
$$y = 3/4 (x + 2)$$
$$y = 3/4 x + 3/2$$
We draw the graph:

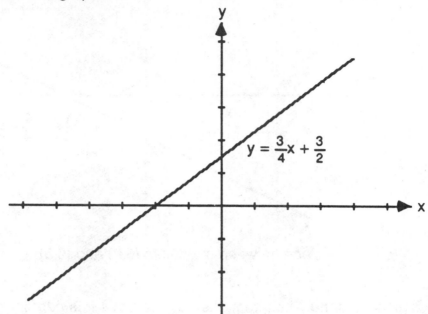

$$y = \frac{3}{4}x + \frac{3}{2}$$

(e)   We first find the slope:
$$m = \frac{6 - 2}{2 - 1} = \frac{4}{1} = 4$$
Using the point (1,2) in the point-slope formula, we have:
$$y - 2 = 4 (x - 1)$$
$$y - 2 = 4x - 4$$
$$y = 4x - 2$$

We draw the graph:

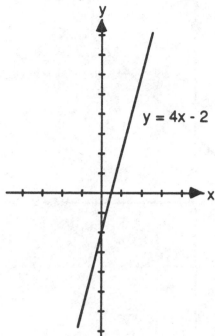

$y = 4x - 2$

23. We first find the x- and y-intercepts of the circle:

x-intercepts: y-intercepts:

$$y = 0$$
$$x^2 + 4x + 4 = 0$$
$$(x + 2)^2 = 0$$
$$x = -2$$

$$x = 0$$
$$y^2 - 4y + 4 = 0$$
$$(y - 2)^2 = 0$$
$$y = 2$$

So the line passes through the points (-2,0) and (0,2). We find its slope:

$$m = \frac{2 - 0}{0 - (-2)} = \frac{2}{2} = 1$$

So $y = x + 2$ is the equation (in slope-intercept form) of the line.

We draw the graph:

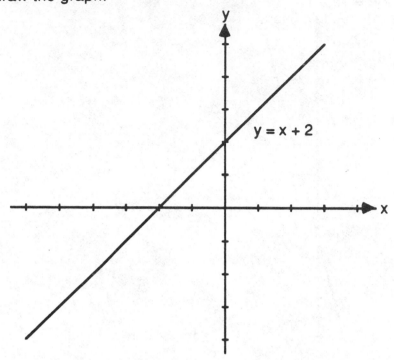

25. If the line is parallel to the x-axis, then its slope is 0. Since this line is of the form y = constant, then for (-3,4) to lie of the line the equation is y = 4, or y - 4 = 0 in the desired form. We draw the graph:

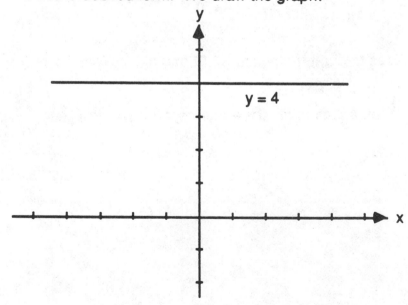

27. (a)   (x + y - 1) (x - y - 1) = 0
           So x + y - 1 = 0   or   x - y - 1 = 0

$$y = -x + 1 \qquad\qquad y = x - 1$$

So the graph has two lines:

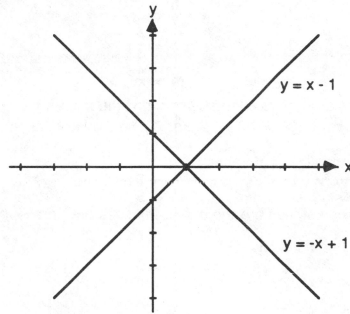

(b) $(2x + 3y + 6)(2x - 3y + 6) = 0$

So $2x + 3y + 6 = 0$ or $2x - 3y + 6 = 0$

$$3y = -2x - 6 \qquad\qquad 3y = 2x + 6$$

$$y = -\frac{2}{3}x - 2 \qquad\qquad y = \frac{2}{3}x + 2$$

So the graph has two lines:

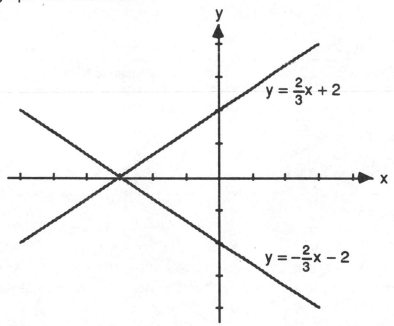

29. (a) We find the slopes of each:

$$3x - 4y = 12 \qquad\qquad 4x - 3y = 12$$
$$-4y = -3x + 12 \qquad\qquad -3y = -4x + 12$$
$$y = \frac{3}{4}x - 3 \qquad\qquad y = \frac{4}{3}x - 4$$
$$m = \frac{3}{4} \qquad\qquad m = \frac{4}{3}$$

The lines are not parallel (slopes aren't the same), the lines are not perpendicular (3/4 • 4/3 = 1, not -1), so they are neither.

(b) We find the slopes of each:

$$y = 5x - 16 \qquad\qquad y = 5x + 2$$
$$m = 5 \qquad\qquad m = 5$$

Since these slopes are the same, the lines are parallel.

(c) We find the slopes of each:

$$5x - 6y = 25 \qquad\qquad 6x + 5y = 0$$
$$-6y = -5x + 25 \qquad\qquad 5y = -6x$$
$$y = \frac{5}{6}x - \frac{25}{6} \qquad\qquad y = -\frac{5}{6}x$$
$$m = \frac{5}{6} \qquad\qquad m = -\frac{6}{5}$$

Since (5/6)(-6/5) = -1, the lines are perpendicular.

(d) We find the slopes of each:

$$y = -\frac{2}{3}x - 1 \qquad\qquad y = \frac{3}{2}x - 1$$
$$m = -\frac{2}{3} \qquad\qquad m = \frac{3}{2}$$

Since (-2/3) (3/2) = -1, the lines are perpendicular.

(e) We find the slopes of each:

$$-2x - 5y = 1 \qquad\qquad y - \frac{2}{5}x - 4 = 0$$
$$-5y = 2x + 1 \qquad\qquad y = \frac{2}{5}x + 4$$
$$y = -\frac{2}{5}x - \frac{1}{5}$$
$$m = -\frac{2}{5} \qquad\qquad m = \frac{2}{5}$$

The lines are not parallel (slopes aren't the same); the lines are not perpendicular (-2/5 • 2/5 = -4/25, not -1), so they are neither.

(f)   We find the slopes of each:

$$x = 8y + 3 \qquad\qquad 4y - \frac{1}{2}x = 32$$

$$8y = x - 3 \qquad\qquad 4y = \frac{1}{2}x + 32$$

$$y = \frac{1}{8}x - \frac{3}{8} \qquad\qquad y = \frac{1}{8}x + 8$$

$$m = \frac{1}{8} \qquad\qquad m = \frac{1}{8}$$

Since these slopes are the same, the lines are parallel.

31.   We first find the slope:

$$2x - 5y = 10$$
$$-5y = -2x + 10$$
$$y = \frac{2}{5}x - 2$$

So the slope is $\frac{2}{5}$. We use the point (-1,2) in the point-slope formula:

$$y - 2 = \frac{2}{5}[x - (-1)]$$

$$y - 2 = \frac{2}{5}(x + 1)$$

$$y - 2 = \frac{2}{5}x + \frac{2}{5}$$

$$y = \frac{2}{5}x + \frac{12}{5} \qquad [\,\text{form } y = mx + b\,]$$

$$5y = 2x + 12$$

$$2x - 5y + 12 = 0 \quad [\,\text{form } Ax + By + C = 0\,]$$

This could also be written as $-2x + 5y - 12 = 0$

33.   We first find the slope of $4y - 3x = 1$:

$$4y = 3x + 1$$
$$y = \frac{3}{4}x + \frac{1}{4}$$

Since this slope is $\frac{3}{4}$, the perpendicular line slope is $-\frac{4}{3}$. We now use the point (4,0) in the point-slope formula:

$$y - 0 = -\frac{4}{3}(x - 4)$$

$$y = -\frac{4}{3}x + \frac{16}{3} \qquad [\,\text{form } y = mx + b\,]$$

$$3y = -4x + 16$$

$$4x + 3y - 16 = 0 \qquad [\,\text{form } Ax + By + C = 0\,]$$

35.   We first find the slope of $3x - 5y = 25$:

$$-5y = -3x + 25$$

$$y = \frac{3}{5}x - 5$$

So the slope is $\frac{3}{5}$. We now find the y-intercept of $6x - y + 11 = 0$:

$$y = 6x + 11$$

So the y-intercept is 11. We write the equation:

$$y = \frac{3}{5}x + 11 \quad [\text{ form } y = mx + b\,]$$

$$5y = 3x + 55$$

$$3x - 5y + 55 = 0 \quad [\text{ form } Ax + By + C = 0\,]$$

This could also be written as $-3x + 5y - 55 = 0$

37.   (a)   Its center is (0,0) and its radius is 5. We draw the graph:

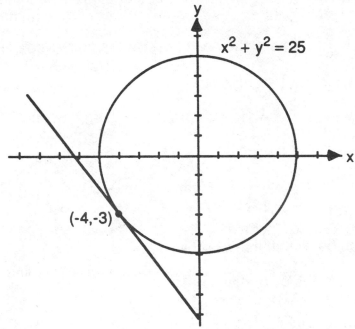

(b)   The tangent line will be perpendicular to the radius drawn from the center (0,0) and the point (-4,-3). We find the slope:

$$m = \frac{-3 - 0}{-4 - 0} = \frac{-3}{-4} = \frac{3}{4}$$

So the perpendicular line will have slope $= -\frac{4}{3}$. We use the point (-4,-3) in the point-slope formula:

$$y - (-3) = -\frac{4}{3}[x - (-4)]$$

$$y + 3 = -\frac{4}{3}(x + 4)$$

$$y + 3 = -\frac{4}{3}x - \frac{16}{3}$$

$$y = -\frac{4}{3}x - \frac{25}{3}$$

39. (a) We let $x = 10$, so $C = 450 + 8x = 450 + 8(10) = \$530$.

    (b) We let $x = 11$, so $C = 450 + 8(11) = \$538$.

    (c) There are two ways to find the marginal cost. One way is to recognize that the marginal cost will be the slope of the line, which is \$8/fan. Another way would be to use the definition of the marginal cost: the cost of producing the <u>next</u> unit. Call C(10) the cost of producing 10 fans and C(11) the cost of producing 11 fans. Then the marginal cost would be C(11) - C(10) = 538 - 530 = \$8/fan. We get the same answer using either approach.

41. (a) Since the velocity is the slope of the line, then it will be 5 ft/sec.

    (b) We let $t = 15$, so $d = 5(15) = 75$ ft.

    (c) We have:
    $$d(16) = d(15) + \text{velocity}$$
    $$= 75 + 5$$
    $$= 80 \text{ ft}$$

43. We use the point-slope formula to find the equation of the line:
$$y - 6 = -5(x - 3)$$
$$y - 6 = -5x + 15$$
$$y = -5x + 21$$
We now find the intercepts:
x-intercept: Let $y = 0$
$$-5x + 21 = 0$$
$$5x = 21$$
$$x = \frac{21}{5}$$
y-intercept: Let $x = 0$
$$y = 21$$

We draw the graph:

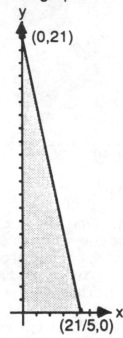

From the figure, we see that   A = (1/2) (base) (height)
= (1/2) (21/5) (21)
= 44.1 sq. units

45. (a)   We first find the slope between (a,0) and (0,b):
$$m = \frac{b - 0}{0 - a} = -\frac{b}{a}$$
So the equation (using the point (0,b)) is:
$$y = -\frac{b}{a}x + b$$
$$ay = -bx + ab$$
$$bx + ay = ab$$
Dividing through by ab, we have:
$$\frac{bx}{ab} + \frac{ay}{ab} = \frac{ab}{ab}$$
$$\frac{x}{a} + \frac{y}{b} = 1$$

(b)   We have: $\frac{x}{6} + \frac{y}{7} = 1$
Multiplying through by 42:
$$7x + 6y = 42$$
$$7x + 6y - 42 = 0$$

47. (a) We draw the graph:

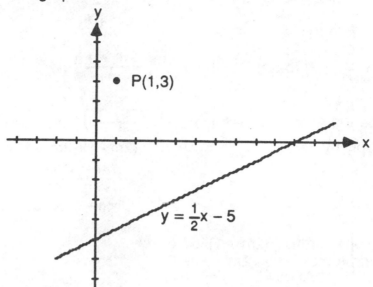

(b) Its slope must be -2, so we use (1,3) in the point-slope formula:
$$y - 3 = -2 (x - 1)$$
$$y - 3 = -2x + 2$$
$$y = -2x + 5$$

(c) We set the two equations equal:
$$-2x + 5 = \frac{1}{2}x - 5$$
$$-4x + 10 = x - 10$$
$$-5x = -20$$
$$x = 4$$
$$y = -2 (4) + 5 = -3$$
The intersection point is (4,-3)

(d) We find the distance from (1,3) to (4,-3):
$$d = \sqrt{(4 - 1)^2 + (-3 - 3)^2} = \sqrt{9 + 36} = \sqrt{45} = 3\sqrt{5}$$

49. (a) Since the slope is m and the point (2,1) lies on the line, we use the point-slope formula to get $y - 1 = m (x - 2)$

(b) For the x-intercept, let y = 0:
$$-1 = m (x - 2)$$
$$-1 = mx - 2m$$
$$mx = 2m - 1$$
$$x = \frac{2m - 1}{m}$$

For the y-intercept, let $x = 0$:
$$y - 1 = m(-2)$$
$$y - 1 = -2m$$
$$y = -2m + 1$$

(c)   Area $= (1/2)$ (base) (height) $= \dfrac{1}{2}\left(\dfrac{2m - 1}{m}\right)(-2m + 1)$

(d)   Since the area is 4, we have: $\dfrac{1}{2}\left(\dfrac{2m - 1}{m}\right)(-2m + 1) = 4$

Multiply by $2m$:
$$(2m - 1)(-2m + 1) = 8m$$
$$-4m^2 + 4m - 1 = 8m$$
$$-4m^2 - 4m - 1 = 0$$
$$4m^2 + 4m + 1 = 0$$

(e)   We solve for m: $(2m + 1)^2 = 0$
Taking roots: $2m + 1 = 0$
$$2m = -1$$
$$m = -\dfrac{1}{2}$$

51. (a)   Since $\dfrac{\Delta x}{\Delta P} = -\dfrac{2}{3}$, we have the equation:
$$x = 280 - (2/3)(P - 195)$$
$$x = 410 - \dfrac{2}{3}P$$

(b)   If $P = 270$, we have: $x = 280 - (2/3)(270 - 195)$
$$= 280 - (2/3)(75)$$
$$= 280 - 50$$
$$= 230$$
So 230 units can be sold in a month.

(c)   If $x = 205$, we have: $205 = 280 - (2/3)(P - 195)$
$$-75 = -(2/3)(P - 195)$$
$$112.5 = P - 195$$
$$307.5 = P$$
The price would be $307.50 per unit.

53. (a)   Since A lies on $y = m_1 x$ and B lies on $y = m_2 x$, and the x-coordinate is 1 in either case, then $y = m_1$ and $y = m_2$, respectively. So $A = (1, m_1)$ and $B = (1, m_2)$.

(b) Using the distance formula, we have:

$$OA^2 = (1 - 0)^2 + (m_1 - 0)^2 = 1 + m_1^2$$
$$OB^2 = (1 - 0)^2 + (m_2 - 0)^2 = 1 + m_2^2$$
$$AB^2 = (1 - 1)^2 + (m_1 - m_2)^2 = m_1^2 + m_2^2 - 2m_1m_2$$

(c) We use the Pythagorean Theorem:

$$OA^2 + OB^2 = AB^2$$
$$(1 + m_1^2) + (1 + m_2^2) = m_1^2 + m_2^2 - 2m_1m_2$$
$$2 = -2m_1m_2$$
$$m_1m_2 = -1$$

55. (a) See the figure:

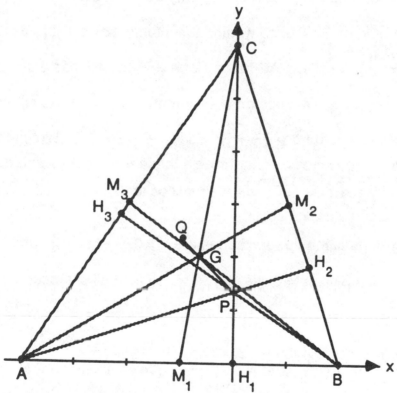

We find the midpoints:

$$M_1 = (-1,0), \quad M_2 = (1,3), \quad M_3 = (-2,3)$$

We plug into the equation $(x - h)^2 + (y - k)^2 = r^2$, and simplify to get the equations:

$$1 + 2h + h^2 + k^2 = r^2$$
$$10 - 2h + h^2 - 6k + k^2 = r^2$$
$$13 + 4h + h^2 - 6k + k^2 = r^2$$

Subtracting the first equation from the other two yields:
$$4h + 6k = 9$$
$$2h - 6k = -12$$
Adding these yields $h = -\frac{1}{2}$, and substituting into the first equation

yields $k = \frac{11}{6}$, and finally we find that $r^2 = \frac{130}{36}$. So the circle is

$(x + \frac{1}{2})^2 + (y - \frac{11}{6})^2 = \frac{130}{36}$.

This can be converted to the form $3x^2 + 3y^2 + 3x - 11y = 0$.

(b) We now find H_1, H_2, and H_3. $H_1 = (0,0)$ by inspection. Since BC has

a slope $= -3$, then AH_2 has a slope $= \frac{1}{3}$, thus $y = \frac{1}{3}x + \frac{4}{3}$. BC has an

equation of $y = -3x + 6$, so we find the intersection point to be $(\frac{7}{5}, \frac{9}{5})$. So

$H_2 = (\frac{7}{5}, \frac{9}{5})$. Similarly AC has a slope $= \frac{3}{2}$, so BH_3 has a slope $= -\frac{2}{3}$,

thus $y = -\frac{2}{3}x + \frac{4}{3}$. AC has an equation of $y = \frac{3}{2}x + 6$, so we find the

intersection point to be $(-\frac{28}{13}, \frac{36}{13})$. So $H_3 = (-\frac{28}{13}, \frac{36}{13})$. We find the

equation of the circle passing through these three points and get

$(x + \frac{1}{2})^2 + (y - \frac{11}{6})^2 = \frac{130}{36}$, which simplifies to $3x^2 + 3y^2 + 3x - 11y = 0$.

(c) The equations of the three altitudes are $x = 0$, $y = \frac{1}{3}x + \frac{4}{3}$, and

$y = -\frac{2}{3}x + \frac{4}{3}$. Since $x = 0$, we get $y = \frac{4}{3}$, so they all intersect at the

point $(0, \frac{4}{3})$.

(d) $N_1 = (-2, \frac{2}{3})$, $N_2 = (1, \frac{2}{3})$, and $N_3 = (0, \frac{11}{3})$. We check that N_1, N_2, and N_3

lie on $3x^2 + 3y^2 + 3x - 11y = 0$, which they all do.

(e) Rather than using the hint, we'll plug into $(x - h)^2 + (y - k)^2 = r^2$ directly
and simplify, yielding:
$$36 + h^2 - 12k + k^2 = r^2$$
$$16 + h^2 + 8h + k^2 = r^2$$
$$4 - 4h + h^2 + k^2 = r^2$$

Subtracting the first equation from the other two yields:

$$2h + 3k = 5$$
$$-h + 3k = 8$$

which has a solution of $h = -1$ and $k = \frac{7}{3}$. So the center of the circle is $(-1, \frac{7}{3})$.

(f)   We find the radius of the circumcircle:

$$r^2 = (0 + 1)^2 + (6 - \frac{7}{3})^2 = \frac{130}{9}, \text{ so } r = \frac{\sqrt{130}}{3}$$

From (a) we have the radius of the nine-point circle is $\frac{\sqrt{130}}{6}$, which is one-half of the radius of the circumcircle.

(g)   Midpoint of $QP = (-\frac{1}{2}, \frac{11}{6})$. Note that this is the center of the nine-point circle from (a).

(h)   We first find the medians:

$$CM_1: \quad m = 6, \text{ so } \quad y = 6x + 6$$
$$BM_3: \quad m = -\frac{3}{4}, \text{ so } \quad y = -\frac{3}{4}x + \frac{3}{2}$$
$$AM_2: \quad m = \frac{3}{5}, \text{ so } \quad y = \frac{3}{5}x + \frac{12}{5}$$

Now find the intersections:

$$6x + 6 = -\frac{3}{4}x + \frac{3}{2}, \text{ so } x = -\frac{2}{3} \text{ and } y = 2$$
$$6x + 6 = \frac{3}{5}x + \frac{12}{5}, \text{ so } x = -\frac{2}{3} \text{ and } y = 2$$
$$-\frac{3}{4}x + \frac{3}{2} = \frac{3}{5}x + \frac{12}{5}, \text{ so } x = -\frac{2}{3} \text{ and } y = 2$$

So the intersection point is $(-\frac{2}{3}, 2)$.

(i)   We find the equation of QP: $m = -1$, so $y = -x + \frac{4}{3}$

$$PG = \sqrt{(-2/3 - 0)^2 + (2 - 4/3)^2} = \frac{2\sqrt{2}}{3}$$
$$GQ = \sqrt{(-1 + 2/3)^2 + (7/3 - 2)^2} = \frac{\sqrt{2}}{3}$$

So $PG = 2 \cdot GQ$

Chapter 3 Review Exercises

1.   We find the slope: $m = \dfrac{6 - 2}{-6 - (-4)} = \dfrac{4}{-2} = -2$

   Using the point (-4,2) in the point-slope formula:
$$y - 2 = -2\,[\,x - (-4)\,]$$
$$y - 2 = -2\,(x + 4)$$
$$y - 2 = -2x - 8$$
$$y = -2x - 6$$

3.   Using the point-slope formula: $y - (-3) = \dfrac{1}{4}\,[\,x - (-2)\,]$

$$y + 3 = \dfrac{1}{4}\,(x + 2)$$
$$y + 3 = \dfrac{1}{4}x + \dfrac{1}{2}$$
$$y = \dfrac{1}{4}x - \dfrac{5}{2}$$

5.   We find the slope between the points (-4,0) and (0,8):
$$m = \dfrac{8 - 0}{0 - (-4)} = \dfrac{8}{4} = 2$$
   Using the slope-intercept formula: $y = 2x + 8$

7.   Since it is parallel to the x-axis, its equation will be of the form y = constant (horizontal line). Since (0,-2) is on the line, its equation is y = -2.

9.   We find the slope of x + y + 1 = 0 by putting it in slope-intercept form, and get y = -x - 1. So its slope is -1, and thus a perpendicular slope would be 1. We use the point (1,2) in the point-slope formula:
$$y - 2 = 1(x - 1)$$
$$y - 2 = x - 1$$
$$y = x + 1$$

11.   We find the center of each circle by completing the square:
$$x^2 + 4x + y^2 + 2y = 0$$
$$(x^2 + 4x + 4) + (y^2 + 2y + 1) = 0 + 4 + 1$$
$$(x + 2)^2 + (y + 1)^2 = 5$$
   center: (-2,-1)

$$x^2 - 4x + y^2 - 16y = 0$$
$$(x^2 - 4x + 4) + (y^2 - 16y + 64) = 0 + 4 + 64$$
$$(x - 2)^2 + (y - 8)^2 = 68$$
   center: (2,8)

We find the slope between (-2,-1) and (2,8):

$$m = \frac{8 - (-1)}{2 - (-2)} = \frac{9}{4}$$

We use the point (2,8) in the point-slope formula:

$$y - 8 = \frac{9}{4}(x - 2)$$

$$y - 8 = \frac{9}{4}x - \frac{9}{2}$$

$$y = \frac{9}{4}x + \frac{7}{2}$$

13. We find the midpoint of the line segment joining (-2,-3) and (6,-5):

$$M = \left(\frac{-2 + 6}{2}, \frac{-3 - 5}{2}\right) = \left(\frac{4}{2}, -\frac{8}{2}\right) = (2,-4)$$

Now we find the slope between (0,0) and (2,-4):

$$m = \frac{-4 - 0}{2 - 0} = \frac{-4}{2} = -2$$

We use the slope-intercept formula to get $y = -2x + 0$, or $y = -2x$.

15. We first find the center of the circle by completing the square:

$$x^2 - 6x + y^2 + 8y = 0$$
$$(x^2 - 6x + 9) + (y^2 + 8y + 16) = 0 + 9 + 16$$
$$(x - 3)^2 + (y + 4)^2 = 25$$

So the center is (3,-4). We now find the slope of the radius drawn from (3,-4) to (0,0):

$$m = \frac{0 - (-4)}{0 - 3} = \frac{4}{-3} = -\frac{4}{3}$$

So the slope of the perpendicular tangent line is $\frac{3}{4}$. We use the slope-intercept formula:

$$y = \frac{3}{4}x + 0$$

$$y = \frac{3}{4}x$$

17. Call the x-intercept a. Then the y-intercept is 2 - a, and we find the slope from each to (2,-1):

$$m = \frac{-1 - 0}{2 - a} = \frac{-1}{2 - a}$$

$$m = \frac{-1 - (2 - a)}{2 - 0} = \frac{-1 - 2 + a}{2} = \frac{a - 3}{2}$$

Since these two slopes must be equal, we have:
$$\frac{-1}{2 - a} = \frac{a - 3}{2}$$

Cross-multiply:
$$-2 = (2 - a)(a - 3)$$
$$-2 = -a^2 + 5a - 6$$
$$0 = a^2 - 5a + 4$$
$$0 = (a - 4)(a - 1)$$
$$a = 1 \quad \text{or} \quad a = 4$$

When a = 1, we have m $= \dfrac{1 - 3}{2} = \dfrac{-2}{2} = -1$

When a = 4, we have m $= \dfrac{-1}{2 - 4} = \dfrac{-1}{-2} = \dfrac{1}{2}$

We use the point (2,-1), and each of these slopes, in the point-slope formula:

$$y - (-1) = -1(x - 2) \qquad y - (-1) = \frac{1}{2}(x - 2)$$

$$y + 1 = -x + 2 \qquad\qquad y + 1 = \frac{1}{2}x - 1$$

$$y = -x + 1 \qquad\qquad\quad y = \frac{1}{2}x - 2$$

Both of these lines satisfy the given conditions.

19. We use the distance formula with $(x_1, y_1) = (-1, 2)$ and $(x_2, y_2) = (4, -10)$:
$$d = \sqrt{[4 - (-1)]^2 + (-10 - 2)^2} = \sqrt{25 + 144} = \sqrt{169} = 13$$

21. We find the distance of each from the origin:
$$d_1 = \sqrt{(15 - 0)^2 + (6 - 0)^2} = \sqrt{225 + 36} = \sqrt{261}$$
$$d_2 = \sqrt{(16 - 0)^2 + (2 - 0)^2} = \sqrt{256 + 4} = \sqrt{260}$$
(15,6) is (barely) farther from the origin.

23. $y = x^4 - 2x^2$
x-axis: Replace y with -y:
$$-y = x^4 - 2x^2$$
$$y = -x^4 + 2x^2 \quad \text{NO}$$
y-axis: Replace x with -x:
$$y = (-x)^4 - 2(-x)^2$$
$$y = x^4 - 2x^2 \quad \text{YES}$$
origin: Replace y with -y and x with -x:
$$-y = (-x)^4 - 2(-x)^2$$
$$-y = x^4 - 2x^2$$
$$y = -x^4 + 2x^2 \quad \text{NO}$$

25. $y = x^3 + 5x$

x-axis: Replace y with -y:

$-y = x^3 + 5x$

$y = -x^3 - 5x$ NO

y-axis: Repalce x with -x:

$y = (-x)^3 + 5(-x)$

$y = -x^3 - 5x$ NO

origin: Replace y with -y and x with -x:

$-y = (-x)^3 + 5(-x)$

$-y = -x^3 - 5x$

$y = x^3 + 5x$ YES

27. $y^2 = (x + y)^4$

x-axis: Replace y with -y:

$(-y)^2 = (x + (-y))^4$

$y^2 = (x - y)^4$ NO

y-axis: Replace x with -x:

$y^2 = (-x + y)^4$ NO

origin: Replace y with -y and x with -x:

$(-y)^2 = (-x + (-y))^4$

$y^2 = (-x - y)^4$

$y^2 = (x + y)^4$ YES   (since $(-1)^4 = (1)^4$)

29. $y = 3x - \dfrac{1}{x}$

x-axis: Replace y with -y:

$-y = 3x - \dfrac{1}{x}$

$y = -3x + \dfrac{1}{x}$ NO

y-axis: Replace x with -x:

$y = 3(-x) - \dfrac{1}{-x}$

$y = -3x + \dfrac{1}{x}$ NO

origin: Replace y with -y and x with -x:

$-y = 3(-x) - \dfrac{1}{-x}$

$-y = -3x + \dfrac{1}{x}$

$y = 3x - \dfrac{1}{x}$ YES

31. $y = 2^x - 2^{-x}$
     x-axis: Replace y with -y:
              $-y = 2^x - 2^{-x}$
              $y = -2^x + 2^{-x}$ NO
     y-axis: Replace x with -x:
              $y = 2^{-x} - 2^{-(-x)}$
              $y = 2^{-x} - 2^x$ NO
     origin: Replace y with -y and x with -x:
              $-y = 2^{-x} - 2^{-(-x)}$
              $-y = 2^{-x} - 2^x$
              $y = 2^x - 2^{-x}$ YES

33. x-axis: Yes
     y-axis: No
     origin: No

35. x-axis: Yes
     y-axis: Yes
     origin: Yes

37. x-axis: Yes
     y-axis: No
     origin: No

39. x-axis: Yes
     y-axis: No
     origin: No

41. x-axis: No
     y-axis: Yes
     origin: No

43. $2x - 5y = 10$
     We put the line into slope-intercept form:
              $2x - 5y = 10$
              $-5y = -2x + 10$
              $y = \frac{2}{5}x - 2$

We draw the graph:

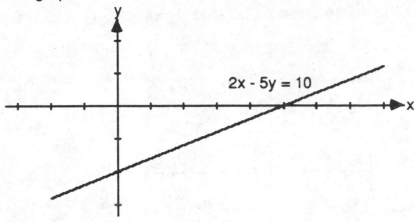

45. $x = 9 - y^2$
We plot points to obtain the graph:

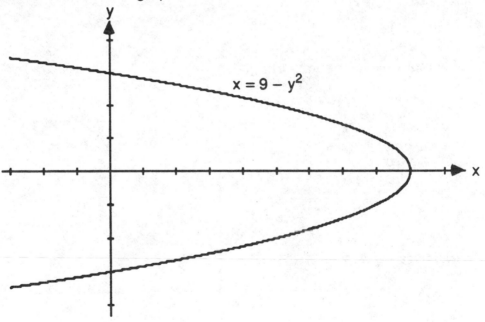

47. $x^2 + y^2 = 1$
     This is a circle with center = (0,0) and radius = 1. We draw the graph:

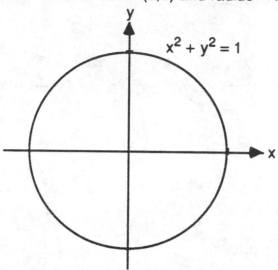

49. $y = |x| + 1$
     We plot points to obtain the graph:

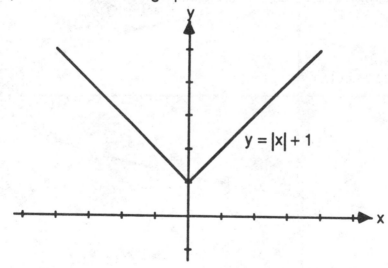

51. $y = x^2 - 4x + 4$
     We plot points to obtain the graph:

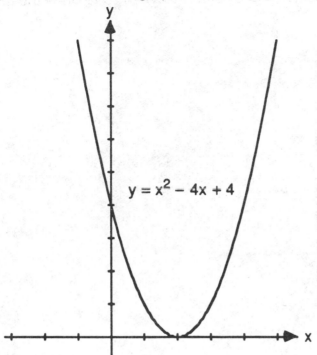

$$y = x^2 - 4x + 4$$

53. $y = |x - 2| + 2$
     We plot points to obtain the graph:

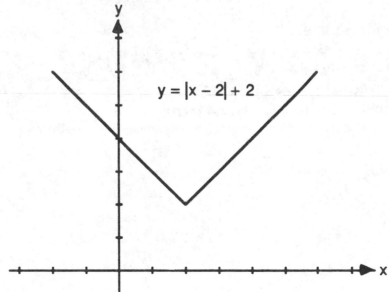

$$y = |x - 2| + 2$$

55. $3x + y = 0$

We put the line in slope-intercept form:
$$3x + y = 0$$
$$y = -3x$$

We draw the graph:

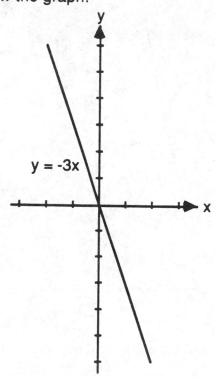

$y = -3x$

57. We complete the square:
$$x^2 - 4x + y^2 + 6y = 0$$
$$(x^2 - 4x + 4) + (y^2 + 6y + 9) = 4 + 9$$
$$(x - 2)^2 + (y + 3)^2 = 13$$

This is a circle with center = (2,-3) and radius = $\sqrt{13}$.

We draw the graph:

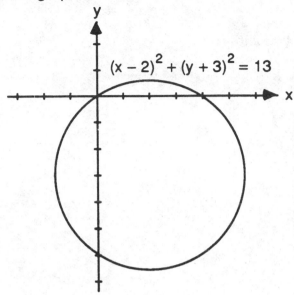

$(x - 2)^2 + (y + 3)^2 = 13$

59. $y = \dfrac{x^2 - 16}{x - 4}$

As long as $x \neq 4$, we can simplify:

$$y = \frac{x^2 - 16}{x - 4} = \frac{(x + 4)(x - 4)}{(x - 4)} = x + 4$$

This is a line in slope intercept form. We draw the graph:

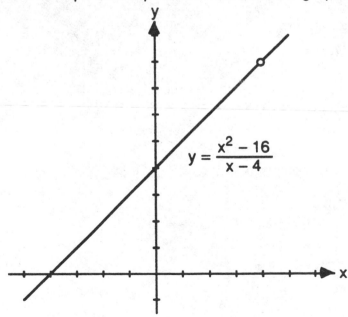

$y = \dfrac{x^2 - 16}{x - 4}$

61. $(4x - y + 4)(4x + y - 4) = 0$
     Then either $4x - y + 4 = 0$ or $4x + y - 4 = 0$
                         $y = 4x + 4$ $y = -4x + 4$
     The graph will consist of two lines:

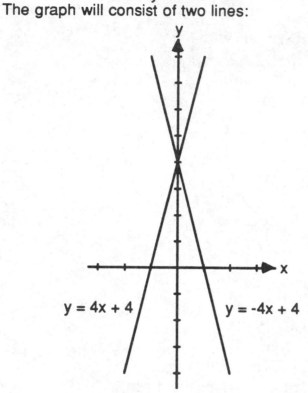

63. We set up the equation involving slope:
     $$\frac{t - 1}{5 - 2} = 6$$
     $$\frac{t - 1}{3} = 6$$
     $$t - 1 = 18$$
     $$t = 19$$

65. The slope between the points $(-2, -8)$ and (x, x^3) is:
     $$m = \frac{x^3 - (-8)}{x - (-2)}$$
     $$= \frac{x^3 + 8}{x + 2}$$
     $$= \frac{(x + 2)(x^2 - 2x + 4)}{x + 2}$$
     $$= x^2 - 2x + 4$$

67. The midpoint of the hypotenuse (BC) would be:

$$M = \left(\frac{0 + 2c}{2}, \frac{2b + 0}{2}\right) = \left(\frac{2c}{2}, \frac{2b}{2}\right) = (c, b)$$

We compute the distances:

$$MA = \sqrt{(c - 0)^2 + (b - 0)^2} = \sqrt{c^2 + b^2}$$
$$MB = \sqrt{(c - 0)^2 + (b - 2b)^2} = \sqrt{c^2 + b^2}$$
$$MC = \sqrt{(c - 2c)^2 + (b - 0)^2} = \sqrt{c^2 + b^2}$$

These distances are all the same.

69. (a) $d = \sqrt{(5 - 2)^2 + (-6 - 5)^2} = \sqrt{9 + 121} = \sqrt{130}$

(b) $m = \dfrac{-6 - 5}{5 - 2} = -\dfrac{11}{3}$

(c) $M = \left(\dfrac{2 + 5}{2}, \dfrac{5 - 6}{2}\right) = \left(\dfrac{7}{2}, -\dfrac{1}{2}\right)$

71. (a) $d = \sqrt{\left(-\dfrac{\sqrt{3}}{2} - \dfrac{\sqrt{3}}{2}\right)^2 + \left(-\dfrac{1}{2} - \dfrac{1}{2}\right)^2}$

$$= \sqrt{(-\sqrt{3})^2 + (-1)^2}$$
$$= \sqrt{3 + 1}$$
$$= \sqrt{4}$$
$$= 2$$

(b) $m = \dfrac{-\dfrac{1}{2} - \dfrac{1}{2}}{-\dfrac{\sqrt{3}}{2} - \dfrac{\sqrt{3}}{2}} = \dfrac{-1}{-\sqrt{3}} = \dfrac{1}{\sqrt{3}} = \dfrac{\sqrt{3}}{3}$

(c) $M = \left(\dfrac{\sqrt{3}/2 - \sqrt{3}/2}{2}, \dfrac{1/2 - 1/2}{2}\right) = (0, 0)$

73. We find the slope:

$$m = \frac{1 - 2}{4 - 1} = -\frac{1}{3}$$

Using (1,2) in the point-slope formula:

$$y - 2 = -\frac{1}{3}(x - 1)$$
$$y - 2 = -\frac{1}{3}x + \frac{1}{3}$$
$$y = -\frac{1}{3}x + \frac{7}{3}$$

We now find the x and y-intercepts:

Let x = 0   Let y = 0

$y = \dfrac{7}{3}$ x = 7

Then the Area $= \dfrac{1}{2}$ (base) (height) $= \dfrac{1}{2}(7)\left(\dfrac{7}{3}\right) = \dfrac{49}{6}$

75. (a) Since the marginal cost is the slope, then C_m = \$12/tire.

   (b) Let x = 1000. C = 8500 + 12(1000) = 8500 + 12000 = \$20,500

   (c) $C(1001)$ = C (1000) + C_m
            = 20,500 + 12
            = \$20,512

   As a check, let x = 1001. Then C = 8500 + 12(1001) = \$20,512.

77. (a) We find the slope of P_1Q:

$$m = \frac{\dfrac{1}{3}y_1 + \dfrac{2}{3}y_2 - y_1}{\dfrac{1}{3}x_1 + \dfrac{2}{3}x_2 - x_1}$$

Multiply by $\dfrac{3}{3}$ to get:

$$m = \frac{y_1 + 2y_2 - 3y_1}{x_1 + 2x_2 - 3x_1}$$

$$= \frac{2y_2 - 2y_1}{2x_2 - 2x_1}$$

$$= \frac{y_2 - y_1}{x_2 - x_1}$$

We find the slope of P_2Q:

$$m = \frac{\dfrac{1}{3}y_1 + \dfrac{2}{3}y_2 - y_2}{\dfrac{1}{3}x_1 + \dfrac{2}{3}x_2 - x_2}$$

Multiply by $\dfrac{3}{3}$ to get:

$$m = \frac{y_1 + 2y_2 - 3y_2}{x_1 + 2x_2 - 3x_2}$$

$$= \frac{y_1 - y_2}{x_1 - x_2}$$

Since the two slopes are the same, P_1, P_2, and Q are collinear.

(b)   We use the distance formula:

$$P_1Q = \sqrt{\left(\frac{1}{3}x_1 + \frac{2}{3}x_2 - x_1\right)^2 + \left(\frac{1}{3}y_1 + \frac{2}{3}y_2 - y_1\right)^2}$$

$$= \sqrt{\left(\frac{2}{3}x_2 - \frac{2}{3}x_1\right)^2 + \left(\frac{2}{3}y_2 - \frac{2}{3}y_2\right)^2}$$

$$= \sqrt{\frac{4}{9}(x_2 - x_1)^2 + \frac{4}{9}(y_2 - y_1)^2}$$

$$= \frac{2}{3}\sqrt{(x_2 - x_1)^2 + (y_2 - y_1)^2}$$

$$P_1P_2 = \sqrt{(x_2 - x_1)^2 + (y_2 - y_1)^2}$$

So $P_1Q = \frac{2}{3}P_1P_2$

79.   We first find the intercepts:

Let $x = 0$

$$(-h)^2 + (y - k)^2 = r^2$$
$$h^2 + (y - k)^2 = r^2$$
$$(y - k)^2 = r^2 - h^2$$

Taking roots:

$$y - k = \pm\sqrt{r^2 - h^2}$$
$$y = k \pm \sqrt{r^2 - h^2}$$
$$y_1 = k + \sqrt{r^2 - h^2}$$
$$y_2 = k - \sqrt{r^2 - h^2}$$

Let $y = 0$

$$(x - h)^2 + (-k)^2 = r^2$$
$$(x - h)^2 + k^2 = r^2$$
$$(x - h)^2 = r^2 - k^2$$

Taking roots:

$$x - h = \pm\sqrt{r^2 - k^2}$$
$$x = h \pm \sqrt{r^2 - k^2}$$
$$x_1 = h + \sqrt{r^2 - k^2}$$
$$x_2 = h - \sqrt{r^2 - h^2}$$

We now compute the quantity $x_1x_2 - y_1y_2$:

$$x_1x_2 - y_1y_2 = (h + \sqrt{r^2 - k^2})(h - \sqrt{r^2 - h^2}) - (k + \sqrt{r^2 - h^2})(k - \sqrt{r^2 - h^2})$$

$$= \left(h^2 - (r^2 - k^2)\right) - \left(k^2 - (r^2 - h^2)\right)$$

$$= h^2 - r^2 + k^2 - k^2 + r^2 - h^2$$

$$= 0$$

81.   We must prove that $BC^2 = \frac{9}{5}(PA^2 + QA^2)$. Using the coordinates given in the hint, where $B(0,3b)$, $C(3c,0)$, $P(c,2b)$, and $Q(2c,b)$, we have:

$$BC^2 = (3c - 0)^2 + (0 - 3b)^2 = 9c^2 + 9b^2 = 9(b^2 + c^2)$$
$$PA^2 = (c - 0)^2 + (2b - 0)^2 = 4b^2 + c^2$$
$$QA^2 = (2c - 0)^2 + (b - 0)^2 = b^2 + 4c^2$$

So $\frac{9}{5}(PA^2 + QA^2) = \frac{9}{5}(4b^2 + c^2 + b^2 + 4c^2)$

$$= \frac{9}{5}(5b^2 + 5c^2)$$

$$= 9(b^2 + c^2)$$

$$= BC^2$$

83. (a) This is the result proved in exercise #48 (a) (section 3.4). We'll redo that. The slope of the radius from (0,0) to (x_1, y_1) is $\frac{y_1}{x_1}$, and so the perdendicular tangent line will have slope $-\frac{x_1}{y_1}$. Using this point in the point-slope formula:

$$y - y_1 = -\frac{x_1}{y_1}(x - x_1)$$
$$y_1 y - y_1{}^2 = -x_1 x + x_1{}^2$$
$$x_1 x + y_1 y = x_1{}^2 + y_1{}^2$$

But since (x_1, y_1) is a point on the circle, we have shown:
$$x_1 x + y_1 y = R^2$$

(b) Since this represents the equation of the tangent line, and since $(x,y) = (a,b)$ lies on that line, we have $x_1 a + y_1 b = R^2$

(c) We can repeat (a) using the point (x_2, y_2). Since it also passes through (a,b), we have $x_2 a + y_2 b = R^2$.

(d) Since $ax + by = R^2$ is a line, and parts (b) and (c) show that both (x_1, y_1) and (x_2, y_2) satisfy this equation, they must lie on the line.

85. Here $(x_0, y_0) = (1,2)$, $m = \frac{1}{2}$ and $b = -5$:

$$d = \frac{2 - \frac{1}{2}(1) - (-5)}{\sqrt{1 + (\frac{1}{2})^2}} = \frac{2 - \frac{1}{2} + 5}{\sqrt{1 + \frac{1}{4}}} = \frac{\frac{13}{2}}{\sqrt{\frac{5}{4}}} = \frac{13\sqrt{5}}{5}$$

87. Here $(x_0, y_0) = (-1, -3)$, $A = 2$, $B = 3$, and $C = -6$:

$$d = \frac{|2(-1) + 3(-3) + (-6)|}{\sqrt{2^2 + 3^3}} = \frac{|-2 - 9 - 6|}{\sqrt{13}} = \frac{17}{\sqrt{13}} = \frac{17\sqrt{13}}{13}$$

CHAPTER 4
FUNCTIONS

4.1 The Definition of a Function

1. (a) All real numbers, or $(-\infty, \infty)$

    (b) We must solve: $-5x + 1 \geq 0$
    $$-5x \geq -1$$
    $$x \leq \frac{1}{5}$$

    So the domain is $(-\infty, \frac{1}{5}]$.

    (c) We must solve: $|-5x + 1| > 0$
    Since $|-5x + 1| \geq 0$ already, we need to find when:
    $$-5x + 1 = 0$$
    $$-5x = -1$$
    $$x = \frac{1}{5}$$

    So the domain is all real numbers except $\frac{1}{5}$, or $(-\infty, \frac{1}{5}) \cup (\frac{1}{5}, \infty)$.

3.   (a)   We must exclude those values of x where: $x - 4 = 0$

$x = 4$

So the domain is all real numbers except 4, or $(-\infty, 4) \cup (4, \infty)$.

(b)   We must exclude those values of x where: $x^2 - 4 = 0$

$x^2 = 4$

$x = \pm 2$

So the domain is all real numbers except ±2, or

$(-\infty, -2) \cup (-2, 2) \cup (2, \infty)$.

(c)   We must solve: $\dfrac{x^2 + 4}{x^2 - 4} \geq 0$

$\dfrac{x^2 + 4}{(x - 2)(x + 2)} \geq 0$

Key numbers: ±2

A sign chart results in the following information:

$(-\infty, -2)$:   positive

$(-2, 2)$:   negative

$(2, \infty)$:   positive

So the domain is $(-\infty, -2) \cup (2, \infty)$.

5.   (a)   We must solve: $x^2 - 4x - 5 \geq 0$

$(x - 5)(x + 1) \geq 0$

Key numbers: 5, -1

A sign chart results in the following information:

$(-\infty, -1)$:   positive

$(-1, 5)$:   negative

$(5, \infty)$:   positive

So the domain is $(-\infty, -1] \cup [5, \infty)$.

(b)   We must solve $x^2 - 4x - 5 > 0$, which has the same solutions as in (a) but excluding the endpoints. So the domain is $(-\infty, -1) \cup (5, \infty)$.

(c)   There are no restrictions on $\sqrt[3]{x^2 - 4x - 5}$, so the domain is all real numbers, or $(-\infty, \infty)$.

7. (a) We solve for x: $y = \dfrac{x + 3}{x - 5}$

$$y(x - 5) = x + 3$$
$$yx - 5y = x + 3$$
$$yx - x = 5y + 3$$
$$x(y - 1) = 5y + 3$$
$$x = \dfrac{5y + 3}{y - 1}$$

We see that $y = 1$ will be excluded from the range. So the range is all real numbers except 1, or $(-\infty,1) \cup (1,\infty)$.

(b) We solve for x: $y = \dfrac{x - 5}{x + 3}$

$$y(x + 3) = x - 5$$
$$yx + 3y = x - 5$$
$$yx - x = -3y - 5$$
$$x(y - 1) = -3y - 5$$
$$x = \dfrac{-3y - 5}{y - 1}$$
$$x = \dfrac{3y + 5}{1 - y}$$

We see that $y = 1$ will be excluded from the range. So the range is all real numbers except 1, or $(-\infty,1) \cup (1,\infty)$.

9. (a) We solve for x: $y = x^2 + 4$

$$y - 4 = x^2$$
$$x = \pm\sqrt{y - 4}$$

We see that $y - 4 \geq 0$, and thus $y \geq 4$. So the range is $[4,\infty)$.

(b) We solve for x: $y = x^3 + 4$

$$y - 4 = x^3$$
$$x = \sqrt[3]{y - 4}$$

Since $\sqrt[3]{y - 4}$ has no restrictions, then the range is all real numbers, or $(-\infty,\infty)$.

11. f: YES; g: YES; F: YES; H: YES
h: NO, since h(x) = 1 and h(x) = 2, which violates the definition of a function.
G: NO, since G(y) has not been assigned a value.

13. (a) Range_f = { 1,2,3 }
          Range_g = { 2,3 }
          Range_F = { 1 }
          Range_H = { 1,2 }

     (b) Range_g = { i,j }
          Range_F = { i,j }
          Range_G = { k }

15. (a) $y = (x - 3)^2$
     (b) $y = x^2 - 3$
     (c) $y = (3x)^2$
     (d) $y = 3x^2$

17. (a) $f(1) = (1)^2 - 3(1) + 1 = 1 - 3 + 1 = -1$

     (b) $f(0) = (0)^2 - 3(0) + 1 = 0 - 0 + 1 = 1$

     (c) $f(-1) = (-1)^2 - 3(-1) + 1 = 1 + 3 + 1 = 5$

     (d) $f(3/2) = (3/2)^2 - 3(3/2) + 1 = 9/4 - 9/2 + 1 = -5/4$

     (e) $f(z) = (z)^2 - 3(z) + 1 = z^2 - 3z + 1$

     (f) $f(x + 1) = (x + 1)^2 - 3(x + 1) + 1$
            $= x^2 + 2x + 1 - 3x - 3 + 1$
            $= x^2 - x - 1$

     (g) $f(a + 1) = (a + 1)^2 - 3(a + 1) + 1$
            $= a^2 + 2a + 1 - 3a - 3 + 1$
            $= a^2 - a - 1$

     (h) $f(-x) = (-x)^2 - 3(-x) + 1 = x^2 + 3x + 1$

     (i) $|f(1)| = |-1| = 1$ from (a)

     (j) $f(\sqrt{3}) = (\sqrt{3})^2 - 3(\sqrt{3}) + 1 = 3 - 3\sqrt{3} + 1 = 4 - 3\sqrt{3}$

     (k) $f(1 + \sqrt{2}) = (1 + \sqrt{2})^2 - 3(1 + \sqrt{2}) + 1$
            $= 1 + 2\sqrt{2} + 2 - 3 - 3\sqrt{2} + 1$
            $= 1 - \sqrt{2}$

(l) $|1 - f(2)| = |-[(2)^2 - 3(2) + 1]|$
$= |1 - [4 - 6 + 1]|$
$= |1 - (-1)|$
$= |1 + 1|$
$= 2$

19. (a) $f(2x) = 3(2x)^2 = 3(4x^2) = 12x^2$

(b) $2f(x) = 2(3x^2) = 6x^2$

(c) $f(x^2) = 3(x^2)^2 = 3x^4$

(d) $[f(x)]^2 = (3x^2)^2 = 9x^4$

(e) $f(x/2) = 3(x/2)^2 - 3(x^2/4) = 3x^2/4$

(f) $f(x)/2 = 3x^2/2$

21. (a) $H(0) = 1 - 2(0)^2 = 1 - 0 = 1$

(b) $H(2) = 1 - 2(2)^2 = 1 - 2(4) = 1 - 8 = -7$

(c) $H(\sqrt{2}) = 1 - 2(\sqrt{2})^2 = 1 - 2(2) = 1 - 4 = -3$

(d) $H(5/6) = 1 - 2(5/6)^2 = 1 - 2(25/36) = 1 - 25/18 = -7/18$

(e) $H(x + 1) = 1 - 2(x + 1)^2$
$= 1 - 2(x^2 + 2x + 1)$
$= 1 - 2x^2 - 4x - 2$
$= -2x^2 - 4x - 1$

(f) $H(x + h) = 1 - 2(x + h)^2 = 1 - 2(x^2 + 2xh + h^2) = 1 - 2x^2 - 4xh - 2h^2$

(g) $H(x + h) - H(x) = (1 - 2x^2 - 4xh - 2h^2) - (1 - 2x^2)$ from (f)
$= 1 - 2x^2 - 4xh - 2h^2 - 1 + 2x^2$
$= -4xh - 2h^2$

(h) $\dfrac{H(x + h) - H(x)}{h} = \dfrac{-4xh - 2h^2}{h}$ from (g)

$= \dfrac{h(-4x - 2h)}{h}$

$= -4x - 2h$

23. (a) For the domain, we must exclude those values which make $x - 2 = 0$, or $x = 2$. So the domain is all real numbers except 2, or

$(-\infty,2) \cup (2,\infty)$. For the range, we solve for x:

$y = \dfrac{2x - 1}{x - 2}$

$y(x - 2) = 2x - 1$

$yx - 2y = 2x - 1$

$yx - 2x = 2y - 1$

$x(y - 2) = 2y - 1$

$x = \dfrac{2y - 1}{y - 2}$

Since the denominator cannot be zero, $y = 2$ is excluded. So the

range is all real numbers except 2, or $(-\infty,2) \cup (2,\infty)$.

(b) $R(0) = \dfrac{2(0) - 1}{0 - 2} = \dfrac{-1}{-2} = \dfrac{1}{2}$

(c) $R(1/2) = \dfrac{2(1/2) - 1}{1/2 - 2} = \dfrac{1 - 1}{-3/2} = 0$

(d) $R(-1) = \dfrac{2(-1) - 1}{-1 - 2} = \dfrac{-2 - 1}{-3} = \dfrac{-3}{-3} = 1$

(e) $R(x^2) = \dfrac{2(x^2) - 1}{x^2 - 2} = \dfrac{2x^2 - 1}{x^2 - 2}$

(f) $R(1/x) = \dfrac{2(1/x) - 1}{1/x - 2} = \dfrac{2/x - 1}{1/x - 2} = \dfrac{2 - x}{1 - 2x}$ by multiplying by $\dfrac{x}{x}$

(g) $R(a) = \dfrac{2a - 1}{a - 2}$

(h) $R(x - 1) = \dfrac{2(x - 1) - 1}{(x - 1) - 2} = \dfrac{2x - 2 - 1}{x - 3} = \dfrac{2x - 3}{x - 3}$

25. (a) $d(1) = -16(1)^2 + 96(1) = -16 + 96 = 80$

$d(3/2) = -16(3/2)^2 + 96(3/2) = -16(9/4) + 144 = 108$

$$d(2) = -16(2)^2 + 96(2) = -64 + 192 = 128$$
$$d(t_0) = -16t_0^2 + 96t_0$$

(b) We set $d(t) = 0$
$$-16t^2 + 96t = 0$$
$$-16t(t - 6) = 0$$
$$t = 0, 6$$

(c) We set $d(t) = 1$
$$-16t^2 + 96t = 1$$
$$16t^2 - 96t + 1 = 0$$
$$t = \frac{96 \pm \sqrt{(-96)^2 - 4(16)(1)}}{2(16)}$$
$$= \frac{96 \pm \sqrt{9216 - 64}}{32}$$
$$= \frac{96 \pm \sqrt{9152}}{32}$$
$$= \frac{96 \pm 8\sqrt{143}}{32}$$
$$= \frac{12 \pm \sqrt{143}}{4}$$

27. $g(3) = |3 - 4| = |-1| = 1$
$g(x + 4) = |x + 4 - 4| = |x|$

29. (a) $f(x + h) = (x + h)^2 = x^2 + 2xh + h^2$
So $\dfrac{f(x + h) - f(x)}{h} = \dfrac{(x^2 + 2xh + h^2) - (x^2)}{h}$
$$= \frac{2xh + h^2}{h}$$
$$= \frac{h(2x + h)}{h}$$
$$= 2x + h$$

(b) $f(x + h) = 2(x + h)^2 - 3(x + h) + 1$
$$= 2(x^2 + 2xh + h^2) - 3x - 3h + 1$$
$$= 2x^2 + 4xh + 2h^2 - 3x - 3h + 1$$

So $\dfrac{f(x + h) - f(x)}{h}$

$$= \dfrac{(2x^2 + 4xh + 2h^2 - 3x - 3h + 1) - (2x^2 - 3x + 1)}{h}$$

$$= \dfrac{2x^2 + 4xh + 2h^2 - 3x - 3h + 1 - 2x^2 + 3x - 1}{h}$$

$$= \dfrac{4xh + 2h^2 - 3h}{h}$$

$$= \dfrac{h(4x + 2h - 3)}{h}$$

$$= 4x + 2h - 3$$

(c) $f(x + h) = (x + h)^3 = x^3 + 3x^2h + 3xh^2 + h^3$

So $\dfrac{f(x + h) - f(x)}{h} = \dfrac{(x^3 + 3x^2h + 3xh^2 + h^3) - (x^3)}{h}$

$$= \dfrac{3x^2h + 3xh^2 + h^3}{h}$$

$$= \dfrac{h(3x^2 + 3xh + h^2)}{h}$$

$$= 3x^2 + 3xh + h^2$$

31. (a) $\dfrac{f(x) - f(a)}{x - a} = \dfrac{\dfrac{x}{x - 1} - \dfrac{a}{a - 1}}{x - a} \cdot \dfrac{(x - 1)(a - 1)}{(x - 1)(a - 1)}$

$$= \dfrac{x(a - 1) - a(x - 1)}{(x - a)(x - 1)(a - 1)}$$

$$= \dfrac{ax - x - ax + a}{(x - a)(x - 1)(a - 1)}$$

$$= \dfrac{-(x - a)}{(x - a)(x - 1)(a - 1)}$$

$$= \dfrac{-1}{(x - 1)(a - 1)}$$

(b)   Using our result from (a) with a = 3, we have:
$$\dfrac{f(x) - f(3)}{x - 3} = \dfrac{-1}{(x - 1)(3 - 1)} = \dfrac{-1}{2(x - 1)}$$

(c) $\dfrac{f(x + h) - f(x)}{h} = \dfrac{\dfrac{x + h}{x + h - 1} - \dfrac{x}{x - 1}}{h} \cdot \dfrac{(x - 1)(x + h - 1)}{(x - 1)(x + h - 1)}$

$$= \dfrac{(x + h)(x - 1) - x(x + h - 1)}{h(x - 1)(x + h - 1)}$$

$$= \frac{x^2 + hx - x - h - x^2 - xh + x}{h(x - 1)(x + h - 1)}$$

$$= \frac{-h}{h(x - 1)(x + h - 1)}$$

$$= \frac{-1}{(x - 1)(x + h - 1)}$$

(d) Using our result from (c) with $x = 3$, we have:

$$\frac{f(3 + h) - f(3)}{h} = \frac{-1}{(3 - 1)(3 + h - 1)} = \frac{-1}{2(2 + h)}$$

33. (a) We set $f(x_0) = g(x_0)$: $4x_0 - 3 = 8 - x_0$

$$5x_0 = 11, \text{ so } x_0 = \frac{11}{5}$$

(b) We set $f(x_0) = g(x_0)$: $x_0^2 - 4 = 4 - x_0^2$

$$2x_0^2 = 8$$

$$x_0^2 = 4$$

Taking roots: $x_0 = \pm 2$

$$x_0 = 2 \text{ or } x_0 = -2$$

(c) We set $f(x_0) = g(x_0)$: $x_0^2 = x_0^3$

$$x_0^3 - x_0^2 = 0$$

$$x_0^2(x_0 - 1) = 0$$

$$x_0 = 0 \text{ or } x_0 = 1$$

(d) We set $f(x_0) = g(x_0)$: $2x_0^2 - x_0 = 3$

$$2x_0^2 - x_0 - 3 = 0$$

$$(2x_0 - 3)(x_0 + 1) = 0$$

$$x_0 = \frac{3}{2} \text{ or } x_0 = -1$$

35. (a) $A(1) = 1000\left(1 + \frac{0.12}{4}\right)^{4(1)} = \$1125.51$

$A(0) = 1000\left(1 + \frac{0.12}{4}\right)^{4(0)} = \$1000.00$

So $A(1) - A(0) = 1125.51 - 1000.00 = \$125.51$

45. $f(x+y) = \dfrac{(x+y) - x}{(x+y) + y} = \dfrac{y}{x + 2y}$ and $f(x-y) = \dfrac{(x-y) - x}{(x-y) + y} = \dfrac{-y}{x}$

$\quad$ So $f(x+y) + f(x-y) = \dfrac{y}{x + 2y} - \dfrac{y}{x}$

$$= \dfrac{yx - y(x + 2y)}{x(x + 2y)}$$

$$= \dfrac{yx - yx - 2y^2}{x^2 + 2xy}$$

$$= \dfrac{-2y^2}{x^2 + 2xy}$$

47. $F\left(\dfrac{ax + b}{cx - a}\right) = \dfrac{a\left(\dfrac{ax + b}{cx - a}\right) + b}{c\left(\dfrac{ax + b}{cx - a}\right) - a}$

$$= \dfrac{a(ax + b) + b(cx - a)}{c(ax + b) - a(cx - a)} \quad \text{by multiplying by} \dfrac{cx - a}{cx - a}$$

$$= \dfrac{a^2x + ab + bcx - ab}{acx + bc - acx + a^2}$$

$$= \dfrac{a^2x + bcx}{a^2 + bc}$$

$$= \dfrac{x(a^2 + bc)}{a^2 + bc}$$

$$= x$$

49. $g(1) = (1)^2 - 3(1)k - 4 = 1 - 3k - 4 = -3k - 3$, so if $g(1) = -2$ we have:

$$-3k - 3 = -2$$
$$-3k = 1$$
$$k = -\dfrac{1}{3}$$

51. (a) $L(1) = 0$, since $2^0 = 1$

$\quad$ (b) $L(2) = 1$, since $2^1 = 1$

$\quad$ (c) $L(4) = 2$, since $2^2 = 4$

$\quad$ (d) $L(64) = 6$, since $2^6 = 64$

$\quad$ (e) $L(1/2) = -1$, since $2^{-1} = \dfrac{1}{2}$

(f) $L(1/4) = -2$, since $2^{-2} = \dfrac{1}{4}$

(g) $L(1/64) = -6$, since $2^{-6} = \dfrac{1}{64}$

(h) $L(\sqrt{2}) = \dfrac{1}{2}$, since $2^{1/2} = \sqrt{2}$

53.   Actually, we already know the answer to this question. Since $\dfrac{-b + \sqrt{b^2 - 4ac}}{2a}$ is one of the roots to the quadratic equation $q(x) = 0$, we know $q\left(\dfrac{-b + \sqrt{b^2 - 4ac}}{2a}\right) = 0$. Let's check our answer manually:

$$q\left(\dfrac{-b + \sqrt{b^2 - 4ac}}{2a}\right)$$

$$= a\left(\dfrac{-b + \sqrt{b^2 - 4ac}}{2a}\right)^2 + b\left(\dfrac{-b + \sqrt{b^2 - 4ac}}{2a}\right) + c$$

$$= a\left(\dfrac{b^2 - 2b\sqrt{b^2 - 4ac} + b^2 - 4ac}{4a^2}\right) + \left(\dfrac{-b^2 + b\sqrt{b^2 - 4ac}}{2a}\right) + c$$

$$= \dfrac{2b^2 - 4ac - 2b\sqrt{b^2 - 4ac}}{4a} + \dfrac{-b^2 + b\sqrt{b^2 - 4ac}}{2a} + c$$

$$= \dfrac{b^2 - 2ac - b\sqrt{b^2 - 4ac} - b^2 + b\sqrt{b^2 - 4ac}}{2a} + c$$

$$= \dfrac{-2ac}{2a} + c$$

$$= -c + c$$

$$= 0 \quad \text{It checks!}$$

55.   (a) $f[f(x)] = f\left(\dfrac{3x - 4}{x - 3}\right)$

$$= \dfrac{3\left(\dfrac{3x - 4}{x - 3}\right) - 4}{\left(\dfrac{3x - 4}{x - 3}\right) - 3}$$

$$= \dfrac{3(3x - 4) - 4(x - 3)}{(3x - 4) - 3(x - 3)} \qquad \text{multiplying by } \dfrac{x - 3}{x - 3}$$

$$= \dfrac{9x - 12 - 4x + 12}{3x - 4 - 3x + 9}$$

$$= \frac{5x}{5}$$
$$= x$$

(b)   Since $f[f(x)] = x$, then $f[f(22/7)] = \frac{22}{7}$

57. The problem here is the word "nearest." $G(4) = 3$, but also $G(4) = 5$, since
     both 3 and 5 are equally "near" 4. So G is not a function, since it assigns
     more than one value to $x = 4$. To alter the definition of G, one could define G
     to assign the closest prime number less than or equal to x (or, for that matter,
     greater than or equal to x). This would provide G with a way of "deciding"
     between 3 and 5, in the previous example. Why do we need the "or equal to"
     portion of the definition? [Hint: How would you define G(5) otherwise?]

59. $P(1) = (1)^2 - 1 + 41 = 41$
       $P(2) = (2)^2 - 2 + 41 = 43$
       $P(3) = (3)^2 - 3 + 41 = 47$
       $P(4) = (4)^2 - 4 + 41 = 53$
     Yes, although one has to search quite a while:
       $P(41) = (41)^2 - (41) + 41$
              $= (41)(41 - 1 + 1)$
              $= (41)(41)$, which is not prime.
     This is the first such number.

4.2 The Graph of a Function

1.   (a)   positive

      (b) $f(-2) = 4; f(1) = 1; f(2) = 2; f(3) = 0$

      (c) $f(2)$, since $f(2) > 0$ and $f(4) < 0$

      (d) $f(4) - f(1) = -2 - 1 = -3$

      (e) $|f(4) - f(1)| = |-3| = 3$

      (f)   Domain $= [-2,4]$; Range $= [-2,4]$

3.   (a) $f(-2) = 0$ and $g(-2) = 1$, so $g(-2)$ is larger.

      (b) $f(0) - g(0) = 2 - (-3) = 2 + 3 = 5$

(c)   f(1) - g(1) = 1 - (-1) = 2
       f(2) - g(2) =   1 - 0   = 1
       f(3) - g(3) =   4 - 1   = 3
       So f(2) - g(2) is the smallest.

(d)   Since f(1) = 1, we see that g(x) = 1 when x = -2 or x = 3

(e)   Since (3,4) is a point on the graph of f, then 4 is in the range of f.

5.   (a)   f(3) = 3; f(π) = 3; f(39/10) = 3; f(-3/2) = -2

      (b)   the integers

7.   (a)   f(x) = x^3

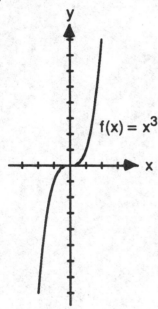

$f(x) = x^3$

(b) $g(x) = |x^3|$

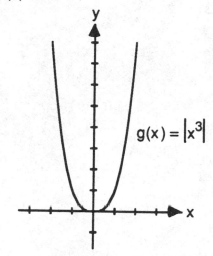

$g(x) = |x^3|$

(c) $h(x) = x^3 + 1$

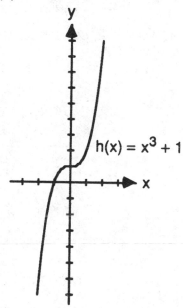

$h(x) = x^3 + 1$

(d) $H(x) = |x^3 + 1|$

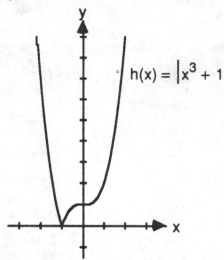

$$h(x) = |x^3 + 1|$$

9.   (a)   [-2,6]

(b) $G(0) = -1$; $G(2) = 5$; $G(3) = 6$; $G(7) = -2$; $G(9) = 2$, so in increasing size, the order is: $G(7) < G(0) < G(9) < G(2) < G(3)$

(c)   The highest point is (3,6)

(d)   The lowest point is (7,-2)

11.   (a)   yes

(b)   no

(c)   no

(d)   yes

13.   The slope is:
$$m = \frac{f(4) - f(3)}{4 - 3} = \frac{4^2 - 3^2}{1} = \frac{16 - 9}{1} = 7$$

We draw the graph:

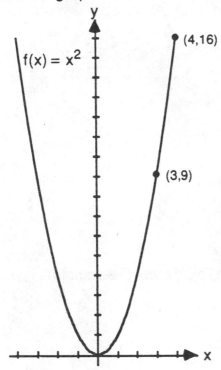

$f(x) = x^2$

(4,16)

(3,9)

15. We find the two slopes:

$$m_1 = \frac{T(4) - T(1)}{4 - 1} \qquad m_2 = \frac{T(9) - T(4)}{9 - 4}$$

$$= \frac{\sqrt{4} - \sqrt{1}}{3} \qquad = \frac{\sqrt{9} - \sqrt{4}}{5}$$

$$= \frac{2 - 1}{3} \qquad = \frac{3 - 2}{5}$$

$$= \frac{1}{3} \qquad = \frac{1}{5}$$

Since $m_1 > m_2$, then the line between $(1, T(1))$ and $(4, T(4))$ has the larger slope.

17.   (a) $k(x) = \sqrt{1 - x^2}$,   [0,1]

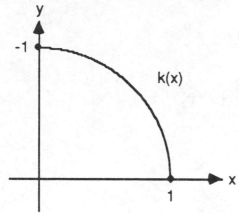

(b) $m(x) = \sqrt{1 - x^2}$,   (0,1)

This graph will be the same as in (a), except the points (0,1) and (1,0) will be excluded.

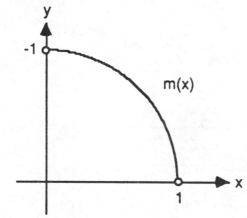

(c)   We graph n(x) with the required domain:

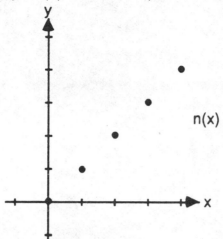

(d)   We graph z(x) on the required domain:

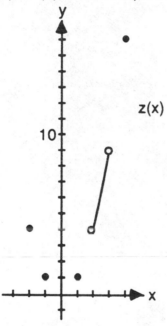

19. We graph f(x):

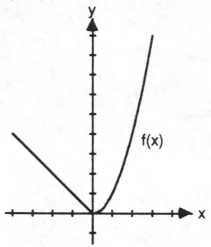

21. We graph A(x):

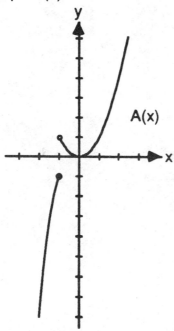

23. We graph C(x):

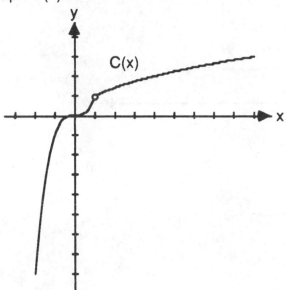

25. (a)   We graph g(x):

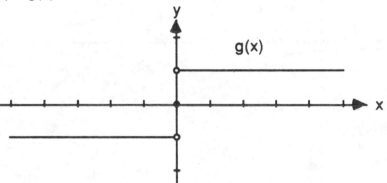

(b)   We graph G(x):

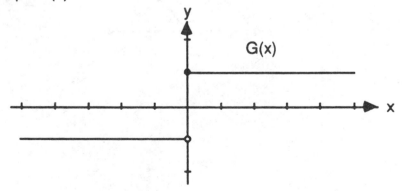

27.   We graph V(x):

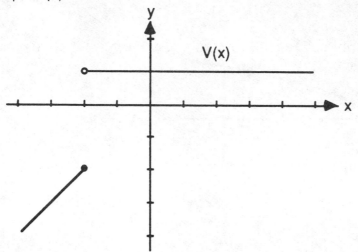

29.   We graph f(x):

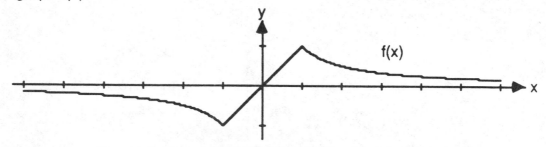

31.   We graph y(x):

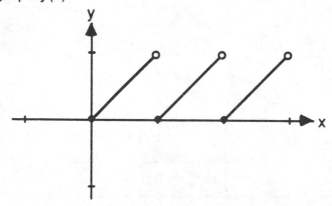

33. (a)   Note that, for $x \neq -5$, we have:

$$\frac{x^2 - 25}{x + 5} = \frac{(x + 5)(x - 5)}{x + 5} = x - 5$$

That makes it much easier to graph. The domain is all real numbers

except -5, or $(-\infty,-5) \cup (-5,\infty)$:

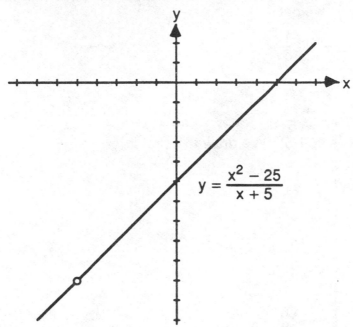

$$y = \frac{x^2 - 25}{x + 5}$$

(b)   This just adds the point (-5,-10) to the graph:

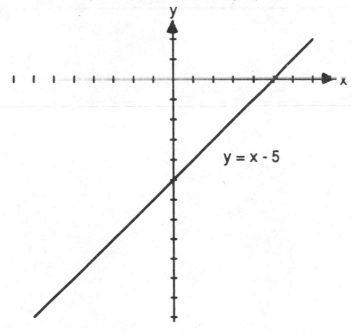

$$y = x - 5$$

35. Let the coordinates of T be $(t, \frac{1}{t})$. Then:

$$m = \frac{\frac{1}{t} - 1}{t - 1} = -\frac{1}{5}$$

Multiplying by $\frac{t}{t}$, we get:

$$\frac{1 - t}{t(t - 1)} = -\frac{1}{5}$$

$$\frac{-1}{t} = \frac{-1}{5}$$

$$-t = -5$$

$$t = 5$$

So the point T is (5,1/5). We draw the sketch:

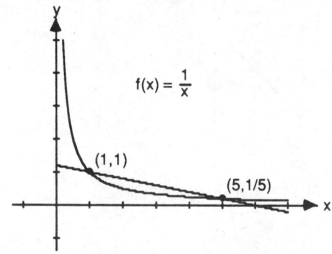

37. p (x) = [2x]

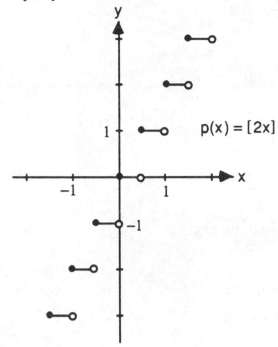

p(x) = [2x]

39. r (x) = x - [x]

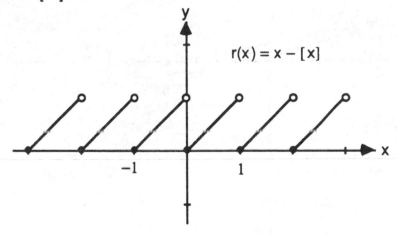

r(x) = x − [x]

41. $f(x) = \left([x] \right)^2$

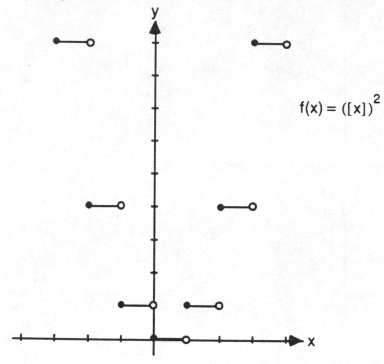

$$f(x) = ([x])^2$$

43. (a) $y = -[-x]$

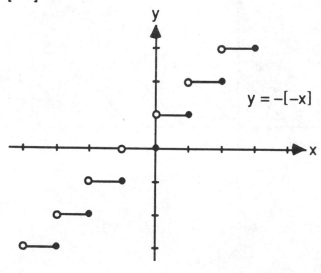

$$y = -[-x]$$

(b)   Notice that f(x) has the same graph as in (a):

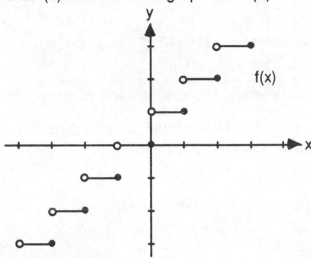

45.   B is the point $(x + h, f(x + h))$
Since A is $(x, f(x))$, then the slope is:
$$m = \frac{f(x + h) - f(x)}{h}$$

47.   (a)   We can see from the figure that the slope of the line segment joining
$(a, f(a))$ and $(b, f(b))$ is $m = \dfrac{f(b) - f(a)}{b - a}$:

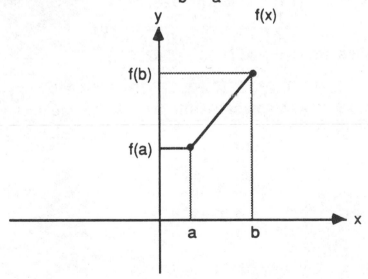

(b)   We compute the slope between (0,0) and (1,1):

$$m = \frac{1 - 0}{1 - 0} = \frac{1}{1} = 1$$

We compute the slope between (10,100) and (11,121):

$$m = \frac{121 - 100}{11 - 10} = \frac{21}{1} = 21$$

Clearly the average rate of change between 10 and 11 is larger.

(c)   We compute the average rate of change for each function:

$f(x) = x^2$, the points are (3,9) and (4,16):

$$m = \frac{16 - 9}{4 - 3} = \frac{7}{1} = 7$$

$g(x) = x^3$, the points are (3,27) and (4,64):

$$m = \frac{64 - 27}{4 - 3} = \frac{37}{1} = 37$$

$h(x) = \frac{1}{x}$, the points are (3,1/3) and (4,1/4):

$$m = \frac{1/4 - 1/3}{4 - 3} = \frac{-1/12}{1} = -\frac{1}{12}$$

So $g(x) = x^3$ has the largest average rate of change between 3 and 4.

(d)   (i)   Points are (1,1) and (1.1,1.21):

$$m = \frac{1.21 - 1}{1.1 - 1} = \frac{0.21}{0.1} = 2.1$$

(ii)   Points are (1,1) and (1.01,1.0201):

$$m = \frac{1.0201 - 1}{1.01 - 1} = \frac{0.0201}{0.01} = 2.01$$

(iii) Points are (1,1) and (1.001,1.002001):

$$m = \frac{1.002001 - 1}{1.001 - 1} = \frac{0.002001}{0.001} = 2.001$$

It appears that, as b approaches 1, the average rate of change is approaching 2.

49. (a) $f(2) - f(1) = 16(2)^2 - 16(1)^2$
            $= 16(4) - 16(1)$
            $= 64 - 16$
            $= 48 \text{ ft}$

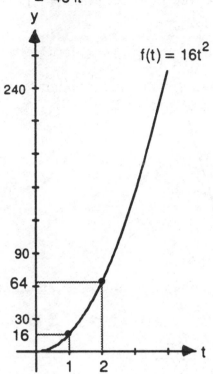

(b)   f (3) - f (2) = $16(3)^2 - 16(2)^2$
                       $= 16 (9) - 16 (4)$
                       $= 144 - 64$
                       $= 80$ ft

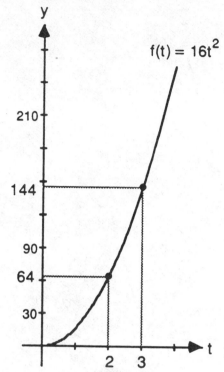

(c)   Avg. vel. $= \dfrac{f(3) - f(1)}{3 - 1}$

$= \dfrac{144 - 16}{3 - 1}$

$= \dfrac{128}{2}$

$= 64$ ft/sec

This is the same as the slope of the line joining the points $(1, f(1))$ and $(3, f(3))$.

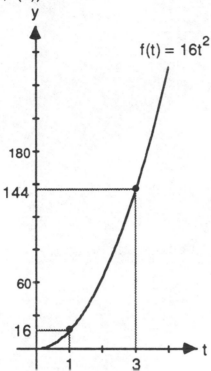

$f(t) = 16t^2$

(d)   (i) $v_{avg} = \dfrac{f(1.1) - f(1)}{1.1 - 1} = \dfrac{19.36 - 16}{0.1} = \dfrac{3.36}{0.1} = 33.6$

(ii) $v_{avg} = \dfrac{f(1.001) - f(1)}{1.001 - 1} = \dfrac{16.032016 - 16}{0.001} = 32.016$

(iii) $v_{avg} = \dfrac{f(1.00001) - f(1)}{1.00001 - 1} = \dfrac{16.0003200016 - 16}{0.00001} = 32.00016$

As b approaches 1, the average velocity seems to be approaching 32 ft/sec. Case (iii) gives the clearest indication of what these values are approaching.

4.3 Techniques in Graphing

1. $y = x^2 - 3$
      This is $y = x^2$ displaced down 3 units. See graph:

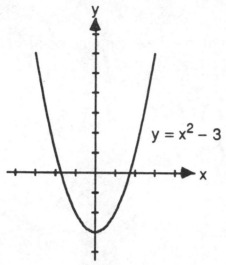

$y = x^2 - 3$

3. $y = (x + 4)^2$
      This is $y = x^2$ displaced 4 units to the left. See graph:

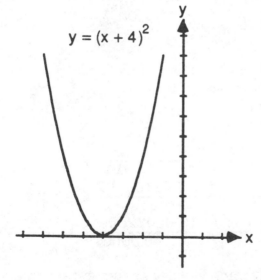

$y = (x + 4)^2$

5. $y = (x - 4)^2$
      This is $y = x^2$ displaced 4 units to the right. See graph:

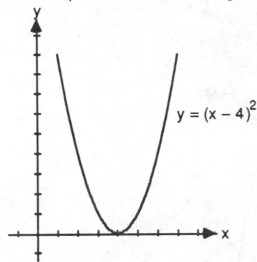

7. $y = -x^2$
      This is $y = x^2$ reflected across the x-axis. See graph:

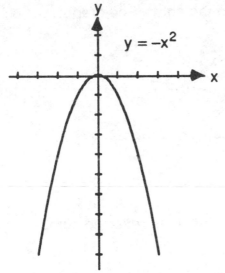

9. $y = -(x - 3)^2$
This is $y = x^2$ displaced 3 units to the right, then reflected across the x-axis.
See graph:

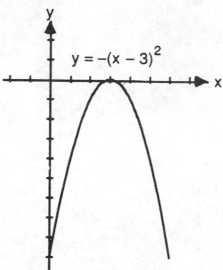

11. $y = \sqrt{x - 3}$
This is $y = \sqrt{x}$ displaced 3 units to the right. See graph:

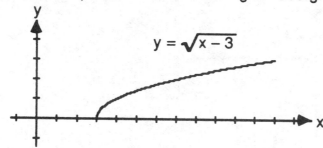

13. $y = -\sqrt{x + 1}$
This is $y = \sqrt{x}$ displaced 1 unit to the left, then reflected across the x-axis.
See graph:

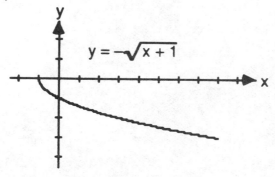

15. $y = \dfrac{1}{x + 2} + 2$

This is $y = \dfrac{1}{x}$ displaced 2 units to the left and 2 units up. See graph:

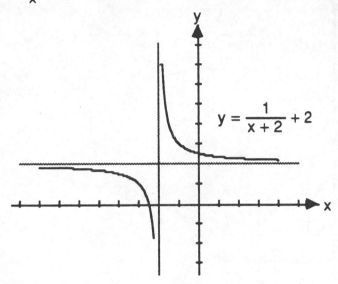

17. $y = (x - 2)^3$

This is $y = x^3$ displaced 2 units to the right. See graph:

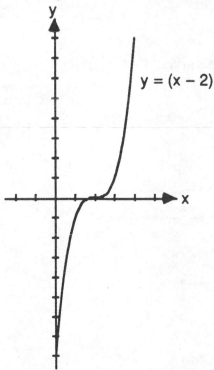

19. $y = -x^3 + 4$
This is $y = x^3$ reflected across the x-axis, then displaced 4 units up. See graph:

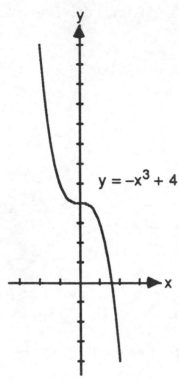

$y = -x^3 + 4$

21. $y = [-x]$
This is $y = [x]$ reflected across the y-axis. See graph:

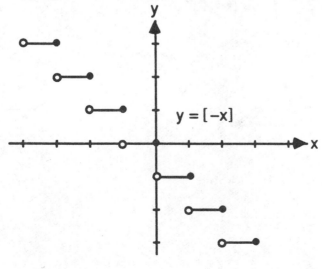

$y = [-x]$

23. y = -[-x]
     This is y = [x] reflected across the y-axis, then reflected across the x-axis.
     See graph:

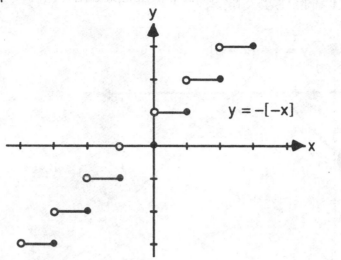

25. y = f(x - 5) = |x - 5|
     This is y = |x| displaced 5 units to the right. See graph:

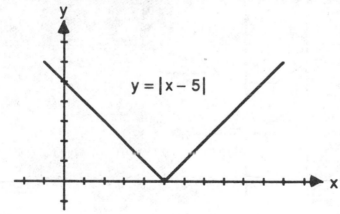

27. $y = 1 - f(x - 5) = 1 - |x - 5|$

This is $y = |x|$ displaced 5 units to the right, then reflected across the x-axis, then displaced up 1 unit. See graph:

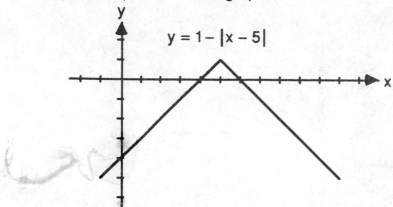

29. $y = F(x + 3) = \dfrac{1}{x + 3}$

This is $y = \dfrac{1}{x}$ displaced 3 units to the left. See graph:

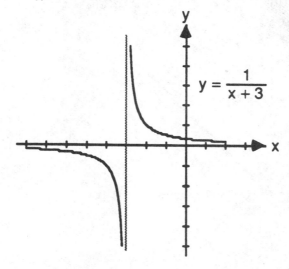

31. $y = -F(x + 3) = \dfrac{-1}{x + 3}$

This is $y = \dfrac{1}{x}$ displaced 3 units to the left and reflected across the x-axis.

See graph:

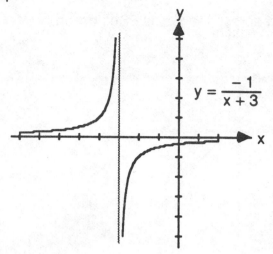

$$y = \frac{-1}{x + 3}$$

33. $y = g(x - 2) = \sqrt{1 - (x - 2)^2}$

This is $y = \sqrt{1 - x^2}$ displaced 2 units to the right. See graph:

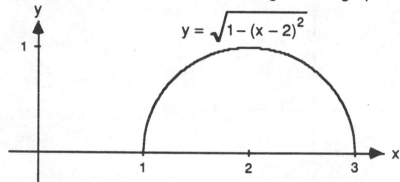

$$y = \sqrt{1 - (x - 2)^2}$$

35. $y = 1 - g(x - 2) = 1 - \sqrt{1 - (x - 2)^2}$

This is $y = \sqrt{1 - x^2}$ displaced 2 units to the right, reflected across the x-axis, and displaced up 1 unit. See graph:

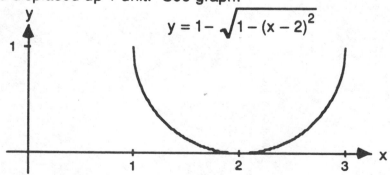

$$y = 1 - \sqrt{1 - (x - 2)^2}$$

(b) $A(10) = 1000\left(1 + \dfrac{0.12}{4}\right)^{4(10)} = \$3262.04$

   $A(9) = 1000\left(1 + \dfrac{0.12}{4}\right)^{4(9)} = \$2898.28$

   So $A(10) - A(9) = 3262.04 - 2898.28 = \$363.76$

37. (a)   We fill in the table:

n	2	3	4	5	6	7	8
g(n)	1.4142	1.4422	1.4142	1.3797	1.3480	1.3205	1.2968

   (b) $g(15) = 1.19786$ and $g(14) = 1.20744$, so 15 is the smallest natural number n such that $g(n) < 1.2$

39. (a) $f(a) = \dfrac{a - a}{a + a} = \dfrac{0}{2a} = 0$

   $f(2a) = \dfrac{2a - a}{2a + a} = \dfrac{a}{3a} = \dfrac{1}{3}$

   $f(3a) = \dfrac{3a - a}{3a + a} = \dfrac{2a}{4a} = \dfrac{1}{2}$

   So $f(3a) \neq f(a) + f(2a)$, since $\dfrac{1}{2} \neq 0 + \dfrac{1}{3}$

   (b) $f(5a) = \dfrac{5a - a}{5a + a} = \dfrac{4a}{6a} = \dfrac{2}{3}$

   So $f(5a) = 2\left(\dfrac{1}{3}\right) = 2f(2a)$

41. $\phi(y^2) = 2(y^2) - 3 = 2y^2 - 3$

   $[\phi(y)]^2 = (2y - 3)^2 = 4y^2 - 12y + 9$

   So $\phi(y^2) \neq [\phi(y)]^2$

43. $f(ax + b) = 2(ax + b) + 3 = 2ax + 2b + 3$

   We set $f(ax + b) = x$: $2ax + 2b + 3 = x$

   Equating constants, we have $2ax = x$ and $2b + 3 = 0$

   $2a = 1$ $2b = -3$

   $a = \dfrac{1}{2}$ $b = -\dfrac{3}{2}$

   So $a = \dfrac{1}{2}$ and $b = -\dfrac{3}{2}$

37. (a)   y = - f (x)
           This is y = f (x) reflected across the x-axis. See graph:

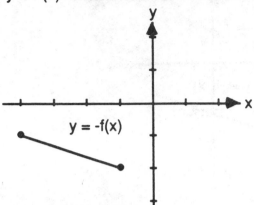

     (b)   y = f (-x)
           This is y = f (x) reflected across the y-axis. See graph:

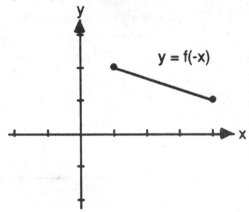

     (c)   y = - f (-x)
           This is y = f (x) reflected across the y-axis and reflected across the
           x-axis. See graph:

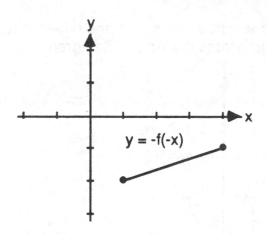

y = -f(-x)

39. (a)   y = g (-x)
     This is y = g (x) reflected across the y-axis. See graph:

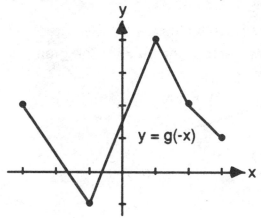

y = g(-x)

(b)   y = - g (x)
     This is y = g (x) reflected across the x-axis. See graph:

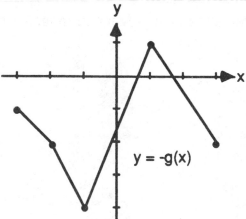

y = -g(x)

(c) $y = -g(-x)$
This is $y = g(x)$ reflected across the y-axis and reflected across the x-axis. See graph:

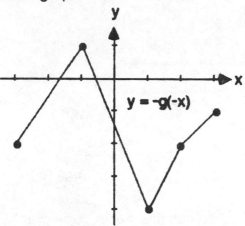

41.   (a) $y = 10^{-x}$
This is $y = 10^x$ reflected across the y-axis. See graph:

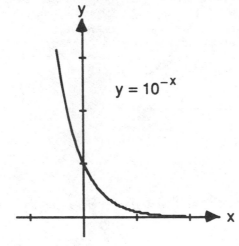

(b) $y = -10^x$

This is $y = 10^x$ reflected across the x-axis. See graph:

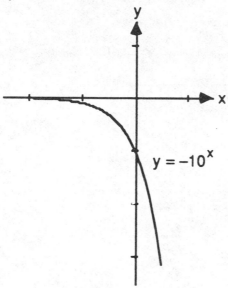

(c) $y = -10^{-x}$

This is $y = 10^x$ reflected across the y-axis and reflected across the x-axis. See graph:

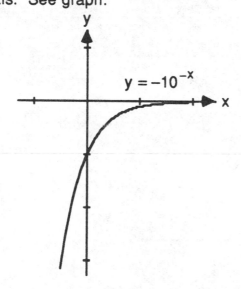

(d) $y = 10^{x-1}$

This is $y = 10^x$ displaced 1 unit to the right. See graph:

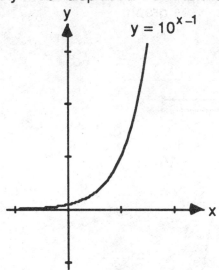

(e) $y = 10^x + 1$

This is $y = 10^x$ displaced up 1 unit. See graph:

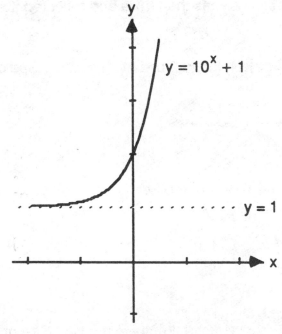

(f) $y = -10^{x-1} - 1$

This is $y = 10^x$ displaced to the right 1 unit, reflected across the x-axis, then displaced down 1 unit. See graph:

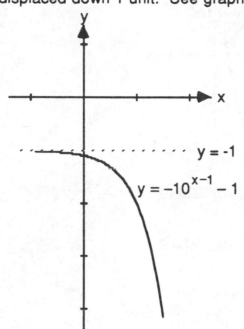

43. (a) $|x - 2| + |y| = 2$

This is $|x| + |y| = 2$ displaced 2 units to the right. See graph:

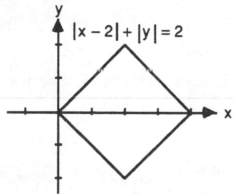

(b) $|x + 2| + |y| = 2$

This is $|x| + |y| = 2$ displaced 2 units to the left. See graph:

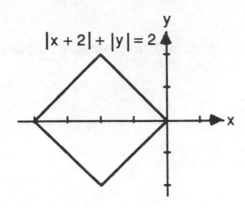

$|x + 2| + |y| = 2$

(c) $|x| + |y - 2| = 2$
This is $|x| + |y| = 2$ displaced 2 units up. See graph:

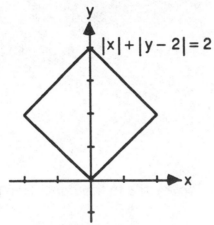

$|x| + |y - 2| = 2$

(d) $|x| + |y + 2| = 2$
This is $|x| + |y| = 2$ displaced 2 units down. See graph:

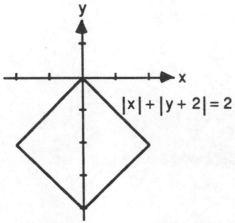

$|x| + |y + 2| = 2$

(e) $|x - 2| + |y + 2| = 2$

This is $|x| + |y| = 2$ displaced 2 units to the right and 2 units down.
See graph:

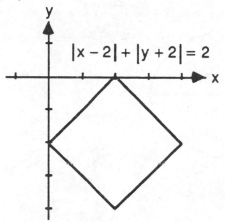

$$|x - 2| + |y + 2| = 2$$

(f) $|x + 2| + |y + 2| = 2$

This is $|x| + |y| = 2$ displaced 2 units to the left and 2 units down.
See graph:

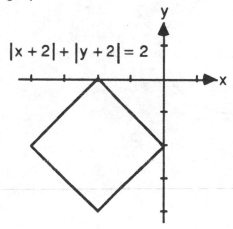

$$|x + 2| + |y + 2| = 2$$

45. (a) $4(x - 1)^2 + 9y^2 = 36$
         This is $4x^2 + 9y^2 = 36$ displaced 1 unit to the right. See graph:

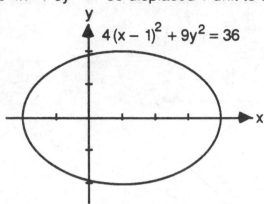

   (b) $4x^2 + 9(y - 1)^2 = 36$
         This is $4x^2 + 9y^2 = 36$ displaced 1 unit up. See graph:

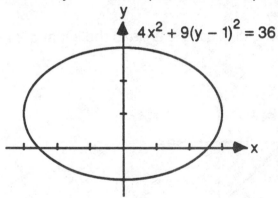

   (c) $4(x + 1)^2 + 9(y + 1)^2 = 36$
         This is $4x^2 + 9y^2 = 36$ displaced 1 unit to the left and 1 unit down.
         See graph:

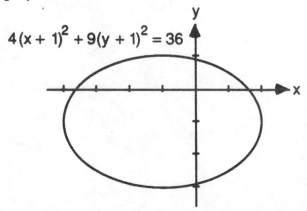

(d) $4(x-1)^2 + 9(y-1)^2 = 36$

This is $4x^2 + 9y^2 = 36$ displaced 1 unit to the right and 1 unit up. See graph:

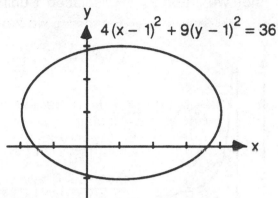

47. (a) $(a+3, b)$, since $f(a+3-3) = f(a) = b$

(b) $(a, b-3)$, since $f(a) - 3 = b - 3$

(c) $(a+3, b-3)$, since $f(a+3-3) - 3 = f(a) - 3 = b - 3$

(d) $(a, -b)$, since $-f(a) = -b$

(e) $(-a, b)$, since $f(-(-a)) = f(a) = b$

(f) $(-a, -b)$, since $-f(-(a)) = -f(a) = -b$

49. We work from the right-hand side of the equality:

$$\frac{1}{x-1} + 1 = \frac{1+x-1}{x-1} = \frac{x}{x-1}$$

Since $g(x) = \frac{1}{x-1} + 1$, then we graph $y = \frac{1}{x}$ displaced 1 unit to the right and 1 unit up. See graph:

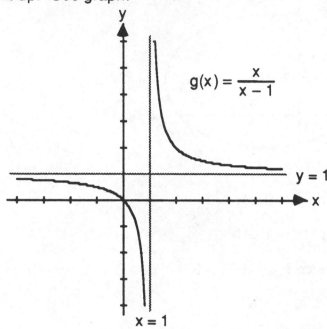

51. We work from the right-hand side of the equality:

$$(x-2)^3 - 1 = x^3 - 6x^2 + 12x - 8 - 1 = x^3 - 6x^2 + 12x - 9$$

Since $y = (x-2)^3 - 1$, then we graph $y = x^3$ displaced 2 units to the right and 1 unit down. See graph:

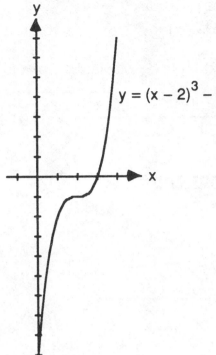

$$y = (x - 2)^3 - 1$$

53. We rationalize the denominator (which is valid for $0 < |x| \leq 1$):

$$\frac{x^2}{1 - \sqrt{1 - x^2}} \cdot \frac{1 + \sqrt{1 - x^2}}{1 + \sqrt{1 - x^2}} = \frac{x^2\left(1 + \sqrt{1 - x^2}\right)}{1 - 1 + x^2}$$

$$= \frac{x^2\left(1 + \sqrt{1 - x^2}\right)}{x^2}$$

$$= 1 + \sqrt{1 - x^2}$$

Now, since $0 \leq \sqrt{1 - x^2} < 1$, then $1 \leq 1 + \sqrt{1 - x^2} < 2$. So the range is $[1,2)$.

55. (a) Call $y = f(x)$. We replace x by -x and y by -y:

$$-y = f(-x)$$
$$-y = -f(x) \quad \text{since } f(-x) = -f(x)$$
$$y = f(x)$$

So the resulting equation is identical to the original equation, and thus the graph of $y = f(x)$ is symmetric about the origin.

(b)   (i) $f(-x) \cong (-x)^3 = -x^3 = -f(x)$

       (ii) $f(-x) = -2(-x)^5 + 4(-x)^3 - (-x)$

                  $= 2x^5 - 4x^3 + x$

                  $= -(-2x^5 + 4x^3 - x)$

                  $= -f(x)$

       (iii) $f(-x) = \dfrac{|-x|}{(-x) + (-x)^7} = \dfrac{|x|}{-x - x^7} = -\dfrac{|x|}{x + x^7} = -f(x)$

4.4 Methods of Combining Functions

1.   (a) $(f + g)(x) = f(x) + g(x)$

                      $= (2x - 1) + (x^2 - 3x - 6)$

                      $= x^2 - x - 7$

      (b) $(f - g)(x) = f(x) - g(x)$

                      $= (2x - 1) - (x^2 - 3x - 6)$

                      $= -x^2 + 5x + 5$

      (c) $(f - g)(0) = -(0)^2 + 5(0) + 5$

                      $= 0 + 0 + 5$

                      $= 5$

3.   (a) $(m - f)(x) = m(x) - f(x)$

                      $= (x^2 - 9) - (2x - 1)$

                      $= x^2 - 9 - 2x + 1$

                      $= x^2 - 2x - 8$

      (b) $(f - m)(x) = f(x) - m(x)$

                      $= (2x - 1) - (x^2 - 9)$

                      $= 2x - 1 - x^2 + 9$

                      $= -x^2 + 2x + 8$

5.   (a) $(fk)(x) = f(x) k(x)$

                    $= (2x - 1)(2)$

                    $= 4x - 2$

      (b) $(kf)(x) = k(x) f(x)$

                    $= 2(2x - 1)$

                    $= 4x - 2$

(c) $(fk)(1) - (kf)(2)$ $= [4(1) - 2] - [4(2) - 2]$
$= 2 - 6$
$= -4$

7.   (a) $\dfrac{f}{m}(x) - \dfrac{m}{f}(x) = \dfrac{f(x)}{m(x)} - \dfrac{m(x)}{f(x)}$

$= \dfrac{[f(x)]^2 - [m(x)]^2}{f(x)m(x)}$

$= \dfrac{(2x - 1)^2 - (x^2 - 9)^2}{(x^2 - 9)(2x - 1)}$

$= \dfrac{(4x^2 - 4x + 1) - (x^4 - 18x^2 + 81)}{2x^3 - x^2 - 18x + 9}$

$= \dfrac{-x^4 + 22x^2 - 4x - 80}{2x^3 - x^2 - 18x + 9}$

(b) $\dfrac{f}{m}(0) - \dfrac{m}{f}(0) = \dfrac{-0^4 + 22(0)^2 - 4(0) - 80}{2(0)^3 - 0^2 - 18(0) + 9} = -\dfrac{80}{9}$

9.   (a) $[m(k - h)](x) = m(x) [k(x) - h(x)]$
$= (x^2 - 9)(2 - x^3)$
$= 2x^2 - 18 - x^5 + 9x^3$
$= -x^5 + 9x^3 + 2x^2 - 18$

(b) $(mk)(x) - (mh)(x) = m(x) k(x) - m(x) h(x)$
$= (x^2 - 9)(2) - (x^2 - 9)(x^3)$
$= 2x^2 - 18 - x^5 + 9x^3$
$= -x^5 + 9x^3 + 2x^2 - 18$

(c) $(mk)(-1) - (mh)(-1) = -(-1)^5 + 9(-1)^3 + 2(-1)^2 - 18$
$= -(-1) + 9(-1) + 2(1) - 18$
$= 1 - 9 + 2 - 18$
$= -24$

11.   (a) $(f \circ g)(x) = f[g(x)]$
$= f(-2x - 5)$
$= 3(-2x - 5) + 1$
$= -6x - 15 + 1$
$= -6x - 14$

(b) $(f \circ g)(10) = -6(10) - 14 = -60 - 14 = -74$

(c) $(g \circ f)(x) = g[f(x)]$
$= g(3x + 1)$

$$= -2(3x + 1) - 5$$
$$= -6x - 2 - 5$$
$$= -6x - 7$$

(d) $(g \circ f)(10) = -6(10) - 7 = -60 - 7 = -67$

13.   (a) $(f \circ g)(x) = f[g(x)]$
$$= f(1 + x)$$
$$= 1 - (1 + x)$$
$$= 1 - 1 - x$$
$$= -x$$
$(f \circ g)(-2) = -(-2) = 2$
$(g \circ f)(x) = g[f(x)]$
$$= g(1 - x)$$
$$= 1 + (1 - x)$$
$$= 2 - x$$
$(g \circ f)(-2) = 2 - (-2) = 2 + 2 = 4$

(b) $(f \circ g)(x) = f[g(x)]$
$$= f(2 - 3x)$$
$$= (2 - 3x)^2 - 3(2 - 3x) - 4$$
$$= 4 - 12x + 9x^2 - 6 + 9x - 4$$
$$= 9x^2 - 3x - 6$$
$(f \circ g)(-2) = 9(-2)^2 - 3(-2) - 6 = 36 + 6 - 6 = 36$
$(g \circ f)(x) = g[f(x)]$
$$= g(x^2 - 3x - 4)$$
$$= 2 - 3(x^2 - 3x - 4)$$
$$= 2 - 3x^2 + 9x + 12$$
$$= -3x^2 + 9x + 14$$
$(g \circ f)(-2) = -3(-2)^2 + 9(-2) + 14 = -12 - 18 + 14 = -16$

(c) $(f \circ g)(x) = f[g(x)]$
$$= f(1 - x^4)$$
$$= \frac{1 - x^4}{3}$$
$(f \circ g)(-2) = \dfrac{1 - (-2)^4}{3} = \dfrac{1 - 16}{3} = \dfrac{-15}{3} = -5$

$$(g \circ f)(x) = g[f(x)]$$

$$= g\left(\frac{x}{3}\right)$$

$$= 1 - \left(\frac{x}{3}\right)^4$$

$$= 1 - \frac{x^4}{81}$$

$$(g \circ f)(-2) = 1 - \frac{(-2)^4}{81} = 1 - \frac{16}{81} = \frac{65}{81}$$

(d) $(f \circ g)(x) = f[g(x)]$

$$= f(x^2 + 1)$$

$$= 2^{x^2+1}$$

$$(f \circ g)(-2) = 2^{(-2)^2+1} = 2^{4+1} = 2^5 = 32$$

$$(g \circ f)(x) = g[f(x)]$$

$$= g(2^x)$$

$$= (2^x)^2 + 1$$

$$= 2^{2x} + 1$$

$$(g \circ f)(-2) = 2^{2(-2)} + 1$$

$$= 2^{-4} + 1$$

$$= \frac{1}{16} + 1$$

$$= \frac{17}{16}$$

(e) $(f \circ g)(x) = f[g(x)]$

$$= f(3x^5 - 4x^2)$$

$$= 3x^5 - 4x^2$$

$$(f \circ g)(-2) = 3(-2)^5 - 4(-2)^2 = -96 - 16 = -112$$

$$(g \circ f)(x) = g[f(x)]$$

$$= g(x)$$

$$= 3x^5 - 4x^2$$

$$(g \circ f)(-2) = 3(-2)^5 - 4(-2)^2 = -96 - 16 = -112$$

(f) $(f \circ g)(x) = f[g(x)]$

$$= f\left(\frac{x+4}{3}\right)$$

$$= 3\left(\frac{x+4}{3}\right) - 4$$

$$= x + 4 - 4$$

$$= x$$

$$(f \circ g)(-2) = -2$$

$$(g \circ f)\,(x) = g\,[\,f(x)\,]$$
$$= g\,(3x - 4)$$
$$= \frac{3x - 4 + 4}{3}$$
$$= \frac{3x}{3}$$
$$= x$$
$$(g \circ f)\,(-2) = -2$$

15. (a) $(F \circ G)\,(x) = F\,[\,G(x)\,]$

$$= F\left(\frac{x + 1}{x - 1}\right)$$

$$= \frac{3\left(\dfrac{x + 1}{x - 1}\right) - 4}{3\left(\dfrac{x + 1}{x - 1}\right) + 3}$$

Multiplying by $\dfrac{x - 1}{x - 1}$ yields:

$$= \frac{3(x + 1) - 4(x - 1)}{3(x + 1) + 3(x - 1)}$$
$$= \frac{3x + 3 - 4x + 4}{3x + 3 + 3x - 3}$$
$$= \frac{-x + 7}{6x}$$

(b) $F\,[\,G(t)\,] = \dfrac{-t + 7}{6t}$

(c) $(F \circ G)\,(2) = F\,[\,G(2)\,] = \dfrac{-2 + 7}{6(2)} = \dfrac{5}{12}$

(d) $(G \circ F)\,(x) = G\,[\,F(x)\,]$

$$= G\left(\frac{3x - 4}{3x + 3}\right)$$

$$= \frac{\dfrac{3x - 4}{3x + 3} + 1}{\dfrac{3x - 4}{3x + 3} - 1}$$

Multiplying by $\dfrac{3x + 3}{3x + 3}$ yields:

$$= \frac{(3x - 4) + 1(3x + 3)}{(3x - 4) - 1(3x + 3)}$$
$$= \frac{3x - 4 + 3x + 3}{3x - 4 - 3x - 3}$$

$$= \frac{6x - 1}{-7}$$

$$= \frac{1 - 6x}{7}$$

(e) $G[F(y)] = \dfrac{1 - 6y}{7}$

(f) $(G \circ F)(2) = G[F(2)] = \dfrac{1 - 6(2)}{7} = \dfrac{-11}{7}$

17. (a) $M(7) = \dfrac{2(7) - 1}{7 - 2} = \dfrac{14 - 1}{5} = \dfrac{13}{5}$

$$M[M(7)] = M\left(\frac{13}{5}\right) = \frac{2\left(\frac{13}{5}\right) - 1}{\frac{13}{5} - 2} = \frac{\frac{26}{5} - 1}{\frac{3}{5}} = \frac{\frac{21}{5}}{\frac{3}{5}} = 7$$

(b) $(M \circ M)(x) = M[M(x)]$

$$= M\left(\frac{2x - 1}{x - 2}\right)$$

$$= \frac{2\left(\frac{2x - 1}{x - 2}\right) - 1}{\left(\frac{2x - 1}{x - 2}\right) - 2}$$

Multiply by $\dfrac{x - 2}{x - 2}$:

$$= \frac{2(2x - 1) - 1(x - 2)}{(2x - 1) - 2(x - 2)}$$

$$= \frac{4x - 2 - x + 2}{2x - 1 - 2x + 4}$$

$$= \frac{3x}{3}$$

$$= x$$

(c) $(M \circ M)(7) = M[M(7)] = 7$. Yes, it agrees!

19. (a) $f[g(3)] = f(0) = 1$

(b) $g[f(3)] = g(4) = -3$

(c) $f[h(3)] = f(2) = -1$

(d) $(h \circ g)(2) = h[g(2)] = h(1) = 2$

(e) $h\{f[g(3)]\} = h[f(0)] = h(1) = 2$

(f) $(g \circ f \circ h \circ f)(2) = (g \circ f \circ h)(-1) = (g \circ f)(3) = g(4) = -3$

21.   (a) $(T \circ I)(x) = T[I(x)] = T(x) = 4x^3 - 3x^2 + 6x - 1$
$(I \circ T)(x) = I[T(x)] = I(4x^3 - 3x^2 + 6x - 1) = 4x^3 - 3x^2 + 6x - 1$

(b) $(G \circ I)(x) = G[I(x)] = G(x) = ax^2 + bx + c$
$(I \circ G)(x) = I[G(x)] = I(ax^2 + bx + c) = ax^2 + bx + c$

(c)   In general, given any function $f(x)$ and $I(x) = x$, then:
$(f \circ I)(x) = f(x)$ and $(I \circ f)(x) = f(x)$
Such a function, $I(x) = x$, is called the identity function.

23. $(f \circ g)(0) = f[g(0)] = f(3) = 1$
$(f \circ g)(1) = f[g(1)] = f(2) = 3$
$(f \circ g)(2) = f[g(2)] = f(0) = 2$
$(f \circ g)(3) = f[g(3)] = f(4) = $ undefined
$(f \circ g)(4) = f[g(4)] = f(-1) = 2$
Thus we have the table:

x	0	1	2	3	4
$(f \circ g)(x)$	1	3	2	und	2

$(g \circ f)(-1) = g[f(-1)] = g(2) = 0$
$(g \circ f)(0) = g[f(0)] = g(2) = 0$
$(g \circ f)(1) = g[f(1)] = g(0) = 3$
$(g \circ f)(2) = g[f(2)] = g(3) = 4$
$(g \circ f)(3) = g[f(3)] = g(1) = 2$
$(g \circ f)(4) = g[f(4)] = $ undefined
Thus we have the table:

x	-1	0	1	2	3	4
$(g \circ f)(x)$	0	0	3	4	2	und

25.   (a) $(f \circ g)(x) = f[g(x)]$
$= f(3x - 4)$
$= 2(3x - 4) + 1$
$= 6x - 8 + 1$
$= 6x - 7$
We draw the graph:

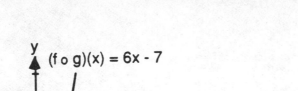

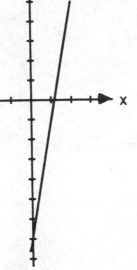

(b) $(g \circ f)(x)$ = $g[f(x)]$
                = $g(2x + 1)$
                = $3(2x + 1) - 4$
                = $6x + 3 - 4$
                = $6x - 1$

We draw the graph:

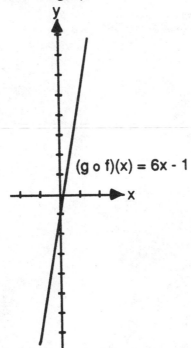

27. (a) $g(x) = \sqrt{x} - 3$

      Domain: $[0, \infty)$

      Range: $[-3, \infty)$

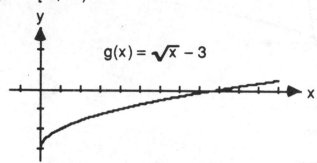

(b) $f(x) = x - 1$
    Domain: All real numbers
    Range: All real numbers

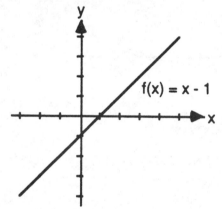

(c) $(f \circ g)(x)$ = $f[g(x)]$
               = $f(\sqrt{x} - 3)$
               = $(\sqrt{x} - 3) - 1$
               = $\sqrt{x} - 4$

    Domain: $[0, \infty)$

    Range: $[-4, \infty)$

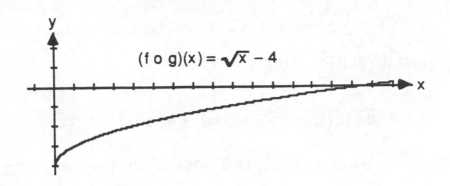

$$(f \circ g)(x) = \sqrt{x} - 4$$

(d) $g[f(x)] = g(x-1) = \sqrt{x-1} - 3$

Domain: $[1, \infty)$

Range: $[-3, \infty)$

(e) We draw the graph:

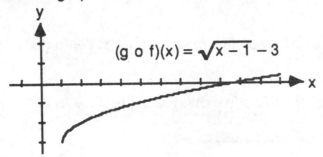

$$(g \circ f)(x) = \sqrt{x-1} - 3$$

29. Let $f(x) = x^4$ and $g(x) = 3x - 1$. Then $C(x) = (f \circ g)(x)$, since $(f \circ g)(x) = f[g(x)] = f(3x-1) = (3x-1)^4$.

31. (a) Let $f(x) = \sqrt[3]{x}$ and $g(x) = 3x + 4$. Then $F(x) = (f \circ g)(x)$, since $(f \circ g)(x) = f[g(x)] = f(3x+4) = \sqrt[3]{3x+4}$.

(b) Let $f(x) = |x|$ and $g(x) = 2x - 3$. Then $G(x) = (f \circ g)(x)$, since $(f \circ g)(x) = f[g(x)] = f(2x-3) = |2x-3|$.

(c) Let $f(x) = x^5$ and $g(x) = ax + b$. Then $H(x) = (f \circ g)(x)$, since $(f \circ g)(x) = f[g(x)] = f(ax+b) = (ax+b)^5$.

(d) Let $f(x) = \dfrac{1}{x}$ and $g(x) = \sqrt{x}$. Then $T(x) = (f \circ g)(x)$,

since $(f \circ g)(x) = f(g(x)) = f(\sqrt{x}) = \dfrac{1}{\sqrt{x}}$.

33. (a) $f(x) = (b \circ c)(x)$, since $(b \circ c)(x) = b[c(x)] = b(2x + 1) = \sqrt[3]{2x + 1}$

(b) $g(x) = (a \circ d)(x)$, since $(a \circ d)(x) = a[d(x)] = a(x^2) = \dfrac{1}{x^2}$

(c) $h(x) = (c \circ d)(x)$, since $(c \circ d)(x) = c[d(x)] = c(x^2) = 2x^2 + 1$

(d) $K(x) = (c \circ b)(x)$, since $(c \circ b)(x) = c[b(x)] = c\left(\sqrt[3]{x}\right) = 2\sqrt[3]{x} + 1$

(e) $l(x) = (c \circ a)(x)$, since $(c \circ a)(x) = c[a(x)] = c\left(\dfrac{1}{x}\right) = 2\left(\dfrac{1}{x}\right) + 1 = \dfrac{2}{x} + 1$

(f) $m(x) = (a \circ c)(x)$, since $(a \circ c)(x) = a[c(x)] = a(2x + 1) = \dfrac{1}{2x + 1}$

(g) $n(x) = (b \circ d)(x)$, since $(b \circ d)(x) = b[d(x)] = b(x^2) = \sqrt[3]{x^2} = x^{2/3}$

Note that we could also use:

$n(x) = (d \circ b)(x)$, since $(d \circ b)(x) = d[b(x)] = d\left(\sqrt[3]{x}\right) = \left(\sqrt[3]{x}\right)^2 = x^{2/3}$

35. $(C \circ f)(t) = C[f(t)] = C\left(\dfrac{1}{t^2 + 1}\right) = 2\pi\left(\dfrac{1}{t^2 + 1}\right) = \dfrac{2\pi}{t^2 + 1}$

When $t = 3$, $(C \circ f)(3) = \dfrac{2\pi}{3^2 + 1} = \dfrac{2\pi}{10} = \dfrac{\pi}{5}$ ft

37. (a) $(C \circ f)(t) = C[f(t)] = C(5t) = 100 + 90(5t) - (5t)^2 = 100 + 450t - 25t^2$

(b) When $t = 3$ hr., we have $C[f(3)] = 100 + 450(3) - 25(3)^2 = \$1225$

(c) When $t = 6$ hr., we have $C[f(6)] = 100 + 450(6) - 25(6)^2 = \$1900$
No, the cost is not twice as much for 6 hours.

39. Call $y = f(x)$. Since $(g \circ f)(x) = g[f(x)] = g(y)$, then:

$$g(y) = x + 5$$
$$4y - 1 = x + 5$$
$$4y = x + 6$$
$$y = \frac{x + 6}{4}$$

So $f(x) = \frac{x + 6}{4}$

41. We set $f[g(x)] = x$

$$f(ax + b) = x$$
$$-2(ax + b) + 1 = x$$
$$-2ax - 2b + 1 = x$$

Since a and b are constants, we can equate components:

$$-2a = 1 \quad \text{and} \quad -2b + 1 = 0$$
$$a = -\frac{1}{2} \qquad\qquad -2b = -1$$
$$b = \frac{1}{2}$$

So $a = -\frac{1}{2}$ and $b = \frac{1}{2}$

43. (a)
$$\frac{f[g(x)] - f[g(a)]}{g(x) - g(a)} = \frac{f(2x - 1) - f(2a - 1)}{(2x - 1) - (2a - 1)}$$
$$= \frac{(2x - 1)^2 - (2a - 1)^2}{2x - 1 - 2a + 1}$$
$$= \frac{[(2x - 1) + (2a - 1)][(2x - 1) - (2a - 1)]}{2x - 2a}$$
$$= \frac{(2x + 2a - 2)(2x - 2a)}{2x - 2a}$$
$$= 2x + 2a - 2$$

(b)
$$\frac{f[g(x)] - f[g(a)]}{x - a} = \frac{(2x + 2a - 2)(2x - 2a)}{x - a}$$
$$= \frac{4(x + a - 1)(x - a)}{x - a}$$
$$= 4x + 4a - 4$$

45. (a)
$$(g \circ h \circ f)(x) = g\{h[f(x)]\}$$
$$= g[h(x^2)]$$
$$= g\left(\frac{x^2}{2}\right)$$
$$= \frac{x^2}{2} + 1$$

(b) $(h \circ f \circ g)(x) = h\{f[g(x)]\}$
$= h[f(x + 1)]$
$= h[(x + 1)^2]$
$= \dfrac{(x + 1)^2}{2}$

(c) $(g \circ f \circ h)(x) = g\{f[h(x)]\}$
$= g[f(\tfrac{x}{2})]$
$= g[(\tfrac{x}{2})^2]$
$= g(\tfrac{x^2}{4})$
$= \dfrac{x^2}{4} + 1$

(d) $(f \circ h \circ g)(x) = f\{h[g(x)]\}$
$= f[h(x + 1)]$
$= f(\dfrac{x + 1}{2})$
$= (\dfrac{x + 1}{2})^2$
$= \dfrac{(x + 1)^2}{4}$

(e) $(h \circ g \circ f)(x) = h\{g[f(x)]\}$
$= h[g(x^2)]$
$= h(x^2 + 1)$
$= \dfrac{x^2 + 1}{2}$

47.   (a) $p(x) = (g \circ f \circ h)(x)$, since $(g \circ f \circ h)(x) = g\{f[h(x)]\}$
$= g[f(3x)]$
$= g[(3x)^2]$
$= g(9x^2)$
$= 1 - 9x^2$

(b) $q(x) = (h \circ g \circ f)(x)$, since $(h \circ g \circ f)(x) = h\{g[f(x)]\}$
$= h[g(x^2)]$
$= h(1 - x^2)$
$= 3(1 - x^2)$
$= 3 - 3x^2$

(c) $r(x) = (f \circ g \circ h)(x)$, since

$$(f \circ g \circ h)(x) = f\{g[h(x)]\}$$
$$= f[g(3x)]$$
$$= f(1 - 3x)$$
$$= (1 - 3x)^2$$
$$= 1 - 6x + 9x^2$$

(d) $s(x) = (h \circ f \circ g)(x)$, since

$$(h \circ f \circ g)(x) = h\{f[g(x)]\}$$
$$= h[f(1 - x)]$$
$$= h[(1 - x)^2]$$
$$= h(1 - 2x + x^2)$$
$$= 3(1 - 2x + x^2)$$
$$= 3 - 6x + 3x^2$$

49. (a)

$$F'[G(x)] \bullet G'(x) = F'(x^2 + 2x + 2) \bullet (2x + 2)$$
$$= \frac{1}{2\sqrt{x^2 + 2x + 2}} \bullet (2x + 2)$$
$$= \frac{x + 1}{\sqrt{x^2 + 2x + 2}}$$

(b)

$$F'[G(9)] \bullet G'(9) = \frac{9 + 1}{\sqrt{9^2 + 2(9) + 2}}$$
$$= \frac{10}{\sqrt{81 + 18 + 2}}$$
$$= \frac{10}{\sqrt{101}}$$
$$= \frac{10\sqrt{101}}{101}$$

51. (a) We have the following compositions:

$(i \circ i)(x)$	$= i(x)$	$= x$	$= i$	$(a \circ i)(x)$	$= a(x)$	$= -x$	$= a$
$(i \circ a)(x)$	$= i(-x)$	$= -x$	$= a$	$(a \circ a)(x)$	$= a(-x)$	$= x$	$= i$
$(i \circ b)(x)$	$= i\left(\frac{1}{x}\right)$	$= \frac{1}{x}$	$= b$	$(a \circ b)(x)$	$= a\left(\frac{1}{x}\right)$	$= -\frac{1}{x}$	$= c$
$(i \circ c)(x)$	$= i\left(-\frac{1}{x}\right)$	$= -\frac{1}{x}$	$= c$	$(a \circ c)(x)$	$= a\left(-\frac{1}{x}\right)$	$= \frac{1}{x}$	$= b$
$(b \circ i)(x)$	$= b(x)$	$= \frac{1}{x}$	$= b$	$(c \circ i)(x)$	$= c(x)$	$= -\frac{1}{x}$	$= c$
$(b \circ a)(x)$	$= b(-x)$	$= -\frac{1}{x}$	$= c$	$(c \circ a)(x)$	$= c(-x)$	$= \frac{1}{x}$	$= b$

$$(b \circ b)(x) = b\left(\frac{1}{x}\right) = x \quad = i \qquad (c \circ b)(x) = c\left(\frac{1}{x}\right) = -x \quad = a$$

$$(b \circ c)(x) = b\left(-\frac{1}{x}\right) = -x \quad = a \qquad (c \circ c)(x) = c\left(-\frac{1}{x}\right) = x \quad = i$$

So we have the composition table:

o	i	a	b	c
i	i	a	b	c
a	a	i	c	b
b	b	c	i	a
c	c	b	a	i

(b) Yes

(c) $a^2 = i$; $b^2 = i$; $c^2 = i$; $c^3 = c \circ c^2 = c \circ i = c$

(d) $(a \circ b) \circ c = (c) \circ c = i$ and $a \circ (b \circ c) = a \circ (a) = i$,
     so $(a \circ b) \circ c = a \circ (b \circ c)$

(e) Since $i^2 = a^2 = b^2 = c^2 = i$, then the range of f is $\{ i \}$.

(f) $f(a \circ b) = f(c) = c^2 = i$
     $[f(a)] \circ [f(b)] = a^2 \circ b^2 = i \circ i = i$, so $f(a \circ b) = [f(a)] \circ [f(b)]$

(g) $f(a \circ b \circ c) = f(a \circ a) = f(i) = i^2 = i$
     $[f(a)] \circ [f(b)] \circ [f(c)] = a^2 \circ b^2 \circ c^2 = i \circ (i \circ i) = i \circ i = i$,
     so $f(a \circ b \circ c) = [f(a) \circ f(b) \circ f(c)]$

4.5 Inverse Functions

1. (a) We need to show that $(f \circ g)(x) = x$ and that $(g \circ f)(x) = x$:

$$(f \circ g)(x) = f[g(x)]$$
$$= f\left(\frac{x}{3}\right)$$
$$= 3\left(\frac{x}{3}\right)$$
$$= x$$

$$(g \circ f)(x) = g[f(x)]$$
$$= g(3x)$$
$$= \frac{3x}{3}$$
$$= x$$

So $f(x)$ and $g(x)$ are inverse functions.

(b)   We need to show $(f \circ g)(x) = x$ and that $(g \circ f)(x) = x$:
$$(f \circ g)(x) = f[g(x)]$$
$$= f\left(\frac{x+1}{4}\right)$$
$$= 4\left(\frac{x+1}{4}\right) - 1$$
$$= x + 1 - 1$$
$$= x$$
$$(g \circ f)(x) = g[f(x)]$$
$$= g(4x - 1)$$
$$= \frac{(4x - 1) + 1}{4}$$
$$= \frac{4x}{4}$$
$$= x$$

So $f(x)$ and $g(x)$ are inverse functions.

(c)   We need to show $(g \circ h)(x) = x$ and that $(h \circ g)(x) = x$:
$$(g \circ h)(x) = g[h(x)]$$
$$= g(x^2)$$
$$= \sqrt{x^2}$$
$$= x, \text{ since } x \geq 0$$
$$(h \circ g)(x) = h[g(x)]$$
$$= h(\sqrt{x})$$
$$= (\sqrt{x})^2$$
$$= x$$

So $g(x)$ and $h(x)$ are inverse functions.

3.   (a)   Since $f[f^{-1}(x)] = x$, then $f[f^{-1}(4)] = 4$

(b)   Since $f^{-1}[f(x)] = x$, then $f^{-1}[f(-1)] = -1$

(c)   Since $(f \circ f^{-1})(x) = x$, then $(f \circ f^{-1})(\sqrt{2}) = \sqrt{2}$

(d)   Since $f[f^{-1}(x)] = x$, then $f[f^{-1}(t + 1)] = t + 1$

(e) $f(0) = 0^3 + 2(0) + 1 = 1$, then $f^{-1}(1) = 0$

(f) $f(-1) = (-1)^3 + 2(-1) + 1 = -1 - 2 + 1 = -2$, then $f^{-1}(2) = -1$

5. (a) Let $y = 3x - 1$
We switch the roles of x and y and solve the resulting equation for y:
$$x = 3y - 1$$
$$3y = x + 1$$
$$y = \frac{x + 1}{3}$$

So the inverse is $f^{-1}(x) = \frac{x + 1}{3}$

(b) $f[f^{-1}(x)] = f\left(\frac{x + 1}{3}\right)$
$$= 3\left(\frac{x + 1}{3}\right) - 1$$
$$= x + 1 - 1$$
$$= x$$
$$f^{-1}[f(x)] = f^{-1}(3x - 1)$$
$$= \frac{(3x - 1) + 1}{3}$$
$$= \frac{3x}{3}$$
$$= x$$

We have $f[f^{-1}(x)] = x$ and $f^{-1}[f(x)] = x$, which verifies that $f(x)$ and $f^{-1}(x)$ are inverse funtions.

(c)   The graphs of each line are given below. Note the symmetry of each line about the line $y = x$:

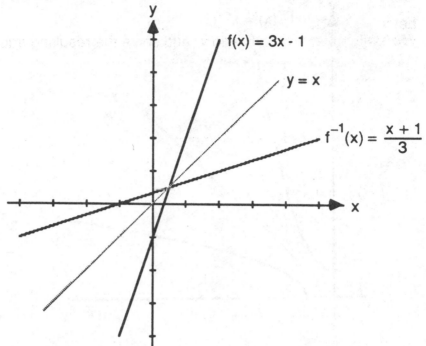

7.   (a)   Let $y = \sqrt{x - 1}$
We switch the roles of x and y and solve the resulting equation for y:
$$x = \sqrt{y - 1}$$
Squaring each side:
$$x^2 = y - 1$$
$$y = x^2 + 1$$
So the inverse is $f^{-1}(x) = x^2 + 1$.

(b) $f[f^{-1}(x)] = f(x^2 + 1)$
$$= \sqrt{(x^2 + 1) - 1}$$
$$= \sqrt{x^2}$$
$$= x, \text{ since } x \geq 0$$
$f^{-1}[f(x)] = f^{-1}(\sqrt{x - 1})$
$$= (\sqrt{x - 1})^2 + 1$$
$$= x - 1 + 1$$
$$= x$$
We have $f[f^{-1}(x)] = x$ and $f^{-1}[f(x)] = x$, which verifies that f (x) and $f^{-1}(x)$ are inverse functions.

(c)   The graphs of each curve are given below. Note the symmetry of each curve about the line y = x:

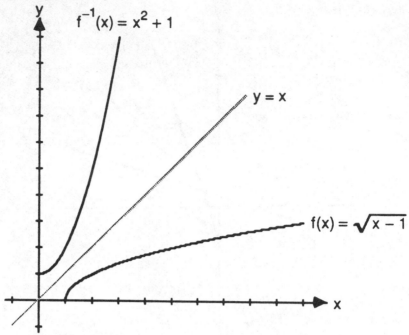

$$f^{-1}(x) = x^2 + 1$$

y = x

$$f(x) = \sqrt{x - 1}$$

9.   (a)   Domain of f: All real numbers except 3, or $(-\infty, 3) \cup (3, \infty)$
        Range of f: We solve for x:

$$y = \frac{x + 2}{x - 3}$$
$$y(x - 3) = x + 2$$
$$yx - 3y = x + 2$$
$$yx - x = 3y + 2$$
$$x(y - 1) = 3y + 2$$
$$x = \frac{3y + 2}{y - 1}$$

So the range of f (x) is all real numbers except 1, or $(-\infty, 1) \cup (1, \infty)$

(b) Let $y = \dfrac{x + 2}{x - 3}$

We switch the roles of x and y and solve the resulting equation for y:

$$x = \frac{y + 2}{y - 3}$$
$$x(y - 3) = y + 2$$
$$xy - 3x = y + 2$$
$$xy - y = 3x + 2$$
$$y(x - 1) = 3x + 2$$
$$y = \frac{3x + 2}{x - 1}$$

So $f^{-1}(x) = \dfrac{3x + 2}{x - 1}$

(c) Domain of f^{-1}: All real numbers except 1, or $(-\infty, 1) \cup (1, \infty)$

Range of f^{-1}: We solve $y = \dfrac{3x + 2}{x - 1}$ for x:

$$y(x - 1) = 3x + 2$$
$$yx - y = 3x + 2$$
$$yx - 3x = y + 2$$
$$x(y - 3) = y + 2$$
$$x = \frac{y + 2}{y - 3}$$

So the range of f^{-1} is all real numbers except 3, or $(-\infty, 3) \cup (3, \infty)$

Notice that: domain of f = range of f^{-1}
range of f = domain of f^{-1}

11. Let $y = 2x^3 + 1$

We switch the roles of x and y and solve the resulting equation for y:

$$x = 2y^3 + 1$$
$$2y^3 = x - 1$$
$$y^3 = \frac{x - 1}{2}$$
$$y = \sqrt[3]{\frac{x - 1}{2}}$$

So $f^{-1}(x) = \sqrt[3]{\dfrac{x - 1}{2}}$

13. $f[f^{-1}(x)] = f\left(\frac{x+4}{3}\right) = 3\left(\frac{x+4}{3}\right) - 4 = x + 4 - 4 = x$

$f^{-1}[f(x)] = f^{-1}(3x-4) = \frac{(3x-4)+4}{3} = \frac{3x}{3} = x$

This verfies that f and f^{-1} are inverse functions. We sketch the graph:

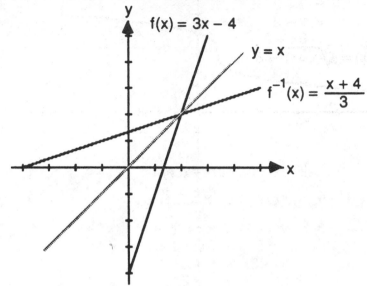

15. (a)   Let $y = (x-3)^3 - 1$
We switch the roles of x and y and solve the resulting equation for y:

$$x = (y-3)^3 - 1$$
$$(y-3)^3 = x + 1$$

Taking the cube root:

$$y - 3 = \sqrt[3]{x+1}$$
$$y = \sqrt[3]{x+1} + 3$$

So $f^{-1}(x) = \sqrt[3]{x+1} + 3$

(b)   The graph of each curve is given below:

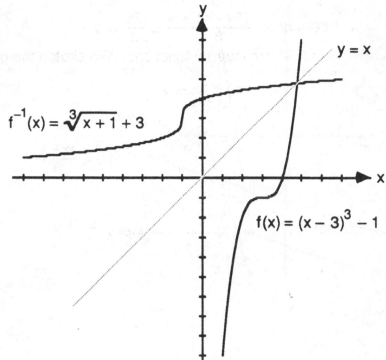

$$f^{-1}(x) = \sqrt[3]{x+1} + 3$$

$y = x$

$$f(x) = (x-3)^3 - 1$$

17.   (a) $y = g^{-1}(x)$

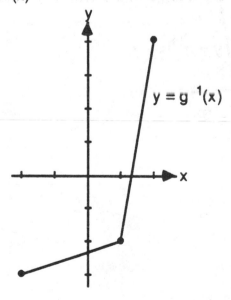

$y = g^{-1}(x)$

(b) $y = g^{-1}(x) - 1$

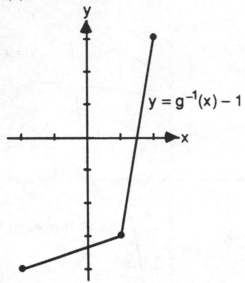

(c) $y = g^{-1}(x - 1)$

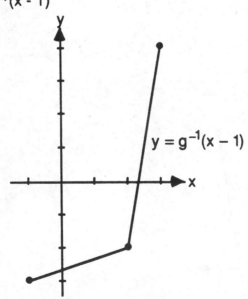

(d) $y = g^{-1}(-x)$

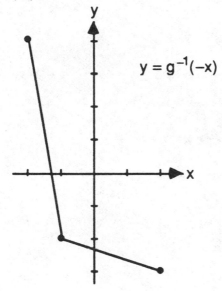

$y = g^{-1}(-x)$

(e) $y = -g^{-1}(x)$

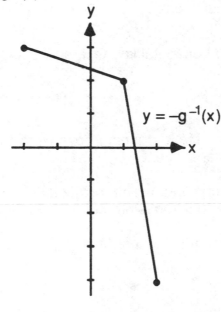

$y = -g^{-1}(x)$

(f) $y = - g^{-1}(-x)$

$y = -g^{-1}(-x)$

19.   The graph of $y = x^2 + 1$ is a parabola opening upward, which fails the horizontal line test, so it is not one-to-one.

21.   The graph of $f(x) = \dfrac{1}{x}$ passes the horizontal line test, so it is one-to-one.

23.   The graph of $y = x^3$ passes the horizintal line test, so it is one-to-one.

25.   The graph of $y = \sqrt{1 - x^2}$ is a semi-circle opening downward, which fails the horizontal line-test, so it is not one-to-one.

27.   The graph of $g(x) = 5$ is a horizontal line, which clearly fails the horizontal line test (it is a horizontal line), so the function is not one-to-one.

29.   The graph of $f(x)$ passes the horizontal line test (even at $y = 1$), so it is one-to-one.

31. $f[f(x)] = f\left(\dfrac{3x - 2}{5x - 3}\right)$

$$= \dfrac{3\left(\dfrac{3x - 2}{5x - 3}\right) - 2}{5\left(\dfrac{3x - 2}{5x - 3}\right) - 3}$$

We multiply by $\frac{5x-3}{5x-3}$:

$$= \frac{3(3x-2)-2(5x-3)}{5(3x-2)-3(5x-3)}$$

$$= \frac{9x-6-10x+6}{15x-10-15x+9}$$

$$= \frac{-x}{-1}$$

$$= x$$

Thus $f^{-1}(x) = f(x)$.

33. (a) Let $y = \frac{ax+b}{cx+d}$

We switch the roles of x and y and solve the resulting equation for y:

$$x = \frac{ay+b}{cy+d}$$
$$x(cy+d) = ay+b$$
$$cxy+dx = ay+b$$
$$cxy-ay = b-dx$$
$$y(cx-a) = b-dx$$
$$y = \frac{b-dx}{cx-a}$$

So $M^{-1}(x) = \frac{b-dx}{cx-a}$

(b) $M[\,M(x)\,] = M\left(\frac{ax+b}{cx+d}\right)$

$$= \frac{a\left(\frac{ax+b}{cx+d}\right)+b}{c\left(\frac{ax+b}{cx+d}\right)+d}$$

Multiply by $\frac{cx+d}{cx+d}$:

$$= \frac{a(ax+b)+b(cx+d)}{c(ax+b)+d(cx+d)}$$

$$= \frac{a^2x+ab+bcx+bd}{acx+bc+cdx+d^2}$$

$$= \frac{(a^2+bc)x+(ab+bd)}{(ac+cd)x+(bc+d^2)}$$

(c) $M[M(0)] = \dfrac{(a^2 + bc)(0) + (ab + b)}{(ac + cd)(0) + (bc + d^2)}$

$= \dfrac{ab + bd}{bc + d^2}$

(d) $M^{-1}[M(x)] = x$

(e) $M^{-1}[M(0)] = 0$

35. $F^{-1}(x)$ is extremely hard (if even possible) to find, so another approach is needed. Note that $F(0) = 0^3 + 7(0) - 5 = -5$, so since $F(0) = -5$ we must have $F^{-1}(-5) = 0$.

37.   Let the points $P = (5,2)$ and $Q = (2,5)$. We must first show that the line segment PQ is perpendicular to the line $y = x$:

$m = \dfrac{5 - 2}{2 - 5} = \dfrac{3}{-3} = -1$

Since $y = x$ has a slope of 1, and $1(-1) = -1$, then the two lines are perpendicular . Next, we must show that P and Q are equidistant from $y = x$. Call the point $C = (c,c)$ on $y = x$. We use the distance formula:

$PC = \sqrt{(5 - c)^2 + (2 - c)^2}$

$QC = \sqrt{(2 - c)^2 + (5 - c)^2}$

So $PC = QC$. So, since PQ is perpendicular to $y = x$, and $PC = QC$, then by the definition of symmetry, P and Q are symmetric about the line $y = x$.

39.   Let $P = (p_1,p_2)$ and $Q = (q_1,q_2)$. Then $P' = (p_2,p_1)$ and $Q' = (q_2,q_1)$. Using the distance formula, we have:

$PQ = \sqrt{(p_1 - q_1)^2 + (p_2 - q_2)^2}$

$P'Q' = \sqrt{(p_2 - q_2)^2 + (p_1 - q_1)^2}$

Since $PQ = P'Q'$, the answer is yes!

41.   Let $P = (8,2)$ and $Q = (4,8)$. We first find the value of m so that the line segment PQ is perpendicular to the line $y = mx + b$:

slope $= \dfrac{8 - 2}{4 - 8} = \dfrac{6}{-4} = -\dfrac{3}{2}$

So $-\dfrac{3}{2}(m) = -1$, and thus $m = \dfrac{2}{3}$. So $y = \dfrac{2}{3}x + b$.

Next, we must find the value of b so that P and Q are equidistant from $y = \frac{2}{3}x + b$. Call the point $A = (a, \frac{2}{3}a + b)$ on $y = \frac{2}{3}x + b$. We use the distance formula:

$$PA = \sqrt{(a-8)^2 + \left(\frac{2}{3}a + b - 2\right)^2}$$

$$QA = \sqrt{(a-4)^2 + \left(\frac{2}{3}a + b - 8\right)^2}$$

Now, since PA = QA, we have

$$\sqrt{(a-8)^2 + \left(\frac{2}{3}a + b - 2\right)^2} = \sqrt{(a-4)^2 + \left(\frac{2}{3}a + b - 8\right)^2}$$

Squaring each side:

$$(a-8)^2 + \left(\frac{2}{3}a + b - 2\right)^2 = (a-4)^2 + \left(\frac{2}{3}a + b - 8\right)^2$$

$$a^2 - 16a + 64 + \left(\frac{2}{3}a + b\right)^2 - 4\left(\frac{2}{3}a + b\right) + 4 = a^2 - 8a + 16 + \left(\frac{2}{3}a + b\right)^2 - 16\left(\frac{2}{3}a + b\right) + 64$$

$$-16a - 4\left(\frac{2}{3}a + b\right) + 4 = -8a + 16 - 16\left(\frac{2}{3}a + b\right)$$

$$12\left(\frac{2}{3}a + b\right) = 8a + 12$$

$$8a + 12b = 8a + 12$$

$$12b = 12$$

$$b = 1$$

So $y = \frac{2}{3}x + 1$ is the line of symmetry: $m = \frac{2}{3}$ and $b = 1$

43. Let $y = f(x-1)$

We switch the roles of x and y and solve the resulting equation for y:

$$x = f(y-1)$$
$$f^{-1}(x) = y - 1$$
$$y = f^{-1}(x) + 1$$

So $F^{-1}(x) = f^{-1}(x) + 1$

45. (a) Let $P = (a,b)$ and $Q = (x,y)$. Q is the point we are trying to find. Since PQ is perpendicular to $y = 3x$, which has a slope of 3, then we have:

$$\frac{y-b}{x-a} = -\frac{1}{3}$$
$$3y - 3b = -x + a$$
$$x + 3y = a + 3b$$

Now call $C(c, 3c)$ a point on the line $y = 3x$:

$$\frac{3c-b}{c-a} = -\frac{1}{3}$$
$$9c - 3b = -c + a$$
$$10c = a + 3b$$

$$c = \frac{a + 3b}{10}$$

Now, since PC = QC, then by the distance formula we have:

$$\sqrt{(a - c)^2 + (b - 3c)^2} = \sqrt{(x - c)^2 + (y - 3c)^2}$$

Squaring each side and substituting $c = \frac{a + 3b}{10}$, we have:

$$\left(a - \frac{a+3b}{10}\right)^2 + \left(b - \frac{3a+9b}{10}\right)^2 = \left(x - \frac{a+3b}{10}\right)^2 + \left(y - \frac{3a+9b}{10}\right)^2$$

Recall that x + 3y = a + 3b, and thus 3x + 9y = 3a + 9b. Substituting these values into the right-hand side, we obtain:

$$\left(a - \frac{a+3b}{10}\right)^2 + \left(b - \frac{3a+9b}{10}\right)^2 = \left(x - \frac{x+3y}{10}\right)^2 + \left(y - \frac{3x+9y}{10}\right)^2$$

$$\left(\frac{9a - 3b}{10}\right)^2 + \left(\frac{b - 3a}{10}\right)^2 = \left(\frac{9x - 3y}{10}\right)^2 + \left(\frac{y - 3x}{10}\right)^2$$

Multiplying by 100 (10^2) and multiply out parantheses, we obtain:

$$81a^2 - 54ab + 9b^2 + b^2 - 6ab + 9a^2 = 81x^2 - 54xy + 9y^2 + y^2 - 6xy + 9x^2$$

$$90a^2 - 60ab + 10b^2 = 90x^2 - 60xy + 10y^2$$

$$9a^2 - 6ab + b^2 = 9x^2 - 6xy + y^2$$

$$(3a - b)^2 = (3x - y)^2$$

$$|3a - b| = |3x - y|$$

So, either 3x - y = 3a - b   or   3x - y = - (3a - b) = -3a + b

Case 1:

x + 3y = a + 3b,   so x = a + 3b - 3y

3x - y = 3a - b

Substituting: 3(a + 3b - 3y) - y = 3a - b

$$3a + 9b - 9y - y = 3a - b$$

$$- 10y = -10b$$

$$y = b$$

$$x = a$$

But if (x,y) = (a,b), then the point lies on the line!

Case 2:

x + 3y = a + 3b,   so x = a + 3b - 3y

3x - y = -3a + b

Substituting: 3(a + 3b - 3y) - y = -3a + b

$$3a + 9b - 9y - y = -3a + b$$

$$-10y = -6a - 8b$$

$$y = \frac{3a + 4b}{5}$$

Then $x = a + 3b - 3\left(\dfrac{3a + 4b}{5}\right)$

$$= a + 3b - \frac{9a + 12b}{5}$$

$$= \frac{5a + 15b - 9a - 12b}{5}$$

$$= \frac{-4a + 3b}{5}$$

So the reflected point, (x,y) is $\left(\dfrac{3b - 4a}{5}, \dfrac{3a + 4b}{5} \right)$

(b) Calling P and Q as in (a), we have:

$$\frac{y - b}{x - a} = -\frac{1}{m}$$

$$my - mb = -x + a$$

$$x + my = a + mb$$

Let C (c,mc) be a point on the line y = mx:

$$\frac{mc - b}{c - a} = -\frac{1}{m}$$

$$m^2c - mb = a - c$$

$$(m^2 + 1)c = a + mb$$

$$c = \frac{a + mb}{m^2 + 1}$$

Now since PC = QC, we have:

$$\sqrt{(a - c)^2 + (b - mc)^2} = \sqrt{(x - c)^2 + (y - mc)^2}$$

Squaring each side and substituting c $= \dfrac{a + mb}{m^2 + 1}$, we have:

$$\left(a - \frac{a+mb}{m^2+1} \right)^2 + \left(b - \frac{am+m^2b}{m^2+1} \right)^2 = \left(x - \frac{a+mb}{m^2+1} \right)^2 + \left(y - \frac{am+m^2b}{m^2+1} \right)^2$$

Recall that x + my = a + mb, and thus mx + m²y = am + m²b.
Substituting these values into the right-hand side, we obtain:

$$\left(a - \frac{a+mb}{m^2+1} \right)^2 + \left(b - \frac{am+m^2b}{m^2+1} \right)^2 = \left(x - \frac{x+my}{m^2+1} \right)^2 + \left(y - \frac{mx+m^2y}{m^2+1} \right)^2$$

$$\left(\frac{m^2a - mb}{m^2 + 1} \right)^2 + \left(\frac{b - am}{m^2 + 1} \right)^2 = \left(\frac{m^2x - my}{m^2 + 1} \right)^2 + \left(\frac{y - mx}{m^2 + 1} \right)^2$$

Multiplying by (m² + 1)², and multiplying out parentheses, we obtain:

$$m^2a^2 - 2abm + b^2 = m^2x^2 - 2mxy + y^2$$

$$(ma - b)^2 = (mx - y)^2$$

$$|ma - b| = |mx - y|$$

So, either mx - y = ma - b   or   mx - y = - (ma + b) = -ma + b

Case 1:

x + my = a + mb,   so x = a + mb - my

mx - y = ma - b

Substituting: $m(a + mb - my) - y = ma - b$

$$ma + m^2b - m^2y - y = ma - b$$

$$(m^2 + 1)b = (m^2 + 1)y$$

$$b = y$$

$$a = x$$

But, if $(x,y) = (a,b)$, then the point lies on the line!

Case 2:

$x + my = a + mb,$ so $x = a + mb - my$

$mx - y = -ma + b$

Substituting: $m(a + mb - my) - y = -ma + b$

$$ma + m^2b - m^2y - y = -ma + b$$

$$-(m^2 + 1)y = -2ma + b(1 - m^2)$$

$$y = \frac{2ma + (m^2 - 1)b}{m^2 + 1}$$

Then $x = a + mb - \dfrac{2m^2a + m(m^2 - 1)b}{m^2 + 1}$

$$= \frac{am^2+a+m^3b+mb-2m^2a-m^3b+mb}{m^2 + 1}$$

$$= \frac{2mb - (m^2 - 1)a}{m^2 + 1}$$

So the reflected point, (x,y), is:

$$\left(\frac{2mb - (m^2 - 1)a}{m^2 + 1}, \frac{2ma + (m^2 - 1)b}{m^2 + 1} \right)$$

Note: Using $m = 3$ and our answer from (a) verifies this formula.

4.6 Variation

1.   (a) $y = kx$

(b) $A = \dfrac{k}{B}$

3.   (a) $x = kuv^2$

(b) $z = kA^2B^3$

5.   (a) $F = \dfrac{k}{r^2}$

(b) $V^2 = k(U^2 + T^2)$

7.   (a)   Since A varies inversely as B, then $A = \dfrac{k}{B}$. We find k by substituting
           A = -1 and B = 2:
           $$-1 = \frac{k}{2}$$
           $$k = -2$$

     (b)   So $A = \dfrac{-2}{B}$

     (c)   When $B = \dfrac{5}{4}$, we have: $A = \dfrac{-2}{\frac{5}{4}} = -\dfrac{8}{5}$

9.   Since x vaies jointly as y and z, then x = kyz. We find k by substituting
     x = 9, y = 2, and z = -3:
     $$9 = k\,(2)\,(-3)$$
     $$9 = -6k$$
     $$k = -\frac{3}{2}$$
     So $x = \dfrac{-3}{2}\,yz$. Thus, when y = 4 and z = 4:
     $$x = -\frac{3}{2}\,(4)\,(4) = -24$$

11. Since A varies jointly as B and C, then A = kBC. Now we substitute 3B and
     2C in for B and C, respectively:
     $$A = k\,(3B)\,(2C)$$
     $$A = 6\,(kBC)$$
     So A is six times the original value of A.

13. Since x varies jointly as B and C and inversly as $\sqrt{A}$, then $x = \dfrac{kBC}{\sqrt{A}}$. Now
     we substitute 4B, 4C, and 4A in for B, C, and A, respectively:
     $$x = \frac{k(4B)(4C)}{\sqrt{4A}} = \frac{16kBC}{2\sqrt{A}} = 8\left(\frac{kBC}{\sqrt{A}}\right)$$
     So x is eight times the original value of x.

15. (a)   Let S = surface area and r = radius. Then $S = kr^2$. When r = 2 and
           S = 16π, we have:
           $$16\pi = k(2)^2$$
           $$16\pi = 4k$$
           $$k = 4\pi$$
           So $S = 4\pi\, r^2$.

(b)   When $r = \sqrt{3}$, we have: $S = 4\pi (\sqrt{3})^2 = 12\pi$ cm^2.

17.   Let m_1 and m_2 be the two masses, F = force, and d = distance. Then $F = \dfrac{km_1m_2}{d^2}$. Now we substitute $3m_1$, $4m_2$, and $\frac{1}{2}d$ in for m_1, m_2, and d, respectively:

$$F = \frac{k(3m_1)(4m_2)}{\left(\frac{d}{2}\right)^2} = \frac{12m_1m_2}{\dfrac{d^2}{4}} = 48\left(\frac{km_1m_2}{d^2}\right)$$

So the force is 48 times the original force.

19.   Let d = distance and t = time. Then $d = kt^2$. We find k by substituting $d = 490$ and $t = 10$:

$$490 = k(10)^2$$
$$490 = 100k$$
$$k = \frac{490}{100} = 4.9$$

So $d = 4.9t^2$
When $t = 5$, we have:
$$d = (4.9)(5)^2 = (4.9)(25) = 122.5 \text{ m}$$

21.   (a)   Let V = volume and P = pressure. Then $V = \dfrac{k}{P}$. We find k by substituting $V = 2$ and $P = 1.025$:

$$2 = \frac{k}{1.025}$$
$$k = 2.05$$
So $V = \dfrac{2.05}{P}$

(b)   When $P = 1$, we have $V = \dfrac{2.05}{1} = 2.05$ liters.

23.   (a)   Let E = kinetic energy, m = mass, and r = radius. Then $E = \dfrac{km}{r}$. Now we substitute $\frac{1}{2}r$ and $3m$ in for r and m, respectively:

$$E = \frac{k(3m)}{\frac{1}{2}r} = \frac{6km}{r} = 6\left(\frac{km}{r}\right)$$

So the kinetic energy is 6 times the original value.

(b)   Let V = velocity and r = radius. Then $V = \dfrac{k}{\sqrt{r}}$. Now we substitute $\dfrac{1}{2}r$ in for r:

$$V = \frac{k}{\sqrt{\dfrac{1}{2}r}} = \frac{k\sqrt{2}}{\sqrt{r}} = \sqrt{2}\left(\frac{k}{\sqrt{r}}\right)$$

So the velocity is $\sqrt{2}$ times the original velocity.

25. Let W = weight and d = distance. Then $W = \dfrac{k}{d^2}$. We find k by substituting W = 140 and d = 4000:

$$140 = \frac{k}{(4000)^2}$$
$$k = 140\,(4000)^2$$
$$k = 2.24 \times 10^9$$

When d = 4500, we have:

$$W = \frac{2.24 \times 10^9}{(4500)^2} = 110.6 \text{ lbs.}$$

27. (a)   We need a graph which is linear with a negative slope. Such a graph is F.

(b)   We need a graph for $y = \dfrac{k}{x}$. Such a graph is C.

(c)   We need a graph which is a parabola pointed upward. Such a graph is D.

(d)   We need a graph which is linear with a positive slope. Such a graph is A.

(e)   We need a graph which is a parabola pointed downward. Such a graph is B.

29. Let P = period and L = length. Then $P = k\sqrt{L}$. We denote the new length and period by L' and P', respectively, where $P' = \dfrac{P}{2}$. Since $P' = k\sqrt{L'}$, we have:

$$\frac{P}{2} = k\sqrt{L'}$$
$$\frac{k\sqrt{L}}{2} = k\sqrt{L'}$$

$$\frac{k^2L}{4} = k^2L'$$

$$L' = \frac{L}{4}$$

So the new length, L', should be $\frac{1}{4}$ of the original length. Thus it must be shortened by $\frac{3}{4}L$.

31. Let I = intensity and d = distance. Then $I = \frac{k}{d^2}$. When d = 6, we have:

$$I = \frac{k}{6^2} = \frac{k}{36}$$

We are asked to find the value of d when $I = 2\left(\frac{k}{36}\right) = \frac{k}{18}$:

$$\frac{k}{18} = \frac{k}{d^2}$$

$$d^2 = 18$$

$$d = 3\sqrt{2} \approx 4.24$$

At a distance of 4.24 ft, the illumination will be twice as great.

33. The area of the triangle is:

$$A = \frac{1}{2}(\text{base})(\text{height})$$

$$= \frac{1}{2}(x)(y)$$

$$= \frac{1}{2}(x)(mx)$$

$$= \frac{1}{2}mx^2$$

Thus, A varies jointly as m and x^2.

35. Let t = time and d = distance. Then $t^2 = kd^3$. We first find k by using d = 1.000000 and t = 365.2564 (information for earth):

$$t^2 = kd^3$$

$$k = \frac{t^2}{d^3} = \frac{(365.2564)^2}{(1.000000)^3} = 133412.2377$$

So $t = \sqrt{kd^3} = \sqrt{133412.2377d^3}$. We now compute t for each planet:

Mercury:	87.9693 days
Venus:	224.7007 days
Earth:	365.2564 days
Mars:	686.9786 days
Jupiter:	4336.6159 days

Saturn: 10826.9994 days
Uranus: 30873.7244 days
Neptune: 60300.6863 days
Pluto: 91814.3739 days

37. (a) Let $x = k_1 z$ and $y = k_2 z$. Then:
$$x + y = k_1 z + k_2 z = (k_1 + k_2) z$$
Call $K = k_1 + k_2$
Then $x + y = Kz$. This shows that $x + y$ varies directly as z.

(b) $xy = (k_1 z)(k_2 z) = k_1 k_2 z^2$
Call $K = k_1 k_2$
Then $xy = Kz^2$. So xy does _not_ vary directly as z.

(c) $\sqrt{xy} = \sqrt{k_1 k_2 z^2} = \sqrt{k_1 k_2}\, z$ since $z > 0$
Call $K = \sqrt{k_1 k_2}$
Then $\sqrt{xy} = Kz$. This shows that $\sqrt{xy}$ varies directly as z.

39. (a) We have:
$$x + y = k(x - y)$$
$$x + y = kx - ky$$
$$y + ky = kx - x$$
$$y(1 + k) = x(k - 1)$$
$$y = \frac{k - 1}{k + 1}x$$
Setting $K = \frac{k - 1}{k + 1}$, we have $y = Kx$. Thus, y varies directly as x.

(b) $x^2 + y^2 = x^2 + (Kx)^2 = x^2 + K^2 x^2 = (K^2 + 1)(x^2)$

Since $y = Kx$, then $x = \frac{y}{K}$, so:
$$x^2 + y^2 = (K^2 + 1)(x^2)$$
$$= (K^2 + 1)\left(\frac{y}{K}\right)(x)$$
$$= \frac{(K^2 + 1)}{K}(xy)$$

Setting $A = \frac{K^2 + 1}{K}$, we have $x^2 + y^2 = Axy$. Thus, $x^2 + y^2$ varies jointly as x and y.

(c) $x^3 + y^3 = (x + y)(x^2 - xy + y^2)$
$$= (x + y)(x^2 + y^2 - xy)$$
$$= (x + y)(Axy - xy) \text{, from part (b)}$$
$$= (x + y)(xy)(A - 1)$$
$$= (A - 1)(x + y)(xy)$$

Let $B = A - 1$. Then $x^3 + y^3 = Bxy(x + y)$. So $x^3 + y^3$ varies jointly as x, y, and $x + y$.

41.   The area of the triangle is:
$$A = \frac{1}{2}(\text{base})(\text{height})$$
$$= \frac{1}{2}(x)(y)$$
$$= \frac{1}{2}(x)\left(\frac{a^2}{x}\right)$$
$$= \frac{1}{2}a^2$$

Thus, A varies directly as a^2.

Chapter 4 Review Exercises

1.   x-intercepts: ± 2
     y-intercept: 4

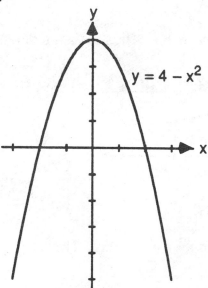

3.   x-intercept: -1
     y-intercept: none

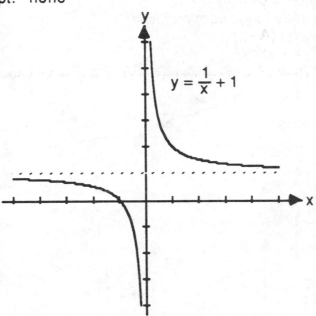

$$y = \frac{1}{x} + 1$$

5.   x-intercept: -2
     y-intercept: 2

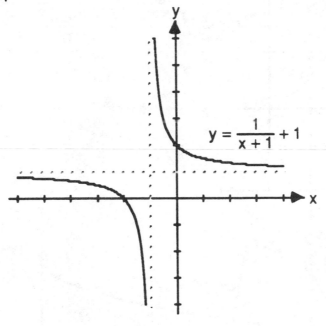

$$y = \frac{1}{x + 1} + 1$$

7.   x-intercept: 4
      y-intercept: none

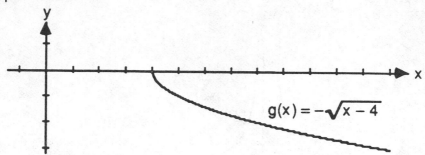

$$g(x) = -\sqrt{x - 4}$$

9.   x-intercept: none
      y-intercept: 2

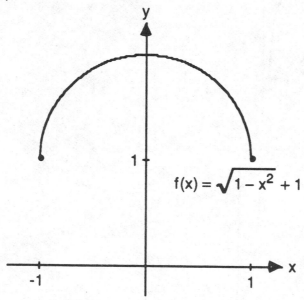

$$f(x) = \sqrt{1 - x^2} + 1$$

11.   x-intercept: -16
      y-intercept: 4

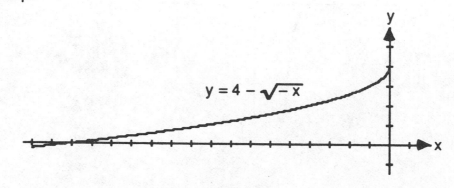

$$y = 4 - \sqrt{-x}$$

13. $(f \circ g)(x) = f(x + 3) = (x + 3)^2$
     x-intercept: -3
     y-intercept: 9

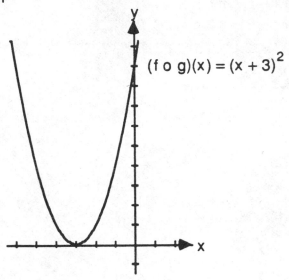

$(f \circ g)(x) = (x + 3)^2$

15. x-intercepts: -1
     y-intercept: 1

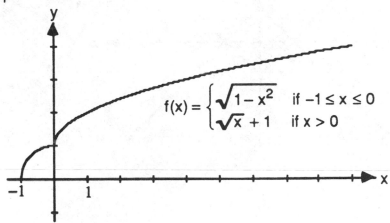

$$f(x) = \begin{cases} \sqrt{1 - x^2} & \text{if } -1 \leq x \leq 0 \\ \sqrt{x} + 1 & \text{if } x > 0 \end{cases}$$

17.   x-intercepts: 1, 3
      y-intercept: 1

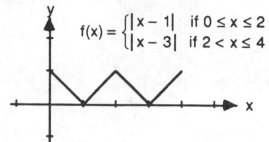

$$f(x) = \begin{cases} |x-1| & \text{if } 0 \le x \le 2 \\ |x-3| & \text{if } 2 < x \le 4 \end{cases}$$

19. $y + |x| - 1 = 0$ or $y - |x| + 1 = 0$
                  $y = -|x| + 1$ $y = |x| - 1$
      x-intercepts: ±1
      y-intercepts: ±1

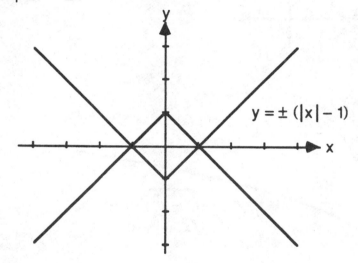

$$y = \pm (|x| - 1)$$

21. $x = \sqrt[3]{y + 2}$
        $x^3 = y + 2$
        $y = x^3 - 2 = g^{-1}(x)$

      x-intercept: $\sqrt[3]{2}$
      y-intercept: -2

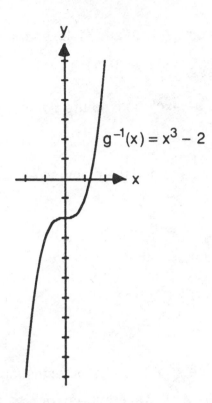

$g^{-1}(x) = x^3 - 2$

23. $(f^{-1} \circ f)(x) = x$, with domain: $x \geq 2$ for $f(x)$
x-intercept: none
y-intercept: none

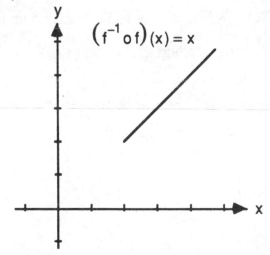

$\left(f^{-1} \circ f\right)(x) = x$

25. The endpoints of $y = f(-x)$ would be $(4,-1)$ and $(0,1)$, so the slope is:

$$m = \frac{1 - (-1)}{0 - 4} = \frac{2}{-4} = -\frac{1}{2}$$

27. The endpoints of $y = f^{-1}(x) + 1$ would be (-1,-3) and (1,1), so the midpoint is:
$$M = \left(\frac{-1+1}{2}, \frac{-3+1}{2}\right) = \left(\frac{0}{2}, -\frac{2}{2}\right) = (0,-1)$$

29. There are no values of x that need to be excluded, so the domain is all real numbers, or $(-\infty, \infty)$.

31. We must be sure that $6x^2 + 7x - 3 \neq 0$. We find the points to exclude:
$$6x^2 + 7x - 3 = 0$$
$$(3x - 1)(2x + 3) = 0$$
$$3x - 1 = 0 \quad \text{or} \quad 2x + 3 = 0$$
$$x = \frac{1}{3} \qquad\qquad x = -\frac{3}{2}$$
So the domain is all real numbers except $\frac{1}{3}$ and $-\frac{3}{2}$, or
$$\left(-\infty, -\frac{3}{2}\right) \cup \left(-\frac{3}{2}, \frac{1}{3}\right) \cup \left(\frac{1}{3}, \infty\right)$$

33. We must be sure that $x^2 + 1 > 0$. Since $x^2 + 1 \geq 1$, this restriction is automatically satisfied. So the domain is all real numbers, or $(-\infty, \infty)$.

35. We must be sure that $5 - x^2 \geq 0$
$$(\sqrt{5} + x)(\sqrt{5} - x) \geq 0$$
These values are satisfied when $-\sqrt{5} \leq x \leq \sqrt{5}$. So the domain is $[-\sqrt{5}, \sqrt{5}]$.

37. We must be sure that $x - [x] \neq 0$. We find the points to exlude:
$$x - [x] = 0$$
$$x = [x]$$
This equality is satisfied by any integer. So the domain is all non-integer real numbers.

39. We solve for x:
$$y = \frac{2x - 3}{x - 2}$$
$$y(x - 2) = 2x - 3$$
$$xy - 2y = 2x - 3$$
$$xy - 2x = 2y - 3$$
$$x(y - 2) = 2y - 3$$
$$x = \frac{2y - 3}{y - 2}$$
Now $y - 2 = 0$ when $y = 2$, so the range is all real numbers except 2, or $(-\infty, 2) \cup (2, \infty)$.

41. $(g \circ f)(x) = g \left(\dfrac{x+2}{x-1}\right) = \dfrac{\left(\dfrac{x+2}{x-1}\right) + 1}{\left(\dfrac{x+2}{x-1}\right) + 4}$

Multiply by $\dfrac{x-1}{x-1}$:

$= \dfrac{(x+2) + 1(x-1)}{(x+2) + 4(x-1)}$

$= \dfrac{x + 2 + x - 1}{x + 2 + 4x - 4}$

$= \dfrac{2x+1}{5x-2}$

We solve $y = \dfrac{2x+1}{5x-2}$ for x:

$y = \dfrac{2x+1}{5x-2}$

$y(5x-2) = 2x+1$

$5xy - 2y = 2x+1$

$5xy - 2x = 2y+1$

$x(5y-2) = 2y+1$

$x = \dfrac{2y+1}{5y-2}$

Now $5y-2 = 0$ when $y = \dfrac{2}{5}$, so the range is all real numbers except $\dfrac{2}{5}$, or

$(-\infty, \dfrac{2}{5}) \cup (\dfrac{2}{5}, \infty)$.

43. Since the range of f^{-1} is the domain of f, we must exclude the values of x where $1 + x = 0$, or $x = -1$. So the range is all real numbers except -1, or

$(-\infty, -1) \cup (-1, \infty)$.

45. $b(x) = (g \circ f)(x)$, since $(g \circ f)(x) = g[f(x)] = g\left(\dfrac{1}{x}\right) = \dfrac{1}{x} - 1$

47. $d(x) = (g \circ G)(x)$, since $(g \circ G)(x) = g[G(x)] = g(\sqrt{x}) = \sqrt{x} - 1$

49. $B(x) = (F \circ g \circ g)(x)$, since:

$(F \circ g \circ g)(x) = (F \circ g)(x-1)$

$= F(x-1-1)$

$= F(x-2)$

$= |x-2|$

51. $D(x) = (f \circ G \circ g \circ g \circ g)(x)$, since:

$$
\begin{aligned}
(f \circ G \circ g \circ g \circ g)(x) &= (f \circ G \circ g \circ g)(x-1) \\
&= (f \circ G \circ g)(x-1-1) \\
&= (f \circ G \circ g)(x-2) \\
&= (f \circ G)(x-2-1) \\
&= (f \circ G)(x-3) \\
&= f(\sqrt{x-3}) \\
&= \frac{1}{\sqrt{x-3}}
\end{aligned}
$$

53. $f(1 + \sqrt{2}) = (1 + \sqrt{2})^2 - (1 + \sqrt{2})$

$$
\begin{aligned}
&= 1 + 2\sqrt{2} + 2 - 1 - \sqrt{2} \\
&= 2 + \sqrt{2}
\end{aligned}
$$

55. $F(t) = t^2 - t$

57. $g(2x) = 1 - 2(2x) = 1 - 4x$

59. $g(x + h) = 1 - 2(x + h) = 1 - 2x - 2h$

61. $f(x) - g(x) = (x^2 - x) - (1 - 2x)$

$$
\begin{aligned}
&= x^2 - x - 1 + 2x \\
&= x^2 + x - 1
\end{aligned}
$$

63. $f(x + h) = (x + h)^2 - (x + h) = x^2 + 2xh + h^2 - x - h$

So: $f(x + h) - f(x) = (x^2 + 2xh + h^2 - x - h) - (x^2 - x)$

$$
\begin{aligned}
&= x^2 + 2xh + h^2 - x - h - x^2 + x \\
&= 2xh + h^2 - h
\end{aligned}
$$

65. $\dfrac{f(x)}{x} = \dfrac{x^2 - x}{x} = \dfrac{x(x-1)}{x} = x - 1$

67. $f[f(x)] = f(x^2 - x)$

$$
\begin{aligned}
&= (x^2 - x)^2 - (x^2 - x) \\
&= x^4 - 2x^3 + x^2 - x^2 + x \\
&= x^4 - 2x^3 + x
\end{aligned}
$$

69. $g[f(3)] = g(3^2 - 3)$
$$= g(9 - 3)$$
$$= g(6)$$
$$= 1 - 2(6)$$
$$= 1 - 12$$
$$= -11$$

71. $(g \circ f)(x) - (f \circ g)(x) = (-2x^2 + 2x + 1) - (4x^2 - 2x),$ [from #68, 70]
$$= -2x^2 + 2x + 1 - 4x^2 + 2x$$
$$= -6x^2 + 4x + 1$$

73. $\dfrac{g(x + h) - g(x)}{h} = \dfrac{(1 - 2x - 2h) - (1 - 2x)}{h}$
$$= \dfrac{1 - 2x - 2h - 1 + 2x}{h}$$
$$= \dfrac{-2h}{h}$$
$$= -2$$

75. $\dfrac{F(x) - F(a)}{x - a} = \dfrac{\dfrac{x - 3}{x + 4} - \dfrac{a - 3}{a + 4}}{x - a}$

Multiply by $\dfrac{(x + 4)(a + 4)}{(x + 4)(a + 4)}$:
$$= \dfrac{(x - 3)(a + 4) - (a - 3)(x + 4)}{(x - a)(x + 4)(a + 4)}$$
$$= \dfrac{(ax - 3a + 4x - 12) - (ax - 3x + 4a - 12)}{(x - a)(x + 4)(a + 4)}$$
$$= \dfrac{ax - 3a + 4x - 12 - ax + 3x - 4a + 12}{(x - a)(x + 4)(a + 4)}$$
$$= \dfrac{7x - 7a}{(x - a)(x + 4)(a + 4)}$$
$$= \dfrac{7(x - a)}{(x - a)(x + 4)(a + 4)}$$
$$= \dfrac{7}{(x + 4)(a + 4)}$$

77. $F[F^{-1}(x)] = x$, by the definition of $F^{-1}(x)$.

79. $F^{-1}(x) = \dfrac{-4x - 3}{x - 1}$ [from # 76], so $F^{-1}(0) = \dfrac{-4(0) - 3}{0 - 1} = \dfrac{-3}{-1} = 3$

   $F(x) = \dfrac{x - 3}{x + 4}$, so $F(0) = \dfrac{0 - 3}{0 + 4} = -\dfrac{3}{4}$

   So $F^{-1}(0) - \dfrac{1}{F(0)} = 3 - \dfrac{1}{-\dfrac{3}{4}} = 3 + \dfrac{4}{3} = \dfrac{13}{3}$

81. Let $y = 1 - 2x$. We switch the roles of x and y and solve the resulting equation for y:

$$x = 1 - 2y$$
$$2y = 1 - x$$
$$y = \frac{1 - x}{2}$$

   So $g^{-1}(x) = \dfrac{1 - x}{2}$

83. $g^{-1}(x + h) = \dfrac{1 - (x + h)}{2} = \dfrac{1 - x - h}{2}$

   So $\dfrac{g^{-1}(x + h) - g^{-1}(x)}{h} = \dfrac{\dfrac{1 - x - h}{h} - \dfrac{1 - x}{2}}{h}$

   Multiply by $\dfrac{2}{2}$:

$$= \frac{(1 - x - h) - (1 - x)}{2h}$$
$$= \frac{1 - x - h - 1 + x}{2h}$$
$$= -\frac{h}{2h}$$
$$= -\frac{1}{2}$$

85. Let $y = \dfrac{f(x)}{x}$. We switch the roles of x and y and solve the resulting equation for y:

$$x = \frac{f(y)}{y}$$
$$xy = f(y)$$
$$xy = y^2 - y$$
$$y^2 - y - xy = 0$$
$$y(y - 1 - x) = 0$$
$$y = 0 \quad \text{or} \quad y - 1 - x = 0$$

   Since $y \neq 0$ by assumption, then $y - 1 - x = 0$, or $y = x + 1$.
   So $T^{-1}(x) = x + 1$.

87.   Domain of f: $-6 \le x \le 8$, or $[-6,8]$
       Range of f: $-2 \le y \le 4$, or $[-2,4]$

89. $f\left(-\frac{5}{2}\right) \approx -1\frac{1}{3}$ and $f\left(-\frac{1}{2}\right) \approx -2$, so $f\left(-\frac{5}{2}\right)$ is larger.

91. $| f(0) - f(8) | = |-1| = 1$ [from #90]

93. $-6 \le x \le -5$, or $[-6,-5]$

95.   No - it fails the horizontal line test. To be more exact, we have f (-4) = 0 and f (2) = 0, which cannot occur with a one-to-one function.

97.   Since f (-4) = 0, then f [f(-4)] = f (0) = -2

99.   g (x) $\le$ f (x) when $0 \le x \le 4$, or $[0,4]$

101.   f (0) = 5 and g (0) = 0, so f (0) + g (0) = 5 + 0 = 5

103.   (a)   f (5) = 2, so g [f(5)] = g (2) = 2

        (b)   g (5) = 4, so f [g(5)] = f (4) = 3

        (c)   (g $\circ$ f) (5) = g [f(5)] = 2, from part (a)

        (d)   (f $\circ$ g) (5) = f [g(5)] = 3, from part (b)

105.   f (10) = 0 and g (10) = 3, so g [f(10)] - f [g(10)] = g (0) - f (3)
                                                              = 0 - 4
                                                              = - 4

107. $| f(x) - 3 | \le 1$ means that $2 \le f(x) \le 4$, which occurs when $3 \le x \le 5$, or $[3,5]$.

109.   (a)   (-6,5)

        (b)   (0,0)

        (c)   (7,5)

        (d)   (0,5)

        (e)   (10,0)

        (f)   (-10,0)

111.   If B varies directly as x and inversely as y^3, then $B = \dfrac{kx}{y^3}$. We find k by plugging in x = 6, y = 2, and B = 9:

$$9 = \frac{k(6)}{2^3}$$
$$9 = \frac{6k}{8}$$
$$72 = 6k$$
$$k = 12$$

So $B = \dfrac{12x}{y^3}$. Now, when x = 3 and y = 4, we have:

$$B = \frac{12(3)}{4^3} = \frac{36}{64} = \frac{9}{16}$$

113.   Let v = velocity and r = radius, so $v = \dfrac{k}{\sqrt{r}}$. If the radius is decreased by 10 percent, then the new radius is 90% of the original radius. We replace r by 0.9r:

$$v = \frac{k}{\sqrt{0.9r}} = \frac{k}{0.95\sqrt{r}} = 1.0541 \left(\frac{k}{\sqrt{r}}\right)$$

So the new velocity will be increased by 5.41%.

115.   Since $f^{-1}(3) = 4$, then $f(4) = 3$.

117.   (a) $F[G(x)] = F\left(\dfrac{1}{x}\right) = \left(\dfrac{1}{x}\right)^2 = \dfrac{1}{x^2}$

$G[F(x)] = G(x^2) = \dfrac{1}{x^2}$

(b)   No. Though $F[G(x)] = G[F(x)]$, these must be equal to x for F and G to be inverse functions.

119.   (a) $y = f(x) + 1$
E, since $f(a) + 1 = b + 1$

(b) $y = f(x + 1)$
C, since $f(a - 1 + 1) = f(a) = b$

(c) $y = f(x - 1) + 1$
L, since $f(a + 1 - 1) + 1 = f(a) + 1 = b + 1$

(d) $y = f(-x)$
A, since $f(-(-a)) = f(a) = b$

(e) $y = -f(x)$
J, since $-f(a) = -b$

(f) $y = -f(-x)$
G, since $-f(-(-a)) = -f(a) = -b$

(g) $y = f^{-1}(x)$
B, since $f^{-1}(b) = a$

(h) $y = f^{-1}(x) + 1$
M, since $f^{-1}(b) + 1 = a + 1$

(i) $y = f^{-1}(x - 1)$
K, since $f^{-1}(b + 1 - 1) = f^{-1}(b) = a$

(j) $y = f^{-1}(-x) + 1$
D, since $f^{-1}(-(-b)) + 1 = f^{-1}(b) + 1 = a + 1$

(k) $y = -f^{-1}(x)$
I, since $-f^{-1}(b) = -a$

(l) $y = -f^{-1}(-x) + 1$
H, since $-f^{-1}(-(-b)) + 1 = -f^{-1}(b) + 1 = -a + 1 = 1 - a$

(m) $y = 1 - f^{-1}(x)$
F, since $1 - f^{-1}(b) = 1 - a$

CHAPTER 5
POLYNOMIAL FUNCTIONS AND RATIONAL FUNCTIONS

5.1 Linear and Quadratic Functions

1. We first find the slope between the points (-1,0) and (5,4):

$$m = \frac{4 - 0}{5 - (-1)} = \frac{4}{6} = \frac{2}{3}$$

Now we use the point (-1,0) in the point-slope formula:

$$y - 0 = \frac{2}{3}[x - (-1)]$$

$$y = \frac{2}{3}(x + 1)$$

$$y = \frac{2}{3}x + \frac{2}{3}$$

Using functional notation, we have $f(x) = \frac{2}{3}x + \frac{2}{3}$.

3. We first find the slope between the points (0,0) and (1, $\sqrt{2}$):

$$m = \frac{\sqrt{2} - 0}{1 - 0} = \sqrt{2}$$

Now, since (0,0) is the y-intercept, we use the slope-intercept formula to write
$y = \sqrt{2}x$.
Using functional notation, we have $g(x) = \sqrt{2}x$.

5.   We find the slope of x - y = 1:
$$-y = -x + 1$$
$$y = x - 1$$

So the parallel slope is 1. We use the point $\left(\frac{1}{2}, -3\right)$ in the point-slope formula:

$$y - (-3) = 1\left(x - \frac{1}{2}\right)$$
$$y + 3 = x - \frac{1}{2}$$
$$y = x - \frac{7}{2}$$

Using functional notation, we have $f(x) = x - \frac{7}{2}$.

7.   We set x = 0 to find the y-intercepts of the circle:
$$0 - 0 + y^2 - 3 = 0$$
$$y^2 = 3$$
$$y = \pm\sqrt{3}$$
So a horizontal line passing through $(0, \sqrt{3})$ is $y = \sqrt{3}$.
Using functional notation, we have $f(x) = \sqrt{3}$.

9. $(f \circ g)(x) = f[g(x)]$
$$= f(1 - 2x)$$
$$= 3(1 - 2x) - 4$$
$$= 3 - 6x - 4$$
$$= -6x - 1$$
So $f \circ g$ is a linear function (it is in standard form).

11.   Call V (t) the value of the machine after t years. When t = 0 we have V = 20,000 and when t = 8 we have V = 1,000. We find the slope of the line between the points (0, 20000) and (8, 1000):
$$m = \frac{1000 - 20000}{8 - 0} = \frac{-19000}{8} = -2375$$
Now, since (0, 20000) is the y-intercept, we use the slope-intercept formula to write V = -2375 t + 20,000.
Using functional notation, we have V(t) = -2375 t + 20,000.

13.   (a)   Call V (t) the value of the machine after t years. Now V = 60,000 when t = 0 and V = 0 when t = 5. We find the slope of the line between (0,60000) and (5,0):
$$m = \frac{0 - 60000}{5 - 0} = \frac{-60000}{5} = -12,000$$
Now, since (0,60000) is the y-intercept, we use the slope-intercept formula to get V = -12,000 t + 60,000.

Using functional notation, we have V(t) = -12,000 t + 60,000.

(b)   The completed schedule is:

End of Year	Yearly Depreciation	Accumulated Depreciation	Value V
0	0	0	60,000
1	12,000	12,000	48,000
2	12,000	24,000	36,000
3	12,000	36,000	24,000
4	12,000	48,000	12,000
5	12,000	60,000	0

15. $y = (x + 2)^2$
vertex: (-2,0)
axis: x = -2
minimum: 0
x-intercept: -2
y-intercept: 4

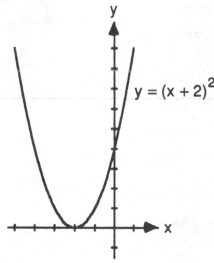

17. $y = 2(x + 2)^2$
     vertex: (-2,0)
     axis: x = -2
     minimum: 0
     x-intercept: -2
     y-intercept: 8

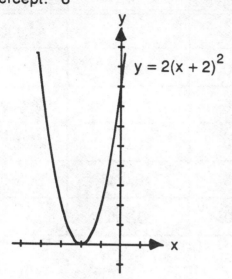

$y = 2(x + 2)^2$

19. $y = -2(x + 2)^2 + 4$
     vertex: (-2,4)
     axis: x = -2
     maximum: 4
     x-intercepts: $-2 \pm \sqrt{2}$
     y-intercept: -4

$y = -2(x + 2)^2 + 4$

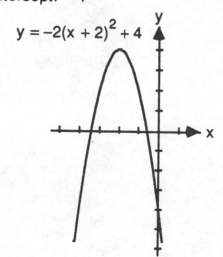

21. $f(x) = x^2 - 4x$
     Complete the square:

$$f(x) = x^2 - 4x = (x^2 - 4x + 4) - 4 = (x - 2)^2 - 4$$

vertex: (2, -4)
axis: x = 2
minimum: -4
x-intercepts: 0, 4
y-intercept: 0

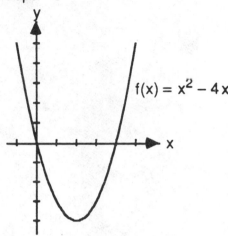

$$f(x) = x^2 - 4x$$

23. $g(x) = 1 - x^2$
     vertex: (0,1)
     axis: x = 0
     maximum: 1
     x-intercepts: ±1
     y-intercept: 1

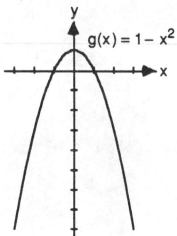

$$g(x) = 1 - x^2$$

25. $y = x^2 - 2x - 3$
Complete the square:
$$y = x^2 - 2x - 3 = (x^2 - 2x + 1) - 3 - 1 = (x - 1)^2 - 4$$
vertex: $(1,-4)$
axis: $x = 1$
minimum: -4
x-intercepts: $3, -1$
y-intercept: -3

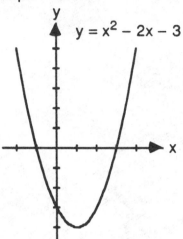

$y = x^2 - 2x - 3$

27. $y = -x^2 + 6x + 2$
Complete the square:
$$y = -x^2 + 6x + 2 = -(x^2 - 6x) + 2 = -(x^2 - 6x + 9) + 2 + 9 = -(x - 3)^2 + 11$$
vertex: $(3,11)$
axis: $x = 3$
maximum: 11
x-intercepts: $3 \pm \sqrt{11}$
y-intercept: 2

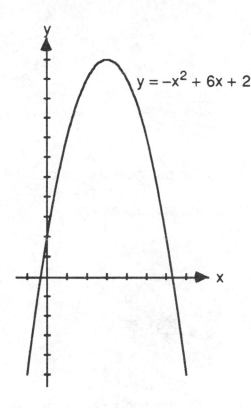

$$y = -x^2 + 6x + 2$$

29. (a)   We complete the square:
$$y = 2x^2 - 4x + 11$$
$$y = 2(x^2 - 2x) + 11$$
$$y = 2(x^2 - 2x + 1) + 11 - 2$$
$$y = 2(x - 1)^2 + 9$$
Since the vertex is (1,9) and the parabola will be pointed up, then x = 1 will yield a minimum output value.

(b)   We complete the square:
$$y = 8x^2 + x - 5$$
$$y = 8\left(x^2 + \frac{1}{8}x\right) - 5$$
$$y = 8\left(x^2 + \frac{1}{8}x + \frac{1}{256}\right) - 5 - \frac{8}{256}$$
$$y = 8\left(x + \frac{1}{16}\right)^2 - \frac{161}{32}$$
Since the vertex is $\left(-\frac{1}{16}, -\frac{161}{32}\right)$ and the parabola will be pointed up, then $x = -\frac{1}{16}$ will yield a minimum output value.

(c) We complete the square:
$$y = -8x^2 + x - 5$$
$$y = -8\left(x^2 - \frac{1}{8}x\right) - 5$$
$$y = -8\left(x^2 - \frac{1}{8}x + \frac{1}{256}\right) - 5 + \frac{8}{256}$$
$$y = -8\left(x - \frac{1}{16}\right)^2 - \frac{159}{32}$$

Since the vertex is $\left(\frac{1}{16}, -\frac{159}{32}\right)$ and the parabola will be pointed

down, then $x = \frac{1}{16}$ will yield a maximum output value.

(d) We complete the square:
$$s = -16t^2 + 196t + 80$$
$$s = -16\left(t^2 - \frac{49}{4}t\right) + 80$$
$$s = -16\left(t^2 - \frac{49}{4}t + \frac{2401}{64}\right) + 80 + \frac{2401}{4}$$
$$s = -16\left(t - \frac{49}{8}\right)^2 + \frac{2721}{4}$$

Since the vertex is $\left(\frac{49}{8}, \frac{2721}{4}\right)$ and the parabola will be pointed

down, then $x = \frac{49}{8}$ will yield a maximum output value.

(e) Since the vertex is $(0,-10)$ and the parabola will be pointed up, then
$x = 0$ will yield a minimum output value.

(f) We complete the square:
$$y = -x^2 + \frac{3}{2}x + 1$$
$$y = -\left(x^2 - \frac{3}{2}x\right) + 1$$
$$y = -\left(x^2 - \frac{3}{2}x + \frac{9}{16}\right) + 1 + \frac{9}{16}$$
$$y = -\left(x - \frac{3}{4}\right)^2 + \frac{25}{16}$$

Since the vertex is $\left(\frac{3}{4}, \frac{25}{16}\right)$ and the parabola will be pointed down,

then $x = \frac{3}{4}$ will yield a maximum output value.

31. We find the vertex of the parabola by completing the square:
$$y = x^2 - 6x + 13$$
$$y = (x^2 - 6x + 9) + 13 - 9$$
$$y = (x - 3)^2 + 4$$
So the vertex is (3,4). We now use the distance formula with the points (0,0) and (3,4):
$$d = \sqrt{(3 - 0)^2 + (4 - 0)^2} = \sqrt{9 + 16} = \sqrt{25} = 5$$
So the vertex is 5 units from the origin.

33. (a) We first complete the square on $x^2 - 6x + 73$:
$$x^2 - 6x + 73 = (x^2 - 6x + 9) + 73 - 9 = (x - 3)^2 + 64$$
So $f(x) = \sqrt{(x - 3)^2 + 64}$
This would achieve a minimum value at $(3, \sqrt{64}) = (3,8)$.

(b) Here $g(x) = \sqrt[3]{(x - 3)^2 + 64}$, which would achieve a minimum value at $(3, \sqrt[3]{64}) = (3,4)$.

(c) We complete the square on $x^4 - 6x^2 + 73$:
$$x^4 - 6x^2 + 73 = (x^4 - 6x^2 + 9) + 73 - 9 = (x^2 - 3)^2 + 64$$
So $h(x) = (x^2 - 3)^2 + 64$, which would achieve a minimum value at $(\pm\sqrt{3}, 64)$.

35. (a) We complete the square on $-x^2 + 4x + 12$:
$$-x^2 + 4x + 12 = -(x^2 - 4x) + 12$$
$$= -(x^2 - 4x + 4) + 12 + 4$$
$$= -(x - 2)^2 + 16$$
So $f(x) = \sqrt{-(x - 2)^2 + 16}$, which has a maximum value at $(2,\sqrt{16}) = (2,4)$

(b) Now $g(x) = \sqrt[3]{-(x - 2)^2 + 16}$, which has a maximum value at $(2,\sqrt[3]{16}) = (2, 2\sqrt[3]{2})$

(c) Here $h(x) = -(x^2 - 2)^2 + 16$, which has a maximum value at $(\pm\sqrt{2}, 16)$

37. We find the slope:
$$m = \frac{5.42 - (-0.83)}{2.06 - 1.27} = \frac{6.25}{0.79} = 7.91$$
We use the point (2.06, 5.42) in the point-slope formula:
$$y - 5.42 = 7.91(x - 2.06)$$

$$y - 5.42 = 7.91x - 16.30$$
$$y = 7.91x - 10.88$$

39. We have $V = 26,450$ when $t = 0$ and $V = -1900$ when $t = 7$, so we find the slope between the points $(0, 26450)$ and $(7, -1900)$:

$$m = \frac{-1900 - 26450}{7 - 0} = \frac{-28350}{7} = -4050$$

Since $(0, 26450)$ is the y-intercept, we use the slope-intercept formula to write $V = -4,050\, t + 26,450$.

Using functional notation, we have $V(t) = -4,050\, t + 26,450$.

41. The vertex will be $(-4,3)$, so its equation will be
$$y = (x + 4)^2 + 3$$
$$= x^2 + 8x + 19$$

43. Since the axis of symmetry is $x = 1$, the parabola will have the form $y = A(x - 1)^2 + B$. Also, if there is only one x-intercept, it must be the vertex. So the vertex is $(1,0)$, and we have the equation $y = A(x - 1)^2$. Since $(0,1)$ must lie on this parabola, we plug the point in to find A:

$$y = A(x - 1)^2$$
$$1 = A(0 - 1)^2$$
$$1 = A$$

So the parabola is $y = (x - 1)^2 = x^2 - 2x + 1$.

45. We find the vertex of the parabola by completing the square:

$$y = 2x^2 + 12x + 14$$
$$y = 2(x^2 + 6x) + 14$$
$$y = 2(x^2 + 6x + 9) + 14 - 18$$
$$y = 2(x + 3)^2 - 4$$

So the vertex is $(-3, -4)$. Thus the circle would have an equation of $(x + 3)^2 + (y + 4)^2 = r^2$. Since $(0,0)$ lies on the circle, we have:

$$(0 + 3)^2 + (0 + 4)^2 = r^2$$
$$r^2 = 9 + 16$$
$$r^2 = 25$$
$$r = 5, \text{ since } r > 0$$

So the circle is $(x + 3)^2 + (y + 4)^2 = 25$.

47. Since a and b will be the x-intercepts of the parabola, and all points with the same y-coordinate will be symmetric about the axis of symmetry, it follows that the midpoint $\left(\frac{a + b}{2}, 0\right)$ must lie on the axis of symmetry. Thus the x-coordinate of the vertex (which also lies on this axis) is $\frac{a + b}{2}$.

49. (a)   We have $\frac{\Delta p}{\Delta x} = \frac{10}{-5} = -2$. Also p = 200 when x = 150. We use the
           point-slope formula with the point (150,200):
$$p - 200 = -2(x - 150)$$
$$p - 200 = -2x + 300$$
$$p = -2x + 500$$
           Using functional notation, we have p(x) = -2x + 500.

     (b)   Since R = xp, we have R = x(-2x + 500) = $-2x^2 + 500x$.
           We complete the square:
$$R = -2x^2 + 500x$$
$$R = -2(x^2 - 250x)$$
$$R = -2(x^2 - 250x + 15625) + 31{,}250$$
$$R = -2(x - 125)^2 + 31{,}250$$
           Using functional notation, we have R(x) = $-2(x - 125)^2 + 31{,}250$. This
           simplifies to R(x) = $-2x^2 + 500x$.

51. (a)   f(1967) = -0.4164(1967) + 1052.0433 $\approx$ 233.0 sec
$$\% \text{ error} = \frac{|231.1 - 233.0|}{231.1} \times 100 \approx 0.82\,\% \text{ error}$$

     (b)   f(1980) = -0.4164(1980) + 1052.0433 $\approx$ 227.6 sec
$$\% \text{ error} = \frac{|228.8 - 227.6|}{228.8} \times 100 \approx 0.52\,\% \text{ error}$$

     (c)   f(1985) = -0.4164(1985) + 1052.0433 $\approx$ 225.49 sec
$$\% \text{ error} = \frac{|226.31 - 225.49|}{226.31} \times 100 \approx 0.36\,\% \text{ error}$$

     (d)   f(2026) = -0.4164(2026) + 1052.0433 $\approx$ 208.42 sec
           The predicted value is 3:30 = 210 sec
           The prediction is close; its percent error is:
$$\% \text{ error} = \frac{|210 - 208.42|}{210} \times 100 = 0.75\,\% \text{ error}$$

53. (a) We complete the square:
$$g(x) = x^2 + 2(a + b)x + 2(a^2 + b^2)$$
$$g(x) = [\,x^2 + 2(a + b)x + (a + b)^2\,] + 2(a^2 + b^2) - (a + b)^2$$
$$g(x) = [\,x + (a + b)\,]^2 + 2a^2 + 2b^2 - a^2 - 2ab - b^2$$
$$g(x) = [\,x + (a + b)\,]^2 + a^2 + b^2 - 2ab$$
$$g(x) = [\,x + (a + b)\,]^2 + (a - b)^2$$
Thus the vertex is $(-(a + b), (a - b)^2)$.

(b) If $a = b$, then $(a - b)^2 = 0$, and thus there is only one x-intercept.
If $a \neq b$, then $(a - b)^2 > 0$. But since $g(x)$ is a parabola opening upward, then it cannot have any x-intercepts.

5.2 Applied Functions: Setting Up Equations

1. (a) We first draw the figure:

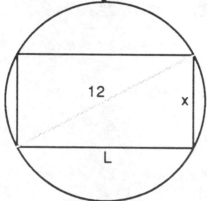

Call P the perimeter. We are asked to come up with a formula for P in terms of x. Since the diameter forms a right triangle, we use the Pythagorean Theorem to get:
$$L^2 + x^2 = 12^2$$
$$L^2 = 144 - x^2$$
$$L = \sqrt{144 - x^2}$$
Now $P = 2x + 2L$
$$= 2x + 2\sqrt{144 - x^2}$$
Using functional notation, we have $P(x) = 2x + 2\sqrt{144 - x^2}$

(b) Let A denote the area of the rectangle. Then $A = xL = x\sqrt{144 - x^2}$
Using functional notation, we have $A(x) = x\sqrt{144 - x^2}$

3.   (a)   We first draw the figure:

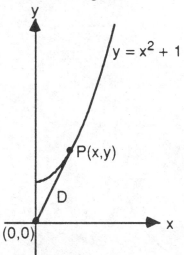

Call D the distance from P(x,y) to the origin. We are asked to come up with a formula for D in terms of x. By the distance formula, we have:

$$D = \sqrt{(x - 0)^2 + (y - 0)^2} = \sqrt{x^2 + y^2}$$

Since P(x,y) lies on the curve, then $y = x^2 + 1$. Substituting this for y in our equation for D, we have:

$$D = \sqrt{x^2 + y^2}$$
$$= \sqrt{x^2 + (x^2 + 1)^2}$$
$$= \sqrt{x^2 + x^4 + 2x^2 + 1}$$
$$= \sqrt{x^4 + 3x^2 + 1}$$

Using functional notation, we have $D(x) = \sqrt{x^4 + 3x^2 + 1}$

   (b)   Let M denote the slope of the line segment from the origin to P(x,y). Then:

$$M = \frac{y - 0}{x - 0} = \frac{y}{x}$$

Substituting $y = x^2 + 1$ in for y in this equation, we have:

$$M = \frac{y}{x} = \frac{x^2 + 1}{x}$$

Using functional notation, we have $M(x) = \frac{x^2 + 1}{x}$

5.   (a)   We first draw the figure:

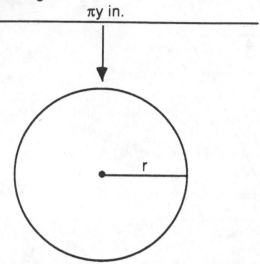

πy in.

Call A the area of the circle and r its radius. We are asked to come up with a formula for A in terms of y. SInce πy is the circumference (C) of the circle, and $C = 2\pi r$, we have:

$$2\pi r = \pi y$$

$$r = \frac{y}{2}$$

Now $A = \pi r^2 = \pi\left(\frac{y}{2}\right)^2 = \frac{\pi y^2}{4}$

Using functional notation, we have $A(y) = \frac{\pi y^2}{4}$

(b)   We draw the figure:

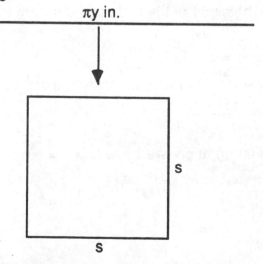

πy in.

Let A denote the area of the square, and s the length of the side.

Since the perimeter (P) is πy and $P = 4s$, we have:
$$4s = \pi y$$
$$s = \frac{\pi y}{4}$$

Now $A = s^2 = \left(\frac{\pi y}{4}\right)^2 = \frac{\pi^2 y^2}{16}$

Using functional notation, we have $A(y) = \frac{\pi^2 y^2}{16}$

7. (a) Let the two numbers be x and $16 - x$. Then the product P would be:
$$P = x(16 - x) = 16x - x^2$$
Using functional notation, we have $P(x) = 16x - x^2$

(b) Since the two numbers are x and $16 - x$, then the sum of squares S would be:
$$\begin{aligned} S &= (x)^2 + (16 - x)^2 \\ &= x^2 + 256 - 32x + x^2 \\ &= 2x^2 - 32x + 256 \end{aligned}$$
Using functional notation, we have $S(x) = 2x^2 - 32x + 256$

(c) There are two ways to set this up. Since the two numbers are x and $16 - x$, then the difference of the cubes D could be:
$$D = (x)^3 - (16 - x)^3 \quad \text{or} \quad D = (16 - x)^3 - x^3$$
Using functional notation, we have:
$$D(x) = x^3 - (16 - x)^3 \quad \text{or} \quad D(x) = (16 - x)^3 - x^3$$

(d) Let A denote the average of the two numbers. Since the two numbers are x and $16 - x$, we have:
$$A = \frac{x + 16 - x}{2} = \frac{16}{2} = 8$$
So $A(x) = 8$. Notice that the average does not depend what the two numbers are!.

9. Let R be the revenue, x be the number of units sold, and p be the demand (price). Then:
$$R = xp = x\left(-\frac{1}{4}x + 8\right) = -\frac{1}{4}x^2 + 8x$$
Using functional notation, we have $R(x) = -\frac{1}{4}x^2 + 8x$

11. (a)   We complete the table:

x	1	2	3	4	5	6	7
P(x)	17.88	19.49	20.83	21.86	22.49	22.58	21.75

(b)   The largest value for P(x) is 22.58, corresponding to $x = 6$.

(c)
$$P(4\sqrt{2}) = 2(4\sqrt{2}) + 2\sqrt{64 - (4\sqrt{2})^2}$$
$$= 8\sqrt{2} + 2\sqrt{64 - 32}$$
$$= 8\sqrt{2} + 2\sqrt{32}$$
$$= 8\sqrt{2} + 8\sqrt{2}$$
$$= 16\sqrt{2}$$
$$\approx 22.63$$

This is indeed larger than any of our table values.

13. (a)   We first draw the figure:

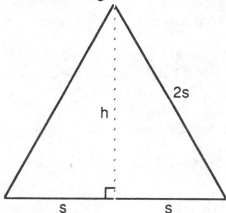

Let h denote the height and 2s denote the sides. Note that the height (called the altitude) bisects the base into the lengths of s and s. We are asked to find h in terms of s, so we use the Pytrhagorean Theorem on the right triangle:

$$h^2 + s^2 = (2s)^2$$
$$h^2 + s^2 = 4s^2$$
$$h^2 = 3s^2$$
$$h = \sqrt{3s^2}$$
$$h = \sqrt{3}\, s$$

Using functional notation we have $h(s) = \sqrt{3}\, s$.

(b) Let A denote the area of the triangle. Then:
$$A = \frac{1}{2}(\text{base})(\text{height}) = \frac{1}{2}(2s)(\sqrt{3}\,s) = \sqrt{3}\,s^2$$
Using functional notation, we have $A(s) = \sqrt{3}\,s^2$.

(c) If each side is 8 cm, then:
$$2s = 8$$
$$s = 4$$
Using the function from (a), we have:
$$h(4) = \sqrt{3}\cdot 4 = 4\sqrt{3}\ \text{cm}.$$

(d) If each side is 5 in., then:
$$2s = 5$$
$$s = \frac{5}{2}$$
Using the function from (b), we have:
$$A\left(\frac{5}{2}\right) = \sqrt{3}\left(\frac{5}{2}\right)^2 = \frac{25\sqrt{3}}{4}\ \text{in}^2$$

15. Let h be the height, r be the radius, and V be the volume. We know that:
$$V = \pi r^2 h$$
We are also given that h = 2r, so we plug into the formula for V:
$$V = \pi r^2(2r) = 2\pi r^3$$
Using functional notation, we have $V(r) = 2\pi\,r^3$.

17. (a) Let h be the height, r be the radius, and V be the volume. We know that $V = 12\pi$ and $V = \pi r^2 h$, so:
$$\pi r^2 h = 12\pi$$
$$h = \frac{12\pi}{\pi r^2}$$
$$h = \frac{12}{r^2}$$
Using functional notation, we have $h(r) = \dfrac{12}{r^2}$

(b) Let S be the total surface area. Then:
$$S = 2\pi r^2 + 2\pi\,rh$$
$$= 2\pi r^2 + 2\pi\,r\left(\frac{12}{r^2}\right)\quad \text{by (a)}$$
$$= 2\pi r^2 + \frac{24\pi r}{r^2}$$
$$= 2\pi r^2 + \frac{24\pi}{r}$$

Using functional notation, we have $S(r) = 2\pi r^2 + \dfrac{24\pi}{r}$

19. We solve $S = 4\pi r^2$ for r:

$$4\pi r^2 = S$$

$$r^2 = \frac{S}{4\pi}$$

$$r = \sqrt{\frac{S}{4\pi}}$$

Now $V = \dfrac{4}{3}\pi r^3$

$$= \frac{4}{3}\pi\left(\sqrt{\frac{S}{4\pi}}\right)^3$$

$$= \frac{4\pi S\sqrt{S}}{3(4\pi)\sqrt{4\pi}}$$

$$= \frac{S\sqrt{S}}{3\sqrt{4\pi}} \quad \text{or} \quad \frac{S\sqrt{4\pi S}}{12\pi}$$

Using functional notation, we have $V(S) = \dfrac{S\sqrt{4\pi S}}{12\pi} = \dfrac{S\sqrt{S\pi}}{6\pi}$

21. We draw a figure:

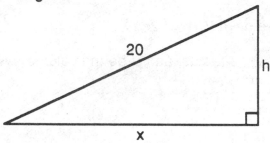

Let A be the area of the triangle, and let x and h be its two legs. By the Pythagorean Theorem, we have:

$$x^2 + h^2 = 20^2$$

$$h^2 = 400 - x^2$$

$$h = \sqrt{400 - x^2}$$

Now $A = \dfrac{1}{2}$ (base) (height)

$$= \frac{1}{2}(x)(h)$$

$$= \frac{1}{2}x\sqrt{400 - x^2}$$

Using functional notation, we have $A(x) = \dfrac{1}{2}x\sqrt{400 - x^2}$

23.   We draw the figure:

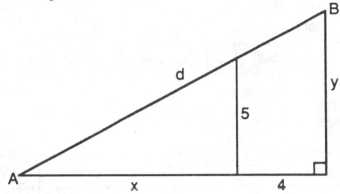

Let $d = AB$.
Using similar triangles, we have:

$$\frac{x}{5} = \frac{x + 4}{y}$$
$$xy = 5(x + 4)$$
$$y = \frac{5(x + 4)}{x}$$

Now:

$$d^2 = (x + 4)^2 + y^2$$
$$= (x + 4)^2 + \left(\frac{5(x + 4)}{x}\right)^2$$
$$= (x + 4)^2 + \frac{25(x + 4)^2}{x^2}$$
$$= \frac{x^2(x + 4)^2 + 25(x + 4)^2}{x^2}$$
$$= \frac{(x + 4)^2(x^2 + 25)}{x^2}$$

So: $$d = \frac{(x + 4)\sqrt{x^2 + 25}}{x}$$

Using functional notation, we have: $d(x) = \dfrac{(x + 4)\sqrt{x^2 + 25}}{x}$

25.   We plug into $A(x) = 50x - x^2$:

x	5	10	20	24	24.8	24.9	25	25.1	25.2	45
A(x)	225	400	600	624	624.96	624.99	625	624.99	624.96	225

$x = 25$ yields the largest area. Since $L = 50 - x = 50 - 25 = 25$, then $L = 25$ is the corresponding value.

27. (a) We plug into $A(x) = 8x - \frac{1}{2}x^3$:

Table 1:

x	1	2	3	4
A	7.5	12	10.5	0

x = 2 yields the largest area

Table 2:

x	1.75	2.00	2.25	2.50	2.75
A	11.3203	12.0000	12.3047	12.1875	11.6016

x = 2.25 yields the largest area.

Table 3:

x	2.15	2.20	2.25	2.30	2.35
A	12.2308	12.2760	12.3047	12.3165	12.3111

x = 2.30 yields the largest area.

(b) Since $x = \frac{4\sqrt{3}}{3} = 2.309$ to four significant places, then x = 2.30 is the closest x-value. This yields an area of 12.3168. Notice that x = 2.30 agrees with this to five significant digits.

29. (a) Since $V = \frac{1}{3}\pi r^2 h$ and $h = \sqrt{3}\,r$, we have:

$$V = \frac{1}{3}\pi r^2 (\sqrt{3}\,r)$$

$$= \frac{\sqrt{3}}{3}\pi r^3$$

Using functional notation, we have $V(r) = \frac{\sqrt{3}}{3}\pi r^3$

(b) Since $S = \pi r \sqrt{r^2 + h^2}$ and $h = \sqrt{3}\,r$, we have:

$$S = \pi r \sqrt{r^2 + h^2}$$
$$= \pi r \sqrt{r^2 + (\sqrt{3}r)^2}$$
$$= \pi r \sqrt{r^2 + 3r^2}$$
$$= \pi r \sqrt{4r^2}$$

$$= \pi r(2r)$$
$$= 2\pi r^2$$

Using functional notation, we have $S(r) = 2\pi r^2$

31. (a)   Since $V = \frac{1}{3}\pi r^2 h$ and $S = \pi r \sqrt{r^2 + h^2}$, and $V = S$, we have:

$$\frac{1}{3}\pi r^2 h = \pi r \sqrt{r^2 + h^2}$$
$$rh = 3\sqrt{r^2 + h^2}$$

Squaring:
$$r^2 h^2 = 9(r^2 + h^2)$$
$$r^2 h^2 = 9r^2 + 9h^2$$
$$r^2 h^2 - 9r^2 = 9h^2$$
$$r^2(h^2 - 9) = 9h^2$$
$$r^2 = \frac{9h^2}{h^2 - 9}$$

Taking roots:
$$r = \sqrt{\frac{9h^2}{h^2 - 9}}$$
$$r = \frac{3h}{\sqrt{h^2 - 9}}$$

Using functional notation, we have $r(h) = \dfrac{3h}{\sqrt{h^2 - 9}}$

(b)   After squaring in (a), we had:
$$r^2 h^2 = 9r^2 + 9h^2$$
$$r^2 h^2 - 9h^2 = 9r^2$$
$$h^2(r^2 - 9) = 9r^2$$
$$h^2 = \frac{9r^2}{r^2 - 9}$$

Taking roots:
$$h = \sqrt{\frac{9r^2}{r^2 - 9}}$$
$$h = \frac{3r}{\sqrt{r^2 - 9}}$$

Using functional notation, we have $h(r) = \dfrac{3r}{\sqrt{r^2 - 9}}$

33. Let x be the length of wire used for the circle. Then 14 - x is the length of wire used for the square. We have:

<u>Circle</u>

$$\text{Circum} = 2\pi r = x$$

$$r = \frac{x}{2\pi}$$

$$\text{Area} = \pi r^2 = \pi\left(\frac{x}{2\pi}\right)^2$$

$$= \frac{\pi x^2}{4\pi^2}$$

<u>Square</u>

$$\text{Perim} = 4S = 14 - x$$

$$S = \frac{14 - x}{4}$$

$$\text{Area} = S^2 = \left(\frac{14 - x}{4}\right)^2$$

$$= \frac{(14 - x)^2}{16}$$

$$= \frac{x^2}{4\pi}$$

So the total combined area is

$$A = \frac{x^2}{4\pi} + \frac{(14 - x)^2}{16}$$

$$= \frac{4x^2 + \pi(14 - x)^2}{16\pi}$$

Using functional notation, we have:

$$A(x) = \frac{4x^2 + \pi(14 - x)^2}{16\pi}$$

35. The perimeter of each semi-circle is $\frac{1}{2}(2\pi r) = \pi r$, so the total perimeter P is given by:

$$P = \pi r + \pi r + l + l$$
$$= 2\pi r + 2l$$

Since $P = \frac{1}{4}$, we have:

$$2\pi r + 2l = \frac{1}{4}$$

$$2l = \frac{1}{4} - 2\pi r$$

$$2l = \frac{1 - 8\pi r}{4}$$

$$l = \frac{1 - 8\pi r}{8}$$

We now find the area A. The area of each semicircle is $\frac{1}{2}(\pi r^2)$, and the area of the rectangle is length • width:

$$A = \frac{1}{2}\pi r^2 + \frac{1}{2}\pi r^2 + lw, \quad \text{but } w = 2r$$

$$= \pi r^2 + \left(\frac{1 - 8\pi r}{8}\right)(2r)$$

$$= \pi r^2 + \frac{r - 8\pi r^2}{4}$$

$$= \frac{4\pi r^2 + r - 8\pi r^2}{4}$$

$$= \frac{r - 4\pi r^2}{4}$$

Using functional notation, we have $A(r) = \dfrac{r(1 - 4\pi r)}{4}$

37. We draw the figure:

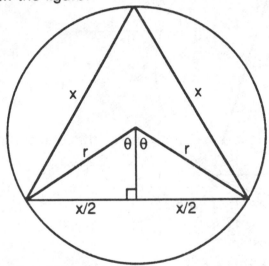

Using geometry, we see that:

$$2\theta = \frac{1}{3}(360°)$$

$$2\theta = 120°$$

$$\theta = 60°$$

Since $\theta = 60°$, then:

$$\frac{x}{2} = \frac{\sqrt{3}}{2}r$$

$$x = \sqrt{3}\,r$$

$$r = \frac{x}{\sqrt{3}}$$

So the area of the circle A is:

$$A = \pi r^2$$

$$= \pi \left(\frac{x}{\sqrt{3}}\right)^2$$

$$= \frac{\pi x^2}{3}$$

Using functional notation, we have $A(x) = \dfrac{\pi x^2}{3}$

39.   We draw the figure:

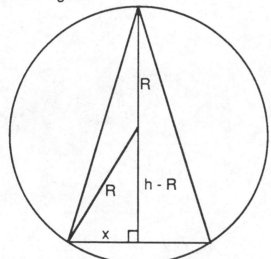

We first find x by the Pythagorean Theorem:

$$x^2 + (h - R)^2 = R^2$$
$$x^2 = R^2 - (h - R)^2$$
$$x^2 = R^2 - (h^2 - 2hR + R^2)$$
$$x^2 = -h^2 + 2hR$$

Taking roots:

$$x = \sqrt{2Rh - h^2}$$

Now the area of the triangle is given by:

$$A_\Delta = \frac{1}{2}(\text{base})(\text{height})$$

$$= \frac{1}{2}(2x)(h)$$

$$= \frac{1}{2}(2\sqrt{2Rh - h^2})(h)$$

$$= h\sqrt{2Rh - h^2}$$

The area of the circle is:

$$A_0 = \pi R^2$$

So the desired area A is given by:

$$A = A_0 - A_\Delta = \pi R^2 - h\sqrt{2Rh - h^2}$$

Since R is a constant, we use functional notation to write:

$$A(h) = \pi R^2 - h\sqrt{2Rh - h^2}$$

41. Since $V = l \cdot w \cdot h$ and $l = 8 - 2x$, $w = 6 - 2x$, $h = x$, we have:

$$\begin{aligned} V &= (8 - 2x)\,(6 - 2x)\,(x) \\ &= (48 - 28x + 4x^2)\,(x) \\ &= 4x^3 - 28x^2 + 48x \end{aligned}$$

Using functional notation, we have $V(x) = 4x^3 - 28x^2 + 48x$

43. (a)   The area of the window would be:

$$A = \frac{1}{2}(\pi r^2) + lw$$

It remains to find l and w in terms of r. We see that $w = 2r$, and the perimeter $P = 32$ and:

$$P = \frac{1}{2}(2\pi r) + 2\,l + w$$

So:

$$\begin{aligned} \frac{1}{2}(2\pi r) + 2\,l + w &= 32 \\ \pi r + 2\,l + 2r &= 32 \\ 2\,l &= 32 - \pi r - 2r \\ l &= \frac{32 - \pi r - 2r}{2} \end{aligned}$$

We now find the area:

$$\begin{aligned} A &= \frac{1}{2}(\pi r^2) + l\,w \\ &= \frac{1}{2}(\pi r^2) + \left(\frac{32 - \pi r - 2r}{2}\right)(2r) \\ &= \frac{\pi r^2}{2} + 32r - \pi r^2 - 2r^2 \\ &= 32r - 2r^2 - \frac{\pi r^2}{2} \end{aligned}$$

Using functional notation, we write $A(r) = 32r - 2r^2 - \dfrac{\pi r^2}{2}$

(b) $A(r) = -\left(\dfrac{4 + \pi}{2}\right)r^2 + 32r$, which will open downward. Since $A(0) = 0$, it does pass through the origin. We complete the square:

$$A(r) = -\left(\frac{4 + \pi}{2}\right)\left(r^2 - \frac{64}{4 + \pi}r\right)$$

$$= -\left(\frac{4 + \pi}{2}\right)\left(r^2 - \frac{64}{4 + \pi}r + \left(\frac{32}{4 + \pi}\right)^2\right) + \left(\frac{4 + \pi}{2}\right)\left(\frac{32}{4 + \pi}\right)^2$$

$$= -\left(\frac{4 + \pi}{2}\right)\left(r - \frac{32}{4 + \pi}\right)^2 + \frac{512}{4 + \pi}$$

So the vertex is $\left(\dfrac{32}{4 + \pi}, \dfrac{512}{4 + \pi}\right)$.

45. (a) We use the Pythagorean Theorem:

$$3^2 + y^2 = z^2$$

Taking roots:

$$z = \sqrt{y^2 + 9}$$

Now $s = \dfrac{y}{z} = \dfrac{y}{\sqrt{y^2 + 9}}$, so $s\sqrt{y^2 + 9} = y$

Squaring, we get:

$$s^2(y^2 + 9) = y^2$$
$$s^2 y^2 + 9s^2 = y^2$$
$$y^2 - s^2 y^2 = 9s^2$$
$$y^2(1 - s^2) = 9s^2$$
$$y^2 = \frac{9s^2}{1 - s^2}$$

Taking roots:

$$y = \frac{3s}{\sqrt{1 - s^2}}$$

Using functional notation, we have $y(s) = \dfrac{3s}{\sqrt{1 - s^2}}$

(b) This was done in (a); we had $s(y) = \dfrac{y}{\sqrt{y^2 + 9}}$

(c) Since $s = \dfrac{y}{z}$, then $z = \dfrac{y}{s}$. Using our result from (a), we have:

$$z = \frac{y}{s} = \frac{\dfrac{3s}{\sqrt{1 - s^2}}}{s} = \frac{3}{\sqrt{1 - s^2}}$$

Using functional notation, we have $z(s) = \dfrac{3}{\sqrt{1 - s^2}}$

(d)   Using our answer from (c), we have:

$$z = \frac{3}{\sqrt{1 - s^2}}$$

$$z\sqrt{1 - s^2} = 3$$

Squaring each side, we get:

$$z^2(1 - s^2) = 9$$

$$z^2 - z^2 s^2 = 9$$

$$-z^2 s^2 = 9 - z^2$$

$$s^2 = \frac{z^2 - 9}{z^2}$$

Taking roots:

$$s = \frac{\sqrt{z^2 - 9}}{z}$$

Using functional notation, we have $s(z) = \dfrac{\sqrt{z^2 - 9}}{z}$

47. (a)   Slope $= \dfrac{a^2 - (-1)}{a - 0} = \dfrac{a^2 + 1}{a}$

(b)   The area of the triangle, A, is:

$$A = \frac{1}{2}(\text{base})(\text{height}) = \frac{1}{2}(a - x_0)(a^2)$$

where x_0 is the x-intercept. To find the x-intercept, we must find the

equation of the line. We use $m = \dfrac{a^2 + 1}{a}$ (from (a) above) and (0,-1)

in the slope-intercept formula to get:

$$y = \frac{a^2 + 1}{a} x - 1$$

We find x_0 by letting $y = 0$:

$$0 = \frac{a^2 + 1}{a} x_0 - 1$$

$$\frac{a^2 + 1}{a} x_0 = 1$$

$$x_0 = \frac{a}{a^2 + 1}$$

So $A = \dfrac{1}{2}(a - x_0) a^2$

$$= \frac{1}{2}\left(a - \frac{a}{a^2 + 1}\right) a^2$$

$$= \frac{a^2}{2}\left(\frac{a(a^2 + 1) - a}{a^2 + 1}\right)$$

$$= \frac{a^2(a^3 + a - a)}{2(a^2 + 1)}$$

$$= \frac{a^2(a^3)}{2(a^2 + 1)}$$

$$= \frac{a^5}{2(a^2 + 1)}$$

49. We re-draw the figure (differently):

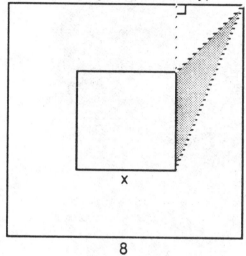

We extend the triangle to form a right triangle as pictured. We find the areas of the large and small right triangles:

$$A_{large} = \frac{1}{2}(base)(height)$$

$$= \frac{1}{2}\left(x + \frac{8 - x}{2}\right)\left(\frac{8 - x}{2}\right)$$

$$= \frac{1}{2}\left(\frac{2x + 8 - x}{2}\right)\left(\frac{8 - x}{2}\right)$$

$$= \frac{(x + 8)(8 - x)}{8}$$

$$= \frac{64 - x^2}{8}$$

$$A_{small} = \frac{1}{2}(base)(height)$$

$$= \frac{1}{2}\left(\frac{8 - x}{2}\right)\left(\frac{8 - x}{2}\right)$$

$$= \frac{64 - 16x + x^2}{8}$$

So A = A_{large} - A_{small}

$$= \frac{64 - x^2}{8} - \frac{64 - 16x + x^2}{8}$$

$$= \frac{64 - x^2 - 64 + 16x - x^2}{8}$$

$$= \frac{16x - 2x^2}{8}$$

$$= \frac{8x - x^2}{4}$$

Using functional notation, we write $A(x) = \frac{8x - x^2}{4}$

Note: A slightly easier approach is to realize that the altitude of the triangle need not lie on the triangle. That is:

$$\text{Area } = \frac{1}{2} \text{(base) (altitude)}$$

$$= \frac{1}{2}(x)\left(\frac{8 - x}{2}\right)$$

$$= \frac{8x - x^2}{4}$$

Both approaches are correct.

51. We draw the diagram:

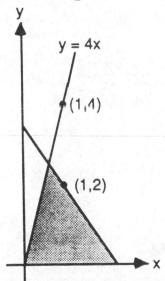

We are asked to find the area A of the shaded triangle. Since the line has slope m and passes through (1,2), then by the point-slope formula, we have:

$$y - 2 = m(x - 1)$$
$$y - 2 = mx - m$$
$$y = mx + (2 - m)$$

Its x-intercept is where $y = 0$:
$$0 = mx + (2 - m)$$
$$mx = m - 2$$
$$x = \frac{m - 2}{m}$$

This is the base of a triangle. To find its height, we must find the value of y where this line and $y = 4x$ intersect. We set the two y-values equal:
$$mx + 2 - m = 4x$$
$$mx - 4x = m - 2$$
$$x(m - 4) = m - 2$$
$$x = \frac{m - 2}{m - 4}$$

Since this point lies on $y = 4x$, its y-coordinate is:
$$y = 4x = 4\left(\frac{m - 2}{m - 4}\right)$$

Finally, we find the area:
$$A = \frac{1}{2}(\text{base})(\text{height})$$
$$= \frac{1}{2}\left(\frac{m - 2}{m}\right)(4)\left(\frac{m - 2}{m - 4}\right)$$
$$= 2\frac{(m - 2)^2}{m(m - 4)}$$
$$= \frac{2(m^2 - 4m + 4)}{m^2 - 4m}$$
$$= \frac{2m^2 - 8m + 8}{m^2 - 4m}$$

Using functional notation, we have $A(m) = \dfrac{2m^2 - 8m + 8}{m^2 - 4m}$

53. We draw a figure:

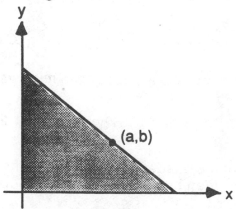

The line has the equation $y - b = m(x - a)$. Since the base and height are the x- and y-intercepts, respectively, we find each intercept:

base:
$$y = 0$$
$$-b = m(x - a)$$
$$-b = mx - ma$$
$$mx = ma - b$$
$$x = \frac{ma - b}{m}$$

height:
$$x = 0$$
$$y - b = m(-a)$$
$$y = b - ma$$

So the area of the triangle is $A = \frac{1}{2}\left(\frac{ma - b}{m}\right)(b - ma) = \frac{(ma - b)^2}{-2m}$

5.3 Maximum and Minimum Problems

1. Call the two numbers x and y. Then $x + y = 5$, so $y = 5 - x$. So the product can be written as:
$$P = xy = x(5 - x) = 5x - x^2$$
We now complete the square:
$$P = -(x^2 - 5x) = -\left(x^2 - 5x + \frac{25}{4}\right) + \frac{25}{4} = -\left(x - \frac{5}{2}\right)^2 + \frac{25}{4}$$
Since this is a parabola opening downward, it will have a maximum value of $\frac{25}{4}$.

3. Call the two numbers x and y. Then $y - x = 1$, so $y = x + 1$. The sum of their squares can be written as:
$$S = x^2 + y^2 = x^2 + (x + 1)^2 = x^2 + x^2 + 2x + 1 = 2x^2 + 2x + 1$$
We now complete the square:
$$S = 2(x^2 + x) + 1 = 2\left(x^2 + x + \frac{1}{4}\right) + 1 - \frac{1}{2} = 2\left(x + \frac{1}{2}\right)^2 + \frac{1}{2}$$

Since this is a parabola opening upward, it will have a minimum value of $\frac{1}{2}$.

5. Let w and l be the width and length, respectively. Since $P = 2w + 2l$, then:
$$2w + 2l = 25$$
$$2l = 25 - 2w$$
$$l = \frac{25 - 2w}{2}$$
So the area is given by:
$$A = wl = w\left(\frac{25 - 2w}{2}\right) = \frac{1}{2}(-2w^2 + 25)$$

We now complete the square:

$$A = -(w^2 - \frac{25}{2}w) = -\left(w^2 - \frac{25}{2}w + \frac{625}{16}\right) = -\left(w - \frac{25}{4}\right)^2 + \frac{625}{16}$$

This is a parabola opening downward, so it will achieve a maximum value when $w = \frac{25}{4}$. We find l:

$$l = \frac{25 - 2\left(\frac{25}{4}\right)}{2} = \frac{25 - \frac{25}{2}}{2} = \frac{25}{4}$$

So the largest such rectangle is a square of dimensions $\frac{25}{4}$ m by $\frac{25}{4}$ m.

7.   Let x and y be the lengths of the two shorter sides, so $x + y = 100$, and $y = 100 - x$. Then the area is given by:

$$A = \frac{1}{2}xy = \frac{1}{2}x(100 - x) = \frac{1}{2}(-x^2 + 100x)$$

We now complete the square:

$$A = -\frac{1}{2}(x^2 - 100x)$$

$$= -\frac{1}{2}(x^2 - 100x + 2500) + 1250$$

$$= -\frac{1}{2}(x - 50)^2 + 1250$$

This is a parabola opening downward, so it will achieve a maximum value of 1250 in^2.

9.   Let x and y be the two numbers, so $x + y = 6$ and thus $y = 6 - x$.

(a) $T = x^2 + y^2$
$$= x^2 + (6 - x)^2$$
$$= x^2 + 36 - 12x + x^2$$
$$= 2x^2 - 12x + 36$$

We now complete the square:

$T = 2(x^2 - 6x) + 36$
$$= 2(x^2 - 6x + 9) + 36 - 18$$
$$= 2(x - 3)^2 + 18$$

This is a parabola opening upward, so it will have a minimum value of 18.

(b) $S = x + y^2$
$$= x + (6 - x)^2$$
$$= x + 36 - 12x + x^2$$
$$= x^2 - 11x + 36$$

We now complete the square:

$$S = (x^2 - 11x) + 36$$

$$= \left(x^2 - 11x + \frac{121}{4}\right) + 36 - \frac{121}{4}$$

$$= \left(x - \frac{11}{2}\right)^2 + \frac{23}{4}$$

This is a parabola opening upward, so it will have a minimum value of $\frac{23}{4}$.

(c) $U = x + 2y^2$

$$= x + 2(6 - x)^2$$

$$= x + 72 - 24x + 2x^2$$

$$= 2x^2 - 23x + 72$$

We now complete the square:

$$U = 2\left(x^2 - \frac{23}{2}x\right) + 72$$

$$= 2\left(x^2 - \frac{23}{2}x + \frac{529}{16}\right) + 72 - \frac{529}{8}$$

$$= 2\left(x - \frac{23}{4}\right)^2 + \frac{47}{8}$$

This is a parabola opening upward, so it will have a minimum value of $\frac{47}{8}$.

(d) $V = x + (2y)^2$

$$= x + 4y^2$$

$$= x + 4(6 - x)^2$$

$$= x + 144 - 40x + 4x^2$$

$$= 4x^2 - 47x + 144$$

We now complete the square:

$$V = 4\left(x^2 - \frac{47}{4}x\right) + 144$$

$$= 4\left(x^2 - \frac{47}{4}x + \frac{2209}{64}\right) + 144 - \frac{2209}{16}$$

$$= 4\left(x - \frac{47}{8}\right)^2 + \frac{95}{16}$$

This is a parabola opening upward, so it will have a minimum value of $\frac{95}{16}$.

11. (a) $h(1) = -16(1)^2 + 32(1) = -16 + 32 = 16$ ft

$h\left(\dfrac{3}{2}\right) = -16\left(\dfrac{3}{2}\right)^2 + 32\left(\dfrac{3}{2}\right) = -16\left(\dfrac{9}{4}\right) + 48 = -36 + 48 = 12$ ft

(b)   We complete the square:

$$\begin{aligned} h &= -16t^2 + 32t \\ &= -16(t^2 - 2t) \\ &= -16(t^2 - 2t + 1) + 16 \\ &= -16(t - 1)^2 + 16 \end{aligned}$$

This is a parabola opening downward, so it will have a maximum height of 16 ft., attained after 1 second.

(c)   We set $h = 7$:

$$7 = -16t^2 + 32t$$
$$16t^2 - 32t + 7 = 0$$
$$(4t - 7)(4t - 1) = 0$$
$$t = \frac{7}{4}, \frac{1}{4}$$

So $h = 7$ ft when $t = \dfrac{7}{4}$ sec or $t = \dfrac{1}{4}$ sec.

13. Every point on the given curve has coordinates of the form $(x, \sqrt{x-2}+1)$, and using the distance formula gives:

$$\begin{aligned} d &= \sqrt{(4-x)^2 + (1 - \sqrt{x-2} - 1)^2} \\ &= \sqrt{16 - 8x + x^2 + x - 2} \\ &= \sqrt{x^2 - 7x + 14} \end{aligned}$$

and we look for a minimum value of the radicand.
We complete the square:

$$(x^2 - 7x) + 14 = \left(x^2 - 7x + \frac{49}{4}\right) + 14 - \frac{49}{4} = \left(x - \frac{7}{2}\right)^2 + \frac{7}{4}$$

This is a parabola opening upward which will achieve a minimum value of

$\sqrt{\dfrac{7}{4}} = \dfrac{\sqrt{7}}{2}$ at $x = \dfrac{7}{2}$. Then:

$$y = \sqrt{\frac{7}{2} - 2} + 1 = \sqrt{\frac{3}{2}} + 1 = \frac{2 + \sqrt{6}}{2}$$

So the point is $\left(\dfrac{7}{2}, \dfrac{2 + \sqrt{6}}{2}\right)$ and the distance is $\dfrac{\sqrt{7}}{2}$.

15. (a) We must find the value of x such that $x - x^2$ is as large as possible.
Call $f(x) = -x^2 + x$. We complete the square:

$$f(x) = -(x^2 - x)$$
$$= -\left(x^2 - x + \frac{1}{4}\right) + \frac{1}{4}$$
$$= -\left(x - \frac{1}{2}\right)^2 + \frac{1}{4}$$

This is a parabola opening downward, so it will achieve a maximum value when $x = \frac{1}{2}$. So the number is $\frac{1}{2}$.

(b) We must find the value of x such that $x - 2x^2$ is as large as possible.
Call $f(x) = -2x^2 + x$. We complete the square:

$$f(x) = -2\left(x^2 - \frac{1}{2}x\right)$$
$$= -2\left(x^2 - \frac{1}{2}x + \frac{1}{16}\right) + \frac{1}{8}$$
$$= -2\left(x - \frac{1}{4}\right)^2 + \frac{1}{8}$$

This is a parabola opening downward, so it will achieve a maximum value when $x = \frac{1}{4}$. So the number is $\frac{1}{4}$.

17. If we choose x for the depth of the pasture, then 500 - 2x is the length paralleling the river. The area of the pasture will then be given by:

$$A = x(500 - 2x) = -2x^2 + 500x$$

We complete the square:

$$A = -2(x^2 - 250x)$$
$$= -2(x^2 - 250x + 125^2) + 2(125)^2$$
$$= -2(x - 125)^2 + 31,250$$

This is a parabola opening downward, so it will achieve a maximum value at x = 125. Then the length = 500 - 2(125) = 500 - 250 = 250. So the dimensions are 125 ft. by 250 ft.

19.
$$R - C = (0.4x^2 + 10x + 5) - (0.5x^2 + 2x + 101)$$
$$= 0.4x^2 + 10x + 5 - 0.5x^2 - 2x - 101$$
$$= -0.1x^2 + 8x - 96$$

We now complete the square:

$$R - C = -0.1(x^2 - 80x) - 96$$
$$= -0.1(x^2 - 80x + 1600) - 96 + 160$$
$$= -0.1(x - 40)^2 + 64$$

This is a parabola opening downward, so it will achieve a maximum value when x = 40.

21.   Recall that revenue, R, is x • p. So:

$$R = x\left(-\frac{1}{4}x + 30\right) = -\frac{1}{4}x^2 + 30x$$

We complete the square:

$$R = -\frac{1}{4}x^2 + 30x$$

$$= -\frac{1}{4}(x^2 - 120x)$$

$$= -\frac{1}{4}(x^2 - 120x + 3600) + 900$$

$$= -\frac{1}{4}(x - 60)^2 + 900$$

This is a parabola opening downward, so it will achieve a maximum value at x = 60. The maximum revenue is $900. The corresponding unit price, p, is

$$p = -\frac{1}{4}(60) + 30 = -15 + 30 = \$15.$$

23.   (a)   To use max/min methods, we need to substitute in the quantity $x^2 + y^2$ and write it strictly in terms of x or y. So take 2x + 3y = 6 and solve for y:

$$3y = 6 - 2x$$

$$y = \frac{6 - 2x}{3}$$

Then substitute, and the quantity $x^2 + y^2$ becomes:

$$Q = x^2 + \left(\frac{6 - 2x}{3}\right)^2$$

$$= x^2 + \frac{36 - 24x + 4x^2}{9}$$

$$= \frac{13}{9}x^2 - \frac{8}{3}x + 4$$

We now complete the square:

$$Q = \frac{13}{9}\left(x^2 - \frac{24}{13}x\right) + 4$$

$$= \frac{13}{9}\left(x^2 - \frac{24}{13}x + \frac{144}{169}\right) + 4 - \frac{13}{9}\left(\frac{144}{169}\right)$$

$$= \frac{13}{9}\left(x - \frac{12}{13}\right)^2 + \frac{36}{13}$$

This is a parabola opening up, so it will achieve a minimum value of $\frac{36}{13}$.

(b)   The equation of a circle with its center at the origin is $x^2 + y^2 = r^2$ where r is the radius. The line $2x + 3y = 6$ will intersect the circle in two points whenever r is sufficiently large. As we reduce r, we gradually reach a position where the circle and line are tangent and this is the minimum value of r or $\sqrt{x^2 + y^2}$. In this case, it is

$\sqrt{\dfrac{36}{13}} = \dfrac{6\sqrt{13}}{13}$. This is the square root of the answer from (a).

25. (a)   We plug $y = 15 - x$ into
$$\begin{aligned} Q &= x^2 + y^2 \\ &= x^2 + (15 - x)^2 \\ &= x^2 + 225 - 30x + x^2 \\ &= 2x^2 - 30x + 225 \end{aligned}$$

We now complete the square:
$$\begin{aligned} Q &= 2x^2 - 30x + 225 \\ &= 2(x^2 - 15x) + 225 \\ &= 2\left(x^2 - 15x + \frac{225}{4}\right) + 225 - \frac{225}{2} \\ &= 2\left(x - \frac{15}{2}\right)^2 + \frac{225}{2} \end{aligned}$$

This is a parabola opening upward, so it will achieve a minimum value of $\dfrac{225}{2}$.

(b)   We plug $y = C - x$ into
$$\begin{aligned} Q &= x^2 + y^2 \\ &= x^2 + (C - x)^2 \\ &= x^2 + C^2 - 2Cx + x^2 \\ &= 2x^2 - 2Cx + C^2 \end{aligned}$$

We now complete the square:
$$\begin{aligned} Q &= 2x^2 - 2Cx + C^2 \\ &= 2(x^2 - Cx) + C^2 \\ &= 2\left(x^2 - Cx + \frac{C^2}{4}\right) + C^2 - \frac{C^2}{2} \\ &= 2\left(x - \frac{C}{2}\right)^2 + \frac{C^2}{2} \end{aligned}$$

This is a parabola opening upward, so it will achieve a minimum value of $\dfrac{C^2}{2}$. When $C = 15$, the result from (a) is verified.

27. Let the other two sides of each of the four triangles be t and 1 - t, respectively. Then the area of the square will be a minimum when the area of these triangles is a maximum. Let's write an expression for the total area of the four triangles.

$$A = 4 \left(\frac{1}{2} \right) (t)(1 - t)$$
$$= 2t - 2t^2$$
$$= -2t^2 + 2t$$

We complete the square:

$$A = -2t^2 + 2t$$
$$= -2(t^2 - t)$$
$$= -2\left(t^2 - t + \frac{1}{4}\right) + \frac{1}{2}$$
$$= -2\left(t - \frac{1}{2}\right)^2 + \frac{1}{2}$$

This is a parabola opening downward, so it will achieve a maximum area of $\frac{1}{2}$ when $t = \frac{1}{2}$. Since the large square has area = 1, then the minimum area is $\frac{1}{2}$ when $x = \frac{1}{\sqrt{2}} = \frac{\sqrt{2}}{2}$.

29. We draw the figure:

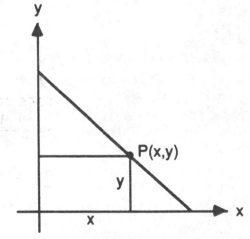

$$A = xy = x(7 - 3x) = -3x^2 + 7x$$

We complete the square:

$$A = -3\left(x^2 - \frac{7}{3}x\right) = -3\left(x^2 - \frac{7}{3}x + \frac{49}{36}\right) + \frac{49}{12} = -3\left(x - \frac{7}{6}\right)^2 + \frac{49}{12}$$

Since this parabola opens downward, the largest possible area is $\frac{49}{12}$.

31. See the figure:

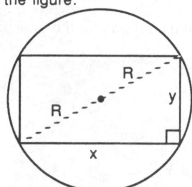

Using the Pythagorean Theorem, we obtain $y = \sqrt{4R^2 - x^2}$. The area A of the rectangle, then, is:

$$A = xy = x\sqrt{4R^2 - x^2}$$

Then:

$$A^2 = x^2(4R^2 - x^2) = 4R^2x^2 - x^4$$

In order to maximize the expression $4R^2x^2 - x^4$, first let $t = x^2$, so that the expression becomes $4R^2t - t^2$.

We complete the square:

$$A^2 = -t^2 + 4R^2t$$
$$= -(t^2 - 4R^2t)$$
$$= -(t^2 - 4R^2t + 4R^4) + 4R^4$$
$$= -(t - 2R^2)^2 + 4R^4$$

This parabola opens downward, so the maximum value of A^2 is $4R^4$, Then the maximum area is $\sqrt{4R^4} = 2R^2$.

33. Let x = east-west dimension, and y = north south dimension. So the cost is given by $C = 12(2x) + 8(2y) = 24x + 16y$. Since this cost is \$4,800, we have $24x + 16y = 4800$, so:

$$y = \frac{4800 - 24x}{16} = \frac{600 - 3x}{2}$$

Now the area is $A = xy = x\left(\dfrac{600 - 3x}{2}\right) = \dfrac{-3}{2}x^2 + 300x$.

So $A(x) = -\dfrac{3}{2}x^2 + 300x$

This will be a parabola opening downward, so it will have a maximum value. We complete the square:

$$A(x) = -\frac{3}{2}x^2 + 300x$$
$$= -\frac{3}{2}(x^2 - 200x)$$

$$= -\frac{3}{2}(x^2 - 200x + 100^2) + 15,000$$

$$= -\frac{3}{2}(x - 100)^2 + 15,000$$

So x = 100 will maximize area, which is 15,000 yd^2. We find y:

$$y = \frac{600 - 3(100)}{2} = \frac{600 - 300}{2} = 150 \text{ yd}$$

So the dimensions are 100 yd by 150 yd.

35. The given function can be rewritten:

$$y = (a_1 + a_2)x^2 - 2(a_1x_1 + a_2x_2)x + (a_1x_1^2 + a_2x_2^2)$$

We complete the square:

$$y = (a_1 + a_2)\left(x^2 - \frac{2(a_1x_1 + a_2x_2)}{a_1 + a_2}x\right) + (a_1x_1^2 + a_2x_2^2)$$

$$= (a_1 + a_2)\left(x - \frac{a_1x_1 + a_2x_2}{a_1 + a_2}\right)^2 + (a_1x_1^2 + a_2x_2^2) - \frac{(a_1x_1 + a_2x_2)^2}{a_1 + a_2}$$

Since a_1 and a_2 are both positive, then $a_1 + a_2 > 0$ and thus this parabola

opens upward. So the minimum must occur where $x = \dfrac{a_1x_1 + a_2x_2}{a_1 + a_2}$.

37. (a)   We have $\dfrac{\Delta p}{\Delta x} = \dfrac{10}{-5} = -2$. Also p = 200 when x = 150. We use the
point-slope formula with the point (150,200):

$$p - 200 = -2(x - 150)$$
$$p - 200 = -2x + 300$$
$$p = -2x + 500$$

Using functional notation, we have p(x) = -2x + 500.

(b)   Since R = xp, we have R = x(-2x + 500) = $-2x^2 + 500x$.
We complete the square:

$$R = -2x^2 + 500x$$
$$R = -2(x^2 - 250x)$$
$$R = -2(x^2 - 250x + 15625) + 31,250$$
$$R = -2(x - 125)^2 + 31,250$$

Using functional notation, we have R(x) = $-2(x - 125)^2 + 31,250$. This
simplifies to R(x) = $-2x^2 + 500x$. Since this parabola opens downward,
we have a maximum revenue of $31,250 when x = 125. We find
p = -2(125) + 500 = $250.

39. Let $x = t^2$, so $f(x) = x - x^2 = -x^2 + x$. We complete the square:

$$f(x) = -(x^2 - x) = -\left(x^2 - x + \frac{1}{4}\right) + \frac{1}{4} = -\left(x - \frac{1}{2}\right)^2 + \frac{1}{4}$$

So $f(x)$ has a maximum value when $x = \frac{1}{2}$. Then $t^2 = \frac{1}{2}$, so $t = \pm\frac{\sqrt{2}}{2}$

41. Let $x = t^2$. Then $y = -t^4 + 6t^2 - 6 = -x^2 + 6x - 6$. We complete the square:

$$\begin{aligned} y &= -x^2 + 6x - 6 \\ &= -(x^2 - 6x) - 6 \\ &= -(x^2 - 6x + 9) - 6 + 9 \\ &= -(x - 3)^2 + 3 \end{aligned}$$

So $x = 3$ will yield the largest output. Since $x = t^2$, we have:

$$t^2 = 3$$
$$t = \pm\sqrt{3}$$

So $t = \sqrt{3}$ or $t = -\sqrt{3}$ will yield the largest output.

43. We complete the square:

$$\begin{aligned} y &= x^2 + bx + 1 \\ &= \left(x^2 + bx + \frac{b^2}{4}\right) + 1 - \frac{b^2}{4} \\ &= \left(x + \frac{b}{2}\right)^2 + \frac{4 - b^2}{4} \end{aligned}$$

Thus the vertex of the parabola is $\left(-\frac{b}{2}, \frac{4 - b^2}{4}\right)$. We use this point, and the point $(0,0)$, in the distance formula:

$$\begin{aligned} d &= \sqrt{\left(-\frac{b}{2} - 0\right)^2 + \left(\frac{4 - b^2}{4} - 0\right)^2} \\ &= \sqrt{\frac{b^2}{4} + \frac{16 - 8b^2 + b^4}{16}} \\ &= \sqrt{\frac{4b^2 + 16 - 8b^2 + b^4}{16}} \\ &= \frac{\sqrt{b^4 - 4b^2 + 16}}{4} \end{aligned}$$

The value for b that will minimize this distance will be the same value that minimizes $y = b^4 - 4b^2 + 16$. Let $t = b^2$, so $y = t^2 - 4t + 16$. We complete the square:

$$\begin{aligned} y &= t^2 - 4t + 16 \\ &= (t^2 - 4t + 4) + 16 - 4 \\ &= (t - 2)^2 + 12 \end{aligned}$$

So this function has a minimum value when $t = 2$. Since $t = b^2$, we have:

$$b^2 = 2$$
$$b = \sqrt{2}, \text{ since } b > 0$$

So $b = \sqrt{2}$ will minimize the distance from the origin to the vertex of the parabola.

45.   The perimeter $P = 2x + 2r + \frac{1}{2}(2\pi r) = 2x + 2r + \pi r$, so $x = \dfrac{P - 2r - \pi r}{2}$.

Now the area of the figure is given by:

$$A = \frac{1}{2}(\pi r^2) + x(2r)$$

$$= \frac{\pi r^2}{2} + \left(\frac{P - 2r - \pi r}{2}\right)(2r)$$

$$= \frac{\pi}{2}r^2 + Pr - 2r^2 - \pi r^2$$

$$= \left(-2 - \frac{\pi}{2}\right)r^2 + Pr$$

$$= \left(\frac{-4 - \pi}{2}\right)r^2 + Pr$$

We complete the square:

$$A = \left(\frac{-4 - \pi}{2}\right)\left(r^2 - \frac{2P}{4 + \pi}r\right)$$

$$= \left(\frac{-4 - \pi}{2}\right)\left(r^2 - \frac{2P}{4 + \pi}r + \frac{P^2}{(4 + \pi)^2}\right) + \frac{P^2}{2(4 + \pi)}$$

$$= \left(\frac{-4 - \pi}{2}\right)\left(r - \frac{P}{4 + \pi}\right)^2 + \frac{P^2}{2(4 + \pi)}$$

This parabola opens downward, and thus has a maximum value when $r = \dfrac{P}{4 + \pi}$ and this maximum area is $\dfrac{P^2}{2(4 + \pi)}$.

47.   (a)   We complete the table:

x	0.5	1	1.5	2	2.5	3	3.5
y	24	12	8	6	4.8	4	3.43
xy	12	12	12	12	12	12	12
x + y	24.5	13	9.5	8	7.3	7	6.93

The x-y pair of (3.5,3.43) appears to yield the smallest sum $x + y$.

(b) Call x, y the two numbers, so $xy = 12$ and thus $y = \dfrac{12}{x}$. Then $x + y$ becomes:

$$x + \frac{12}{x} = \left(\sqrt{x} - \sqrt{\frac{12}{x}}\right)^2 + 2\sqrt{12}$$

This will have a minimum value of $2\sqrt{12} = 4\sqrt{3}$ when $\sqrt{x} = \sqrt{\dfrac{12}{x}}$,

since $\left(\sqrt{x} - \sqrt{\dfrac{12}{x}}\right)^2 \geq 0$. We solve for x:

$$\sqrt{x} = \sqrt{\frac{12}{x}}$$

Squaring we get:

$$x = \frac{12}{x}$$
$$x^2 = 12$$
$$x = \sqrt{12}$$

So both numbers are $\sqrt{12} = 2\sqrt{3}$.

(c) $\sqrt{12} + \sqrt{12} = 2\sqrt{12} = 4\sqrt{3} \approx 3.464$, which is smaller than our table values.

49. (a) Note: For calculation purposes, it is easier to write the function as

$$f(x) = x - 2 + \frac{1}{2x}$$

x	0.4	0.5	0.6	0.7	0.8	0.9
f(x)	-.350000	-.500000	-.566667	-.585714	-.575000	-.544444

smallest output: x = 0.7

x	0.68	0.69	0.70	0.71	0.72	0.73
f(x)	-.584706	-.585362	-.585714	-.585775	-.585556	-.585068

smallest output: x = 0.71

(b) $f(x) = \left(x + \dfrac{1}{2x}\right) - 2$

$$= \left(\sqrt{x} - \frac{1}{\sqrt{2x}}\right)^2 - 2 + \frac{2}{\sqrt{2}}$$

$$= \left(\sqrt{x} - \frac{1}{\sqrt{2x}}\right)^2 - 2 + \sqrt{2}$$

This will have a minimum value of $-2 + \sqrt{2}$ when:

$$\sqrt{x} = \frac{1}{\sqrt{2x}}$$

$$x = \frac{1}{2x}$$

$$2x^2 = 1$$

$$x^2 = \frac{1}{2}$$

$$x = \frac{1}{\sqrt{2}} = \frac{\sqrt{2}}{2}$$

(c) $-2 + \sqrt{2} \approx -0.585786$, which is smaller than the table value of -0.585775.

5.4 Polynomial Functions

1.   Yes

3.   Yes

5.   No - It cannot approach a horizontal asymptote

7. $y = (x - 2)^2 + 1$
This is $y = x^2$ shifted 2 units to the right and 1 unit up. See graph:

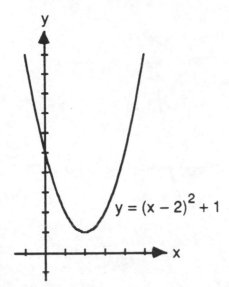

x-intercept: none
y-intercept: 5

9. $y = -(x - 1)^4$
This is $y = x^4$ reflected about the x-axis and shifted 1 unit to the right. See graph:

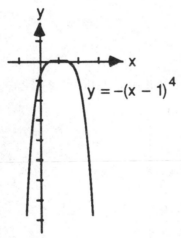

x-intercept: 1
y-intercept: -1

11. $y = (x - 4)^3 - 2$
This is $y = x^3$ shifted 4 units to the right and 2 units down. See graph:

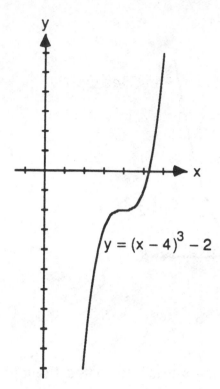

$$y = (x - 4)^3 - 2$$

x-intercept: $4 + \sqrt[3]{2}$
y-intercept: -66

13. $y = -2(x + 5)^4$
This is $y = 2x^4$ shifted 5 units to the left and reflected about the x-axis. See graph:

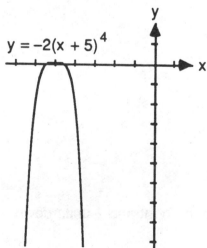

$$y = -2(x + 5)^4$$

x-intercept: -5
y-intercept: -1250

15. $y = \dfrac{1}{2}(x + 1)^5$

This is $y = \dfrac{1}{2}x^5$ shifted 1 unit to the left. See graph:

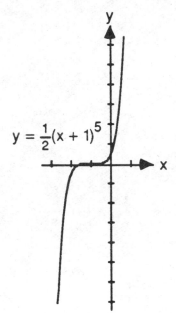

x-intercept: -1

y-intercept: $\dfrac{1}{2}$

17. $y = -(x - 1)^3 - 1$

This is $y = x^3$ shifted 1 unit to the right, 1 unit down, and reflected about the x-axis. See graph:

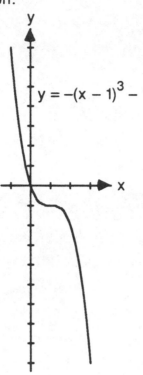

$y = -(x - 1)^3 - 1$

x-intercept: 0
y-intercept: 0

19. $y = (x - 2)(x - 1)(x + 1)$

The roots can be found by inspection. If x = 2, then the (x - 2) factor is zero. The roots of -1 and 1 can be found the same way. Near x = -1, y is near $(-1 - 2)(-1 - 1)(x + 1)$ or $6x + 6$. It rises fairly steeply to the right. At x = 1 the curve is like the line $y = -2x + 2$ and near x = 2 it approximates $y = 3x - 6$. To complete the sketch we need to pick points between the roots and get an idea how high turning points may be. Incidentally, such turning points are not necessarily halfway between the roots, but they are usually in the general area. Here we might choose to find f(0) (always a good choice) and $f\left(\frac{3}{2}\right)$.

$f(0) = 2$ and $f\left(\frac{3}{2}\right) = -\frac{5}{8}$. We sketch the graph:

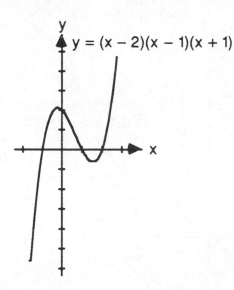

$$y = (x - 2)(x - 1)(x + 1)$$

21. $y = 2x(x + 1)(x + 3)$

The roots of $y = 2x(x + 1)(x + 3)$ are 0, -1, and -3. We will also want to know when $x = -2$ and $-\frac{1}{2}$. Again, we look at the behavior of y near the roots. For example, when x is close to -3, y is like $12x + 36$, rising steeply to the right. We sketch the graph:

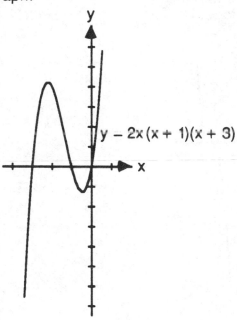

$$y - 2x(x + 1)(x + 3)$$

23. $y = x^3(x + 2)$

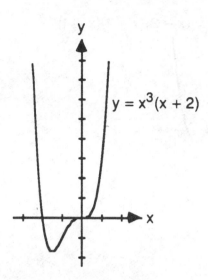

$y = x^3(x + 2)$

25. $y = 2(x - 1)(x - 4)^3$
The roots are 1 and 4. Look at f(0). Its enormous!
$f(0) = 2(0 - 1)(0 - 4)^3 = 128$. The graph must be very steep between x = 0 and x = 1. Let's find f(2) and f(3) to help. We discover that the curve passes through (2,-16) and (3,-4). Near x = 4 it behaves like $y = 6(x - 4)^3$, a tall, thin version of $y = x^3$. Put it together and you have a sketch like:

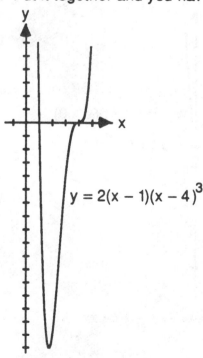

$y = 2(x - 1)(x - 4)^3$

27. $y = (x + 1)^2(x - 1)(x - 3)$

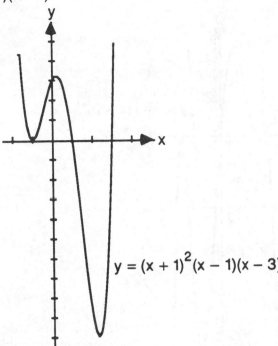

$$y = (x + 1)^2(x - 1)(x - 3)$$

29. $y = -x^3(x - 4)(x + 2)$

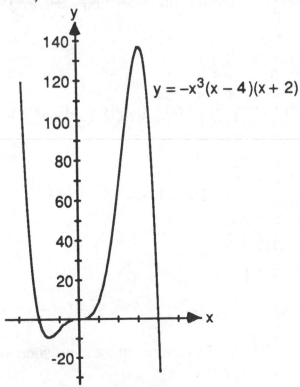

$$y = -x^3(x - 4)(x + 2)$$

31. $y = -4x(x - 2)^2(x + 2)^3$

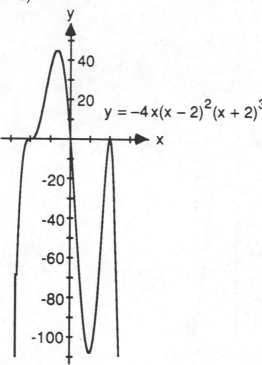

$$y = -4x(x - 2)^2(x + 2)^3$$

33. From left to right, they are: $f(x) = x$, $g(x) = x^2$, $h(x) = x^3$, $F(x) = x^4$, $G(x) = x^5$, $H(x) = x^6$.

35. We must find where $0 \le H(x) < 0.1$
$$0 \le x^6 < 0.1$$
Taking roots: $0 \le x < 0.68$
So, when x lies in the interval [0,0.68), then H(x) will lie in the interval [0,0.1).

37. We must find where:
$$g(t) - F(t) = 0.26$$
$$t^2 - t^4 = 0.26$$
$$t^4 - t^2 + 0.26 = 0$$
Using the quadratic formula:
$$t^2 = \frac{1 \pm \sqrt{1 - 4(0.26)}}{2}$$
$$= \frac{1 \pm \sqrt{1 - 1.04}}{2}$$
$$= \frac{1 \pm \sqrt{-0.04}}{2}$$
Since this equation has no real solutions, there is no such value of t.

39. We set them equal:

$$x = \frac{1}{100}x^2$$

$$0 = \frac{1}{100}x^2 - x$$

$$0 = \frac{1}{100}(x^2 - 100x)$$

$$0 = \frac{1}{100} \cdot x(x - 100)$$

The graph intersects at the origin but also at the point (100,100).

41. $y = 2x^3 - x^4$
     $y = x^3(2 - x)$

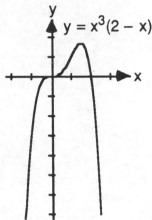

43. $y = x^3 + x^2 - 2x$
     $y = x(x^2 + x - 2)$
     $y = x(x + 2)(x - 1)$

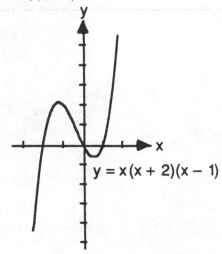

45. $y = 4x^2 - x^4$

$y = x^2(4 - x^2)$

$y = x^2(2 + x)(2 - x)$

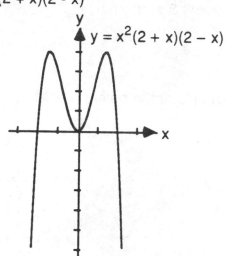

$y = x^2(2 + x)(2 - x)$

5.5 Graphs of Rational Functions

1.   Domain: We must exclude those values of x where:

$$4x - 12 = 0$$
$$4x = 12$$
$$x = 3$$

So the domain is all real numbers except 3, or $(-\infty, 3) \cup (3, \infty)$.

x-intercepts: We must find where:

$$3x + 15 = 0$$
$$3x = -15$$
$$x = -5$$

So the x-intercept is -5.

y-intercepts: Let $x = 0$

$$y = \frac{0 + 15}{0 - 12} = -\frac{5}{4}$$

So the y-intercept is $-\frac{5}{4}$.

3.   Domain: We must exclude those values of x where:
$$x^2 - x - 6 = 0$$
$$(x - 3)(x + 2) = 0$$
$$x = 3, -2$$
So the domain is all real numbers except 3 and -2, or

$(-\infty,-2) \cup (-2,3) \cup (3,\infty)$.

x-intercepts: We must find where:
$$x^2 - 8x - 9 = 0$$
$$(x - 9)(x + 1) = 0$$
$$x = 9, -1$$
So the x-intercepts are 9 and -1.

y-intercepts: Let x = 0
$$y = \frac{-9}{-6} = \frac{3}{2}$$
So the y-intercept is $\frac{3}{2}$.

5.   Domain: We must exclude those values of x where:
$$x^6 = 0$$
Taking roots: $x = 0$

So the domain is all real numbers except 0, or $(-\infty,0) \cup (0,\infty)$.

x-intercepts: We must find where:
$$(x^2 - 4)(x^3 - 1) = 0$$
$$x^2 - 4 = 0 \quad \text{or} \quad x^3 - 1 = 0$$
$$x^2 = 4 \qquad\qquad x^3 = 1$$

Taking roots:
$$x = \pm 2 \qquad\qquad x = 1$$
So the x-intercepts are -2, 2, and 1.

y-intercepts: Let x = 0
$$y = \frac{(-4)(-1)}{0}, \text{ which is undefined.}$$
So there are no y-intercepts.

7. $y = \dfrac{1}{x + 4}$

x-intercept: none

y-intercept: $\dfrac{1}{4}$

horizontal asymptote: $y = 0$ (x-axis)
vertical asymptote: $x = -4$

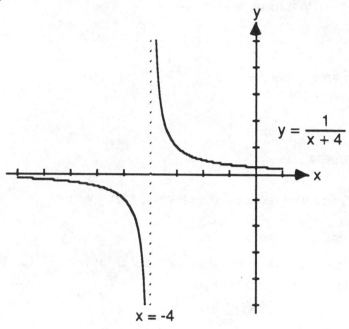

9. $y = \dfrac{3}{x + 2}$

x-intercept: none

y-intercept: $\dfrac{3}{2}$

horizontal asymptote: $y = 0$ (x-axis)
vertical asymptote: $x = -2$

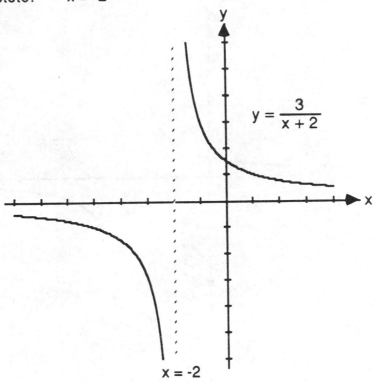

11. $y = \dfrac{-2}{x - 3}$

     x-intercept: none

     y-intercept: $\dfrac{2}{3}$

     horizontal asymptote: $y = 0$ (x-axis)
     vertical asymptote: $x = 3$

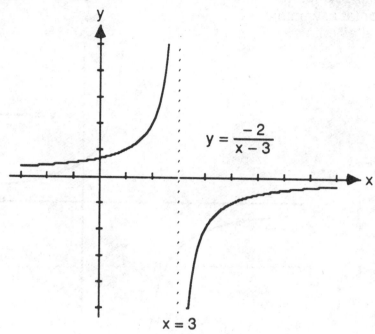

$$y = \dfrac{-2}{x - 3}$$

$x = 3$

13. $y = \dfrac{x - 3}{x - 1}$

Using long division, we have.

$$\dfrac{x - 3}{x - 1} = 1 - \dfrac{2}{x - 1}$$

x-intercept: 3
y-intercept: 3
horizontal asymptote: $y = 1$
vertical asymtote: $x = 1$

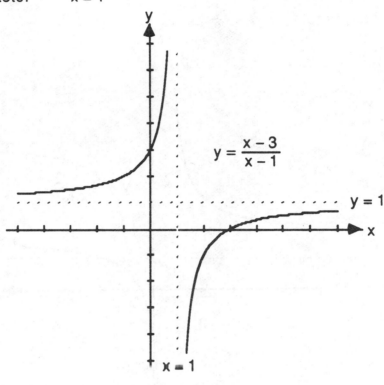

$$y = \dfrac{x - 3}{x - 1}$$

$y = 1$

$x = 1$

15. $y = \dfrac{4x - 2}{2x + 1}$

Using long division, we have:
$$\dfrac{4x - 2}{2x + 1} = 2 - \dfrac{4}{2x + 1}$$

x-intercept: $\dfrac{1}{2}$

y-intercept: -2

horizontal asymptote: $y = 2$

vertical asymptote: $x = -\dfrac{1}{2}$

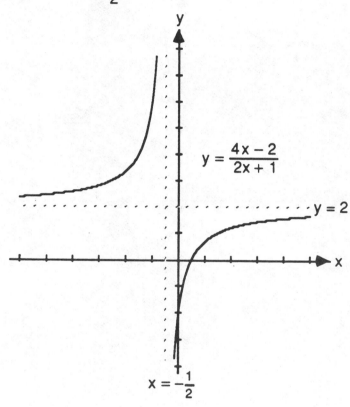

17. $y = \dfrac{1}{(x - 2)^2}$

x-intercept: none

y-intercept: $\dfrac{1}{4}$

horizontal asymptote: $y = 0$ (x-axis)

vertical asymptote: $x = 2$

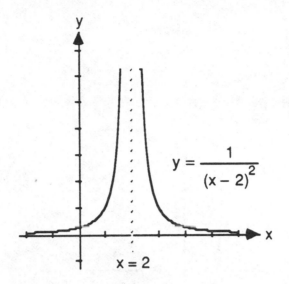

$$y = \frac{1}{(x-2)^2}$$

x = 2

19. $y = \dfrac{3}{(x + 1)^2}$

x-intercept: none
y-intercept: 3
horizontal asymptote: $y = 0$ (x-axis)
vertical asymptote: $x = -1$

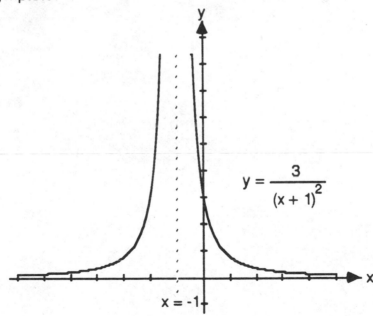

$$y = \frac{3}{(x + 1)^2}$$

x = -1

21. $y = \dfrac{1}{(x + 2)^3}$

x-intercept: none

y-intercept: $\dfrac{1}{8}$

horizontal asymptote: $y = 0$ (x-axis)
vertical asymptote: $x = -2$

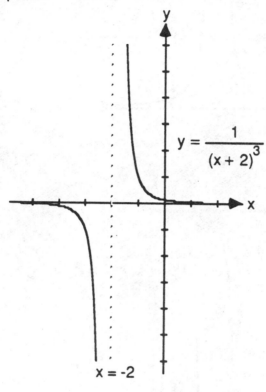

23. $y = \dfrac{-4}{(x + 5)^3}$

x-intercept: none

y-intercept: $-\dfrac{4}{125}$

horizontal asymptote: $y = 0$ (x-axis)
vertical asymptote: $x = -5$

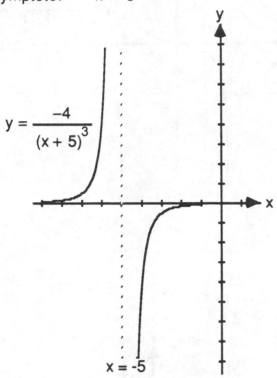

$y = \dfrac{-4}{(x + 5)^3}$

x = -5

25. $y = \dfrac{-x}{(x + 2)(x - 2)}$

x-intercept: 0
y-intercept: 0
horizontal asymptote: $y = 0$ (x-axis)
vertical asymptotes: $x = -2$, $x = 2$

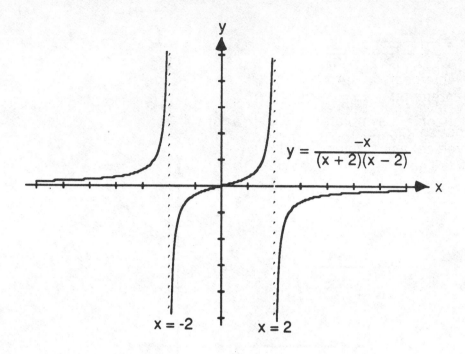

$$y = \frac{-x}{(x + 2)(x - 2)}$$

x = -2   x = 2

27. $y = \dfrac{x}{(x - 1)(x + 3)}$
    x-intercept: 0
    y-intercept: 0
    horizontal asymptote: y = 0 (x-axis)
    vertical asymptotes: x = -3 , x = 1

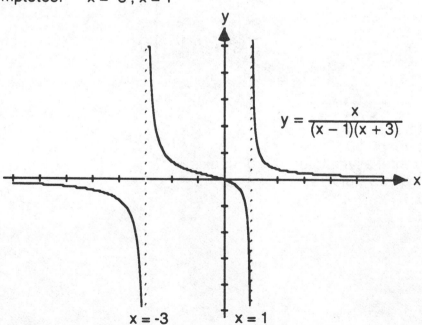

$$y = \frac{x}{(x - 1)(x + 3)}$$

x = -3   x = 1

29. $y = \dfrac{(x - 4)(x + 2)}{(x - 1)(x - 3)}$

x-intercepts: -2, 4

y-intercept: $-\dfrac{8}{3}$

horizontal asymptote: $y = 1$
vertical asymptotes: $x = 1$, $x = 3$
We find where the curve crosses the horizontal asymptote:

$$\frac{(x - 4)(x + 2)}{(x - 1)(x - 3)} = 1$$
$$(x - 4)(x + 2) = (x - 1)(x - 3)$$
$$x^2 - 2x - 8 = x^2 - 4x + 3$$
$$-2x - 8 = -4x + 3$$
$$2x = 11$$
$$x = \frac{11}{2}$$

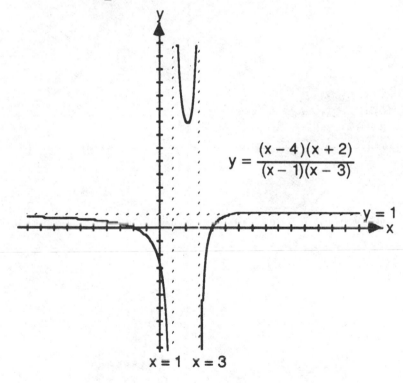

$$y = \frac{(x - 4)(x + 2)}{(x - 1)(x - 3)}$$

$y = 1$

$x = 1$ $x = 3$

31. $y = \dfrac{(x + 1)^2}{(x - 1)(x - 3)}$

x-intercept: -1

y-intercept: $\dfrac{1}{3}$

horizontal asymptote: $y = 1$
vertical asymptotes: $x = 1$, $x = 3$
We find where the curve crosses the horizontal asymptote:

$$\dfrac{(x + 1)^2}{(x - 1)(x - 3)} = 1$$
$$(x + 1)^2 = (x - 1)(x - 3)$$
$$x^2 + 2x + 1 = x^2 - 4x + 3$$
$$2x + 1 = -4x + 3$$
$$6x = 2$$
$$x = \dfrac{1}{3}$$

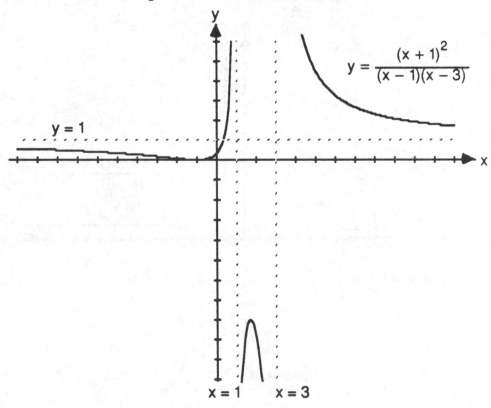

$y = \dfrac{(x + 1)^2}{(x - 1)(x - 3)}$

$y = 1$

$x = 1$ $x = 3$

33. (a)   x near -2: $y \approx \dfrac{(-5)(x+2)}{(-1)(-4)} = -\dfrac{5}{4}(x+2) = -\dfrac{5}{4}x - \dfrac{5}{2}$

(b)   x near -1: $y \approx \dfrac{(-4)(1)}{(x+1)(-3)} = \dfrac{4/3}{x+1}$

(c)   x near 2: $y \approx \dfrac{(-1)(4)}{(3)(x-2)} = \dfrac{-4/3}{x-2}$

35. (a)   For $x \neq 3$, $y = \dfrac{x^2 - 9}{x+3} = \dfrac{(x+3)(x-3)}{x+3} = x - 3$. So this is the graph of $y = x - 3$, without the point at $(-3,-6)$:

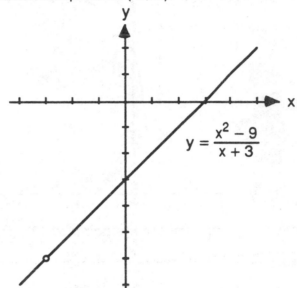

$$y = \frac{x^2 - 9}{x + 3}$$

(b) $y = \dfrac{x^2 - 5x + 6}{x^2 - 2x - 3} = \dfrac{(x-2)(x-3)}{(x+1)(x-3)} = \dfrac{x-2}{x+1}$ If $x \neq 3$. So this is the graph of $y = \dfrac{x-2}{x+1}$, without the point at $\left(3, \dfrac{1}{4}\right)$:

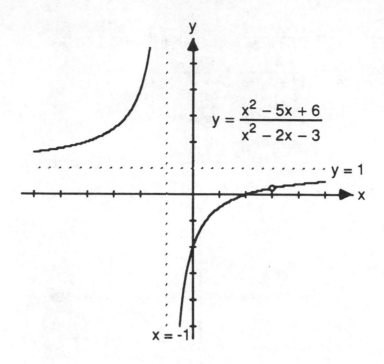

$$y = \frac{x^2 - 5x + 6}{x^2 - 2x - 3}$$

(c)   For $x \neq 1, 2, 3$, $y = \dfrac{(x - 1)(x - 2)(x - 3)}{(x - 1)(x - 2)(x - 3)(x - 4)} = \dfrac{1}{x - 4}$. So this is

the graph of $y = \dfrac{1}{x - 4}$, without the points at $\left(1, -\dfrac{1}{3}\right)$, $\left(2, -\dfrac{1}{2}\right)$, $(3, -1)$:

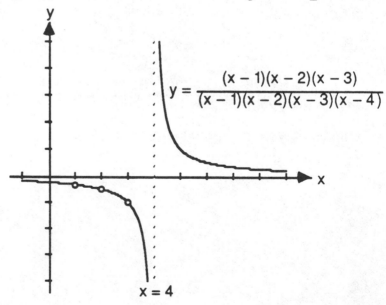

$$y = \frac{(x - 1)(x - 2)(x - 3)}{(x - 1)(x - 2)(x - 3)(x - 4)}$$

37. $y = \dfrac{x}{(x-3)^2}$

horizontal asymptote: $y = 0$
vertical asymptote: $x = 3$

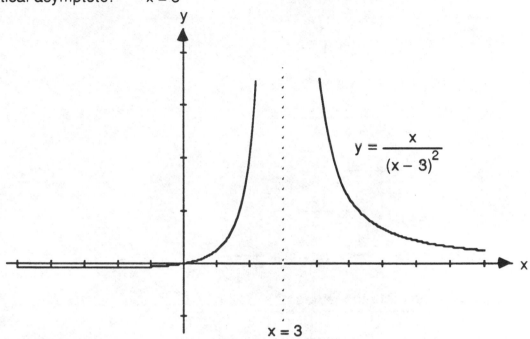

We find the value of k where $k = \dfrac{x}{(x-3)^2}$

$$k(x-3)^2 = x$$
$$kx^2 - 6kx + 9k = x$$
$$kx^2 - (6k+1)x + 9k = 0$$

Since this equation must have only one solution, we set the discriminant equal to zero:

$$(-(6k+1))^2 - 4k(9k) = 0$$
$$(6k+1)^2 - 36k^2 = 0$$
$$(6k+1+6k)(6k+1-6k) = 0$$
$$(12k+1)(1) = 0$$

So $12k + 1 = 0$, thus $k = -\dfrac{1}{12}$

Thus $y = -\dfrac{1}{12}$. We find x:

$$-\dfrac{1}{12} = \dfrac{x}{(x-3)^2}$$
$$-(x-3)^2 = 12x$$

$$(x - 3)^2 = -12x$$
$$x^2 - 6x + 9 = -12x$$
$$x^2 + 6x + 9 = 0$$
$$(x + 3)^2 = 0$$
$$x = -3$$

So the low point is $\left(-3, -\frac{1}{12}\right)$.

39. (a)   We use long division:

$$
\begin{array}{r}
x + 4 \\
x - 3 \overline{\big)\ x^2 + x - 6} \\
\underline{x^2 - 3x} \\
4x - 6 \\
\underline{4x - 12} \\
6
\end{array}
$$

So $\dfrac{x^2 + x - 6}{x - 3} = (x + 4) + \dfrac{6}{x - 3}$

(b)   We complete the tables:

x	$x+4$	$\dfrac{x^2 + x - 6}{x - 3}$
10	14	14.8571
100	104	104.0619
1000	1004	1004.0060

x	$x+4$	$\dfrac{x^2 + x - 6}{x - 3}$
-10	-6	-6.4615
-100	-96	-96.0583
-1000	-996	-996.0600

(c)   vertical asymptote: $x = 3$
       x-intercepts: $x^2 + x - 6 = 0$
                            $(x + 3)(x - 2) = 0$
                                         $x = -3, 2$

       y-intercept: $F(0) = \dfrac{-6}{-3} = 2$

(d)   We graph F(x):

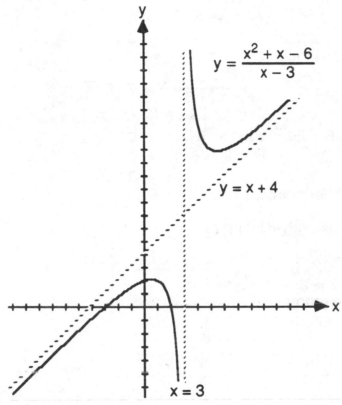

$$y = \frac{x^2 + x - 6}{x - 3}$$

$$y = x + 4$$

$$x = 3$$

(e)   We find where $\dfrac{x^2 + x - 6}{x - 3} = k$

$$x^2 + x - 6 = kx - 3k$$
$$x^2 + (1 - k)x + (3k - 6) = 0$$

Set the discriminant equal to 0:
$$(1 - k)^2 - 4(1)(3k - 6) = 0$$
$$1 - 2k + k^2 - 12k + 24 = 0$$
$$k^2 - 14k + 25 = 0$$
$$(k - 7)^2 = -25 + 49$$
$$(k - 7)^2 = 24$$

$$k - 7 = \pm\sqrt{24}$$
$$k = 7 \pm 2\sqrt{6}$$

So either $y = 7 + 2\sqrt{6}$ or $y = 7 - 2\sqrt{6}$
For each of these values, we find x:

$$\frac{x^2 + x - 6}{x - 3} = 7 + 2\sqrt{6}$$
$$x^2 + x - 6 = (7 + 2\sqrt{6})x - 21 - 6\sqrt{6}$$
$$x^2 + (-6 - 2\sqrt{6})x + (15 + 6\sqrt{6}) = 0$$
$$(x - (3 + \sqrt{6}))^2 = 0$$
$$x = 3 + \sqrt{6}$$

So one point is $(3 + \sqrt{6}, 7 + 2\sqrt{6})$

$$\frac{x^2 + x - 6}{x - 3} = 7 - 2\sqrt{6}$$
$$x^2 + x - 6 = (7 - 2\sqrt{6})x - 21 + 6\sqrt{6}$$
$$x^2 + (-6 + 2\sqrt{6})x + (15 - 6\sqrt{6}) = 0$$
$$(x - (3 - \sqrt{6}))^2 = 0$$
$$x = 3 - \sqrt{6}$$

So the other point is $(3 - \sqrt{6}, 7 - 2\sqrt{6})$.

41.   Using long division, we find that:

$$\frac{-x^2 + 1}{x} = -x + \frac{1}{x},$$

and thus $y = -x$ is a slant asymptote.
We sketch the graph:

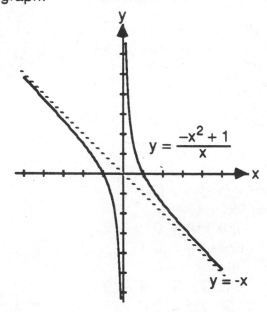

$$y = \frac{-x^2 + 1}{x}$$

$$y = -x$$

Chapter 5 Review Exercises

1. We find the slope between the points (3,5) and (-2,0):
    $$m = \frac{0 - 5}{-2 - 3} = \frac{-5}{-5} = 1$$
    We use the point (3,5) in the point-slope formula:
    $$y - 5 = 1\,(x - 3)$$
    $$y - 5 = x - 3$$
    $$y = x + 2$$
    Using functional notation, we have $f(x) = x + 2$.

3. We find the slope of the line $3x - 8y = 16$
    $$-8y = -3x + 16$$
    $$y = \frac{3}{8}x - 2$$

    We use $m = \frac{3}{8}$ and the point (4,-1) in the point-slope formula:

    $$y - (-1) = \frac{3}{8}(x - 4)$$

    $$y + 1 = \frac{3}{8}x - \frac{3}{2}$$

    $$y = \frac{3}{8}x - \frac{5}{2}$$

    Using functional notation, we have $f(x) = \frac{3}{8}x - \frac{5}{2}$

5. If the graph of the inverse function passes through (2,1), then (1,2) must lie
    on the graph of the function. We find the slope between the points (1,2) and
    (-3,5):
    $$m = \frac{5 - 2}{-3 - 1} = \frac{3}{-4} = -\frac{3}{4}$$
    We use the point (1,2) in the point-slope formula:

    $$y - 2 = -\frac{3}{4}(x - 1)$$

    $$y - 2 = -\frac{3}{4}x + \frac{3}{4}$$

    $$y = -\frac{3}{4}x + \frac{11}{4}$$

    Using functional notation, we have $f(x) = -\frac{3}{4}x + \frac{11}{4}$

7.
$$y = x^2 + 2x - 3$$
$$y + 3 = x^2 + 2x$$
$$y + 3 + 1 = x^2 + 2x + 1$$
$$y + 4 = (x + 1)^2$$
vertex: $(-1, -4)$
x-intercepts: $1, -3$
y-intercept: -3

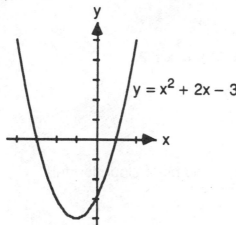

$$y = x^2 + 2x - 3$$

9.
$$y = -x^2 + 2\sqrt{3}\,x + 3$$
$$y - 3 = -(x^2 - 2\sqrt{3}\,x)$$
$$y - 3 - 3 = -(x^2 - 2\sqrt{3}\,x + 3)$$
$$y - 6 = -(x - \sqrt{3})^2$$
vertex: $(\sqrt{3}, 6)$
x-intercepts: $\sqrt{3} + \sqrt{6},\ \sqrt{3} - \sqrt{6}$
y-intercept: 3

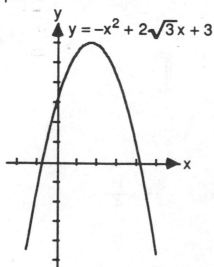

$$y = -x^2 + 2\sqrt{3}\,x + 3$$

11. $y = -3x^2 + 12x$
        $y = -3(x^2 - 4x)$
   $y - 12 = -3(x^2 - 4x + 4)$
   $y - 12 = -3(x - 2)^2$
vertex: (2,12)
x-intercepts: 0, 4
y-intercept: 0

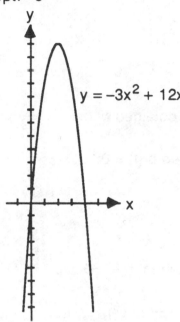

$y = -3x^2 + 12x$

13. We find the two vertices:

$y = x^2 - 4x + 6$ $y = -x^2 - 4x - 5$
$y - 6 = x^2 - 4x$ $y + 5 = -(x^2 + 4x)$
$y - 6 + 4 = x^2 - 4x + 4$ $y + 5 - 4 = -(x^2 + 4x + 4)$
$y - 2 = (x - 2)^2$ $y + 1 = -(x + 2)^2$
vertex: (2,2)   vertex: (-2,-1)

We now find the distance between (2,2) and (-2,-1):

$$d = \sqrt{(-2 - 2)^2 + (-1 - 2)^2} = \sqrt{16 + 9} = \sqrt{25} = 5$$

15. Call x and y the two numbers, so $x + y = \sqrt{3}$, and thus $y = \sqrt{3} - x$.
     We find their product:

$$P = xy = x(\sqrt{3} - x) = -x^2 + \sqrt{3}\,x$$

We now complete the square:

$$P = -(x^2 - \sqrt{3}\,x) = -\left(x^2 - \sqrt{3}\,x + \frac{3}{4}\right) + \frac{3}{4} = -\left(x - \frac{\sqrt{3}}{2}\right)^2 + \frac{3}{4}$$

The maximum product is $\frac{3}{4}$.

17. (a) $h(t) = v_0 t - 16t^2$
We complete the square:
$$h = -16t^2 + v_0 t$$
$$= -16\left(t^2 - \frac{v_0}{16}t\right)$$
$$= -16\left(t^2 - \frac{v_0}{16}t + \frac{v_0^2}{1024}\right) + \frac{v_0^2}{64}$$
$$= -16\left(t - \frac{v_0}{32}\right)^2 + \frac{v_0^2}{64}$$

So the maximum height of $\frac{v_0^2}{64}$ ft. is obtained when $t = \frac{v_0}{32}$ sec.

(b)   The object will strike the ground when $h(t) = 0$:
$$-16t^2 + v_0 t = 0$$
$$t(-16t + v_0) = 0$$
$$t = 0 \quad \text{or} \quad t = \frac{v_0}{16}$$

So the object will strike the ground when $t = \frac{v_0}{16}$ sec.

19. (a)   We find the distance between $(0,2)$ and (x, x^2):
$$d = \sqrt{(x - 0)^2 + (x^2 - 2)^2}$$
$$= \sqrt{x^2 + x^4 - 4x^2 + 4}$$
$$= \sqrt{x^4 - 3x^2 + 4}$$

(b)   We want to minimize d. This will occur at the same x-coordinate as the minimum of d^2. We complete the square:
$$d^2 = x^4 - 3x^2 + 4$$
$$= \left(x^4 - 3x^2 + \frac{9}{4}\right) + 4 - \frac{9}{4}$$
$$= \left(x^2 - \frac{3}{2}\right)^2 + \frac{7}{4}$$

So the minimum occurs where $x^2 = \frac{3}{2}$, so $x = \pm\sqrt{\frac{3}{2}} = \frac{\pm\sqrt{6}}{2}$. Since the point is in the second quadrant, we know $x < 0$, and thus the point on the parabola is $\left(\frac{-\sqrt{6}}{2}, \frac{3}{2}\right)$.

21. We find the distance from $(2,0)$ and $(x, \frac{4}{3}x + b)$:

$$d = \sqrt{(x-2)^2 + \left(\frac{4}{3}x + b\right)^2}$$

$$= \sqrt{x^2 - 4x + 4 + \frac{16}{9}x^2 + \frac{8b}{3}x + b^2}$$

$$= \sqrt{\frac{25}{9}x^2 + \left(\frac{8b}{3} - 4\right)x + (4 + b^2)}$$

We complete the square on d^2:

$$d^2 = \frac{25}{9}\left(x^2 + \frac{9}{25}\left(\frac{8b}{3} - 4\right)x\right) + (4 + b^2)$$

$$= \frac{25}{9}\left(x^2 + \frac{12}{25}(2b - 3)x\right) + (4 + b^2)$$

$$= \frac{25}{9}\left(x^2 + \frac{12}{25}(2b - 3)x + \frac{36}{625}(2b - 3)^2\right) + (4 + b^2) - \frac{4}{25}(2b - 3)^2$$

$$= \frac{25}{9}\left(x + \frac{6}{25}(2b - 3)\right)^2 + \frac{25(4 + b^2) - 4(4b^2 - 12b + 9)}{25}$$

$$= \frac{25}{9}\left(x + \frac{6}{25}(2b - 3)\right)^2 + \frac{(3b + 8)^2}{25}$$

Since the minimum distance is 5, then $5 = \left|\dfrac{3b + 8}{5}\right|$. We now solve for b:

$$|3b + 8| = 25$$

$$3b + 8 = 25 \quad \text{or} \quad 3b + 8 = -25$$
$$3b = 17 \qquad\qquad 3b = -33$$
$$b = \frac{17}{3} \qquad\qquad b = -11$$

23. Since $x + y = \sqrt{2}$, then $y = \sqrt{2} - x$. Then:

$$s = x^2 + y^2$$
$$= x^2 + (\sqrt{2} - x)^2$$
$$= x^2 + 2 - 2\sqrt{2}x + x^2$$
$$= 2x^2 - 2\sqrt{2}x + 2$$

We complete the square:

$$s = 2(x^2 - \sqrt{2}x) + 2$$

$$= 2\left(x^2 - \sqrt{2}x + \frac{1}{2}\right) + 2 - 1$$

$$= 2\left(x - \frac{\sqrt{2}}{2}\right)^2 + 1$$

So the minimum value of s is 1.

25. Let x and h be the two legs. We have:
$$x^2 + h^2 = 15^2$$
$$h^2 = 225 - x^2$$
$$h = \sqrt{225 - x^2}$$

So $A = \frac{1}{2}$ (base) (height) $= \frac{1}{2} x \sqrt{225 - x^2}$

We find $A^2 = \frac{1}{4} x^2 (225 - x^2) = -\frac{1}{4} x^4 + \frac{225}{4} x^2$

We now complete the square on A^2:

$$A^2 = -\frac{1}{4} (x^4 - 225x^2)$$

$$= -\frac{1}{4} \left(x^4 - 225x^2 + \left(\frac{225}{2}\right)^2 \right) + \left(\frac{225}{4}\right)^2$$

$$= -\frac{1}{4} \left(x^2 - \frac{225}{2} \right)^2 + \left(\frac{225}{4}\right)^2$$

So the maximum of $A^2 = \left(\frac{225}{4}\right)^2$, thus $A = \frac{225}{4} cm^2$.

27. $f(x) = x^2 - (a^2 + 2a) x + 2a^3$
$$= (x - a^2) (x - 2a)$$

So the x-intercepts are a^2 and 2a. Since $2a > a^2$ when $0 < a < 2$, then the distance between $(a^2, 0)$ and $(2a, 0)$ will be $D = 2a - a^2 = -a^2 + 2a$

We now complete the square:
$$D = -(a^2 - 2a) = -(a^2 - 2a + 1) + 1 = -(a - 1)^2 + 1$$

So D is maximum when $a = 1$.

29. $R = xp = x(160 - \frac{1}{5} x) = -\frac{1}{5} x^2 + 160 x$

We now complete the square:

$$R = -\frac{1}{5} (x^2 - 800x)$$

$$= -\frac{1}{5} (x^2 - 800x + 160,000) + 32,000$$

$$= -\frac{1}{5} (x - 400)^2 + 32,000$$

So x = 400 units will maximize the revenue. Then $p = 160 - \frac{1}{5} (400) = \$80$.

31. $y = (x + 4)(x - 2)$
     x-intercepts: -4, 2
     y-intercept: -8
     vertex: (-1,-9)

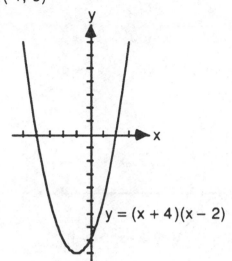

$y = (x + 4)(x - 2)$

33. $y = -(x + 5)^3$
     x-intercept: -5
     y-intercept: -125

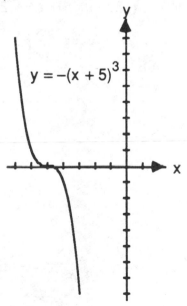

$y = -(x + 5)^3$

35. $y = -x^2(x + 1)$
     x-intercepts: -1, 0
     y-intercept: 0

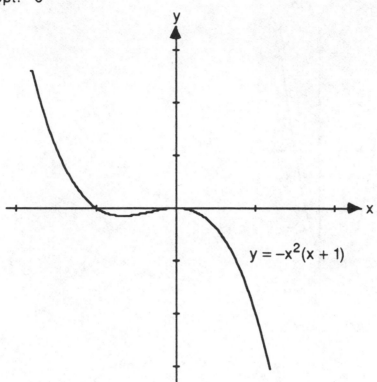

37. $y = x(x - 2)(x + 2)$
     x-intercepts: 0, 2, -2
     y-intercept: 0

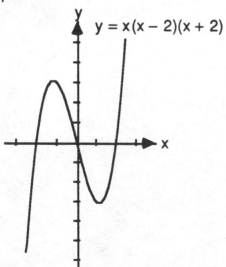

39. $y = \dfrac{3x + 1}{x}$

x-intercept: $-\dfrac{1}{3}$

y-intercept: none
horizontal asymptote: $y = 3$
vertical asymptote: $x = 0$

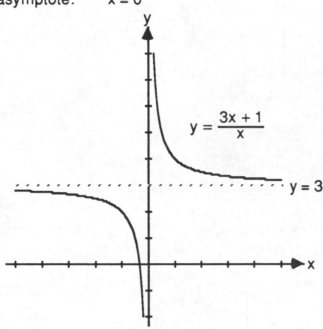

$y = \dfrac{3x + 1}{x}$

$y = 3$

41. $y = \dfrac{-1}{(x - 1)^2}$

x-intercept: none
y-intercept: -1
horizontal asymptote: $y = 0$
vertical asymptote: $x = 1$

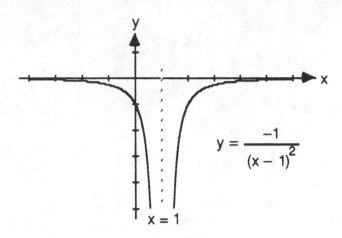

$$y = \frac{-1}{(x-1)^2}$$

$x = 1$

43. $y = \dfrac{x - 2}{x - 3}$

x-intercept: 2

y-intercept: $\dfrac{2}{3}$

horizontal asymptote: y = 1
vertical asymptote: x = 3

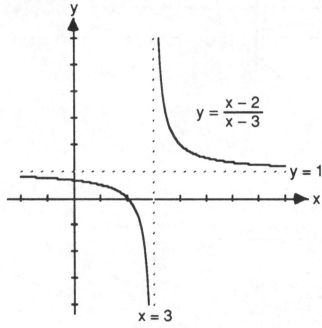

$$y = \frac{x-2}{x-3}$$

$y = 1$

$x = 3$

45. $y = \dfrac{(x-1)^2}{(x-2)^2}$

x-intercept: 1

y-intercept: $\dfrac{1}{4}$

horizontal asymptote: $y = 1$
vertical asymptote: $x = 2$

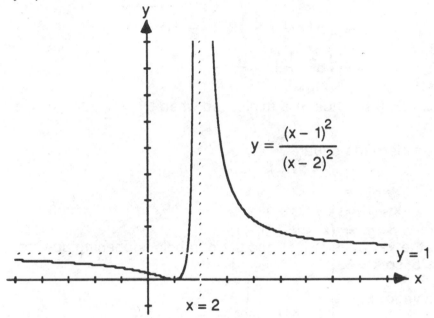

47. (a) If $b = 1$, then $f(x) = x^2 + 2x + 1 = (x+1)^2$, so the vertex is (-1,0). By the distance formula :

$$d = \sqrt{(-1-0)^2 + (0-0)^2} = 1$$

(b) If $b = 2$, then $f(x) = x^2 + 4x + 1$. We complete the square:

$$f(x) = (x^2 + 4x + 4) + 1 - 4 = (x+2)^2 - 3$$

So the vertex is (-2,-3). By the distance formula:

$$d = \sqrt{(-2-0)^2 + (-3-0)^2} = \sqrt{4+9} = \sqrt{13}$$

(c) We complete the square:

$$\begin{aligned}
f(x) &= x^2 + 2bx + 1 \\
&= (x^2 + 2bx + b^2) + 1 - b^2 \\
&= (x+b)^2 + 1 - b^2
\end{aligned}$$

So the vertex is $(-b, 1 - b^2)$. By the distance formula:

$$d = \sqrt{(-b)^2 + (1 - b^2)^2}$$
$$= \sqrt{b^2 + 1 - 2b^2 + b^4}$$
$$= \sqrt{b^4 - b^2 + 1}$$

We now complete the square on d^2:

$$d^2 = b^4 - b^2 + 1$$
$$= \left(b^4 - b^2 + \frac{1}{4}\right) + 1 - \frac{1}{4}$$
$$= \left(b^2 - \frac{1}{2}\right)^2 + \frac{3}{4}$$

So d^2 (and thus d) is minimized when $b^2 = \frac{1}{2}$, thus $b = \pm\frac{1}{\sqrt{2}} = \frac{\pm\sqrt{2}}{2}$.

49.   We complete the square:

$$y = x^2 - 2x + k$$
$$y - k = x^2 - 2x$$
$$y - k + 1 = x^2 - 2x + 1$$
$$y = (x - 1)^2 + (k - 1)$$

Since the vertex is $(1, k-1)$ and the parabola is opening upward, then $k - 1 = 5$, so $k = 6$.

51.   We solve for x:

$$y = \frac{(x - 1)(x - 3)}{x - 4}$$
$$y(x - 4) = (x - 1)(x - 3)$$
$$yx - 4y = x^2 - 4x + 3$$
$$0 = x^2 - (4 + y)x + (4y + 3)$$

Using the quadratic formula:

$$x = \frac{4 + y \pm \sqrt{(4 + y)^2 - 4(4y + 3)}}{2}$$
$$= \frac{4 + y \pm \sqrt{16 + 8y + y^2 - 16y - 12}}{2}$$
$$= \frac{4 + y \pm \sqrt{y^2 - 8y + 4}}{2}$$

So we must make sure that $y^2 - 8y + 4 \geq 0$
We find the key numbers by using the quadratic formula:

$$y = \frac{8 \pm \sqrt{64 - 16}}{2} = \frac{8 \pm 4\sqrt{3}}{2} = 4 \pm 2\sqrt{3}$$

From a sign chart, we see that the range is $y \leq 4 - 2\sqrt{3}$ or $y \geq 4 + 2\sqrt{3}$.

We write this as $(-\infty, 4 - 2\sqrt{3}] \cup [4 + 2\sqrt{3}, \infty)$.

53. We first draw a figure:

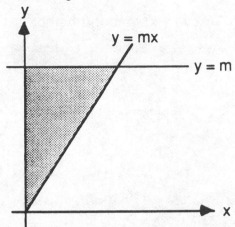

We find the intersection point of these two lines:

$$mx = m$$
$$x = 1$$
$$y = m$$

So the point is $(1,m)$. Since these are the base and height, respectively, of the triangle, we have:

$$A = \frac{1}{2}(1)(m) = \frac{m}{2}$$

Using functional notation, $A(m) = \frac{m}{2}$

55. We re-draw the figure and label essential parts:

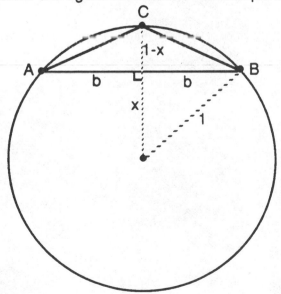

By the labeled parts of the figure, we have:

$$x^2 + b^2 = 1^2, \text{ so } b = \sqrt{1 - x^2}$$

Thus the base of the triangle is $2b = 2\sqrt{1 - x^2}$ and the height is $1 - x$, thus the area is given by:

$$A = \frac{1}{2} \cdot 2\sqrt{1 - x^2} \cdot (1 - x)$$

$$= (1 - x)\sqrt{1 - x^2}$$

Using functional notation, $A(x) = (1 - x)\sqrt{1 - x^2}$

CHAPTER 6
EXPONENTIAL AND LOGARITHMIC FUNCTIONS

6.1 Exponential Functions

1. Since $2^{10} \approx 10^3$, then $2^{30} = (2^{10})^3 \approx (10^3)^3 = 10^9$

3. $2^{90} = (2^{10})^9 \approx (10^3)^9 = 10^{27}$

5. All real numbers, or $(-\infty, \infty)$

7. Since $2^{x-1} \neq 0$ (even if $x = 1$), then domain is all real numbers, or $(-\infty, \infty)$.

9.   We graph $y = 2^x$ and $y = 2^{-x}$:

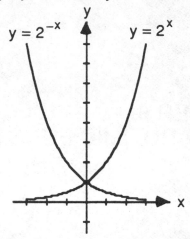

11.   We graph $y = 3^x$ and $y = -3^x$ (note that $y = -3^x$ is a reflection about the x-axis):

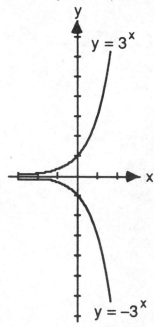

13. We graph $y = 2^x$ and $y = 3^x$:

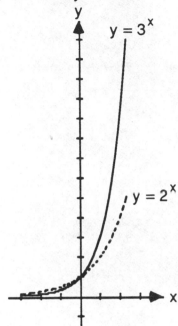

15. We graph $y = \left(\dfrac{1}{2}\right)^x = 2^{-x}$ and $y = \left(\dfrac{1}{3}\right)^x = 3^{-x}$:

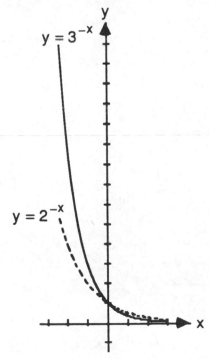

17. $y = -2^x + 1$

    domain: $(-\infty, \infty)$; range: $(-\infty, 1)$
    x-intercept: 0
    y-intercept: 0
    asymptote: $y = 1$

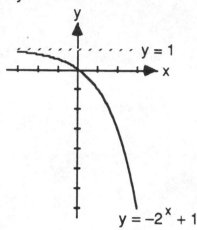

19. $y = 3^{-x} + 1$

    domain: $(-\infty, \infty)$; range: $(1, \infty)$
    x-intercept: none
    y-intercept: 2
    asymptote: $y = 1$

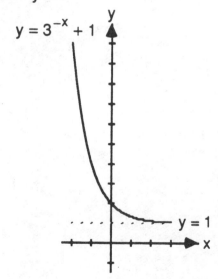

21. $y = 2^{x-1}$

domain: $(-\infty,\infty)$; range: $(0,\infty)$
x-intercept: none
y-intercept: $\dfrac{1}{2}$
asymptote: $y = 0$

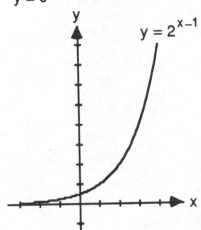

23. $y = 3^{x+1} + 1$

domain: $(-\infty,\infty)$; range: $(1,\infty)$
x-intercept: none
y-intercept: 4
asymptote: $y = 1$

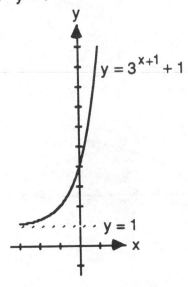

25. $3x(10^x) + 10^x = 0$

   $10^x(3x + 1) = 0$

   $3x + 1 = 0$ or $10^x = 0$

   $x = -\dfrac{1}{3}$, since $10^x \neq 0$

27. $3(3^x) - 5x(3^x) + 2x^2(3^x) = 0$

   $3^x(3 - 5x + 2x^2) = 0$

   $3^x(3 - 2x)(1 - x) = 0$

   $3^x = 0$ or $3 - 2x = 0$ or $1 - x = 0$

   $x = \dfrac{3}{2}$ or $x = 1$, since $3^x \neq 0$

29. $\dfrac{f(x + h) - f(x)}{h}$ $= \dfrac{2^{x+h} - 2^x}{h}$

   $= \dfrac{2^x 2^h - 2^x}{h}$

   $= \dfrac{2^x(2^h - 1)}{h}$

   $= 2^x \left(\dfrac{2^h - 1}{h}\right)$

31. (a) We know the graph of $y = 2^x$ and the graph of g, the inverse of f, should contain these points with the x and y coordinates interchanged. g(x) will be reflected across the line y = x:

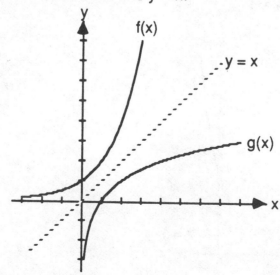

(b) domain: $(0,\infty)$; range: $(-\infty,\infty)$
intercept: $x = 1$ (no y-intercept)
asymptote: $x = 0$ (the negative y-axis)

33. (a) $\sqrt{2} = 2^{1/2} = 2^{0.5} \approx 1.4$

(b) $\sqrt[5]{2} = 2^{1/5} = 2^{.2} \approx 1.15$

(c) $\sqrt[5]{8} = 8^{1/5} = (2^3)^{1/5} = 2^{3/5} = 2^{.6} \approx 1.5$

35. (a) Since $10^0 = 1$, the entry in the table corresponding to $x = 1$ is 0. Since $10^1 = 10$, the entry corresponding to $x = 10$ is 1.

(b) Since $10^{.3} \approx 2$, we have $(10^{.3})^2 \approx 2^2$. That is, $10^{.6} \approx 4$. Therefore, the entry in the table corresponding to $x = 4$ is 0.6. Similarly, by cubing both sides of the approximation $10^{.3} \approx 2$, we obtain $10^{.9} \approx 8$. Thus, the entry in the table corresponding to $x = 8$ is 0.9.

(c) Using the hint that is given, we have $5 \approx \dfrac{10}{10^{.3}} = 10^{.7}$. Thus, the entry in the table corresponding to $x = 5$ is 0.7.

(d) We have $7^2 \approx (5)(10) \approx (10^{.7})(10^1) = 10^{1.7}$. Therefore, $(7^2)^{1/2} \approx (10^{1.7})^{1/2}$, or $7 \approx 10^{.85}$. Thus the power to which 10 must be raised to yield 7 is approximately 0.85.

(e) We have $3^4 \approx (8)(10) \approx (10^{.9})(10^1) = 10^{1.9}$. Therefore, $(3^4)^{1/4} \approx (10^{1.9})^{1/4} \approx 10^{.475}$. Thus, the power to which 10 must be raised to yield 3 is approximately 0.48.

(f) We have $6 = (2)(3) \approx (10^{.3})(10^{.48}) = 10^{.78}$. Thus, the power to which 10 must be raised to yield 6 is approximately 0.78. We also have $9 = (3)(3) \approx (10^{.475})(10^{.475}) = 10^{.95}$. Thus, the power to which 10 must be raised to yield 9 is approximately 0.95. We

complete the table:

x	$\log_{10} x$
1	0
2	0.3
3	0.48
4	0.6
5	0.7
6	0.78
7	0.85
8	0.9
9	0.95
10	1

6.2 The Exponential Function $y = e^x$

1. $y = e^x$

    domain: $(-\infty,\infty)$; range: $(0,\infty)$
    x-intercept: none
    y-intercept: 1
    asymptote: $y = 0$

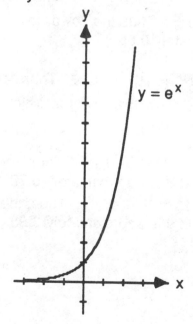

3. $y = -e^x$

domain: $(-\infty,\infty)$; range: $(-\infty,0)$

x-intercept: none
y-intercept: -1
asymptote: $y = 0$

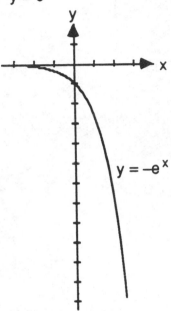

$y = -e^x$

5. $y = e^x + 1$

domain: $(-\infty,\infty)$; range: $(1,\infty)$

x-intercept: none
y-intercept: 2
asymptote: $y = 1$

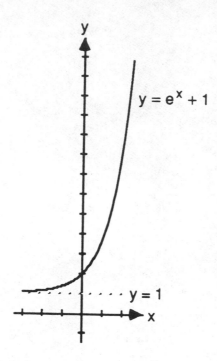

7. $y = e^{x+1} + 1$

domain: $(-\infty, \infty)$; range: $(1, \infty)$

x-intercept: none
y-intercept: $e + 1$
asymptote: $y = 1$

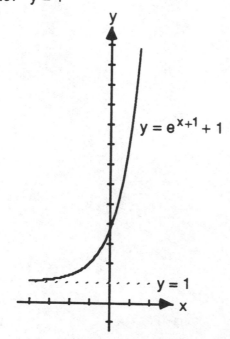

9. $y = -e^{x-2}$

   domain: $(-\infty,\infty)$; range: $(-\infty,0)$
   x-intercept: none
   y-intercept: $-\dfrac{1}{e^2}$
   asymptote: $y = 0$

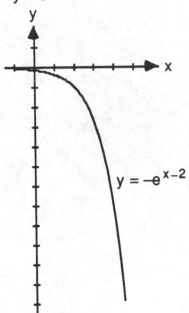

$y = -e^{x-2}$

11. $y = e - e^x$

   domain: $(-\infty,\infty)$; range: $(-\infty,e)$
   x-intercept: 1
   y-intercept: e - 1
   asymptote: $y = e$

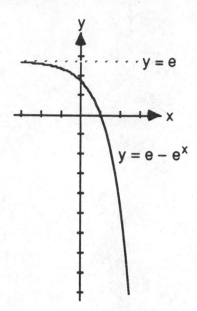

13. $y = e^x$ and $y = 2^x$

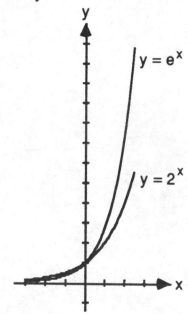

15. $e^{5k} = (e^k)^5$, so:
   $(e^k)^5 = 32$
   $e^k = 32^{1/5}$
   $e^k = 2$

17. $e^{3t} = (e^t)^3$, so:

$$(e^t)^3 = 4$$

$$e^t = \sqrt[3]{4}$$

19. (a) Given the growth law $N = N_0 e^{kt}$, and $N_0 = 2000$, $N = 6000$, $t = 2$, we have:

$$6000 = 2000\, e^{k(2)}$$
$$3 = e^{2k}$$
$$\sqrt{3} = 3^k$$

(b) When $t = 10$, we have $N = 2000\, e^{10k}$

$$= 2000\, (e^k)^{10}$$
$$= 2000\, (\sqrt{3})^{10}$$
$$= 2000\, (243)$$
$$= 486{,}000$$

21. Given the growth law $N = N_0 e^{kt}$, and $N_0 = 3200$, $e^k = \sqrt[5]{2}$, $t = 5$, we have:

$$N = 3200\, e^{5k}$$
$$= 3200\, (e^k)^5$$
$$= 3200\, (\sqrt[5]{2})^5$$
$$= 3200\, (2)$$
$$= 6400 \text{ bacteria}$$

23. Given the decay law $N = N_0 e^{kt}$, and $N = \frac{1}{2} N_0$ when $t = 8$, we have:

$$\frac{1}{2}N_0 = N_0 e^{8k}$$
$$\frac{1}{2} = e^{8k}$$
$$\left(\frac{1}{2}\right)^{1/8} = e^k$$

So when $t = 7$ and $N_0 = 1$, we have:

$$N = 1e^{7k} = (3^k)^7 = \left(\frac{1}{2}\right)^{7/8} \approx 0.55 \text{ grams}$$

25. Given the decay law $N = N_0 e^{kt}$, and $N = \frac{1}{2} N_0$ when $t = 24000$, we have:

$$\frac{1}{2} N_0 = N_0 e^{24000k}$$

$$\frac{1}{2} = e^{24000k}$$

$$\left(\frac{1}{2}\right)^{1/24000} = e^k$$

So when $t = 1000$, we have:

$$N = N_0 e^{1000k} = N_0 \left(\frac{1}{2}\right)^{1/24} \approx 0.9715 N_0$$

So about 97.15 % will still be remaining.

27.
$$\frac{E(x + h) - E(x)}{h} = \frac{e^{x+h} - e^x}{h}$$
$$= \frac{e^x e^h - e^x}{h}$$
$$= \frac{e^x (e^h - 1)}{h}$$
$$= e^x \left(\frac{e^h - 1}{h}\right)$$

29. $C(x) = \dfrac{e^x + e^{-x}}{2}$

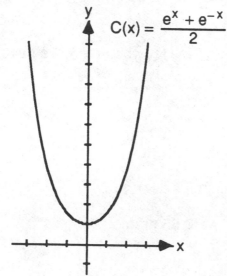

$C(x) = \dfrac{e^x + e^{-x}}{2}$

31. We complete the table:

n	$1 + \frac{1}{n}$	$\left(1 + \frac{1}{n}\right)^n$
1	2	2.0000
10	1.1	2.5937
100	1.01	2.7048
1000	1.001	2.7169
10,000	1.0001	2.7181
100,000	1.00001	2.7183

33. (a)   Since $N = N_0 e^{kt}$

$N = 1 e^{kt}$ using $N_0 = 1$ billion

$2 = e^{k \cdot 80}$

$e^k = 2^{1/80}$

So N in 1985 should be given by:

$N = (2^{1/80})^{135}$

$N = 2^{27/16}$ or about 3.22 billion

(b)   It's too low, by about 1.6 billion people!

35. (a)   We draw the graphs:

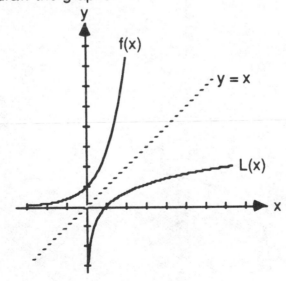

(b)   domain: $(0, \infty)$; range: $(-\infty, \infty)$
x-intercept: 1
asymptote: $x = 0$

(c)   (i) $y = -L(x)$
        x-intercept: 1
        asymptote: $x = 0$

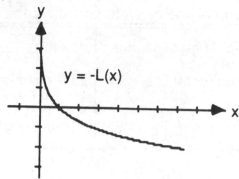

$y = -L(x)$

(ii) $y = L(-x)$
        x-intercept: -1
        asymptote: $x = 0$

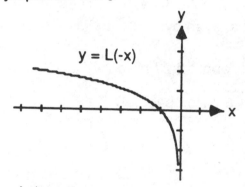

$y = L(-x)$

(iii) $y = L(x - 1)$
        x-intercept: 2
        asymptote: $x = 1$

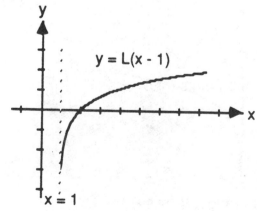

$y = L(x - 1)$

$x = 1$

6.3 Logarithmic Functions

1. (a) No, because a horizontal line can intersect the parabola twice.

    (b) Yes, because any horizontal line intersects the line only once.

    (c) Yes, because any horizontal line intersects the curve only once.

3. (a) Let $y = \dfrac{2x - 1}{3x + 4}$. We switch the roles of x and y and solve the resulting equation for y:

$$x = \frac{2y - 1}{3y + 4}$$
$$x(3y + 4) = 2y - 1$$
$$3xy + 4x = 2y - 1$$
$$3xy - 2y = -1 - 4x$$
$$y(3x - 2) = -1 - 4x$$
$$y = \frac{-1 - 4x}{3x - 2}$$
$$y = \frac{4x + 1}{2 - 3x}$$

So $f^{-1}(x) = \dfrac{4x + 1}{2 - 3x}$

(b) $\dfrac{1}{f(x)} = \dfrac{3x + 4}{2x - 1}$

(c) $f^{-1}(0) = \dfrac{4(0) + 1}{2 - 3(0)} = \dfrac{1}{2}$

(d) $\dfrac{1}{f(0)} = \dfrac{3(0) + 4}{2(0) - 1} = \dfrac{4}{-1} = -4$

5. $y = f^{-1}(x)$ would join the points $(-2,3)$ and $(5,-1)$, so $y = f^{-1}(x - 1)$ will join the points $(-1,3)$ and $(6,-1)$.

7. (a) $\log_3 9 = 2$
    (b) $\log_{10} 1000 = 3$
    (c) $\log_7 343 = 3$
    (d) $\log_2 \sqrt{2} = \dfrac{1}{2}$

9. (a) $2^5 = 32$
   (b) $10^0 = 1$
   (c) $e^{1/2} = \sqrt{e}$
   (d) $3^{-4} = \dfrac{1}{81}$
   (e) $t^v = u$

11. $\log_5 30$ represents the power to which 5 must be raised to get 30. It is clearly greater than 2, since $5^2 = 25$. $\log_8 60$ is less than 2 since $8^2 = 64$. Hence, $\log_5 30$ is larger.

13. (a) $\log_9 27$ is the power to which 9 must be raised to get 27. We can see it's between 1 and 2 since $9^1 = 9$ while $9^2 = 81$. To find it let $\log_9 27 = n$ then $9^n = 27$ in exponential form and $3^{2n} = 3^3$. So, $2n = 3$ and $n = \dfrac{3}{2}$.

   (b) If $\log_4 \dfrac{1}{32} = n$ then $4^n = \dfrac{1}{32}$ or $2^{2n} = 2^{-5}$. So $2n = -5$, and $n = -\dfrac{5}{2}$. So $\log_4 \dfrac{1}{32} = -\dfrac{5}{2}$.

   (c) Follow the same steps. If $\log_5 5\sqrt{5} = n$, then:
   $$5^n = 5\sqrt{5}$$
   $$5^n = 5^{3/2}$$
   $$n = \frac{3}{2}$$

15. (a) $\log_x 256 = 8$
   $$x^8 = 256 = 2^8$$
   So $x = 2$

   (b) $\log_5 x = -1$
   $$5^{-1} = x$$
   So $x = \dfrac{1}{5}$

   The solution to problems of this type frequently depends on our ability to move back and forth between the logarithmic and exponential form.

17. (a) We must have $5x > 0$, so $x > 0$. So the domain is $(0,\infty)$.

    (b) We must have $3 - 4x > 0$, so $3 > 4x$ and $x < \frac{3}{4}$. So the domain is

    $(-\infty,\frac{3}{4})$

    (c) We must have $x^2 > 0$, so $x \neq 0$. So the domain is all real numbers
    except 0, or $(-\infty,0) \cup (0,\infty)$.

    (d) We must have $x > 0$. So the domain is $(0,\infty)$.

    (e) We must have $x^2 - 25 > 0$
    $$(x - 5)(x + 5) > 0$$
    Key numbers: ± 5
    From a sign chart, we see that $x < -5$ or $x > 5$. So the domain is

    $(-\infty,-5) \cup (5,\infty)$.

19. We must make sure that $1 - \ln x \neq 0$. We find where $1 - \ln x = 0$:
    $$1 - \ln x = 0$$
    $$1 = \ln x$$
    $$e^1 = x$$
    So $x = e$ must be excluded from the domain. For the logarithm to be defined,
    however, we must also make sure that $x > 0$. So the domain is

    $(0, e) \cup (e, \infty)$.
    For the range, we switch the roles of x and y and solve that resulting equation
    for y:
    $$x = \frac{1}{1 - \ln y}$$
    $$1 - \ln y = \frac{1}{x}$$
    $$\ln y = 1 - \frac{1}{x}$$
    $$y = e^{1-1/x}$$
    So $x \neq 0$

    So the range is all real numbers except 0, or $(-\infty, 0) \cup (0, \infty)$.

21. (a) $y = \log_{10}(x + 1)$

    domain: $(-1,\infty)$; range: $(-\infty,\infty)$
    x-intercept: 0
    y-intercept: 0
    asymptote: $x = -1$

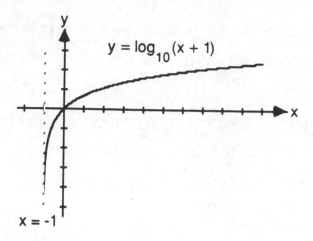

(b) $y = -\log_{10}(x + 1)$

domain: $(-1, \infty)$; range: $(-\infty, \infty)$
x-intercept: 0
y-intercept: 0
asymptote: $x = -1$

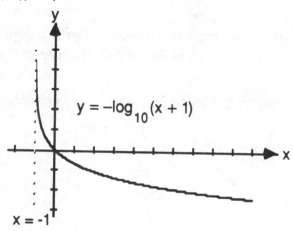

23. (a) $y = \ln x$

domain: $(0, \infty)$; range: $(-\infty, \infty)$
x-intercept: 1
y-intercept: none
asymptote: $x = 0$

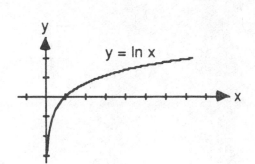

(b) y = ln (-x)

   domain: (-∞,0); range: (-∞,∞)
   x-intercept: -1
   y-intercept: none
   asymptote: x = 0

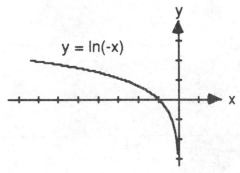

(c) y = -1 + ln (-x)

   domain: (-∞,0); range: (-∞,∞)
   x-intercept: -e
   y-intercept: none
   asymptote: x = 0

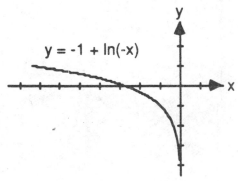

25. (a)   Let $x = \ln e^4$
$$e^x = e^4$$
$$x = 4$$

(b)   Let $x = \ln \dfrac{1}{e}$
$$e^x = \dfrac{1}{e}$$
$$e^x = e^{-1}$$
$$x = -1$$

(c)   Let $x = \ln \sqrt{e}$
$$e^x = \sqrt{e}$$
$$e^x = e^{1/2}$$
$$x = \dfrac{1}{2}$$

27. $10^x = 25$
$$x = \log_{10} 25$$
$$x \approx 1.40$$

29. $10^{(x^2)} = 40$
$$x^2 = \log_{10} 40$$
$$x = \pm\sqrt{\log_{10} 40}$$
$$x = \pm\sqrt{1 + \log_{10} 4}$$
$$x \approx \pm 1.27$$

31. $e^{2t+3} = 10$
$$2t + 3 = \ln 10$$
$$2t = -3 + \ln 10$$
$$t = \dfrac{-3 + \ln 10}{2}$$
$$t \approx -0.35$$

33. $e^{1-4t} = 12.405$
$$1 - 4t = \ln 12.405$$
$$-4t = -1 + \ln 12.405$$
$$t = \dfrac{1 - \ln 12.405}{4}$$
$$t \approx -0.38$$

35. (a) Use the decay equation $N = N_0 e^{kt}$, when $N = \frac{1}{2} N_0$ when $t = 4.5 \times 10^9$:

$$\frac{1}{2} N_0 = N_0 \, e^{(4.5 \times 10^9) \, k}$$

$$\frac{1}{2} = e^{(4.5 \times 10^9) \, k}$$

$$\ln \frac{1}{2} = (4.5 \times 10^9) \, k$$

$$k = \frac{\ln 0.5}{4.5 \times 10^9} \approx -1.54 \times 10^{-10}$$

(b) Use $t = 1000$:

$$N = N_0 e^{1000(-1.54 \times 10^{-10})}$$

$$= (0.999999846) \, N_0$$

So 99.9999846 % is still remaining.

37. (a) Starting with $N = N_0 e^{kt}$, we have:

$$\frac{1}{2} N_0 = N_0 \, e^{k \bullet 1}$$

$$e^k = \frac{1}{2}$$

$$k = \ln \frac{1}{2}$$

(b) If 90% is gone, the amount remaining will be 10%, or .4 g, and we have:

$$.4 = 4 \, e^{(\ln .5) \, t}$$

$$.1 = e^{(\ln .5) \, t}$$

$$\ln .1 = \ln (e^{(\ln .5) \, t})$$

$$\ln .1 = (\ln .5) \, t$$

$$t = \frac{\ln .1}{\ln .5} \approx 3.32 \text{ years}$$

39. (a)   We start with:
$$3 \times 10^8 = (2 \times 10^7) e^{k \bullet 2}$$
$$e^{2k} = 15$$
$$2k = \ln 15$$
$$k = \frac{\ln 15}{2}$$
$$2N_0 = N_0 e^{[(\ln 15)/2]t}$$
$$2 = e^{[(\ln 15)/2]t}$$
$$\ln 2 = \frac{\ln 15}{2} \bullet t$$
$$t = \frac{2 \ln 2}{\ln 15} \approx 0.51 \text{ hours}$$

(b)   Since 1 billion = 10^9, we want:
$$10^9 = 2 \times 10^7 e^{[(\ln 15)/2]t}$$
$$t = \frac{2 \ln 50}{\ln 15} \approx 2.89 \text{ hours}$$

41. Our rule for finding inverses is to interchange x and y and then solve for y, so:
$$f(x) = e^{x+1}$$
$$y = e^{x+1}$$
becomes
$$x = e^{y+1}$$
$$\ln x = \ln (e^{y+1})$$
$$\ln x = y + 1$$
$$y = -1 + \ln x$$
$$f^{-1}(x) = -1 + \ln x$$
A word of caution here. Be careful about writing an answer like this as
$\ln x - 1$. It can be incorrectly read as $\ln (x - 1)$ instead of $(\ln x) - 1$. The form of
our anser avoids this problem.
The x-intercept will be e and x = 0 is the asymptote:

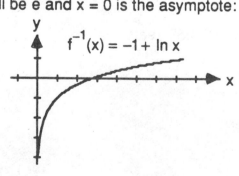

43.   We graph the region:

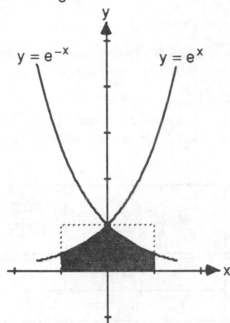

$y = e^{-x}$ $y = e^{x}$

The area is less than the rectangle (shown dotted on the graph), which has an area of 2 square units.

45. $e^{2x} - 5e^{x} - 6 = 0$ has the form of a quadratic in e^{x}. To see this let $e^{x} = n$, then the equation becomes $n^{2} - 5n - 6 = 0$ and we factor:

$$(e^{x} - 6)(e^{x} + 1) = 0$$

If $e^{x} - 6 = 0$, then $e^{x} = 6$ and $x = \ln 6$, but e^{x} can never equal -1, so there is no root corresponding to this factor, and $x = \ln 6$ is the only solution.

47.   If $\log_{2} x = 100$, then $x = 2^{100} = (2^{10})^{10} \approx (10^{3})^{10} = 10^{30}$

49.   We set $A = B$:

$$A_{0}e^{k_{1}t} = B_{0}e^{k_{2}t}$$

$$\frac{A_{0}}{B_{0}} = \frac{e^{k_{2}t}}{e^{k_{1}t}}$$

$$\frac{A_{0}}{B_{0}} = e^{(k_{2} - k_{1})t}$$

$$\ln\left(\frac{A_{0}}{B_{0}}\right) = (k_{2} - k_{1})t$$

$$t = \frac{\ln\left(\frac{A_0}{B_0}\right)}{k_2 - k_1}$$

This represents the amount of time it takes for two radioactive substances to decay to the same mass.

51. (a) $P(10) = 4$, since 2, 3, 5, 7 do not exceed 10.
         $P(18) = 7$, since 2, 3, 5, 7, 11, 13, 17, do not exceed 18.
         $P(19) = 8$, since 2, 3, 5, 7, 11, 13, 17, 19, do not exceed 19.

     (b) We complete the table:

x	$P(x)$	$\dfrac{x}{\ln x}$	$\dfrac{P(x)}{x/\ln x}$
10^2	25	21.715	1.151
10^4	1229	1,085.736	1.132
10^6	78,498	72,382.414	1.084
10^8	5,761,455	5,428,681.024	1.061
10^9	50,847,534	48,254,942.43	1.054
10^{10}	455,052,512	434,294,481.9	1.048

6.4 Properties of Logarithms

1. $\log_{10} 70 - \log_{10} 7 = \log_{10} \frac{70}{7} = \log_{10} 10 = 1$

3. $\log_7 \sqrt{7} = \log_7 (7^{1/2}) = \frac{1}{2}$

5. $\log_3 108 + \log_3 \frac{3}{4} = \log_3 \left(\frac{108 \cdot 3}{4}\right)$
    $= \log_3 81$
    $= \log_3 3^4$
    $= 4$

7. $-\dfrac{1}{2} + \ln \sqrt{e} = -\dfrac{1}{2} + \ln e^{1/2} = -\dfrac{1}{2} + \dfrac{1}{2} = 0$

9. $2^{\log_2 5} - 3 \log_5 \sqrt[3]{5} = 5 - 3 \log_5 5^{1/3}$

$$= 5 - 3\left(\dfrac{1}{3}\right)$$
$$= 5 - 1$$
$$= 4$$

11. $\log_{10} 30 + \log_{10} 2 = \log_{10}(30 \cdot 2) = \log_{10} 60$

13. $\log_5 6 + \log_5 \dfrac{1}{3} + \log_5 10 = \log_5 \left(6 \cdot \dfrac{1}{3} \cdot 10\right) = \log_5 20$

15. (a) $\ln 3 - 2 \ln 4 + \ln 32 = \ln 3 - \ln(4^2) + \ln 32$

$$= \ln \left(\dfrac{3 \cdot 32}{4^2}\right)$$
$$= \ln 6$$

(b) $\ln 3 - 2(\ln 4 + \ln 32) = \ln 3 - 2[\ln(4 \cdot 32)]$
$$= \ln 3 - 2 \ln 128$$
$$= \ln 3 - \ln(128^2)$$
$$= \ln \left(\dfrac{3}{128^2}\right)$$
$$= \ln \left(\dfrac{3}{16384}\right)$$

17. $\log_b 4 + 3\left[\log_b(1+x) - \dfrac{1}{2}\log_b(1-x)\right]$

$$= \log_b 4 + 3\left(\log_b(1+x) - \log_b\sqrt{1-x}\right)$$
$$= \log_b 4 + \log_b(1+x)^3 - \log_b(1-x)^{3/2}$$
$$= \log_b \left(\dfrac{4(1+x)^3}{(1-x)^{3/2}}\right)$$

19. $4 \log_{10} 3 - 6 \log_{10}(x^2+1) + \dfrac{1}{2}\left[\log_{10}(x+1) - 2 \log_{10} 3\right]$

$$= \log_{10} 3^4 - \log_{10}(x^2+1)^6 + \dfrac{1}{2}\left[\log_{10}(x+1) - \log_{10} 3^2\right]$$
$$= \log_{10} 81 - \log_{10}(x^2+1)^6 + \dfrac{1}{2} \log_{10}\left(\dfrac{x+1}{9}\right)$$

$$= \log_{10} 81 - \log_{10}(x^2 + 1)^6 + \log_{10}\left(\frac{x + 1}{9}\right)^{1/2}$$

$$= \log_{10}\left(\frac{81\frac{\sqrt{x + 1}}{3}}{(x^2 + 1)^6}\right)$$

$$= \log_{10}\left(\frac{27\sqrt{x + 1}}{(x^2 + 1)^6}\right)$$

21. (a) $\log_{10}\left(\dfrac{x^2}{1 + x^2}\right) = \log_{10} x^2 - \log_{10}(1 + x^2)$

$$= 2\log_{10} x - \log_{10}(1 + x^2)$$

(b) $\ln\left(\dfrac{x^2}{\sqrt{1 + x^2}}\right) = \ln x^2 - \ln\sqrt{1 + x^2}$

$$= 2\ln x - \frac{1}{2}\ln(1 + x^2)$$

23. (a) $\log_{10}\sqrt{9 - x^2} = \dfrac{1}{2}\log_{10}(9 - x^2)$

$$= \frac{1}{2}\log_{10}[(3 + x)(3 - x)]$$

$$= \frac{1}{2}\log_{10}(3 + x) + \frac{1}{2}\log_{10}(3 - x)$$

(b) $\ln\left(\dfrac{\sqrt{4 - x^2}}{(x - 1)(x + 1)^{3/2}}\right)$

$$= \frac{1}{2}\ln(4 - x^2) - \ln(x - 1) - \ln(x + 1)^{3/2}$$

$$= \frac{1}{2}\ln[(2 + x)(2 - x)] - \ln(x - 1) - \frac{3}{2}\ln(x + 1)$$

$$= \frac{1}{2}\ln(2 + x) + \frac{1}{2}\ln(2 - x) - \ln(x - 1) - \frac{3}{2}\ln(x + 1)$$

25. (a) $\log_b\sqrt{\dfrac{x}{b}} = \dfrac{1}{2}\log_b\dfrac{x}{b}$

$$= \frac{1}{2}\log_b x - \frac{1}{2}\log_b b$$

$$= \frac{1}{2}\log_b x - \frac{1}{2}$$

(b) $\quad 2 \ln \sqrt{(1 + x^2)(1 + x^4)(1 + x^6)} = \ln[\,(1 + x^2)(1 + x^4)(1 + x^6)\,]$
$$= \ln(1 + x^2) + \ln(1 + x^4) + \ln(1 + x^6)$$

27. (a) $\quad \log_{10}(AB^2C^3) = \log_{10}A + \log_{10}B^2 + \log_{10}C^3$
$$= \log_{10}A + 2\log_{10}B + 3\log_{10}C$$
$$= a + 2b + 3c$$

(b) $\quad \log_{10}\sqrt{10ABC} = \dfrac{1}{2}\log_{10}(10ABC)$
$$= \dfrac{1}{2}\log_{10}10 + \dfrac{1}{2}\log_{10}A + \dfrac{1}{2}\log_{10}B + \dfrac{1}{2}\log_{10}C$$
$$= \dfrac{1}{2}(1) + \dfrac{1}{2}a + \dfrac{1}{2}b + \dfrac{1}{2}c$$
$$= \dfrac{1}{2}(1 + a + b + c)$$

(c) $\quad \log_{10}\left(\dfrac{10A}{\sqrt{BC}}\right) = \log_{10}(10A) - \dfrac{1}{2}\log_{10}(BC)$
$$= \log_{10}10 + \log_{10}A - \dfrac{1}{2}\log_{10}B - \dfrac{1}{2}\log_{10}C$$
$$= 1 + a - \dfrac{1}{2}b - \dfrac{1}{2}c$$

(d) $\quad \log_{10}\left(\dfrac{100A^2}{B^4\sqrt[3]{C}}\right) = \log_{10}10^2 + \log_{10}A^2 - \log_{10}B^4 - \log_{10}C^{1/3}$
$$= 2\log_{10}10 + 2\log_{10}A - 4\log_{10}B - \dfrac{1}{3}\log_{10}C$$
$$= 2(1) + 2a - 4b - \dfrac{1}{3}c$$
$$= 2 + 2a - 4b - \dfrac{1}{3}c$$

(e) $\quad \log_{10}\left(\dfrac{(AB)^5}{C}\right) = \log_{10}A^5 + \log_{10}B^5 - \log_{10}C$
$$= 5\log_{10}A + 5\log_{10}B - \log_{10}C$$
$$= 5a + 5b - c$$

29. $5 = 2e^{2x-1}$

Taking the natural log of each side, we have:

$$\ln 5 = \ln 2 + \ln e^{2x-1}$$
$$\ln 5 = \ln 2 + (2x - 1)$$
$$\ln 5 = \ln 2 + 2x - 1$$
$$2x = \ln 5 - \ln 2 + 1$$
$$x = \frac{\ln 5 - \ln 2 + 1}{2}$$

31.

$$3e^{1+t} = 2$$
$$\ln 3 + \ln e^{1+t} = \ln 2$$
$$\ln 3 + 1 + t = \ln 2$$
$$t = \ln 2 - \ln 3 - 1$$

33.

$$2^x = 9$$
$$\ln 2^x = \ln 9$$
$$x \ln 2 = \ln 9$$
$$x = \frac{\ln 9}{\ln 2}$$

35.

$$10 \cdot 2^x = 5^x$$
$$\ln 10 + \ln 2^x = \ln 5^x$$
$$\ln 10 + x \ln 2 = x \ln 5$$
$$\ln 10 = x \ln 5 - x \ln 2$$
$$\ln 10 = x (\ln 5 - \ln 2)$$
$$x = \frac{\ln 10}{\ln 5 - \ln 2}$$
$$x = \frac{\ln 5 + \ln 2}{\ln 5 - \ln 2}$$

37.

$$\log_9 (x + 1) = \frac{1}{2} + \log_9 x$$
$$\log_9 (x + 1) - \log_9 x = \frac{1}{2}$$
$$\log_9 \left(\frac{x + 1}{x}\right) = \frac{1}{2}$$
$$9^{1/2} = \frac{x + 1}{x}$$
$$3 = \frac{x + 1}{x}$$
$$3x = x + 1$$
$$2x = 1$$
$$x = \frac{1}{2}$$

39. $\log_{10} (2x + 4) + \log_{10} (x - 2) = 1$

$\log_{10} [(2x + 4)(x - 2)] = 1$

$(2x + 4)(x - 2) = 10^1$

$2x^2 - 8 = 10$

$2x^2 = 18$

$x^2 = 9$

$x = \pm 3$

But x = -3 is an extraneous root ($\log_{10}$ -2 is undefined), so x = 3.

41. $\log_{10} (x + 3) - \log_{10} (x - 2) = 2$

$\log_{10} \left(\dfrac{x + 3}{x - 2} \right) = 2$

$10^2 = \dfrac{x + 3}{x - 2}$

$100(x - 2) = x + 3$

$100x - 200 = x + 3$

$99x = 203$

$x = \dfrac{203}{99}$

43. $\log_b (x + 1) = 2 \log_b (x - 1)$

$\log_b (x + 1) = \log_b (x - 1)^2$

$x + 1 = (x - 1)^2$

$x + 1 = x^2 - 2x + 1$

$x^2 - 3x = 0$

$x(x - 3) = 0$

$x = 0, 3$

But x = 0 is an extraneous root ($\log_b$ -1 is undefined), so x = 3.

45. $\log_{10} (x - 6) + \log_{10} (x + 3) = 1$

$\log_{10} [(x - 6)(x + 3)] = 1$

$10^1 = (x - 6) (x + 3)$

$x^2 - 3x - 18 = 10$

$x^2 - 3x - 28 = 0$

$(x - 7)(x + 4) = 0$

x = 7 and x = -4 are roots of this equation.
However, we must check to make sure both roots work in the original equation. 7 does, but when we try -4 we have $\log_{10}$ -10 and $\log_{10}$ -1, neither of which are defined.

47.   (a) $\log_{10} x - y = \log_{10} (3x - 1)$

         $\log_{10} x - \log_{10} (3x - 1) = y$

$$\log_{10} \left(\frac{x}{3x - 1} \right) = y$$

$$10^y = \frac{x}{3x - 1}$$

$$10^y (3x - 1) = x$$

$$3(10^y)x - 10^y = x$$

$$3(10^y)x - x = 10^y$$

$$x[3(10^y) - 1] = 10^y$$

$$x = \frac{10^y}{3(10^y) - 1}$$

(b) $\log_{10} (x - y) = \log_{10} (3x - 1)$ is easier to solve, for we can conclude directly that:

$$x - y = 3x - 1$$
$$-2x = y - 1$$
$$x = \frac{y - 1}{-2} \quad \text{or} \quad \frac{1 - y}{2}$$

49.   There is a formula which shows us how to convert to logs in any base, but let's do one the longer way and review how the formula is derived. Given $\log_2 5$, we are asked to write it as a base 10 log:

$$\log_2 5 = N$$
$$2^N = 5$$
$$\log_{10} 2^N = \log_{10} 5$$
$$N \bullet \log_{10} 2 = \log_{10} 5$$
$$N = \frac{\log_{10} 5}{\log_{10} 2}$$
$$\log_2 5 = \frac{\log_{10} 5}{\log_{10} 2}$$

51. $\ln 3 = \log_e 3 = \dfrac{\log_{10} 3}{\log_{10} e}$

53. $\log_b 2 = \dfrac{\log_{10} 2}{\log_{10} b}$

55. $\log_{10} 6 = \dfrac{\ln 6}{\ln 10}$

57. $\log_{10} e = \dfrac{\ln e}{\ln 10} = \dfrac{1}{\ln 10}$

59. $\log_{10}(\log_{10} x) = \log_{10}\left(\dfrac{\ln x}{\ln 10}\right)$

$$= \dfrac{\ln\left(\dfrac{\ln x}{\ln 10}\right)}{\ln 10}$$

$$= \dfrac{\ln(\ln x) - \ln(\ln 10)}{\ln 10}$$

61. (a) true
    (b) true
    (c) true
    (d) false -- $\ln x^3 = 3\ln x$, not $\ln 3x$
    (e) true
    (f) false -- $\ln(2x)^3 = 3\ln 2x$, but $\ln 2x^3 = \ln 2 + 3\ln x$
    (g) true
    (h) false -- $\log_5 24$ is between 1 and 2, not 5^1 and 5^2
    (i) true
    (j) false -- $\log_5 24$ is close to 2 ($2 = \log_5 25$)
    (k) false -- it is $x > 0$
    (l) true
    (m) true

63. $\ln(P + Q) = \ln(3 + 4) = \ln 7 \approx 1.94591$

$\ln P + \ln Q = \ln 3 + \ln 4 \approx 1.09861 + 1.38629 \approx 2.48490$

So $\ln(3 + 4) \neq \ln 3 + \ln 4$

65. $\ln(PQ) = \ln(10 \cdot 20) = \ln 200 \approx 5.29832$

$(\ln P)(\ln Q) = (\ln 10)(\ln 20) \approx (2.30259)(2.99573) \approx 6.89794$

So $\ln(10 \cdot 20) \neq (\ln 10)(\ln 20)$

67. $\dfrac{\log_{10} 19}{\log_{10} 89} \approx \dfrac{1.27875}{1.94939} \approx 0.65598$

$\log_{10} 19 - \log_{10} 89 \approx 1.27875 - 1.94939 \approx -0.67064$

So $\dfrac{\log_{10} 19}{\log_{10} 89} \neq \log_{10} 19 - \log_{10} 89$

69. $\log_{10} \pi^7 \approx 3.48005$

$7 \log_{10} \pi \approx 7 \,(0.49715) \approx 3.48005$

So $\log_{10} \pi^7 = 7 \log_{10} \pi$

71. $b^{\log_b P} = 10^{\log_{10} 1776} = 10^{3.24944} = 1776$

$10^{\log_{10} 1776} = 1776$

73. $\log_{10} A + \log_{10} B + \log_{10} C = \log_{10} 11 + \log_{10} 12 + \log_{10} 13$

$$\approx 1.04139 + 1.07918 + 1.11394$$

$$\approx 3.23451$$

$\log_{10}(ABC) = \log_{10}(11 \bullet 12 \bullet 13) = \log_{10} 1716 \approx 3.23451$

So $\log_{10} A + \log_{10} B + \log_{10} C = \log_{10}(ABC)$

75. $g\,(f\,(0.123456)) = g\,(10^{0.123456})$

$$\approx g\,(1.3287889)$$

$$\approx \log_{10} 1.3287889$$

$$\approx 0.123456$$

77. (a)   We substitute for x:

$3e^{1 - (\ln 0.3 + 1)} = 3e^{-\ln 0.3}$

$$= 3e^{\ln (0.3)^{-1}}$$

$$= 3\,(0.3)^{-1}$$

$$= 3\left(\frac{10}{3}\right)$$

$$= 10$$

(b) $\dfrac{\ln 0.3 + 1}{2} = \dfrac{1}{2}\ln 0.3 + \dfrac{1}{2} = \ln (0.3)^{1/2} + \dfrac{1}{2} = \dfrac{1}{2} + \ln \sqrt{0.3}$

(c)   Since $\ln e = 1$, then $\dfrac{1}{2} = \dfrac{1}{2}\ln e = \ln \sqrt{e}$. So:

$$\frac{1}{2} + \ln \sqrt{0.3} = \ln \sqrt{e} + \ln \sqrt{0.3} = \ln \sqrt{\frac{3e}{10}}$$

79. $\log_b\left(\dfrac{\sqrt{3} + \sqrt{2}}{\sqrt{3} - \sqrt{2}}\right) = \log_b\left(\dfrac{\sqrt{3} + \sqrt{2}}{\sqrt{3} - \sqrt{2}} \bullet \dfrac{\sqrt{3} + \sqrt{2}}{\sqrt{3} + \sqrt{2}}\right)$

$$= \log_b\left(\frac{(\sqrt{3} + \sqrt{2})^2}{3 - 2}\right)$$

$$= \log_b (\sqrt{3} + \sqrt{2})^2$$
$$= 2 \log_b (\sqrt{3} + \sqrt{2})$$

81. $b^{3 \log_b x} = b^{\log_b x^3} = x^3$

83. $\log_2 \sqrt[5]{4\sqrt{2}} = \frac{1}{5} \log_2 4\sqrt{2}$

$$= \frac{1}{5} \log_2 (2^2 \bullet 2^{1/2})$$

$$= \frac{1}{5} \log_2 (2^{5/2})$$

$$= \frac{1}{5} \bullet \frac{5}{2}$$

$$= \frac{1}{2}$$

85. $\quad\quad\quad 3 \ln x = \alpha + 3 \ln \beta$

$3\ln x - 3\ln \beta = \alpha$

$3(\ln x - \ln \beta) = \alpha$

$\quad 3 \ln \dfrac{x}{\beta} = \alpha$

$\quad\quad \ln \dfrac{x}{\beta} = \dfrac{\alpha}{3}$

$\quad\quad\quad \dfrac{x}{\beta} = e^{\alpha/3}$

$\quad\quad\quad x = \beta e^{\alpha/3}$

87. Using the change of base formula, we have:

$$\log_b a = \frac{\log_a a}{\log_a b} = \frac{1}{\log_a b}$$

89. Using the change of base formula, we have:

$$\log_{ab} x = \frac{\log_a x}{\log_a ab} = \frac{\log_a x}{\log_a a + \log_a b} = \frac{\log_a x}{1 + \log_a b}$$

So $\dfrac{\log_a x}{\log_{ab} x} = \dfrac{\log_a x}{\dfrac{\log_a x}{1 + \log_a b}} = 1 + \log_a b$

This proves the desired result.

91.   We work from the right-hand side:
$$\frac{1}{2}(\log a + \log b) = \frac{1}{2}\log(ab) = \log\sqrt{ab}$$
So, proving the desired equality is equivalent to proving:
$$\frac{1}{3}(a+b) = \sqrt{ab}, \text{ since log is a 1-1 function.}$$
If a and b are both positive, we can square each side:
$$\frac{1}{9}(a^2 + 2ab + b^2) = ab$$
We now work with the left-hand side:
$$\frac{1}{9}(a^2 + 2ab + b^2) = \frac{1}{9}(7ab + 2ab) \text{ by our assumption } a^2 + b^2 = 7ab$$
$$= \frac{1}{9}(9ab)$$
$$= ab$$
This proves the result.

93.   Let $y = \ln(x + \sqrt{x^2 + 1})$. We interchange the roles of x and y, then solve for y:
$$x = \ln(y + \sqrt{y^2 + 1})$$
$$e^x = y + \sqrt{y^2 + 1}$$
$$e^x - y = \sqrt{y^2 + 1}$$
Squaring each side:
$$e^{2x} - 2ye^x + y^2 = y^2 + 1$$
$$e^{2x} - 2ye^x = 1$$
$$e^{2x} - 1 = 2ye^x$$
$$\frac{e^{2x} - 1}{2e^x} = y$$
So $f^{-1}(x) = \dfrac{e^{2x} - 1}{2e^x}$

95.   We complete the table:

x	10^2	10^3	10^6	10^{20}	10^{50}	10^{99}
y	0.4234	0.6589	0.9654	1.3428	1.5573	1.6918

As x approaches infinity, so does ln x, and thus ln (ln x), and finally ln [ln(ln x)]. The table is misleading -- it only indicates that y approaches infinity much slower!

An actual proof of the result is more complicated:
Assume that y does <u>not</u> approach infinity, so there is some number N such that $y < N$, then $\ln[\ln(\ln x)] < N$, so $\ln(\ln x) < e^N$.

But since $\ln(\ln x) < e^N$, then $\ln x < e^{(e^N)}$, and finally $x < e^{e^{(e^N)}}$. But clearly this is false, since x approaches infinity and thus cannot be bounded. Thus y must approach infinity.

6.5 <u>Applications</u>

1. For annual compounding of money we use the formula $A = P(1 + r)^t$. We want A when P = \$800, r = 0.06 and t = 4 years:

$$A = 800(1 + 0.06)^4$$
$$= 800(1.06)^4$$
$$\approx \$1009.98$$

3. For annual compounding of money we use the formula $A = P(1 + r)^t$. We want r when A = \$6000, P = \$4000 and t = 5:

$$6000 = 4000(1 + r)^5$$
$$1.5 = (1 + r)^5$$
$$(1.5)^{1/5} = 1 + r$$
$$r = (1.5)^{1/5} - 1$$
$$r \approx 0.0845$$

So the interest rate is 8.45 %.

5. In the first bank, we have P = \$500, r = 0.05, and t = 4:

$$A = 500(1 + 0.05)^4$$
$$= 500(1.05)^4$$
$$\approx 607.75$$

We now deposit P = \$607.75, r = 0.06, and t = 4:

$$A = 607.75(1 + 0.06)^4$$
$$= 607.75(1.06)^4$$
$$\approx 767.27$$

So the new balance will be \$767.27.

7. (a) We use $A = P(1 + r)^t$ with P = 1000, r = 0.07, and t = 20:

$$A = 1000(1 + 0.07)^{20}$$
$$= 1000(1.07)^{20}$$
$$\approx 3869.69$$

The new balance is \$3869.68

(b)   We use $A = P\left(1 + \dfrac{r}{N}\right)^{Nt}$ with $P = 1000$, $r = 0.07$, $N = 4$, $t = 20$:

$$A = 1000\left(1 + \frac{0.07}{4}\right)^{4(20)}$$

$$= 1000\,(1.0175)^{80}$$

$$\approx 4006.39$$

The new balance is \$4006.39

9.   For compounding quarterly we use the formula:

$$A = P\left(1 + \frac{r}{N}\right)^{Nt}.$$

So here $P = \$100$, $r = 6\%$ and we have $N = 4$ compoundings per year.
We want the value of t for which $A \geq \$120$:

$$120 \leq 100\left(1 + \frac{0.06}{4}\right)^{4t}$$

$$1.2 \leq (1.015)^{4t}$$

$$\ln 1.2 \leq 4t \ln 1.015$$

$$4t \geq \frac{\ln 1.2}{\ln 1.015}$$

$$t \geq \frac{\ln 1.2}{4 \ln 1.015}$$

$$t \geq 3.06$$

This is slightly over 3 years, and so 13 quarters will be required.

11.   We use $A = P\left(1 + \dfrac{r}{N}\right)^{Nt}$ where $r = 0.055$, $N = 2$, $A = 6000$, $t = 10$:

$$6000 = P\left(1 + \frac{0.55}{2}\right)^{2(10)}$$

$$6000 = P\,(1.0275)^{20}$$

$$P = \frac{6000}{(1.0275)^{20}}$$

$$P \approx 3487.50$$

You must deposit a principal of \$3487.50

13.   We use $A = Pe^{rt}$ where $A = 5000$, $t = 10$, and $r = 0.065$:

$$5000 = Pe^{(0.065)(10)}$$

$$5000 = Pe^{0.65}$$

$$P = \frac{5000}{e^{0.65}}$$

$$P \approx 2610.23$$

A principal of \$2610.23 will grow to \$5000 in 10 years.

15. Since the effective rate is $r = 0.06$, we have:
$$A = P(1 + 0.06)^1$$
$$A = (1.06)P$$
The nominal rate r would yield a balance of:
$$A = Pe^{r(1)}$$
$$A = Pe^r$$
Setting these equal:
$$Pe^r = P(1.06)$$
$$e^r = 1.06$$
$$r = \ln 1.06$$
$$r \approx 0.0583$$
So the nominal rate is 5.83%

17. Let's take the 6% investment first:
$$A = 10{,}000(1 + 0.06)^5$$
$$= 10{,}000(1.3382)$$
$$\approx \$13382.26$$
The second choice will be:
$$A = 10{,}000e^{0.05\,(5)}$$
$$= 10{,}000e^{.25}$$
$$\approx \$12840.25, \quad \text{considerably less.}$$

19. (a) $T_2 \approx \dfrac{0.7}{r} = \dfrac{0.7}{0.05} = 14$ years

    (b) $T_2 = \dfrac{\ln 2}{r} = \dfrac{\ln 2}{0.05} = 13.86$ years

    (c) Here $d_1 = 13.86$, $d_2 = 14$, so $d = |13.86 - 14| = 0.14$

    This represents $\dfrac{0.14}{13.86}(100) \approx 1.01$ % of the actual doubling time.

21. Here: $A = 1000e^{(.08)\,300}$
$$A = 1000e^{24}$$
$$A = 1000(2.65 \times 10^{10})$$
$$A = \$2.65 \times 10^{13}$$
That's $26.5 trillion, a nice inheritance.

23. (a) $T_2 \approx \dfrac{0.7}{0.05} = 14$ years

    (b) We sketch the graph:

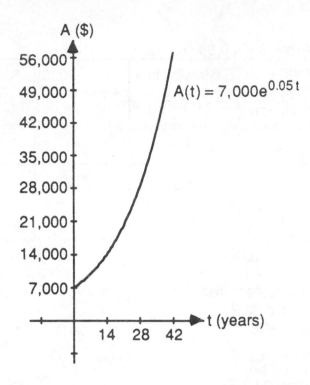

25. The growth problems are solved by assuming an exponential growth rate:
$$N = N_0 e^{kt}$$
First we find the percent distribution by dividing the total population into each of the two regions:
$$\frac{1.131}{4.090} \approx 27.7\% \text{ for more developed regions.}$$
Applying the growth formula to the total world population, we have:
$$N = N_0 e^{kt}$$
$$N = 4.090 e^{0.18 \, (25)}$$
$$N = 4.090 \, e^{.45}$$
$$N \approx 6.414 \text{ billion}$$
The other calculations are similar to these two. The completed table is:

	1975 Population (billions)	% Population in 1975	Growth Rate (% per year)	Year 2000 Population (billions)	% of World Population in 2000
World	4.090	100	1.8	6.414	100
More Dev.	1.131	27.7	0.6	1.314	20.5
Less Dev.	2.959	72.3	2.1	5.002	78.0

27. We complete the table:

	1975 Population (billions)	Growth Rate (% per year)	Year 2000 Population (billions)	% Increase in Population
Low	4.043	1.5	5.883	45.5
Medium	4.090	1.8	6.414	56.8
High	4.134	2.0	6.816	64.9

29. (a)   Use $N = N_0 e^{kt}$:

$$62,947,714 = 23,191,876\ e^{k\,(50)}$$
$$2.7142 = e^{50k}$$
$$\ln 2.7142 = 50k$$
$$k = \frac{\ln 2.7142}{50}$$
$$k \approx 0.0200$$

  (b)   In 1950, we have:
$$N = (62,947,714)\ e^{(0.02)\,(50)}$$
$$\approx 170,853,155$$
(Your answer may differ slightly due to round-off error)

  (c)   The actual growth over that period was slower than that predicted from (b) with a constant growth rate.

31. (a) $k \approx 0.0068$, or 0.68%

  (b) $k \approx 0.0096$, or 0.96%
  (c)   It would be 19,751,512
  (d)   Our prediction is higher than the actual population.

33.   (a)   We draw the graph:

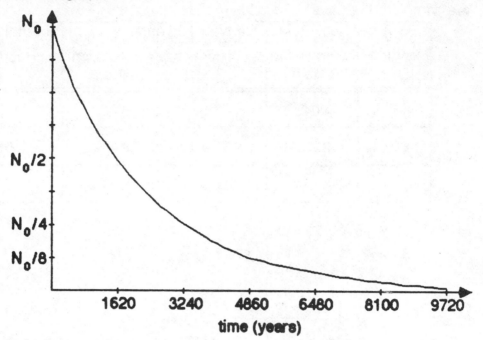

(b)   We draw the graph:

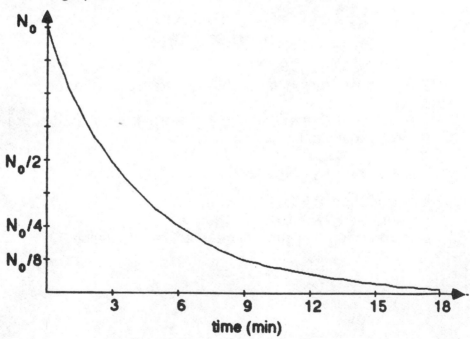

35. (a) $N = N_0 e^{kt}$

$\frac{1}{2} N_0 = N_0 e^{k \cdot 13}$ because after 13 years, N will be one-half of the original amount. So, dividing by N_0, we get:

$$e^{13k} = .5$$
$$13k = \ln .5$$
$$k = \frac{\ln .5}{13} \approx -0.0533$$

Once you understand this, it will be convenient for you to remember that k always equals ln .5 divided by the length of a half life for decay problems.

(b) $N = N_0 e^{(-.0533)(10)}$

$N \approx .587 \, N_0$ or about 58.7% of N_0 after 10 years.

If t = 100, $N \approx .5\%$ of N_0.

37. (a) $k = \frac{\ln 0.5}{28} \approx -0.0248$

(b) We set $\frac{N_0}{1000} = N_0 e^{kt}$

$$0.001 = e^{-0.0248\,t}$$
$$\ln 0.001 = -0.0248\,t$$
$$t = \frac{\ln 0.001}{-0.0248} \approx 279 \text{ years}$$

(c) Since $2^{10} \approx 1000$, then after 10 half lives, it shoud be reduced to $\frac{N_0}{1000}$. Since each half life is 28 years, this is approximately 280 years. Note that this is close to our answer from (b).

39. (a) We use $N = N_0 e^{kt}$ with $N = 10 \times 10^9$, $N_0 = 3.6 \times 10^9$, and $k = 0.02$:

$$10 \times 10^9 = (3.6 \times 10^9) e^{0.02\,t}$$
$$\frac{10}{3.6} = e^{0.02\,t}$$
$$\ln \frac{10}{3.6} = 0.02\,t$$
$$t = \frac{\ln \frac{10}{3.6}}{0.02}$$
$$t \approx 51 \text{ years}$$

So 51 years after 1969, or 2020, the carrying capacity will be reached.

(b)   We use $N = N_0 e^{kt}$ with $N = 10 \times 10^9$, $N_0 = 4.043 \times 10^9$, and $k = 0.015$:

$$10 \times 10^9 = (4.043 \times 10^9) e^{0.015 t}$$

$$\frac{10}{4.043} = e^{0.015 t}$$

$$\ln \frac{10}{4.043} = 0.015 t$$

$$t = \frac{\ln \dfrac{10}{4.043}}{0.015}$$

$$t \approx 60 \text{ years}$$

So 60 years after 1975, or 2035, the carrying capacity will be reached.

(c)   We use $N = N_0 e^{kt}$ with $N = 10 \times 10^9$, $N_0 = 4.134 \times 10^9$, and $k = 0.02$:

$$10 \times 10^9 = (4.134 \times 10^9) e^{0.02 t}$$

$$\frac{10}{4.134} = e^{0.02 t}$$

$$\ln \frac{10}{4.134} = 0.02 t$$

$$t = \frac{\ln \dfrac{10}{4.134}}{0.02}$$

$$t \approx 44 \text{ years}$$

So 44 years after 1975, or 2019, the carrying capacity will be reached.

41.   (a) $T = \dfrac{\ln \left(\dfrac{Ak}{A_0} + 1 \right)}{k} = \dfrac{\ln \left(\dfrac{161241(0.01)}{250} + 1 \right)}{0.01} \approx 201 \text{ years}$

(b) $T = \dfrac{\ln \left(\dfrac{Ak}{A_0} + 1 \right)}{k} = \dfrac{\ln \left(\dfrac{161241(0.02)}{250} + 1 \right)}{0.02} \approx 132 \text{ years}$

43.   (a) $\log_{10} E = 11.4 + 1.5M$

$$E = 10^{11.4 + 1.5M}$$

$$E = 10^{11.4} \cdot 10^{1.5M}$$

(b) $\dfrac{E_2}{E_1} = \dfrac{10^{11.4} \cdot 10^{1.5M_2}}{10^{11.4} \cdot 10^{1.5M_1}}$

$= 10^{1.5\,(M_2 - M_1)}$

$= 10^{1.5\,(7.8 - 6.8)}$

$= 10^{1.5\,(1.0)}$

≈ 31.6

45. $k = \dfrac{\ln 0.5}{4.7 \times 10^{10}} \approx -1.4748 \times 10^{-11}$

47. $T = \dfrac{\ln\left(\dfrac{N_s}{N_r} + 1\right)}{-k} = \dfrac{\ln\,(0.0636 + 1)}{-\,(-1.4748 \times 10^{-11})} \approx 4.181 \times 10^9$ years

The rock is approximately 4.181 billion years old.

49. $T = \dfrac{5730 \ln \dfrac{N}{920}}{\ln \dfrac{1}{2}} = \dfrac{5730 \ln \dfrac{141}{920}}{\ln \dfrac{1}{2}} \approx 15505$

The two paintings are 15,505 years old.

51. $T = \dfrac{5730 \ln \dfrac{N}{920}}{\ln \dfrac{1}{2}} = \dfrac{5730 \ln \dfrac{226}{920}}{\ln \dfrac{1}{2}} \approx 11,605$

This is 11,500 years (to the nearest 500 years).

Chapter 6 Review Exercises

1.　$y = e^x$
horizontal asymptote:　$y = 0$
vertical asymptote:　none
x-intercept:　none
y-intercept:　1

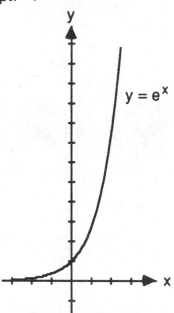

3.　$y = \ln x$
horizontal asymptote:　none
vertical asymptote:　$x = 0$
x-intercept:　1
y-intercept:　none

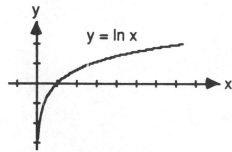

5. $y = 2^{x+1} + 1$
     horizontal asymptote: $y = 1$
     vertical asymptote: none
     x-intercept: none
     y-intercept: 3

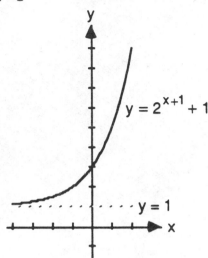

7. $y = \left(\frac{1}{e}\right)^x$
     horizontal asymptote: $y = 0$
     vertical asymptote: none
     x-intercept: none
     y-intercept: 1

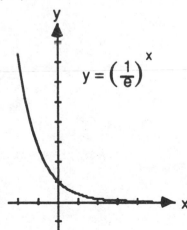

9. $y = e^{x+1} + 1$
      horizontal asymptote: $y = 1$
      vertical asymptote: none
      x-intercept: none
      y-intercept: $e + 1$

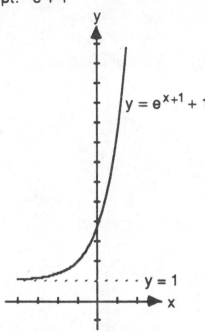

11. $y = \ln(e^x)$
      horizontal asymptote: none
      vertical asymptote: none
      x-intercept: 0
      y-intercept: 0

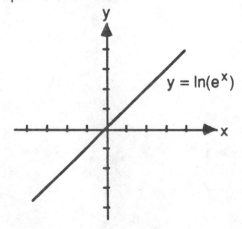

13. $\log_4 x + \log_4 (x - 3) = 1$

$\log_4 [x(x - 3)] = 1$

$x(x - 3) = 4^1$

$x^2 - 3x = 4$

$x^2 - 3x - 4 = 0$

$(x - 4)(x + 1) = 0$

$x = 4, -1$

But $x = -1$ is an extraneous root [$\log_4 -1$ is undefined], so $x = 4$.

15. $\ln x + \ln (x + 2) = \ln 15$

$\ln [x(x + 2)] = \ln 15$

$x(x + 2) = 15$

$x^2 + 2x = 15$

$x^2 + 2x - 15 = 0$

$(x + 5)(x - 3) = 0$

$x = -5, 3$

But $x = -5$ is an extraneous root [$\ln -5$ is undefined], so $x = 3$.

17. $\log_2 x + \log_2 (3x + 10) - 3 = 0$

$\log_2 [x(3x + 10)] = 3$

$x(3x + 10) = 2^3$

$3x^2 + 10x = 8$

$3x^2 + 10x - 8 = 0$

$(3x - 2)(x + 4) = 0$

$x = \dfrac{2}{3}, -4$

But $x = -4$ is an extraneous root [$\log_2 -4$ is undefined], so $x = \dfrac{2}{3}$.

19. $3 \log_9 x = \dfrac{1}{2}$

$\log_9 x = \dfrac{1}{6}$

$x = 9^{1/6}$

$x = \sqrt[6]{9} = \sqrt[3]{3}$

21. $e^{1-5x} = 3\sqrt{e}$

$1 - 5x = \ln 3\sqrt{e}$

$1 - 5x = \ln 3 + \dfrac{1}{2} \ln e$

$1 - 5x = \ln 3 + \dfrac{1}{2}$

$$-5x = \ln 3 - \frac{1}{2}$$
$$x = \frac{1 - 2 \ln 3}{10}$$

23.
$$\log_{10} x - 2 = \log_{10} (x - 2)$$
$$\log_{10} x - \log_{10} (x - 2) = 2$$
$$\log_{10} \frac{x}{x - 2} = 2$$
$$\frac{x}{x - 2} = 100$$
$$x = 100(x - 2)$$
$$x = 100x - 200$$
$$200 = 99x$$
$$x = \frac{200}{99}$$

25.
$$\ln (x + 2) = \ln x + \ln 2$$
$$\ln (x + 2) = \ln 2x$$
$$x + 2 = 2x$$
$$2 = x$$

27. $\ln (x^4) = 4 \ln x$

This is an identity, so the solution is all real numbers $x > 0$, or $(0, \infty)$.

29.
$$\log_{10} x = \ln x$$
$$\frac{\ln x}{\ln 10} = \ln x$$
$$\ln x = (\ln 10) (\ln x)$$
$$\ln x - (\ln 10)(\ln x) = 0$$
$$\ln x (1 - \ln 10) = 0$$
$$\ln x = 0, \text{ so } x = 1$$

31. $\log_{10} \sqrt{10} = \log_{10} (10^{1/2}) = \dfrac{1}{2}$

33. $\ln (\sqrt[5]{e}) = \ln (e^{1/5}) = \dfrac{1}{5}$

35.
$$\begin{aligned}
\log_{10} \pi - \log_{10} 10\pi &= \log_{10} \pi - (\log_{10} 10 + \log_{10} \pi) \\
&= \log_{10} \pi - \log_{10} 10 - \log_{10} \pi \\
&= - \log_{10} 10 \\
&= -1
\end{aligned}$$

37. $10^{\log_{10} 16} = 16$

39. $\ln(e^4) = 4$

41. $\log_{12} 2 + \log_{12} 18 + \log_{12} 4 = \log_{12}(2 \cdot 18 \cdot 4) = \log_{12} 144 = \log_{12}(12^2) = 2$

43. $\dfrac{\ln 100}{\ln 10} = \dfrac{\ln(10^2)}{\ln 10} = \dfrac{2 \ln 10}{\ln 10} = 2$

45. $\log_2 \sqrt[7]{16 \sqrt[3]{2\sqrt{2}}} = \dfrac{1}{7} \log_2 16 \sqrt[3]{2\sqrt{2}}$

$$= \dfrac{1}{7}(\log_2 16 + \log_2 \sqrt[3]{2\sqrt{2}}$$

$$= \dfrac{1}{7}[\log_2(2^4) + \dfrac{1}{3}\log_2 2\sqrt{2}]$$

$$= \dfrac{1}{7}[4 + \dfrac{1}{3}(\log_2 2 + \log_2 \sqrt{2})]$$

$$= \dfrac{1}{7}[4 + \dfrac{1}{3}(1 + \log_2(2^{1/2}))]$$

$$= \dfrac{1}{7}\left(4 + \dfrac{1}{3} \cdot \dfrac{3}{2}\right)$$

$$= \dfrac{1}{7}\left(4 + \dfrac{1}{2}\right)$$

$$= \dfrac{1}{7} \cdot \dfrac{9}{2}$$

$$= \dfrac{9}{14}$$

47. $\log_{10}(A^2 B^3 \sqrt{C}) = \log_{10} A^2 + \log_{10} B^3 + \log_{10} \sqrt{C}$

$$= 2 \log_{10} A + 3 \log_{10} B + \dfrac{1}{2} \log_{10} C$$

$$= 2a + 3b + \dfrac{c}{2}$$

49. $16 \log_{10} \sqrt{A} \sqrt[4]{B} = 16(\log_{10} \sqrt{A} + \log_{10} \sqrt[4]{B})$

$$= 16\left(\dfrac{1}{2} \log_{10} A + \dfrac{1}{4} \log_{10} B\right)$$

$$= 8 \log_{10} A + 4 \log_{10} B$$

$$= 8a + 4b$$

51. $\log_{10}100 = 2$ and $\log_{10}1000 = 3$, so $\log_{10}209$ lies between 2 and 3.

53. $\log_6 36 = 2$ and $\log_6 216 = 3$, so $\log_6 100$ lies between 2 and 3.

55. $\log_{10} 0.010 = -2$ and $\log_{10} 0.001 = -3$, so $\log_{10} 0.003$ lies between -2 and -3.

57.   (a)   We graph $y = \ln (x + 2)$ and $y = \ln (-x) - 1$:

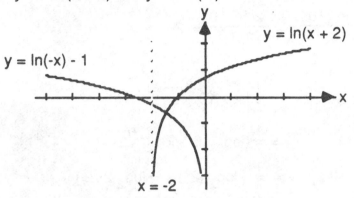

The graph shows these two curves intersect in the third quadrant.

(b)   We set $\ln (x + 2) = \ln (-x) - 1$
$$\ln (x + 2) - \ln (-x) = -1$$
$$\ln \frac{x + 2}{-x} = -1$$
$$\frac{x + 2}{-x} = e^{-1}$$
$$e(x + 2) = -x$$
$$ex + 2e = -x$$
$$ex + x = -2e$$
$$x(e + 1) = -2e$$
$$x = \frac{-2e}{e + 1} \approx -1.46$$

So $y = \ln \left(\frac{-2e}{e + 1} + 2 \right) = \ln \left(\frac{-2e + 2e + 2}{e + 1} \right) = \ln \frac{2}{e + 1} \approx -0.62$
So the two curves intersect in the third quadrant.

59.   We know $N = N_0 e^{kt}$, and $N = \frac{1}{2} N_0$ when $t = T$:
$$\frac{1}{2} N_0 = N_0 e^{kT}$$
$$\frac{1}{2} = e^{kT}$$

$$\ln \frac{1}{2} = kT$$

$$k = \frac{\ln \frac{1}{2}}{T}$$

61. Since 4 half-lives have passed, we will have

$\frac{1}{2}\left(\frac{1}{2}\left(\frac{1}{2}\left(\frac{1}{2}N_0\right)\right)\right) = \frac{1}{16}N_0$ of the subtance left, or 6.25% remaining.

63. $k = \dfrac{\ln \frac{1}{2}}{d}$, and $N_0 = b$. We want to find the value of t when N = c:

$$N = N_0 e^{kt},$$

$$c = b e^{kt}$$

$$\frac{c}{b} = e^{kt}$$

$$\ln \frac{c}{b} = kt$$

$$\ln \frac{c}{b} = \frac{\ln \frac{1}{2}}{d} \cdot t$$

$$t = \frac{d \ln \frac{c}{b}}{\ln \frac{1}{2}}$$

65. $\log_{10} 8 + \log_{10} 3 - \log_{10} 12 = \log_{10}\left(\frac{8 \cdot 3}{12}\right) = \log_{10} 2$

67. $\ln 5 - 3\ln 2 + \ln 16$
$\begin{aligned}
&= \ln 5 - \ln 2^3 + \ln 16 \\
&= \ln 5 - \ln 8 + \ln 16 \\
&= \ln\left(\frac{5 \cdot 16}{8}\right) \\
&= \ln 10
\end{aligned}$

69. $a \ln x + b \ln y = \ln x^a + \ln y^b = \ln x^a y^b$

71. $\ln \sqrt{(x-3)(x+4)} = \frac{1}{2}\ln\left((x-3)(x+4)\right) = \frac{1}{2}\ln(x-3) + \frac{1}{2}(x+4)$

73. $\log_{10} \dfrac{x^3}{\sqrt{1 + x}}$ $= \log_{10} x^3 - \log_{10} \sqrt{1 + x}$

$= \log_{10} x^3 - \log_{10} (1 + x)^{1/2}$

$= 3 \log_{10} x - \dfrac{1}{2} \log_{10} (1 + x)$

75. $\log_{10} \sqrt[3]{\dfrac{x}{100}}$ $= \log_{10} \left(\dfrac{x}{100}\right)^{1/3}$

$= \dfrac{1}{3} \log_{10} \dfrac{x}{100}$

$= \dfrac{1}{3} \log_{10} x - \dfrac{1}{3} \log_{10} 100$

$= \dfrac{1}{3} \log_{10} x - \dfrac{1}{3} \log_{10} 100$

$= \dfrac{1}{3} \log_{10} x - \dfrac{2}{3}$

77. $\ln \left(\dfrac{1 + 2e}{1 - 2e}\right)^3$ $= 3 \ln \dfrac{1 + 2e}{1 - 2e} = 3 \ln (1 + 2e) - 3 \ln (1 - 2e)$

79. We use $B = P(1 + r)^t$ where $P = A$, $B = 2A$, $r = \dfrac{R}{100}$:

$$2A = A \left(1 + \dfrac{R}{100}\right)^t$$

$$2 = \left(1 + \dfrac{R}{100}\right)^t$$

$$\ln 2 = t \ln \left(1 + \dfrac{R}{100}\right)$$

$$t = \dfrac{\ln 2}{\ln \left(1 + \dfrac{R}{100}\right)}$$

81. The balance after 1 year will be $A = P\left(1 + \dfrac{0.095}{12}\right)^{12}$. We must find the effective interest rate r where $A = P(1 + r)^1$. We set these equal:

$$P(1 + r) = P \left(1 + \dfrac{0.095}{12}\right)^{12}$$

$$1 + r = \left(1 + \dfrac{0.095}{12}\right)^{12}$$

$$r = \left(1 + \dfrac{0.095}{12}\right)^{12} - 1$$

$$r \approx 0.0992$$

So the effective interest rate is 9.92%.

83.   We use $A = Pe^{rt}$ where $P = D$, $A = 2D$, and $r = \dfrac{R}{100}$:

$$2D = De^{(R/100)t}$$

$$2 = e^{(R/100)t}$$

$$\ln 2 = \frac{R}{100}(t)$$

$$t = \frac{100 \ln 2}{R}$$

85.   (a)   We use $A = P\left(1 + \dfrac{r}{N}\right)^{Nt}$ where $P = \$660$, $r = .055$, $N = 4$, and $A = \$1000$:

$$1000 = 660\left(1 + \frac{.055}{4}\right)^{4t}$$

$$\frac{50}{33} = (1.01375)^{4t}$$

$$\ln \frac{50}{33} = 4t \ln 1.01375$$

$$t = \frac{\ln \dfrac{50}{33}}{4 \ln 1.01375} \approx 7.61 \text{ years}$$

So the balance will reach $1000 after $7\frac{3}{4}$ years.

(b)   We use $A = P\left(1 + \dfrac{r}{N}\right)^{Nt}$ where $P = D$, $r = \dfrac{R}{100}$, $N = 4$, and $A = nD$:

$$nD = D\left(1 + \frac{R}{400}\right)^{t}$$

$$n = \left(1 + \frac{R}{400}\right)^{t}$$

$$\ln n = t \ln\left(1 + \frac{R}{400}\right)$$

$$t = \frac{\ln n}{\ln\left(1 + \dfrac{R}{400}\right)}$$

87.   (a)   Domain is $x > 0$, or $(0,\infty)$

(b)   We must make sure $\log_{10} x \geq 0$, so $x \geq 1$

So the domain is $x \geq 1$, or $[1,\infty)$

89.   (a)   We must make sure $x^2 - 2x - 15 \neq 0$
$$(x - 5)(x + 3) \neq 0$$
$$x \neq 5, -3$$
So the domain is all real numbers except 5 and -3, or

$(-\infty,-3) \cup (-3,5) \cup (5,\infty)$.

(b)   We must make sure $x^2 - 2x - 15 > 0$
$$(x - 5)(x + 3) > 0$$
Key numbers: -3,5
From a sign chart, we find the domain is $x < -3$ or $x > 5$, or

$(-\infty,-3) \cup (5,\infty)$.

91.   We solve for x:
$$y = \frac{e^x + 1}{e^x - 1}$$
$$y(e^x - 1) = e^x + 1$$
$$ye^x - y = e^x + 1$$
$$ye^x - e^x = y + 1$$
$$e^x(y - 1) = y + 1$$
$$e^x = \frac{y + 1}{y - 1}$$
$$x = \ln \frac{y + 1}{y - 1}$$

So we must make sure $\frac{y + 1}{y - 1} > 0$:

Key numbers: 1, -1

Using a sign chart, the intervals are $y < -1$ or $y > 1$. So the range is

$(-\infty,-1) \cup (1,\infty)$.

93. $\ln 0.5 = \ln (2^{-1})$
$= -\ln 2$
≈ -0.7

95. $\ln \frac{1}{9}$ = $\ln (3^{-2})$

$= -2 \ln 3$

$\approx -2 (1.1)$

≈ -2.2

97. $\ln 72$ = $\ln (3^2 \cdot 2^3)$

$= \ln (3^2) + \ln (2^3)$

$= 2 \ln 3 + 3 \ln 2$

$\approx 2(1.1) + 3(0.7)$

$\approx 2.2 + 2.1$

≈ 4.3

99.   Let $x = e$, then $\ln x = 1$. From the graph, we see $x \approx 2.7$.

101. $\log_2 3$ $= \dfrac{\ln 3}{\ln 2}$

$\approx \dfrac{1.1}{0.7}$

≈ 1.6

103.   (a)   We complete the table:

Region	1990 Population (millions)	Growth Rate (%)	2025 Population
North America	275.2	0.7	351.6
Soviet Union	291.3	0.7	372.2
Europe	499.5	0.2	535.7
Nigeria	113.3	3.1	335.3

(b)   It will be 335.3 mil - 113.3 mil = 222.0 million

(c)   North America: 351.6 mil - 275.2 mil = 76.4 mil
Soviet Union: 372.2 mil - 291.3 mil = 80.9 mil
Europe: 535.7 mil - 499.5 mil = 36.2 mil
combined: 193.5 million

(d)   For Nigeria, our results support his projection.

105.   (a)   The corresponding x-coordinate when $y = 3.000$ is $x \approx 1.0986$

(b)   % error $= \dfrac{|1.0986 - \ln 3|}{\ln 3} \cdot 100 = 0.00112\,\%$

(c) $\ln \sqrt{3} = \dfrac{1}{2} \ln 3 \approx \dfrac{1}{2}(1.0986) \approx 0.5493$

$\ln 9 = \ln (3^2) = 2 \ln 3 \approx 2(1.0986) \approx 2.1972$

$\ln \dfrac{1}{3} = \ln (3^{-1}) = - \ln 3 \approx -1.0986$

CHAPTER 7
TRIGONOMETRIC FUNCTIONS OF ANGLES

7.1 Trigonometric Functions of Acute Angles

1.   (a) $8^2 + 15^2 = 17^2$
           $64 + 225 = 289$ $\sqrt{}$

    (b) $\sin \theta = \dfrac{\text{opposite}}{\text{hypotenuse}} = \dfrac{15}{17}$

           $\cos \beta = \dfrac{\text{adjacent}}{\text{hypotenuse}} = \dfrac{15}{17}$

    (c) $\cos \theta = \dfrac{\text{adjacent}}{\text{hypotenuse}} = \dfrac{8}{17}$

           $\sin \beta = \dfrac{\text{opposite}}{\text{hypotenuse}} = \dfrac{8}{17}$

    (d) $\tan \theta = \dfrac{\text{opposite}}{\text{adjacent}} = \dfrac{15}{8}$

           $\csc \theta = \dfrac{\text{hypotenuse}}{\text{opposite}} = \dfrac{17}{15}$

           $\sec \theta = \dfrac{\text{hypotenuse}}{\text{adjacent}} = \dfrac{17}{8}$

           $\cot \theta = \dfrac{\text{adjacent}}{\text{opposite}} = \dfrac{8}{15}$

(e) $\tan \beta = \dfrac{\text{opposite}}{\text{adjacent}} = \dfrac{8}{15}$

$\csc \beta = \dfrac{\text{hypotenuse}}{\text{opposite}} = \dfrac{17}{8}$

$\sec \beta = \dfrac{\text{hypotenuse}}{\text{adjacent}} = \dfrac{17}{15}$

$\cot \beta = \dfrac{\text{adjacent}}{\text{opposite}} = \dfrac{15}{8}$

3.   We draw the figure:

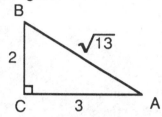

(a) $\sin A = \dfrac{2}{\sqrt{13}} = \dfrac{2\sqrt{13}}{13}$; $\cos A = \dfrac{3}{\sqrt{13}} = \dfrac{3\sqrt{13}}{13}$; $\tan A = \dfrac{2}{3}$

(b) $\sin^2 A + \cos^2 A = \left(\dfrac{2}{\sqrt{13}}\right)^2 + \left(\dfrac{3}{\sqrt{13}}\right)^2 = \dfrac{4}{13} + \dfrac{9}{13} = 1$

$\dfrac{\sin A}{\cos A} = \dfrac{2/\sqrt{13}}{3/\sqrt{13}} = \dfrac{2}{3} = \tan A$

(c) $\cos B = \dfrac{2}{\sqrt{13}} = \dfrac{2\sqrt{13}}{13}$

$\sin^2 A + \cos^2 B = \left(\dfrac{2}{\sqrt{13}}\right)^2 + \left(\dfrac{2}{\sqrt{13}}\right)^2 = \dfrac{4}{13} + \dfrac{4}{13} = \dfrac{8}{13} \neq 1$

5.   We draw the figure:

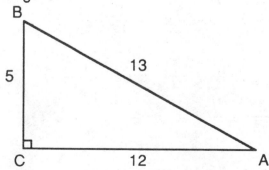

$\sin A = \dfrac{5}{13}$; $\cos A = \dfrac{12}{13}$; $\tan A = \dfrac{5}{12}$; $\sec A = \dfrac{13}{12}$; $\csc A = \dfrac{13}{5}$; $\cot A = \dfrac{12}{5}$

7.   We draw the figure:

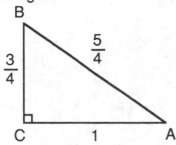

(a) $\sin B = \dfrac{1}{5/4} = \dfrac{4}{5}$; $\cos A = \dfrac{1}{5/4} = \dfrac{4}{5}$

(b) $\cos B = \dfrac{3/4}{5/4} = \dfrac{3}{5}$; $\sin A = \dfrac{3/4}{5/4} = \dfrac{3}{5}$

(c) $\tan A = \dfrac{3/4}{1} = \dfrac{3}{4}$ and $\tan B = \dfrac{1}{3/4} = \dfrac{4}{3}$, so:

$(\tan A)(\tan B) = \left(\dfrac{3}{4}\right)\left(\dfrac{4}{3}\right) = 1$

9.   We draw the figure:

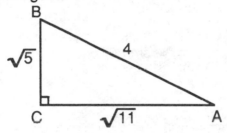

(a) $\sin A = \dfrac{\sqrt{5}}{4}$; $\cos A = \dfrac{\sqrt{11}}{4}$

$\sin^2 A + \cos^2 A = \left(\dfrac{\sqrt{5}}{4}\right)^2 + \left(\dfrac{\sqrt{11}}{4}\right)^2 = \dfrac{5}{16} + \dfrac{11}{16} = 1$

(b) $\tan B = \dfrac{\sqrt{11}}{\sqrt{5}} = \dfrac{\sqrt{55}}{5}$; $\sin B = \dfrac{\sqrt{11}}{4}$; $\cos B = \dfrac{\sqrt{5}}{4}$

$\dfrac{\sin B}{\cos B} = \dfrac{\sqrt{11}/4}{\sqrt{5}/4} = \dfrac{\sqrt{11}}{\sqrt{5}} = \dfrac{\sqrt{55}}{5} = \tan B$

11. $\cos 60° = \dfrac{1}{2}$

$\cos^2 30° - \sin^2 30° = \left(\dfrac{\sqrt{3}}{2}\right)^2 - \left(\dfrac{1}{2}\right)^2 = \dfrac{3}{4} - \dfrac{1}{4} = \dfrac{1}{2}$

So $\cos 60° = \cos^2 30° - \sin^2 30°$.

13. $\sin^2 30° + \sin^2 45° + \sin^2 60° = \left(\dfrac{1}{2}\right)^2 + \left(\dfrac{\sqrt{2}}{2}\right)^2 + \left(\dfrac{\sqrt{3}}{2}\right)^2$

$= \dfrac{1}{4} + \dfrac{1}{2} + \dfrac{3}{4}$

$= \dfrac{6}{4}$

$= \dfrac{3}{2}$

15. $2 \sin 30° \cos 30° = 2 \left(\dfrac{1}{2}\right)\left(\dfrac{\sqrt{3}}{2}\right) = \dfrac{\sqrt{3}}{2}$

$\sin 60° = \dfrac{\sqrt{3}}{2}$

So $2 \sin 30° \cos 30° = \sin 60°$

17. $\sqrt{\dfrac{1 - \cos 60°}{2}} = \sqrt{\dfrac{1 - \dfrac{1}{2}}{2}} = \sqrt{\dfrac{1}{4}} = \dfrac{1}{2} = \sin 30°$

19. $\dfrac{\sin 60°}{1 + \cos 60°} = \dfrac{\dfrac{\sqrt{3}}{2}}{1 + \dfrac{1}{2}} = \dfrac{\sqrt{3}/2}{3/2} = \dfrac{\sqrt{3}}{3} = \tan 30°$

21. $1 + \tan^2 45° = 1 + (1)^2 = 2$

$\sec^2 45° = \left(\dfrac{2}{\sqrt{2}}\right)^2 = \dfrac{4}{2} = 2$

So $1 + \tan^2 45° = \sec^2 45°$

23. We draw the figure:

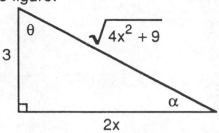

(a) $\sin \theta = \dfrac{2x}{\sqrt{4x^2 + 9}} = \dfrac{2x\sqrt{4x^2 + 9}}{4x^2 + 9}$; $\cos \theta = \dfrac{3}{\sqrt{4x^2 + 9}} = \dfrac{3\sqrt{4x^2 + 9}}{4x^2 + 9}$

$\tan \theta = \dfrac{2x}{3}$

(b) $\sin^2\theta = \dfrac{4x^2}{4x^2 + 9}$; $\cos^2\theta = \dfrac{9}{4x^2 + 9}$; $\tan^2\theta = \dfrac{4x^2}{9}$

(c) $\sin (90° - \theta) = \sin \alpha = \dfrac{3}{\sqrt{4x^2 + 9}} = \dfrac{3\sqrt{4x^2 + 9}}{4x^2 + 9}$;

$\cos (90° - \theta) = \cos \alpha = \dfrac{2x}{\sqrt{4x^2 + 9}} = \dfrac{2x\sqrt{4x^2 + 9}}{4x^2 + 9}$;

$\tan (90° - \theta) = \tan \alpha = \dfrac{3}{2x}$

25. We draw the figure:

(a) $\sin \beta = \dfrac{\sqrt{16x^2 - 1}}{4x}$; $\cos \beta = \dfrac{1}{4x}$; $\tan \beta = \dfrac{\sqrt{16x^2 - 1}}{1} = \sqrt{16x^2 - 1}$

(b) $\csc \beta = \dfrac{4x}{\sqrt{16x^2 - 1}} = \dfrac{4x\sqrt{16x^2 - 1}}{16x^2 - 1}$

$\sec \beta = \dfrac{4x}{1} = 4x$

$\cot \beta = \dfrac{1}{\sqrt{16x^2 - 1}} = \dfrac{\sqrt{16x^2 - 1}}{16x^2 - 1}$

(c) $\sin (90° - \beta) = \sin \omega = \dfrac{1}{4x}$

$\cos (90° - \beta) = \cos \omega = \dfrac{\sqrt{16x^2 - 1}}{4x}$

$\tan (90° - \beta) = \tan \omega = \dfrac{1}{\sqrt{16x^2 - 1}} = \dfrac{\sqrt{16x^2 - 1}}{16x^2 - 1}$

27.   We draw the figure:

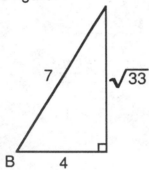

$\sin B = \dfrac{\sqrt{33}}{7}$; $\tan B = \dfrac{\sqrt{33}}{4}$; $\sec B = \dfrac{7}{4}$; $\csc B = \dfrac{7}{\sqrt{33}} = \dfrac{7\sqrt{33}}{33}$;

$\cot B = \dfrac{4}{\sqrt{33}} = \dfrac{4\sqrt{33}}{33}$

29.   We draw the figure:

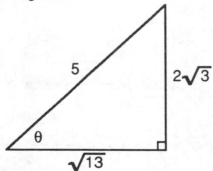

$$\cos \theta = \frac{\sqrt{13}}{5} \; ; \tan \theta = \frac{2\sqrt{3}}{\sqrt{13}} = \frac{2\sqrt{39}}{13} \; ; \sec \theta = \frac{5}{\sqrt{13}} = \frac{5\sqrt{13}}{13} \; ;$$

$$\csc \theta = \frac{5}{2\sqrt{3}} = \frac{5\sqrt{3}}{6} \; ; \cot \theta = \frac{\sqrt{13}}{2\sqrt{3}} = \frac{\sqrt{39}}{6}$$

31. We draw the figure:

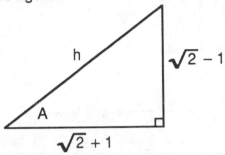

We find side h:

$$(\sqrt{2} + 1)^2 + (\sqrt{2} - 1)^2 = h^2$$
$$3 + 2\sqrt{2} + 3 - 2\sqrt{2} = h^2$$
$$6 = h^2$$
$$h = \sqrt{6}$$

$$\sin A = \frac{\sqrt{2} - 1}{\sqrt{6}} = \frac{2\sqrt{3} - \sqrt{6}}{6} \; ; \cos A = \frac{\sqrt{2} + 1}{\sqrt{6}} = \frac{2\sqrt{3} + \sqrt{6}}{6} \; ;$$

$$\sec A = \frac{\sqrt{6}}{\sqrt{2} + 1} = 2\sqrt{3} - \sqrt{6} \; ; \csc A = \frac{\sqrt{6}}{\sqrt{2} - 1} = 2\sqrt{3} + \sqrt{6} \; ;$$

$$\cot A = \frac{\sqrt{2} + 1}{\sqrt{2} - 1} = 3 + 2\sqrt{2}$$

33. We draw the figure:

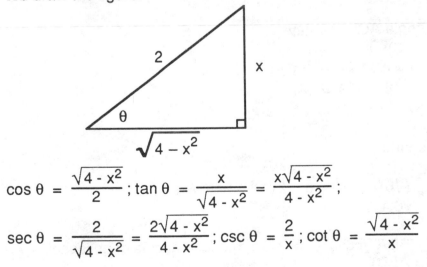

$$\cos \theta = \frac{\sqrt{4 - x^2}}{2} \; ; \tan \theta = \frac{x}{\sqrt{4 - x^2}} = \frac{x\sqrt{4 - x^2}}{4 - x^2} \; ;$$

$$\sec \theta = \frac{2}{\sqrt{4 - x^2}} = \frac{2\sqrt{4 - x^2}}{4 - x^2} \; ; \csc \theta = \frac{2}{x} \; ; \cot \theta = \frac{\sqrt{4 - x^2}}{x}$$

35.   We draw the figure:

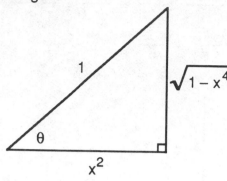

$$\sin \theta = \frac{\sqrt{1 - x^4}}{1} = \sqrt{1 - x^4}; \ \tan \theta = \frac{\sqrt{1 - x^4}}{x^2}; \ \sec \theta = \frac{1}{x^2};$$

$$\csc \theta = \frac{1}{\sqrt{1 - x^4}} = \frac{\sqrt{1 - x^4}}{1 - x^4}; \ \cot \theta = \frac{x^2}{\sqrt{1 - x^4}} = \frac{x^2\sqrt{1 - x^4}}{1 - x^4}$$

37.   (a) $\cos 30° \approx .86603$; $\cos 45° \approx .70711$; $\sin 60° \approx .86603$

(b) $\cos 30° = \sin 60° = \dfrac{\sqrt{3}}{2} \approx .86603$; $\cos 45° = \dfrac{\sqrt{2}}{2} \approx .70711$

39. $\csc 25° \approx 2.36620$; $\sec 25° \approx 1.10338$; $\cot 25° \approx 2.14451$

41.   (a)   By the Pythagorean Theorem:
$$(BC)^2 + (1)^2 = 2^2$$
$$(BC)^2 = 3$$
$$BC = \sqrt{3}$$

(b)   Using triangle ACD, we have:
$$(2 + \sqrt{3})^2 + (1)^2 = (AD)^2$$
$$4 + 4\sqrt{3} + 4 = (AD)^2$$
$$8 + 4\sqrt{3} = (AD)^2$$
$$AD = \sqrt{8 + 4\sqrt{3}} = 2\sqrt{2 + \sqrt{3}}$$

(c)   Using the hint:
$$(AD)^2 = 8 + 4\sqrt{3}$$
$$(\sqrt{6} + \sqrt{2})^2 = 6 + 2\sqrt{12} + 2 = 8 + 4\sqrt{3}$$
So $AD = \sqrt{6} + \sqrt{2}$

(d) $\angle BAD = \angle BDA$ because they are the base angles of an isoceles triangle ($\triangle ABD$)

(e) By the theorem, $\angle BAD + \angle BDA = 30°$, and since part (d) shows that these angles are equal, then:
$$2 (\angle BAD) = 30°$$
$$\angle BAD = 15°$$

(f) $\sin 15° = \dfrac{1}{\sqrt{6} + \sqrt{2}}$ and $\cos 15° = \dfrac{2 + \sqrt{3}}{\sqrt{6} + \sqrt{2}}$

(g) Rationalizing denominators:
$$\sin 15° = \frac{\sqrt{6} - \sqrt{2}}{6 - 2} = \frac{\sqrt{6} - \sqrt{2}}{4}$$
$$\cos 15° = \frac{(2 + \sqrt{3})(\sqrt{6} - \sqrt{2})}{6 - 2}$$
$$= \frac{2\sqrt{6} + \sqrt{18} - 2\sqrt{2} - \sqrt{6}}{4}$$
$$= \frac{\sqrt{6} + \sqrt{2}}{4}$$

(h) $\sin 15° \approx 0.25882$ and $\cos 15° \approx 0.96593$, which agree with the radical calculations

43. Extending AB to D an equal distance to AB guarantees $\triangle DBC$ congruent to $\triangle ABC$. Now $\triangle ADC$ is equilateral as each angle is 60°. By construction $AD = 2AB$ and since the triangle is equilateral, $AC = AD$, hence $AC = 2AB$.

7.2 Right Triangle Applications

1. We draw the figure:

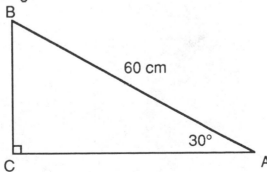

$\sin 30° = \dfrac{BC}{60}$, so $BC = 60 \sin 30° = 60\left(\dfrac{1}{2}\right) = 30$ cm

$\cos 30° = \dfrac{AC}{60}$, so $AC = 60 \cos 30° = 60\left(\dfrac{\sqrt{3}}{2}\right) = 30\sqrt{3}$ cm

3.   We draw the figure:

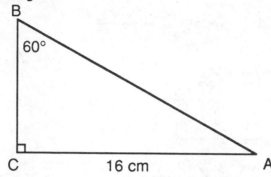

$\sin 60° = \dfrac{16}{AB}$, so $AB = \dfrac{16}{\sin 60°} = \dfrac{16}{\sqrt{3}/2} = \dfrac{32}{\sqrt{3}} = \dfrac{32\sqrt{3}}{3}$ cm

$\tan 60° = \dfrac{16}{BC}$, so $BC = \dfrac{16}{\tan 60°} = \dfrac{16}{\sqrt{3}} = \dfrac{16\sqrt{3}}{3}$ cm

5.   We draw the figure:

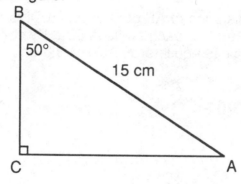

$\sin 50° = \dfrac{AC}{15}$, so $AC = 15 \sin 50° \approx 11.5$ cm

$\cos 50° = \dfrac{BC}{15}$, so $BC = 15 \cos 50° \approx 9.6$ cm

7.   We draw a figure:

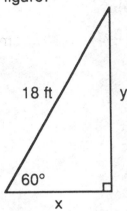

(a)   We are asked to find y:

$$\sin 60° = \frac{y}{18}$$
$$y = 18 \sin 60°$$
$$y = 18 \left(\frac{\sqrt{3}}{2}\right)$$
$$y = 9\sqrt{3} \text{ ft}$$

Using a calculator, this is approximately 15.59 ft

(b)   We are asked to find x:

$$\cos 60° = \frac{x}{18}$$
$$x = 18 \cos 60°$$
$$x = 18 \left(\frac{1}{2}\right)$$
$$x = 9 \text{ ft}$$

9.   Using the sine function we have that $\sin \angle SEM = \frac{MS}{SE}$, so:

$$\sin 21.16° = \frac{MS}{93000000}$$

Thus MS is about 34 million miles.

11.   (a)   The height is 3 sin 30°, so:
$$\text{Area} = \frac{1}{2} (2 \text{ in.})(3 \sin 30° \text{ in.}) = 1.5 \text{ in.}^2$$

(b)   The height is 6 sin 70°, so:
$$\text{Area} = \frac{1}{2} (4 \text{ cm})(6 \sin 70° \text{ cm}) \approx 11.28 \text{ cm}^2$$

13. We form 10 triangles, each with a central angle of 36°. Then:

$$\text{Area of decagon} = 10 \text{ (area of triangle)}$$
$$= 10 \left(\frac{1}{2}\right) (20) (20 \sin 36°)$$
$$= 2000 \sin 36° \text{ cm}^2$$
$$\approx 1175.6 \text{ cm}^2$$

15. We draw the figure:

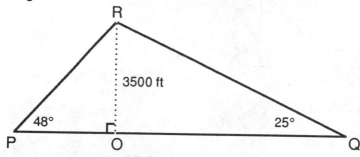

$$\tan 48° = \frac{3500}{PO} \text{ and } \tan 25° = \frac{3500}{OQ}$$
$$\text{So } PO = \frac{3500}{\tan 48°} \text{ and } OQ = \frac{3500}{\tan 25°}$$
$$\text{Thus } PQ = \frac{3500}{\tan 48°} + \frac{3500}{\tan 25°} \approx 10{,}660 \text{ ft}$$

17. We draw a figure:

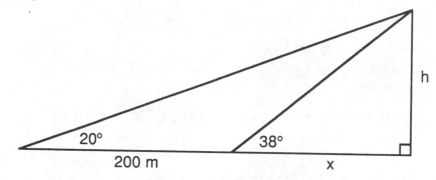

Now $\tan 38° = \frac{h}{x}$, so $x = \frac{h}{\tan 38°}$

Also $\tan 20° = \frac{h}{200 + x}$, so $h = (200 + x) \tan 20°$

Substituting, we have:

$$h = \left(200 + \frac{h}{\tan 38°}\right)\tan 20°$$

$$h \tan 38° = 200 \tan 38° \tan 20° + h \tan 20°$$

$$h(\tan 38° - \tan 20°) = 200 \tan 38° \tan 20°$$

$$h = \frac{200 \tan 38° \tan 20°}{\tan 38° - \tan 20°}$$

$$h \approx 136 \text{ m}$$

19. We draw the figure:

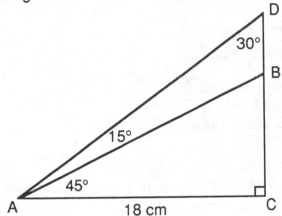

$\tan 45° = \dfrac{BC}{18}$, so $BC = 18 \tan 45°$

$\tan 60° = \dfrac{CD}{18}$, so $CD = 18 \tan 60°$

So $BD = CD - BC$

$= 18(\tan 60° - \tan 45°)$

$= 18(\sqrt{3} - 1) \text{ cm}$

21. (a) $\angle OBA = 90°$

$\angle OAB = \theta$, since both angles are complementary to the same angle ($\angle AOB$).

$\angle BAP = 90° - \theta$

$\angle BPA = \theta$, since $\angle BPA$ and $\angle OAB$ are both complementary to the same angle ($\angle BAP$)

(b)   Using triangle AOP, we have:

$$\sin \theta = \frac{AO}{OP} = \frac{AO}{1}, \text{ so } AO = \sin \theta$$

$$\cos \theta = \frac{AP}{OP} = \frac{AP}{1}, \text{ so } AP = \cos \theta$$

Using triangle AOB, we have:

$$\sin \theta = \frac{OB}{OA} = \frac{OB}{\sin \theta}, \text{ so } OB = \sin^2\theta$$

Using triangle ABP, we have:

$$\cos \theta = \frac{BP}{AP} = \frac{BP}{\cos \theta}, \text{ so } BP = \cos^2\theta$$

23.   (a) $\sin \theta = \frac{4}{5} = 0.8$, so $\theta \approx 53.1°$

(b) $\tan \theta = \frac{12}{5} = 2.4$, so $\theta \approx 67.4°$

(c) $\sin \theta = \frac{6}{8} = 0.75$, so $\theta \approx 48.6°$

25.   Examine the similar triangles having AB and BC as hypotenuses, and notice that θ is also the angle at B in the smaller triangle. We will write trigonometric relationships for each triangle, solve for AB and BC, and then add to get AC:

$$\sin \theta = \frac{5}{BC}, \text{ so } BC = \frac{5}{\sin \theta}$$

$$\cos \theta = \frac{4}{AB}, \text{ so } AB = \frac{4}{\cos \theta}$$

Now AC = AB + BC and therefore:

$$AC = \frac{4}{\cos \theta} + \frac{5}{\sin \theta}$$

$$= \frac{4 \sin \theta + 5 \cos \theta}{\sin \theta \cos \theta}$$

$$= 4 \sec \theta + 5 \csc \theta$$

27.   First observe that the figure $x^2 + y^2 = 1$ is a circle with a radius of one. Then any segment which is a radius can be replaced by one. In each case, we will look for a trigonometric relationship involving the required segment:

(a) $\sin \theta = \frac{DE}{OD}$, so $DE = \sin \theta$

(b) $\cos \theta = \frac{OE}{OD}$, so $OE = \cos \theta$

(c) $\tan \theta = \frac{CF}{OF}$, so $CF = \tan \theta$

(d) $\sec \theta = \dfrac{OC}{OF}$, so $OC = \sec \theta$

Going to $\triangle OAB$, $\angle B = \theta$, and

(e) $\cot \theta = \dfrac{AB}{OA}$, so $AB = \cot \theta$

(f) $\csc \theta = \dfrac{OB}{OA}$, so $OB = \csc \theta$

These segments are sometimes called the line values of the six trigonometric functions.

29.   Since $\sin \theta = \dfrac{r}{PS + r}$ then:

(a) $(r + PS) \sin \theta = r$ and $r(1 - \sin \theta) = PS \sin \theta$

So $r = PS \left(\dfrac{\sin \theta}{1 - \sin \theta} \right)$

(b) $r = (238{,}857) \left(\dfrac{\sin (0.257°)}{1 - \sin (0.257°)} \right) \approx 1080$ miles

31.   (a)   We draw the figure:

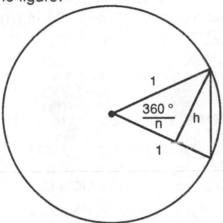

Since $h = \sin \dfrac{360°}{n}$, then the area of this triangle is $\dfrac{1}{2} \left(\sin \dfrac{360°}{n} \right)$.
Since there are n congruent triangles in an n-gon, then the area is
$\dfrac{n}{2} \sin \left(\dfrac{360°}{n} \right)$

(b)   We complete the table:

n	5	10	50	100	1,000	5,000	10,000
A_n	2.38	2.94	3.1333	3.1395	3.141572	3.1415918	3.1415924

(c)   As n gets larger, A_n becomes closer to the area of the circle, which is π.

33.   We first draw a figure:

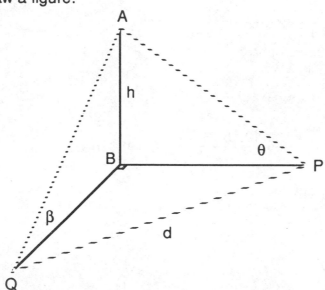

Denote the top of the tower by A, and the bottom by B. Then in right triangle PBA we have $\cot \theta = \dfrac{BP}{h}$, and therefore $BP = h \cot \theta$. Similarly in right triangle QBA, we have $\cot \beta = \dfrac{QB}{h}$, and therefore $QB = h \cot \beta$, Now apply the Pythagorean Theorem in right triangle QBP to obtain:

$$d^2 = (QB)^2 + (BP)^2 = h^2 \cot^2\beta + h^2 \cot^2\theta$$

Therefore $h^2 = \dfrac{d^2}{\cot^2\beta + \cot^2\theta}$

Finally, taking square roots: $h = \dfrac{d}{\sqrt{\cot^2\beta + \cot^2\theta}}$

7.3 Trigonometric Functions of General Angles

1.   (a)   reference angle: 70°

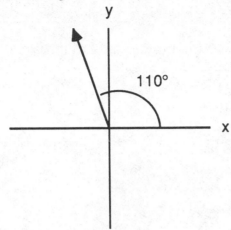

110°

   (b)   reference angle: 60°

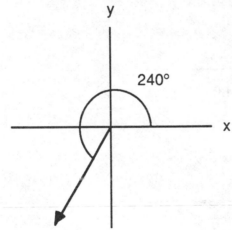

240°

(c)   reference angle: 60°

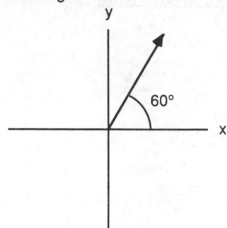

(d)   reference angle: 60°

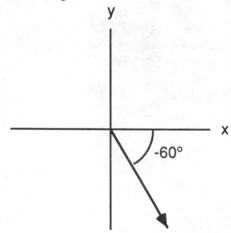

3.   (a)   cos 0° = 1

(b)   sin 450° = sin 90° = 1

(c)   sin 270° = - sin 90° = -1

(d)   sin (-630°) = sin 90° = 1

5.   (a)   csc (-90°) = $\dfrac{1}{\sin(-90°)}$ = $\dfrac{1}{-1}$ = -1

(b)   cot 720° = cot 0° = $\dfrac{\cos 0°}{\sin 0°}$ which is undefined

(c) $\cos(-540) = \cos 180° = -1$

(d) $\sin 810° = \sin 90° = 1$

7.   (a) $\cos\theta = \dfrac{3}{4}$

(b) $\sin\theta = \sqrt{1 - \left(\dfrac{3}{4}\right)^2} = \sqrt{\dfrac{7}{16}} = \dfrac{\sqrt{7}}{4}$

$\tan\theta = \dfrac{\sqrt{7}/4}{3/4} = \dfrac{\sqrt{7}}{3}$

Both values are positive, since 0 is in the first quadrant.

(c)   Since $\cos(\beta - 90°) > 0$ and $\cos(\theta + 90°) < 0$, then $\cos(\beta - 90°)$ is larger.

9.   In each case we will follow a three-step procedure: find the reference angle, recall the value of the trigonometric function for that angle, and then apply a positive or negative value depending on the quadrant.

(a) $\sin 315°$:   reference angle is $45°$

$\sin 45° = \dfrac{\sqrt{2}}{2}$

4th quadrant therefore negative

So $\sin 315° = -\dfrac{\sqrt{2}}{2}$

(b) $\cos 300°$: reference angle is $60°$

$\cos 60° = \dfrac{1}{2}$

4th quadrant, so it's positive

So $\cos 300° = \dfrac{1}{2}$

(c)   Using a similar process, we find:

$\tan 330° = -\tan 30° = -\dfrac{\sqrt{3}}{3}$

(d) $\sin(-315°) = \sin 45° = \dfrac{\sqrt{2}}{2}$

11. (a) $\tan 135° = -\tan 45° = -1$

(b) $\cot 120° = -\cot 60° = -\dfrac{\sqrt{3}}{3}$

(c) $\cot 480° = -\cot 60° = -\dfrac{\sqrt{3}}{3}$

(d) $\tan (-135°) = \tan 45° = 1$

13. $\sin (-30°) = -\dfrac{1}{2}$; $\csc (-30°) = -2$; $\cos (-30°) = \dfrac{\sqrt{3}}{2}$

$\sec (-30°) = \dfrac{2}{\sqrt{3}} = \dfrac{2\sqrt{3}}{3}$; $\cot (-30°) = -\dfrac{3}{\sqrt{3}} = -\sqrt{3}$; $\tan (-30°) = -\dfrac{\sqrt{3}}{3}$

15. (a)   We draw the chart:

θ	0°	90°	180°	270°	360°	450°	540°	630°	720°
$\sin\theta$	0	1	0	−1	0	1	0	−1	0
$\cos\theta$	1	0	−1	0	1	0	−1	0	1

(b)   We draw the chart:

θ	30°	60°	90°	120°	150°	180°	210°	240°	270°	300°	330°	360°
$\sin\theta$	$\dfrac{1}{2}$	$\dfrac{\sqrt{3}}{2}$	1	$\dfrac{\sqrt{3}}{2}$	$\dfrac{1}{2}$	0	$-\dfrac{1}{2}$	$-\dfrac{\sqrt{3}}{2}$	−1	$-\dfrac{\sqrt{3}}{2}$	$-\dfrac{1}{2}$	0

17. We draw the angle:

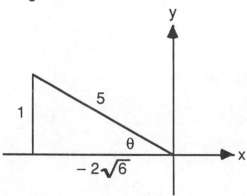

$$\cos\theta = \frac{-2\sqrt{6}}{5}; \tan\theta = \frac{1}{-2\sqrt{6}} = \frac{-\sqrt{6}}{12}; \sec\theta = \frac{-5}{2\sqrt{6}} = \frac{-5\sqrt{6}}{12};$$

$$\csc\theta = \frac{5}{1} = 5; \cot\theta = \frac{-2\sqrt{6}}{1} = -2\sqrt{6}$$

19. We draw the angle:

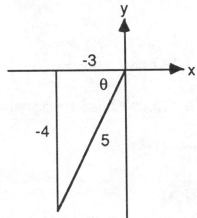

$$\sin\theta = \frac{-4}{5}; \tan\theta = \frac{4}{3}; \sec\theta = \frac{-5}{3}; \csc\theta = \frac{-5}{4}; \cot\theta = \frac{3}{4}$$

21. We draw the figure:

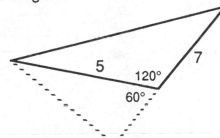

$$\text{Area} = \frac{1}{2}(7)\,(5\sin 60°) = \left(\frac{35}{2}\right)\left(\frac{\sqrt{3}}{2}\right) = \frac{35\sqrt{3}}{4}\ \text{cm}^2$$

23.   We draw the figure:

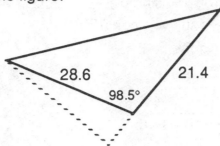

Area $= \frac{1}{2}$ (21.4) (28.6 sin 98.5°) $\approx$ 302.7 cm^2

25.   sin 90° = 1, sin 450° = 1, sin (-270°) = 1 (other answers possible)

27.   (a)   sin 10° $\approx$ 0.17
               cos 10° $\approx$ 0.99

       (b)   sin 20° $\approx$ 0.34
               cos 20° $\approx$ 0.94

       (c)   sin 30° $\approx$ 0.50
               cos 30° $\approx$ 0.87

       (d)   sin 40° $\approx$ 0.64
               cos 40° $\approx$ 0.77

       (e)   sin 50° $\approx$ 0.77
               cos 50° $\approx$ 0.64

       (f)   sin 70° $\approx$ 0.94
               cos 70° $\approx$ 0.34

       (g)   sin 80° $\approx$ 0.99
               cos 80° $\approx$ 0.17

       (h)   sin 100° $\approx$ 0.99 , since sin 100° = sin 80°
               cos 100° $\approx$ -0.17 , since cos 100° = - cos 80°

(i) $\sin 130° \approx 0.77$, since $\sin 130° = \sin 50°$

$\cos 130° \approx -0.64$, since $\cos 130° = -\cos 50°$

29. (a) $\sin 195° = -\sin 15° = \dfrac{1}{4}(\sqrt{2} - \sqrt{6})$

(b) $\cos 162° = -\cos 18° = -\dfrac{1}{4}\sqrt{10 + 2\sqrt{5}}$

(c) $\tan 345° = -\dfrac{\sin 15°}{\cos 15°}$

$$= \dfrac{\dfrac{1}{4}(\sqrt{2} - \sqrt{6})}{\sqrt{1 - \left(\dfrac{1}{4}(\sqrt{6} - \sqrt{2})\right)^2}}$$

$$= \dfrac{\dfrac{1}{4}(\sqrt{2} - \sqrt{6})}{\sqrt{1 - \dfrac{1}{16}(6 - 4\sqrt{3} + 2)}}$$

$$= \dfrac{\dfrac{1}{4}(\sqrt{2} - \sqrt{6})}{\sqrt{1 - \dfrac{1}{2} + \dfrac{\sqrt{3}}{4}}}$$

$$= \dfrac{\dfrac{1}{4}(\sqrt{2} - \sqrt{6})}{\sqrt{\dfrac{1}{2} + \dfrac{\sqrt{3}}{4}}}$$

$$= \dfrac{1}{2}\left(\dfrac{\sqrt{2} - \sqrt{6}}{\sqrt{2 + \sqrt{3}}}\right)$$

(d) $\sin(-15°) = -\sin 15° = \dfrac{1}{4}(\sqrt{2} - \sqrt{6})$

(e) $\cos(-18°) = \cos 18° = \dfrac{1}{4}\sqrt{10 + 2\sqrt{5}}$

(f) $\cos(918°) = -\cos 18° = -\dfrac{1}{4}\sqrt{10 + 2\sqrt{5}}$

31. (a) P: $(\cos\theta, \sin\theta)$; Q: $(\cos\phi, \sin\phi)$

    (b) Using the distance formula:
$$PQ = \sqrt{(\cos\theta - \cos\phi)^2 + (\sin\theta - \sin\phi)^2}$$
$$= \sqrt{\cos^2\theta - 2\cos\theta\cos\phi + \cos^2\phi + \sin^2\theta - 2\sin\theta\sin\phi + \sin^2\phi}$$
$$= \sqrt{2 - 2\cos\theta\cos\phi - 2\sin\theta\sin\phi}$$
$$= \sqrt{2}\sqrt{1 - \cos\theta\cos\phi - \sin\theta\sin\phi}$$

33. $2\log_{10}\sin\theta = \log_{10}\sin^2\theta$
$$= \log_{10}(1 - \cos^2\theta)$$
$$= \log_{10}[(1 - \cos\theta)(1 + \cos\theta)]$$
$$= \log_{10}(1 - \cos\theta) + \log_{10}(1 + \cos\theta)$$

The expression $2\log_{10}\sin^2\theta$ is valid only if $\sin\theta$ is positive. The restriction $0° < \theta < 180°$ quarantees that $\sin\theta$ will be positive, and thus $\log_{10}\sin\theta$ is defined.

35. (a) Since OP and OQ are both radii of the same circle then they are equal. So $\triangle$ OPQ is isosceles and the base angles PQO and QPO are equal, and thus $\angle PQO = 30°$.

    (b) They are opposite interior angles and thus equal.

    (c) Since $\angle QCO$ and $\angle PCO$ are 90°, then $\angle QOC$ and $\angle POC$ are each 60°, thus we have side-angle-side equality and thus the two triangles are congruent.

    (d) CQ = CP as they are corresponding parts of congruent triangles, and hence the x-coordinate are equal but of opposite sign.

37. For $\theta = 0°$:
    $\cos(180° - 0°) = \cos 180° = -1$ and $-\cos 0° = -1$, so:
    $\cos(180° - 0°) = -\cos 0°$
    $\sin(180° - 0°) = \sin 180° = 0$ and $\sin 0° = 0$, so:
    $\sin(180° - 0°) = \sin 0°$
    For $\theta = 90°$:
    $\cos(180° - 90°) = \cos 90° = 0$ and $-\cos 90° = 0$, so:
    $\cos(180° - 90°) = -\cos 90°$
    $\sin(180° - 90°) = \sin 90° = 1$ and $\sin 90° = 1$, so:
    $\sin(180° - 90°) = \sin 90°$

For $\theta = 180°$:

$\cos (180° - 180°) = \cos 0° = 1$ and $-\cos 180° = 1$, so:
$\cos (180° - 180°) = -\cos 180°$
$\sin (180° - 180°) = \sin 0° = 0$ and $\sin 180° = 0$, so:
$\sin (180° - 180°) = \sin 180°$

7.4 Algebra and the Trigonometric Functions

1.   (a) $(1 - \cos \theta)^2 = 1 - 2 \cos \theta + \cos^2\theta$

(b) $(\sin \theta + \cos \theta)^2 = \sin^2\theta + 2 \sin \theta \cos \theta + \cos^2\theta$
$= 1 + 2 \sin \theta \cos \theta$

(c) $\cos \theta + \dfrac{1}{\sin \theta} = \dfrac{\cos \theta \sin \theta + 1}{\sin \theta}$

3.   (a) $\tan^2\theta - 5 \tan \theta - 6 = (\tan \theta - 6)(\tan \theta + 1)$

(b) $\sin^2 B - \cos^2 B = (\sin B + \cos B)(\sin B - \cos B)$

(c) $\cos^2 A + 2 \cos A + 1 = (\cos A + 1)^2$

5. $\dfrac{\dfrac{\cos \theta + 1}{\cos \theta} + 1}{\dfrac{\cos \theta - 1}{\cos \theta} - 1} = \dfrac{\cos \theta + 1 + \cos \theta}{\cos \theta - 1 - \cos \theta}$

$= \dfrac{2 \cos \theta + 1}{-1}$

$= -2 \cos \theta - 1$

7. $\dfrac{1 - \tan \theta}{\dfrac{\sin \theta}{\cos \theta} - 1} = \dfrac{1 - \tan \theta}{\tan \theta - 1} = -1$

9. $\dfrac{\sin^2 A - \cos^2 A}{\sin A - \cos A} = \dfrac{(\sin A - \cos A)(\sin A + \cos A)}{\sin A - \cos A}$

$= \sin A + \cos A$

11. $\sin^2\theta \cos\theta \csc^3\theta \sec\theta = \dfrac{\sin^2\theta \cos\theta}{\sin^3\theta \cos\theta} = \dfrac{1}{\sin\theta} = \csc\theta$

13. $\cot B \sin^2 B \cot B = \dfrac{\cos B \sin^2 B \cos B}{\sin B \sin B} = \cos^2 B$

15. $\dfrac{\cos^2 A + \cos A - 12}{\cos A - 3} = \dfrac{(\cos A - 3)(\cos A + 4)}{\cos A - 3} = \cos A + 4$

17. $\dfrac{\cos A - 2 \sin A \cos A}{\cos^2 A - \sin^2 A + \sin A - 1}$

$= \dfrac{\cos A (1 - 2 \sin A)}{1 - \sin^2 A - \sin^2 A + \sin A - 1}$

$= \dfrac{\cos A (1 - 2 \sin A)}{\sin A - 2 \sin^2 A}$

$= \dfrac{\cos A (1 - 2 \sin A)}{\sin A (1 - 2 \sin A)}$

$= \dfrac{\cos A}{\sin A}$

$= \cot A$

19. $\sec A \csc A - \tan A - \cot A = \dfrac{1}{\cos A} \cdot \dfrac{1}{\sin A} - \dfrac{\sin A}{\cos A} - \dfrac{\cos A}{\sin A}$

$= \dfrac{1 - \sin^2 A - \cos^2 A}{\sin A \cos A}$

$= \dfrac{1 - (\sin^2 A + \cos^2 A)}{\sin A \cos A}$

$= \dfrac{1 - 1}{\sin A \cos A}$

$= 0$

21. $\dfrac{\sec\theta - 1}{\sec\theta + 1} - \dfrac{\tan\theta - \sin\theta}{\tan\theta + \sin\theta} = \dfrac{\dfrac{1}{\cos\theta} - 1}{\dfrac{1}{\cos\theta} + 1} - \dfrac{\dfrac{\sin\theta}{\cos\theta} - \sin\theta}{\dfrac{\sin\theta}{\cos\theta} + \sin\theta}$

$$= \dfrac{1 - \cos\theta}{1 + \cos\theta} - \dfrac{\sin\theta - \sin\theta\cos\theta}{\sin\theta\,(1 + \cos\theta)}$$

$$= \dfrac{\sin\theta\,(1 - \cos\theta) - \sin\theta + \sin\theta\cos\theta}{\sin\theta\,(1 + \cos\theta)}$$

$$= \dfrac{\sin\theta - \sin\theta\cos\theta - \sin\theta + \sin\theta\cos\theta}{\sin\theta\,(1 + \cos\theta)}$$

$$= 0$$

23. $\dfrac{\cot^2\theta}{\csc^2\theta} + \dfrac{\tan^2\theta}{\sec^2\theta} = \dfrac{\dfrac{\cos^2\theta}{\sin^2\theta}}{\dfrac{1}{\sin^2\theta}} + \dfrac{\dfrac{\sin^2\theta}{\cos^2\theta}}{\dfrac{1}{\cos^2\theta}} = \cos^2\theta + \sin^2\theta = 1$

25. $\sin\theta\cos\theta\sec\theta\csc\theta = \dfrac{\sin\theta\cos\theta}{\sin\theta\cos\theta} = 1$

27. $\dfrac{\sin\theta\sec\theta}{\tan\theta} = \dfrac{\sin\theta\left(\dfrac{1}{\cos\theta}\right)}{\dfrac{\sin\theta}{\cos\theta}} = \dfrac{\sin\theta\cos\theta}{\sin\theta\cos\theta} = 1$

29. $\sec x - 5\tan x = \dfrac{1}{\cos x} - \dfrac{5\sin x}{\cos x} = \dfrac{1 - 5\sin x}{\cos x}$

31. $\cos A\,(\sec A - \cos A) = \cos A\left(\dfrac{1}{\cos A} - \cos A\right) = 1 - \cos^2 A = \sin^2 A$

33. $(1 - \sin \theta)(\sec \theta + \tan \theta)$

$$= \sec \theta + \tan \theta - \sin \theta \sec \theta - \sin \theta \tan \theta$$

$$= \sec \theta + \tan \theta - \tan \theta - \frac{\sin^2\theta}{\cos \theta}$$

$$= \frac{1}{\cos \theta} - \frac{\sin^2\theta}{\cos \theta}$$

$$= \frac{\cos^2\theta}{\cos \theta}$$

$$= \cos \theta$$

35. $(\sec \alpha - \tan \alpha)^2 = \sec^2\alpha - 2 \tan \alpha \sec \alpha + \tan^2\alpha$

$$= \frac{1}{\cos^2\alpha} - \frac{2 \sin \alpha}{\cos^2\alpha} + \frac{\sin^2\alpha}{\cos^2\alpha}$$

$$= \frac{1 - 2 \sin \alpha + \sin^2\alpha}{\cos^2\alpha}$$

$$= \frac{(1 - \sin \alpha)^2}{1 - \sin^2\alpha}$$

$$= \frac{(1 - \sin \alpha)^2}{(1 - \sin \alpha)(1 + \sin \alpha)}$$

$$= \frac{1 - \sin \alpha}{1 + \sin \alpha}$$

37. $\dfrac{\sin A}{1 - \cot A} - \dfrac{\cos A}{\tan A - 1}$

$$= \frac{\sin A}{1 - \dfrac{\cos A}{\sin A}} - \frac{\cos A}{\dfrac{\sin A}{\cos A} - 1}$$

$$= \frac{\sin^2 A}{\sin A - \cos A} - \frac{\cos^2 A}{\sin A - \cos A}$$

$$= \frac{(\sin A - \cos A)(\sin A + \cos A)}{\sin A - \cos A}$$

$$= \sin A + \cos A$$

39. $\csc^2\theta + \sec^2\theta$
$= \dfrac{1}{\sin^2\theta} + \dfrac{1}{\cos^2\theta}$

$= \dfrac{\cos^2\theta + \sin^2\theta}{\sin^2\theta \cos^2\theta}$

$= \dfrac{1}{\sin^2\theta \cos^2\theta}$

$= \left(\dfrac{1}{\sin^2\theta}\right) \left(\dfrac{1}{\cos^2\theta}\right)$

$= \csc^2\theta \sec^2\theta$

41. $\dfrac{2\sin^3\beta}{1 - \cos\beta}$
$= \dfrac{2\sin\beta (\sin^2\beta)}{1 - \cos\beta}$

$= \dfrac{2\sin\beta (1 - \cos^2\beta)}{1 - \cos\beta}$

$= \dfrac{2\sin\beta (1 - \cos\beta)(1 + \cos\beta)}{1 - \cos\beta}$

$= 2\sin\beta (1 + \cos\beta)$

$= 2\sin\beta + 2\sin\beta \cos\beta$

43. $\dfrac{\sin^3\theta + \cos^3\theta}{\sin\theta + \cos\theta}$
$= \dfrac{(\sin\theta + \cos\theta)(\sin^2\theta - \sin\theta \cos\theta + \cos^2\theta)}{\sin\theta + \cos\theta}$

$= \sin^2\theta + \cos^2\theta - \sin\theta \cos\theta$

$= 1 - \sin\theta \cos\theta$

45. $\dfrac{\sec\theta - \csc\theta}{\sec\theta + \csc\theta}$
$= \dfrac{\dfrac{1}{\cos\theta} - \dfrac{1}{\sin\theta}}{\dfrac{1}{\cos\theta} + \dfrac{1}{\sin\theta}}$

$= \dfrac{\dfrac{\sin\theta}{\cos\theta} - \dfrac{\sin\theta}{\sin\theta}}{\dfrac{\sin\theta}{\cos\theta} + \dfrac{\sin\theta}{\sin\theta}}$

$= \dfrac{\tan\theta - 1}{\tan\theta + 1}$

47. $(r \sin \theta \cos \phi)^2 + (r \sin \theta \sin \phi)^2 + (r \cos \theta)^2$

$$= r^2 (\sin^2\theta \cos^2\phi + \sin^2\theta \sin^2\phi + \cos^2\theta)$$
$$= r^2 \left(\sin^2\theta (\cos^2\phi + \sin^2\phi) + \cos^2\theta\right)$$
$$= r^2 (\sin^2\theta + \cos^2\theta)$$
$$= r^2$$

49.   Using the hint, we first solve each equation for A and B, respectively:

$$A \sin \theta + \cos \theta = 1$$
$$A \sin \theta = 1 - \cos \theta$$
$$A = \frac{1 - \cos \theta}{\sin \theta}$$

$$B \sin \theta - \cos \theta = 1$$
$$B \sin \theta = 1 + \cos \theta$$
$$B = \frac{1 + \cos \theta}{\sin \theta}$$

So $AB = \left(\dfrac{1 - \cos \theta}{\sin \theta}\right)\left(\dfrac{1 + \cos \theta}{\sin \theta}\right)$

$$= \frac{1 - \cos^2\theta}{\sin^2\theta}$$
$$= \frac{\sin^2\theta}{\sin^2\theta}$$
$$= 1$$

51.   Let x_0, y_0 be the x,y intercepts respectively. Then:

$$\cos \theta = \frac{d}{x_0} \quad \text{and} \quad \cos (90° - \theta) = \frac{d}{y_0}$$

$$x_0 = \frac{d}{\cos \theta} \quad \text{and} \quad y_0 = \frac{d}{\cos (90° - \theta)} = \frac{d}{\sin \theta}$$

Hence, the two points on line L are:

$$\left(\frac{d}{\cos \theta}, 0\right) \text{ and } \left(0, \frac{d}{\sin \theta}\right)$$

So the slope of the line is:

$$\frac{\dfrac{d}{\sin \theta} - 0}{0 - \dfrac{d}{\cos \theta}} = -\frac{\cos \theta}{\sin \theta}$$

Thus, by the slope-intercept formula, we have:

$$y = -\frac{\cos\theta}{\sin\theta}x + \frac{d}{\sin\theta}$$

$$y\sin\theta = -(\cos\theta)x + d$$

$$x\cos\theta + y\sin\theta = d$$

53. $a + b = (\sin\alpha + \cos\alpha) + (\sin\alpha - \cos\alpha) = 2\sin\alpha$

   $a - b = (\sin\alpha + \cos\alpha) - (\sin\alpha - \cos\alpha) = 2\cos\alpha$

   So $\dfrac{a+b}{a-b} = \dfrac{2\sin\alpha}{2\cos\alpha} = \tan\alpha$

55. $\dfrac{\tan\theta + \sec\theta - 1}{\tan\theta - \sec\theta + 1}$

$$= \frac{\dfrac{\sin\theta}{\cos\theta} + \dfrac{1}{\cos\theta} - 1}{\dfrac{\sin\theta}{\cos\theta} - \dfrac{1}{\cos\theta} + 1}$$

$$= \frac{\sin\theta + 1 - \cos\theta}{\sin\theta - 1 + \cos\theta}$$

$$= \frac{(\sin\theta + 1) - \cos\theta}{(\sin\theta - 1) + \cos\theta} \cdot \frac{(\sin\theta + 1) - \cos\theta}{(\sin\theta + 1) - \cos\theta}$$

$$= \frac{(\sin\theta + 1)^2 - 2\cos\theta(\sin\theta + 1) + \cos^2\theta}{(\sin^2\theta - 1) + \cos\theta(\sin\theta + 1) - \cos\theta(\sin\theta - 1) - \cos^2\theta}$$

$$= \frac{\sin^2\theta + 2\sin\theta + 1 - 2\sin\theta\cos\theta - 2\cos\theta + \cos^2\theta}{\sin^2\theta - 1 + \sin\theta\cos\theta + \cos\theta - \sin\theta\cos\theta + \cos\theta - \cos^2\theta}$$

$$= \frac{2 + 2\sin\theta - 2\sin\theta\cos\theta - 2\cos\theta}{\sin^2\theta - \cos^2\theta - 1 + 2\cos\theta}$$

$$= \frac{2(1 - \cos\theta) + 2\sin\theta(1 - \cos\theta)}{1 - \cos^2\theta - \cos^2\theta - 1 + 2\cos\theta}$$

$$= \frac{2(1 - \cos\theta)(1 + \sin\theta)}{-2\cos^2\theta + 2\cos\theta}$$

$$= \frac{(1 - \cos\theta)(1 + \sin\theta)}{\cos\theta(1 - \cos\theta)}$$

$$= \frac{1 + \sin\theta}{\cos\theta}$$

Chapter 7 Review Exercises

1. $\sin 135° = \sin 45° = \dfrac{\sqrt{2}}{2}$

3. $\tan(-240°) = \tan 120° = -\tan 60° = -\sqrt{3}$

5. $\csc 210° = \dfrac{1}{\sin 210°} = -\dfrac{1}{\sin 30°} = -\dfrac{1}{1/2} = -2$

7. $\sin 270° = -1$

9. $\cos(-315°) = \cos 45° = \dfrac{\sqrt{2}}{2}$

11. $\cos 1800° = \cos 0° = 1$

13. $\csc 240° = \dfrac{1}{\sin 240°} = \dfrac{1}{-\sqrt{3}/2} = -\dfrac{2}{\sqrt{3}} = -\dfrac{2\sqrt{3}}{3}$

15. $\sec 780° = \sec 60° = \dfrac{1}{\cos 60°} = \dfrac{1}{1/2} = 2$

17.   (a) $\sin^2(A + B) \neq \sin^2 A + \sin^2 B$, so $\sin^2 33° + \sin^2 57° \neq \sin^2(33° + 57°)$

$\quad$ (b) $\begin{aligned} \sin^2 33° + \sin^2 57° &= \sin^2 33° + \cos^2(90° - 57°) \\ &= \sin^2 33° + \cos^2 33° \\ &= 1 \end{aligned}$

$\qquad$ The correct answer is 1, but not for the reasons the student gave.

19.   We draw a triangle:

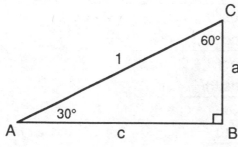

$$\sin 30° = \frac{a}{1}, \text{ so } a = \sin 30° = \frac{1}{2}$$

$$\cos 30° = \frac{c}{1}, \text{ so } c = \cos 30° = \frac{\sqrt{3}}{2}$$

21. We draw a triangle:

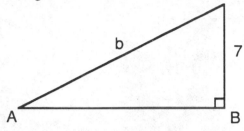

$$\sin A = \frac{7}{b}, \text{ so } b = \frac{7}{\sin A} = \frac{7}{2/5} = \frac{35}{2}$$

23. We draw a triangle:

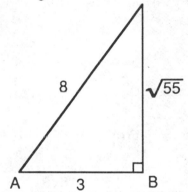

So $\sin A = \dfrac{\sqrt{55}}{8}$ and $\cot A = \dfrac{3}{\sqrt{55}} = \dfrac{3\sqrt{55}}{55}$

25. We draw a triangle:

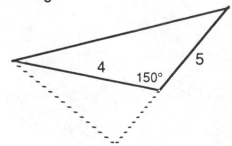

So Area $= \dfrac{1}{2}(5)(4\sin 150°) = \dfrac{1}{2}(10) = 5$

27. We draw a triangle:

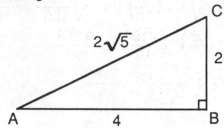

$$\sin A = \frac{2}{2\sqrt{5}} = \frac{1}{\sqrt{5}} \text{ and } \cos B = 0, \text{ so:}$$

$$\sin^2 A + \cos^2 B = \frac{1}{5} + 0 = \frac{1}{5}$$

29. We draw a triangle:

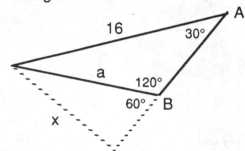

We first find x:

$$\sin 30° = \frac{x}{16}, \text{ so } x = 16 \sin 30° = \frac{1}{2}(16) = 8$$

Now, using the smaller triangle:

$$\sin 60° = \frac{8}{a}, \text{ so } a = \frac{8}{\sin 60°} = \frac{8}{\sqrt{3}/2} = \frac{16}{\sqrt{3}} = \frac{16\sqrt{3}}{3}$$

31. We draw a triangle:

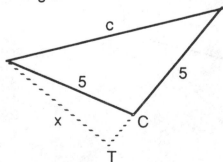

Since $\sin \frac{C}{2} = \frac{9}{10}$, then $\cos \frac{C}{2} = \sqrt{1 - \left(\frac{9}{10}\right)^2} = \sqrt{\frac{19}{100}} = \frac{\sqrt{19}}{10}$

Now $\sin C = 2 \sin \frac{C}{2} \cos \frac{C}{2} = 2 \left(\frac{9}{10}\right) \left(\frac{\sqrt{19}}{10}\right) = \frac{9\sqrt{19}}{50}$

Thus Area $= \frac{1}{2}(5)(5 \sin C) = \frac{25}{2}\left(\frac{9\sqrt{19}}{50}\right) = \frac{9\sqrt{19}}{4}$

We know $x = \frac{45\sqrt{19}}{50} = \frac{9\sqrt{19}}{10}$

Using the small triangle, we find TC:

$$\left(\frac{9\sqrt{19}}{10}\right)^2 + (TC)^2 = 5^2$$

$$\frac{1539}{100} + (TC)^2 = 25$$

$$(TC)^2 = \frac{961}{100}$$

$$TC = \frac{31}{10}$$

Now for the larger right triangle, we have:

$$\left(5 + \frac{31}{10}\right)^2 + \left(\frac{9\sqrt{19}}{10}\right)^2 = c^2$$

$$\frac{6561}{100} + \frac{1539}{100} = c^2$$

$$c^2 = \frac{8100}{100}$$

$$c^2 = 81$$

$$c = 9$$

33. Letting z be the side opposite $(90° - \beta)$, we have:

$$\cot \alpha = \frac{x + z}{y}, \quad \cot \beta = \frac{z}{y}$$

$$\cot \alpha - \cot \beta = \frac{x}{y}$$

So $y = \dfrac{x}{\cot \alpha - \cot \beta}$

35. Since $\sin^2\theta + \cos^2\theta = 1$, we have:

$$\left(\frac{2p^2q^2}{p^4 + q^4}\right)^2 + \cos^2\theta = 1$$

$$\frac{4p^4q^4}{(p^4 + q^4)^2} + \cos^2\theta = 1$$

$$\cos^2\theta = \frac{(p^4 + q^4)^2 - 4p^4q^4}{(p^4 + q^4)^2}$$

$$\cos^2\theta = \frac{p^8 - 2p^4q^4 + q^4}{(p^4 + q^4)^2}$$

$$\cos^2\theta = \frac{(p^4 - q^4)^2}{(p^4 + q^4)^2}$$

$$\cos\theta = \frac{p^4 - q^4}{p^4 + q^4}$$

Now find $\tan\theta$:

$$\tan\theta = \frac{\sin\theta}{\cos\theta} = \frac{2p^2q^2}{p^4 - q^4}$$

37.
$$\frac{\sin A + \cos A}{\sec A + \csc A} = \frac{\sin A + \cos A}{\dfrac{1}{\cos A} + \dfrac{1}{\sin A}}$$

$$= \frac{\sin A \cos A \,(\sin A + \cos A)}{\sin A + \cos A}$$

$$= \sin A \cos A$$

39.
$$\frac{\sin A \sec A}{\tan A + \cot A} = \frac{\dfrac{\sin A}{\cos A}}{\dfrac{\sin A}{\cos A} + \dfrac{\cos A}{\sin A}}$$

$$= \frac{\sin^2 A}{\sin^2 A + \cos^2 A}$$

$$= \sin^2 A$$

41.
$$\frac{\cos A}{1 - \tan A} + \frac{\sin A}{1 - \cot A} = \frac{\cos^2 A}{\cos A - \sin A} + \frac{\sin^2 A}{\sin A - \cos A}$$

$$= \frac{\cos^2 A - \sin^2 A}{\cos A - \sin A}$$

$$= \frac{(\cos A + \sin A)(\cos A - \sin A)}{\cos A - \sin A}$$

$$= \cos A + \sin A$$

43. $(\sec A + \csc A)^{-1}\left((\sec A)^{-1} + (\csc A)^{-1}\right) = \dfrac{\cos A + \sin A}{\dfrac{1}{\cos A} + \dfrac{1}{\sin A}}$

$= \dfrac{\sin A \cos A (\cos A + \sin A)}{\sin A + \cos A}$

$= \sin A \cos A$

45. $\dfrac{\dfrac{\sin A + \cos A}{\sin A - \cos A} - \dfrac{\sin A - \cos A}{\sin A + \cos A}}{\dfrac{\sin A + \cos A}{\sin A - \cos A} + \dfrac{\sin A - \cos A}{\sin A + \cos A}}$

$= \dfrac{(\sin A + \cos A)^2 - (\sin A - \cos A)^2}{(\sin A + \cos A)^2 + (\sin A - \cos A)^2}$

$= \dfrac{1 + 2\sin A \cos A - 1 + 2\sin A \cos A}{1 + 2\sin A \cos A + 1 - 2\sin A \cos A}$

$= \dfrac{4\sin A \cos A}{2}$

$= 2\sin A \cos A$

47. $\sin 20° = \sqrt{1 - \cos^2 20°} = \sqrt{1 - a^2}$

49. $\cos 70° = \sin 20° = \sqrt{1 - a^2}$

51. $\cos 160° = -\cos 20° = -a$

53. $\cos(-160°) = \cos 200° = -\cos 20° = -a$

55. $\sin 200° = -\sin 20° = -\sqrt{1 - a^2}$

57. $\dfrac{\sin^4\theta - \cos^4\theta}{\sin^2\theta - \cos^2\theta} \div \dfrac{1 + \sin\theta\cos\theta}{\sin^3\theta - \cos^3\theta}$

$= \dfrac{(\sin^2\theta - \cos^2\theta)(\sin^2\theta + \cos^2\theta)}{\sin^2\theta - \cos^2\theta} \bullet \dfrac{(\sin\theta - \cos\theta)(\sin^2\theta + \sin\theta\cos\theta + \cos^2\theta)}{1 + \sin\theta\cos\theta}$

$= \dfrac{(\sin\theta - \cos\theta)(\sin^2\theta + \sin\theta\cos\theta + \cos^2\theta)}{1 + \sin\theta\cos\theta}$

$= \sin\theta - \cos\theta$

59.   Since $\dfrac{\tan \alpha}{\tan \beta} = \sqrt{3}$, then:

$$\frac{\sin \alpha}{\sin \beta} = \sqrt{3} \cdot \frac{\cos \alpha}{\cos \beta}$$

$$\sqrt{2} = \sqrt{3} \cdot \frac{\cos \alpha}{\cos \beta}$$

$$\sqrt{2} \cos \beta = \sqrt{3} \cos \alpha$$

$$2 \cos^2 \beta = 3 \cos^2 \alpha$$

$$\frac{2}{3} \cos^2 \beta = \cos^2 \alpha$$

Now $\sin \alpha = \sqrt{2} \sin \beta$, so $\sin^2 \alpha = 2 \sin^2 \alpha$. Thus:

$$\sin^2 \alpha + \cos^2 \alpha = 1$$

$$2 \sin^2 \beta + \frac{2}{3} \cos^2 \beta = 1$$

$$2 \sin^2 \beta + \frac{2}{3}(1 - \sin^2 \beta) = 1$$

$$\frac{4}{3} \sin^2 \beta = \frac{1}{3}$$

$$\sin^2 \beta = \frac{1}{4}$$

$$\sin \beta = \frac{1}{2}$$

$$\beta = 30°$$

Thus $\sin \alpha = \sqrt{2}\left(\frac{1}{2}\right) = \dfrac{\sqrt{2}}{2}$, and so $\alpha = 45°$

61.   We draw a triangle:

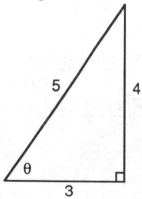

$\sin \theta = \dfrac{4}{5}$ and $\tan \theta = \dfrac{4}{3}$

63.   We draw a triangle:

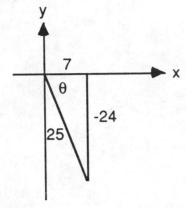

$$\tan \theta = \frac{-24}{7}$$

65.   We draw a triangle:

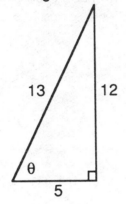

$$\cot \theta = \frac{5}{12}$$

67. We draw a triangle:

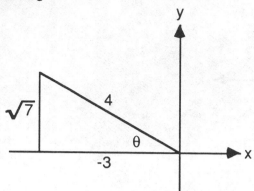

$$\tan(90° - \theta) = \frac{-3}{\sqrt{7}} = \frac{-3\sqrt{7}}{7}$$

69. Since $\cos(180° - \theta) = -\cos\theta$ for $0° < \theta < 90°$, then $\cos(180° - \theta) = \frac{-7}{9}$

71. $\tan\theta + \cot\theta = 2$

$$\frac{\sin\theta}{\cos\theta} + \frac{\cos\theta}{\sin\theta} = 2$$

$$\frac{\sin^2\theta + \cos^2\theta}{\sin\theta\cos\theta} = 2$$

$$1 = 2\sin\theta\cos\theta$$

Now $(\sin\theta + \cos\theta)^2 = \sin^2\theta + 2\sin\theta\cos\theta + \cos^2\theta = 1 + 1 = 2$, so
$\sin\theta + \cos\theta = \sqrt{2}$ since $0° < \theta < 90°$

73. We draw the figure:

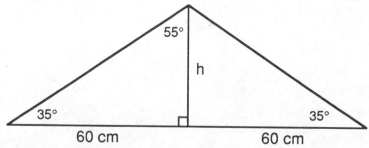

Now $\tan 35° = \frac{h}{60}$, so $h = 60\tan 35°$

Thus Area $= \frac{1}{2}(120)(60\tan 35°) = 3600\tan 35°$ cm$^2 \approx 2521$ cm^2

75. We draw the figure:

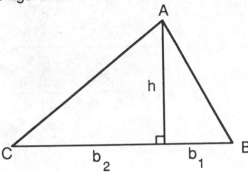

Now:

$$\cot B = \frac{b_1}{h}, \text{ so } b_1 = h \cot B$$

$$\cot C = \frac{b_2}{h}, \text{ so } b_2 = h \cot C$$

So we have:

$$b_1 + b_2 = a$$
$$h \cot B + h \cot C = a$$
$$h (\cot B + \cot C) = a$$
$$h = \frac{a}{\cot B + \cot C}$$

77. We draw the figure:

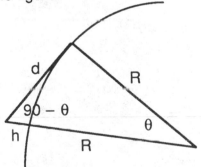

We have:

$$d^2 + R^2 = (R + h)^2$$
$$d^2 = h^2 + 2Rh$$
$$d = \sqrt{2Rh + h^2}$$

So:

$$\cot \theta = \frac{R}{d} = \frac{R}{\sqrt{2Rh + h^2}}$$

79. $\sin^2(90° - \theta) \csc \theta - \tan^2(90° - \theta) \sin \theta \quad = \cos^2\theta \cdot \dfrac{1}{\sin \theta} - \cot^2\theta \sin \theta$

$$= \dfrac{\cos^2\theta}{\sin \theta} - \dfrac{\cos^2\theta}{\sin^2\theta} \cdot \sin \theta$$

$$= \dfrac{\cos^2\theta}{\sin \theta} - \dfrac{\cos^2\theta}{\sin \theta}$$

$$= 0$$

81. $\csc A - \sin A = \dfrac{1}{\sin A} - \sin A$

$$= \dfrac{1 - \sin^2 A}{\sin A}$$

$$= \dfrac{\cos^2 A}{\sin A}$$

$$= \left(\dfrac{\cos A}{\sin A}\right) \cos A$$

$$= \cos A \cot A$$

83. $\dfrac{\cos A - \sin A}{\cos A + \sin A} = \dfrac{\dfrac{\cos A}{\sin A} - 1}{\dfrac{\cos A}{\sin A} + 1} = \dfrac{\cot A - 1}{\cot A + 1}$

85. $\cos^2\theta - \sin^2\theta = \cos^2\theta - (1 - \cos^2\theta) = 2 \cos^2\theta - 1$

87. $\sin A \tan A = \dfrac{\sin^2 A}{\cos A} = \dfrac{1 - \cos^2 A}{\cos A}$

89. $-\cot^4 A + \csc^4 A = \dfrac{-\cos^4 A}{\sin^4 A} + \dfrac{1}{\sin^4 A}$

$$= \dfrac{(1 - \cos^2 A)(1 + \cos^2 A)}{\sin^4 A}$$

$$= \dfrac{\sin^2 A (1 + \cos^2 A)}{\sin^4 A}$$

$$= \dfrac{1 + \cos^2 A}{\sin^2 A}$$

$$= \dfrac{1}{\sin^2 A} + \dfrac{\cos^2 A}{\sin^2 A}$$

$$= \cot^2 A + \csc^2 A$$

91. $\dfrac{\cot^2 A - \tan^2 A}{(\cot A + \tan A)^2}$

$= \dfrac{\cot A - \tan A}{\cot A + \tan A}$

$= \dfrac{\dfrac{\cos A}{\sin A} - \dfrac{\sin A}{\cos A}}{\dfrac{\cos A}{\sin A} + \dfrac{\sin A}{\cos A}}$

$= \dfrac{\cos^2 A - \sin^2 A}{\cos^2 A + \sin^2 A}$

$= \cos^2 A - (1 - \cos^2 A)$

$= 2\cos^2 A - 1$

93. $\dfrac{\cos A - \sin A}{\cos A + \sin A} = \dfrac{1 - \dfrac{\sin A}{\cos A}}{1 + \dfrac{\sin A}{\cos A}} = \dfrac{1 - \tan A}{1 + \tan A}$

95. $\dfrac{1}{\sec A + \tan A}$

$= \dfrac{1}{\dfrac{1}{\cos A} + \dfrac{\sin A}{\cos A}}$

$= \dfrac{\cos A}{1 + \sin A}$

$= \dfrac{(1 - \sin A)\cos A}{1 - \sin^2 A}$

$= \dfrac{(1 - \sin A)\cos A}{\cos^2 A}$

$= \dfrac{1 - \sin A}{\cos A}$

Thus: $\dfrac{1 - \sin A}{\cos A} - \dfrac{1}{\sec A + \tan A} = 0$

97. $\dfrac{\tan A + \tan B}{\cot A + \cot B}$

$= \dfrac{\dfrac{\sin A}{\cos A} + \dfrac{\sin B}{\cos B}}{\dfrac{\cos A}{\sin A} + \dfrac{\cos B}{\sin B}}$

$= \dfrac{(\sin A \sin B)(\cos A \sin B + \sin A \cos B)}{(\cos A \cos B)(\sin A \cos B + \cos A \sin B)}$

$= \left(\dfrac{\sin A}{\cos A}\right)\left(\dfrac{\sin B}{\cos B}\right)$

$= \tan A \tan B$

99. $\tan A - \dfrac{\sec A \sin^3 A}{1 + \cos A}$ $= \dfrac{\sin A}{\cos A} - \dfrac{\sin^3 A}{\cos A \,(1 + \cos A)}$

$= \dfrac{(\sin A)(1 + \cos A) - \sin^3 A}{\cos A \,(1 + \cos A)}$

$= \dfrac{\sin A \,(1 + \cos A) - \sin A \,(1 - \cos^2 A)}{\cos A \,(1 + \cos A)}$

$= \dfrac{\sin A - \sin A \,(1 - \cos A)}{\cos A}$

$= \dfrac{\sin A \cos A}{\cos A}$

$= \sin A$

101. $\dfrac{1}{\csc A - \cot A} - \dfrac{1}{\csc A + \cot A}$ $= \dfrac{2 \cot A}{\csc^2 A - \cot^2 A}$

$= \dfrac{2 \cot A}{\dfrac{1 - \cos^2 A}{\sin^2 A}}$

$= 2 \cot A$

103. Since $\dfrac{1}{1 + \sec^2 A} = \dfrac{\cos^2 A}{\cos^2 A + 1}$ and $\dfrac{1}{1 + \csc^2 A} = \dfrac{\sin^2 A}{\sin^2 A + 1}$

The left-hand side becomes:

$\dfrac{1}{1 + \sin^2 A} + \dfrac{1}{1 + \cos^2 A} + \dfrac{\cos^2 A}{1 + \cos^2 A} + \dfrac{\sin^2 A}{1 + \sin^2 A}$

$= \dfrac{1 + \sin^2 A}{1 + \sin^2 A} + \dfrac{1 + \cos^2 A}{1 + \cos^2 A}$

$= 2$

105. $\dfrac{\sec A - \csc A}{\sec A + \csc A} = \dfrac{1 - \dfrac{\cos A}{\sin A}}{1 + \dfrac{\cos A}{\sin A}} = \dfrac{\sin A - \cos A}{\sin A + \cos A}$

107. $\dfrac{\tan A}{1 + \tan^2 A} = \dfrac{\sin A}{\cos A + \dfrac{\sin^2 A}{\cos A}} = \dfrac{\sin A \cos A}{\cos^2 A + \sin^2 A} = \sin A \cos A$

109. (a)   PN $= \sin \theta$

(b)   ON $= \cos \theta$

(c)   Since $\cos \theta = \dfrac{PN}{PT}$ (note $\theta = \angle TPN$), then $\cos \theta = \dfrac{\sin \theta}{PT}$

Hence, PT $= \tan \theta$

(d)   Here $\cos \theta = \dfrac{1}{OT}$ (using $\triangle$ OPT), so OT $= \dfrac{1}{\cos \theta} = \sec \theta$

(e)   NA $= 1 - ON = 1 - \cos \theta$

(f)   NT $\;= OT - ON$

$= \sec \theta - \cos \theta$

$= \dfrac{1}{\cos \theta} - \cos \theta$

$= \dfrac{1 - \cos^2\theta}{\cos \theta}$

$= \dfrac{\sin^2\theta}{\cos \theta}$

$= \sin \theta \left(\dfrac{\sin \theta}{\cos \theta} \right)$

$= \sin \theta \tan \theta$

111. (a) $\cos 30° = \dfrac{\sqrt{3}}{2}$

(b) $\tan 60° = \dfrac{\sin 60°}{\cos 60°} = \dfrac{\sqrt{3}/2}{1/2} = \sqrt{3}$

(c) $\sin^2 7° + \cos^2 7° = 1$

113. (a) $\cos 330° = \cos 30° = \dfrac{\sqrt{3}}{2}$

(b) $\csc 315° = \dfrac{1}{\sin 315°} = \dfrac{1}{-\sin 45°} = \dfrac{1}{-1/\sqrt{2}} = -\sqrt{2}$

115. $6 \tan^2\theta + 11 \tan \theta + 3 = (3 \tan \theta + 1)(2 \tan \theta + 3)$

117. $\dfrac{\dfrac{\tan\theta+1}{\tan\theta}+1}{\dfrac{\tan\theta-1}{\tan\theta}-1} = \dfrac{\tan\theta+1+\tan\theta}{\tan\theta-1-\tan\theta} = \dfrac{2\tan\theta+1}{-1} = -2\tan\theta-1$

119. We draw a figure:

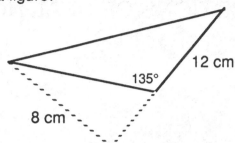

$$\text{Area} = \frac{1}{2}(12)(8\sin 135°) = 48\left(\frac{\sqrt{2}}{2}\right) = 24\sqrt{2}\ \text{cm}^2$$

121. We have:

$$\tan 25° = \frac{DB}{50}, \text{ so } DB = 50\tan 25°$$

$$\tan 55° = \frac{CB}{50}, \text{ so } CB = 50\tan 55°$$

So $CD = CB - DB = 50(\tan 55° - \tan 25°)$

123. $\dfrac{1}{\sin\theta+\cot\theta\cos\theta}$

$$= \dfrac{1}{\sin\theta+\dfrac{\cos\theta}{\sin\theta}\bullet\cos\theta}$$

$$= \dfrac{\sin\theta}{\sin^2\theta+\cos^2\theta}$$

$$= \sin\theta$$

125. Since $AP = \cos\theta$ and $\angle BPA = \theta$, then $\cos\theta = \dfrac{BP}{AP}$ implies $BP = \cos^2\theta$

Therefore:

$$AB = \sqrt{(AP)^2-(BP)^2}$$

$$= \sqrt{\cos^2\theta-\cos^4\theta}$$

$$= \cos\theta\sqrt{1-\cos^2\theta}$$

$$= \cos\theta\sin\theta$$

CHAPTER 8
TRIGONOMETRIC FUNCTIONS OF REAL NUMBERS

8.1 Radian Measure

1. Remember, to convert from degrees to radians, we must multiply by $\frac{\pi}{180°}$:

(a) $60° \left(\frac{\pi}{180°} \right) = \frac{\pi}{3}$ radians

(b) $225° \left(\frac{\pi}{180°} \right) = \frac{5\pi}{4}$ radians

(c) $36° \left(\frac{\pi}{180°} \right) = \frac{\pi}{5}$ radians

(d) $450° \left(\frac{\pi}{180°} \right) = \frac{5\pi}{2}$ radians

(e) $0° \left(\frac{\pi}{180°} \right) = 0$ radians

3. To convert from radians to degrees, we multiply by $\dfrac{180°}{\pi}$:

   (a) $\left(\dfrac{\pi}{12}\right)\left(\dfrac{180°}{\pi}\right) = 15°$

   (b) $\left(\dfrac{3\pi}{2}\right)\left(\dfrac{180°}{\pi}\right) = 270°$

   (c) $(6\pi)\left(\dfrac{180°}{\pi}\right) = 1080°$

   (d) $\left(\dfrac{\pi}{10}\right)\left(\dfrac{180°}{\pi}\right) = 18°$

   (e) $\left(\dfrac{\pi}{2}\right)\left(\dfrac{180°}{\pi}\right) = 90°$

   (f) $(3)\left(\dfrac{180°}{\pi}\right) = \dfrac{540°}{\pi}$

5. Since $90° = \dfrac{\pi}{2}$, which is about $\dfrac{3.14}{2}$ radians, then $\dfrac{3}{2}$ radians is smaller than a right angle.

7. We complete the table:

θ	0	$\pi/2$	π	$3\pi/2$	2π
$\cos \theta$	1	0	-1	0	1

9. (a) $\sin 2$ is positive, since $\dfrac{\pi}{2} < 2 < \pi$

   (b) $\sin 3$ is positive, since $\dfrac{\pi}{2} < 3 < \pi$

11. (a) $\sin 3.16$ is negative, since $\pi < 3.16 < \dfrac{3\pi}{2}$

    (b) $\tan 3.16$ is positive, since $\pi < 3.16 < \dfrac{3\pi}{2}$

13. $s = r\theta = 3\left(\dfrac{4\pi}{3}\right) = 4\pi$ ft

15. $s = r\theta = 2\left(\dfrac{45\pi}{180}\right) = \dfrac{\pi}{2}$ cm

17. Since s = rθ, and s = 1 cm while r = 6 cm, we have:

$$1 = 6\theta$$

$$\theta = \frac{1}{6}$$

The radian measure of θ is $\frac{1}{6}$

19. (a) Each revolution of the wheel is 2π radians, so in 6 revolutions there are θ = 6(2π) = 12π radians.
Consequently, we have:

$$\omega = \frac{\theta}{t} = \frac{12\pi \text{ radians}}{1 \text{ sec}} = 12\pi \text{ radians/sec}$$

(b) Using the formula s = rθ, where r = 12 cm and θ = 12π radians, we have s = (12 cm)(12π radians) = 122π cm.
The linear speed, therefore, is:

$$v = \frac{d}{t} = \frac{144\pi \text{ cm}}{1 \text{ sec}} = 144\pi \text{ cm/sec}$$

(c) Using the formula s = rθ, where r = 6 cm and θ = 12π radians, we have s = (6 cm)(12π rad) = 72π cm.
Thus, we have:

$$v = \frac{d}{t} = \frac{72\pi \text{ cm}}{1 \text{ sec}} = 72\pi \text{ cm/sec}$$

21. (a) In 1 second, the wheel has rotated $1080° \cdot \frac{\pi \text{ rad}}{180°} = 6\pi$ radians.
Consequently, we have:

$$\omega = \frac{\theta}{t} = \frac{6\pi \text{ rad}}{1 \text{ sec}} = 6\pi \text{ rad/sec}$$

(b) Using θ = 6π radians and r = 25 cm, then:

$$s = r\theta = (25 \text{ cm})(6\pi \text{ rad}) = 150\pi \text{ cm}$$

Thus, we have:

$$v = \frac{150\pi \text{ cm}}{1 \text{ sec}} = 150\pi \text{ cm/sec}$$

(c)   Using $\theta = 6\pi$ radians and $r = \dfrac{25}{2}$ cm, then:

$$s = r\theta = \left(\frac{25}{2} \text{ cm}\right)(6\pi \text{ rad}) = 75\pi \text{ cm}$$

Thus, we have:

$$v = \frac{75\pi \text{ cm}}{1 \text{ sec}} = 75\pi \text{ cm/sec}$$

23.   (a)   In 1 minute, the wheel has rotated 500 rev. Since each revolution is equal to 2π radians, then we have:

$$\theta = (500)(2\pi) = 1000\pi \text{ radians}$$

Consequently, we have:

$$\omega = \frac{\theta}{t} = \frac{1000\pi \text{ rad}}{60 \text{ sec}} = \frac{50\pi}{3} \text{ rad/sec}$$

(b)   Using $\theta = 1000\pi$ radians and $r = 45$ cm, then:

$$s = r\theta = (45 \text{ cm})(1000\pi \text{ rad}) = 45000\pi \text{ cm}$$

Thus, we have:

$$v = \frac{45000\pi \text{ cm}}{60 \text{ sec}} = 750\pi \text{ cm/sec}$$

(c)   Using $\theta = 1000\pi$ radians and $r = \dfrac{45}{2}$ cm, then:

$$s = r\theta = \left(\frac{45}{2} \text{ cm}\right)(1000\pi \text{ rad}) = 22500\pi \text{ cm}$$

Thus, we have:

$$v = \frac{22500\pi \text{ cm}}{60 \text{ sec}} = 375\pi \text{ cm/sec}$$

25.   (a)   Here $r = 5$ cm and $\theta = 210° \cdot \dfrac{\pi \text{ rad}}{180°} = \dfrac{7\pi}{6}$ radians, so:

$$A = \frac{1}{2} r^2\theta = \frac{1}{2}(5 \text{ cm})^2 \left(\frac{7\pi}{6}\right) = \frac{175\pi}{12} \text{ cm}^2$$

(b)   Here $r = 2$ in. and $\theta = 15° \cdot \dfrac{\pi \text{ rad}}{180°} = \dfrac{\pi}{12}$ radians, so:

$$A = \frac{1}{2} r^2\theta = \frac{1}{2}(2 \text{ in.})^2 \left(\frac{\pi}{12}\right) = \frac{\pi}{6} \text{ in.}^2$$

27. The area of the shaded region $=$ area of sector - area of triangle

$$= \frac{1}{2}(10 \text{ cm})^2 \left(\frac{\pi}{3}\right) - \frac{1}{2}(10 \text{ cm})(10 \text{ cm}) \sin\frac{\pi}{3}$$

$$= \left[\frac{50\pi}{3} - 50\left(\frac{\sqrt{3}}{2}\right)\right] \text{cm}^2$$

$$= \frac{50\pi}{3} - 25\sqrt{3} \text{ cm}^2$$

29. With arc length 1 ft and radius 1 ft, then angle A = 1 radian, which is approximately 57.3°, slightly less than 60°.

31. Since each revolution results in a distance traveled of $(2\pi)\left(\frac{3}{2}\text{ft}\right) = 3\pi$ ft, then in x revolutions the point on the circumference has traveled $3\pi x$ ft. Thus:

$$3\pi x = 22619$$
$$x = \frac{22619}{3\pi} \text{ rev}$$
$$x \approx 600 \text{ rev}$$

33. (a) Each revolution is 2π radians, and 24 hr = 86400 sec, so:

$$w = \frac{\theta}{t} = \frac{2\pi \text{ rad}}{86400 \text{ sec}} \approx 0.000073 \text{ rad/sec}$$

(b) Using $\theta = 2\pi$ rad and r = 3960 mi, then:

$$s = r\theta = (3960 \text{ mi})(2\pi \text{ rad}) = 7920\pi \text{ mi}$$

Thus, we have:

$$v = \frac{s}{t} = \frac{7920\pi \text{ mi}}{24 \text{ hr}} = 330\pi \text{ mi/hr} \approx 1040 \text{ mph}$$

35. (a) $\text{Area}_1 = \frac{1^2(\pi - \theta)}{2}$, $\text{Area}_2 = \frac{1^2(\theta)}{2}$, hence:

$$P = \frac{\pi - \theta}{2} \cdot \frac{\theta}{2} = \frac{\pi\theta - \theta^2}{4}$$

This is a quadratic function.

(b)   We complete the square:

$$P = \frac{-\theta^2}{4} + \frac{\pi}{4}\theta$$

$$= -\frac{1}{4}(\theta^2 - \pi\theta)$$

$$= -\frac{1}{4}\left(\theta^2 - \pi\theta + \frac{\pi^2}{4}\right) + \frac{\pi^2}{16}$$

$$= -\frac{1}{4}\left(\theta - \frac{\pi}{2}\right)^2 + \frac{\pi^2}{16}$$

Thus P has a maximum value of $\frac{\pi^2}{16}$ when $\theta = \frac{\pi}{2}$.

8.2 Trigonometric Functions of Real Numbers

1.   We complete the table:

θ	$\sin\theta$	$\cos\theta$	$\tan\theta$	$\csc\theta$	$\sec\theta$	$\cot\theta$
0	0	1	0	undef.	1	undef.
$\frac{\pi}{6}$	$\frac{1}{2}$	$\frac{\sqrt{3}}{2}$	$\frac{\sqrt{3}}{3}$	2	$\frac{2\sqrt{3}}{3}$	$\sqrt{3}$
$\frac{\pi}{4}$	$\frac{\sqrt{2}}{2}$	$\frac{\sqrt{2}}{2}$	1	$\sqrt{2}$	$\sqrt{2}$	1
$\frac{\pi}{3}$	$\frac{\sqrt{3}}{2}$	$\frac{1}{2}$	$\sqrt{3}$	$\frac{2\sqrt{3}}{3}$	2	$\frac{\sqrt{3}}{3}$
$\frac{\pi}{2}$	1	0	undef.	1	undef.	0
$\frac{2\pi}{3}$	$\frac{\sqrt{3}}{2}$	$-\frac{1}{2}$	$-\sqrt{3}$	$\frac{2\sqrt{3}}{3}$	-2	$-\frac{\sqrt{3}}{3}$
$\frac{3\pi}{4}$	$\frac{\sqrt{2}}{2}$	$-\frac{\sqrt{2}}{2}$	-1	$\sqrt{2}$	$-\sqrt{2}$	-1
$\frac{5\pi}{6}$	$\frac{1}{2}$	$-\frac{\sqrt{3}}{2}$	$-\frac{\sqrt{3}}{3}$	2	$-\frac{2\sqrt{3}}{3}$	$-\sqrt{3}$
π	0	-1	0	undef.	1	undef.

3. $\cos \theta = \pm \sqrt{1 - \sin^2\theta} = \pm \sqrt{1 - \frac{9}{25}} = \pm \frac{4}{5}$. Now, since $\pi < \theta < \frac{3\pi}{2}$,

then $\cos \theta = -\frac{4}{5}$, and thus $\tan \theta = \frac{\sin \theta}{\cos \theta} = \frac{3}{4}$

5. With $\sin t = \frac{\sqrt{3}}{4}$ and $\frac{\pi}{2} < t < \pi$, so $\cos t = -\sqrt{1 - \frac{3}{16}}$, which is equal to

$-\sqrt{\frac{13}{16}} = -\frac{\sqrt{13}}{4}$, thus $\tan t = -\frac{\sqrt{3}}{\sqrt{13}} = -\frac{\sqrt{39}}{13}$.

7. $\tan \alpha = \frac{12}{5}$, so: $1 + \left(\frac{12}{5}\right)^2 = \sec^2\alpha$

$$1 + \frac{144}{25} = \sec^2\alpha$$

$$\frac{169}{25} = \sec^2\alpha$$

$$\pm\frac{13}{5} = \sec \alpha$$

Since $\cos \alpha > 0$, so is $\sec \alpha$ and thus we pick $\sec \alpha = \frac{13}{5}$. Thus

$\cos \alpha = \frac{5}{13}$, and we use $\sin^2\alpha + \cos^2\alpha = 1$ to get:

$$\sin^2\alpha = 1 - \left(\frac{5}{13}\right)^2 = \frac{144}{169}, \text{ thus } \sin \alpha = \pm\frac{12}{13}$$

We pick the positive value since, if both the tangent and cosine are positive, then so is the sine. Thus $\sin \alpha = \frac{12}{13}$.

9. For $0 < \theta < \frac{\pi}{2}$, we have:

$$\sqrt{9 - x^2} = \sqrt{9 - (3 \sin \theta)^2}$$
$$= \sqrt{9(1 - \sin^2\theta)}$$
$$= \sqrt{9 \cos^2\theta}$$
$$= 3 \cos \theta$$

11. $\dfrac{1}{(u^2 - 25)^{3/2}} = \dfrac{1}{(25 \sec^2\theta - 25)^{3/2}} = \dfrac{1}{125 \tan^3\theta}$

Since $0 < \theta < \frac{\pi}{2}$, then $\tan \theta > 0$. This can also be written as $\dfrac{\cot^3\theta}{125}$.

13. Since $\sec \theta > 0$, we have:

$$\frac{1}{\sqrt{u^2 + 7}} = \frac{1}{\sqrt{7 \tan^2\theta + 7}} = \frac{1}{\sqrt{7} \sec \theta}$$

This can also be written as $\dfrac{\cos \theta}{\sqrt{7}} = \dfrac{\sqrt{7} \cos \theta}{7}$

15. (a) $\sin (-\theta) = -\sin \theta = -\dfrac{2}{3}$

(b) $\sin (-\phi) = -\sin \phi = \dfrac{1}{4}$

(c) $\cos (-\alpha) = \cos \alpha = \dfrac{1}{5}$

(d) $\cos (-\beta) = \cos \beta = -\dfrac{1}{5}$

17. (a) Since $\cos \theta = -\dfrac{1}{3}$ then, since $\dfrac{\pi}{2} < \theta < \pi$, we have $\sin \theta > 0$ and

$\sin \theta = \sqrt{1 - \dfrac{1}{9}} = \sqrt{\dfrac{8}{9}} = \dfrac{2\sqrt{2}}{3}$. Hence $\sin (-\theta) = -\dfrac{2\sqrt{2}}{3}$ and

$\cos (-\theta) = -\dfrac{1}{3}$, thus $\sin (-\theta) + \cos (-\theta) = -\dfrac{2\sqrt{2}}{3} - \dfrac{1}{3}$, which is

$-\dfrac{1 + 2\sqrt{2}}{3}$.

(b) This is 1, regardless of θ.

19. (a) $\cos \left(\dfrac{\pi}{4} + 2\pi\right) = \cos \dfrac{\pi}{4} = \dfrac{\sqrt{2}}{2}$

(b) $\sin \left(\dfrac{\pi}{3} + 2\pi\right) = \sin \dfrac{\pi}{3} = \dfrac{\sqrt{3}}{2}$

(c) $\sin \left(\dfrac{\pi}{2} - 6\pi\right) = \sin \dfrac{\pi}{2} = 1$

21. $\dfrac{\sin^2\theta + \cos^2\theta}{\tan^2\theta + 1} = \dfrac{1}{\sec^2\theta} = \cos^2\theta$

23. $\dfrac{\sec^2\theta - \tan^2\theta}{1 + \cot^2\theta} = \dfrac{\tan^2\theta + 1 - \tan^2\theta}{\csc^2\theta} = \dfrac{1}{\csc^2\theta} = \sin^2\theta$

25.
$$\sin\theta + \cot\theta\cos\theta = \sin\theta + \frac{\cos\theta}{\sin\theta}(\cos\theta)$$
$$= \frac{\sin^2\theta}{\sin\theta} + \frac{\cos^2\theta}{\sin\theta}$$
$$= \frac{\sin^2\theta + \cos^2\theta}{\sin\theta}$$
$$= \frac{1}{\sin\theta}$$
$$= \csc\theta$$

27.
$$\frac{1}{1 + \sec\theta} + \frac{1}{1 - \sec\theta} = \frac{(1 - \sec\theta) + (1 + \sec\theta)}{(1 - \sec\theta)(1 + \sec\theta)}$$
$$= \frac{2}{1 - \sec^2\theta}$$
$$= \frac{-2}{\tan^2\theta}$$
$$= -2\cot^2\theta$$

29. Denoting $\sin\theta$ by S and $\cos\theta$ by C, we have:
$$\frac{\cot\theta}{1 - \tan\theta} + \frac{\tan\theta}{1 - \cot\theta} = \frac{\frac{C}{S}}{1 - \frac{S}{C}} + \frac{\frac{S}{C}}{1 - \frac{C}{S}} = \frac{C^2}{S(C - S)} - \frac{S^2}{C(C - S)}$$

which simplifies to $\dfrac{1}{SC} + 1$. Now we replace C with $\cos\theta$ and S with $\sin\theta$:
$$\frac{1}{SC} + 1 = \frac{\cos^2\theta + \sin^2\theta}{\sin\theta\cos\theta} + 1$$
$$= \frac{\cos\theta}{\sin\theta} + \frac{\sin\theta}{\cos\theta} + 1$$
$$= \cot\theta + \tan\theta + 1$$

31. The expression on the left-hand side becomes:
$$\tan\theta - (\tan\theta\cot\theta)(\cot\theta) + \cot\theta - (\cot\theta\tan\theta)(\tan\theta),$$
which multiplies out to become $\tan\theta - \cot\theta + \cot\theta - \tan\theta$, which is 0.

33. We have:
$$\sin t = \frac{y}{\sqrt{x^2 + y^2}} \text{ and } \cos t = \frac{x}{\sqrt{x^2 + y^2}}$$

Similarly:
$$\sin(t + \pi) = \frac{-y}{\sqrt{x^2 + y^2}} \text{ and } \cos(t + \pi) = \frac{-x}{\sqrt{x^2 + y^2}}$$

And:
$$\sin(t - \pi) = \frac{-y}{\sqrt{x^2 + y^2}} \text{ and } \cos(t - \pi) = \frac{-x}{\sqrt{x^2 + y^2}}$$

Thus we have the results:
$$\sin(t + \pi) = -\sin t$$
$$\sin(t - \pi) = -\sin t$$
$$\cos(t + \pi) = -\cos t$$
$$\cos(t - \pi) = -\cos t$$

35. The substitutions are $x = \frac{\sqrt{2}}{2}(X - Y)$ and $y = \frac{\sqrt{2}}{2}(X + Y)$. Thus we have:

$$x^2 = \frac{1}{2}(X^2 - 2XY + Y^2) \text{ and } y^2 = \frac{1}{2}(X^2 + 2XY + Y^2)$$

and thus:

$$x^4 = \frac{1}{4}(X^4 - 4X^3Y + 6X^2Y^2 - 4XY^3 + Y^4)$$

$$y^4 = \frac{1}{4}(X^4 + 4X^3Y + 6X^2Y^2 + 4XY^3 + Y^4)$$

We also find $x^2y^2 = \frac{1}{4}(X^2 - Y^2)^2 = \frac{1}{4}(X^4 - 2X^2Y^2 + Y^4)$

Now we use the expressions that have been found for x^2, y^2, x^4, and y^4 to substitute in the expression $x^4 + 6x^2y^2 + y^4$ to get:

$$\frac{X^4}{4} - X^3Y + \frac{3}{2}X^2Y^2 - XY^3 + \frac{Y^4}{4} + \frac{3}{2}X^4 - 3X^2Y^2 + \frac{3}{2}Y^4 + \frac{X^4}{4} + X^3Y + \frac{3}{2}X^2Y^2 + XY^3 + \frac{Y^4}{4}$$

which is $2X^4 + 2Y^4$. In light of this result, the equation $x^4 + 6x^2y^2 + y^4 = 32$ is equivalent to $2X^4 + 2Y^4 = 32$, or $X^4 + Y^4 = 16$, as required.

37. We complete the chart:

θ	$1 - \dfrac{\theta^2}{2}$	$\cos \theta$
0.1	0.995	0.995004...
0.2	0.980	0.980066...
0.3	0.955	0.955336...

39. $\begin{aligned}
a + b - c &= (\sin^2\theta + \csc^2\theta) + (\cos^2\theta + \sec^2\theta) - (\tan^2\theta + \cot^2\theta) \\
&= (\sin^2\theta + \cos^2\theta) + (\csc^2\theta - \cot^2\theta) + (\sec^2\theta - \tan^2\theta) \\
&= 1 + 1 + 1 \\
&= 3
\end{aligned}$

41. (a) $0, \pi, 2\pi, 3\pi$

    (b) The domain of $f(\theta)$ are those real numbers for which $\sin\theta \neq 0$, that is all reals except $0, \pm\pi, \pm2\pi, \ldots$ This can be written as all real numbers except $k\pi$, where k is any integer.

    (c) All reals except the integers.

8.3 The Addition Formulas

1. (a) $\sin\theta \cos 2\theta + \cos\theta \sin 2\theta = \sin(\theta + 2\theta) = \sin 3\theta$

    (b) $\sin\dfrac{\pi}{6}\cos\dfrac{\pi}{3} + \cos\dfrac{\pi}{6}\sin\dfrac{\pi}{3} = \sin\left(\dfrac{\pi}{6} + \dfrac{\pi}{3}\right) = \sin\dfrac{\pi}{2} = 1$

3. (a) $\cos 2u \cos 3u - \sin 2u \sin 3u = \cos(2u + 3u) = \cos 5u$

    (b) $\cos 2u \cos 3u + \sin 2u \sin 3u = \cos(2u - 3u) = \cos(-u) = \cos u$

5. $\sin(A + B)\cos A - \cos(A + B)\sin A = \sin(A + B - A) = \sin B$

7. $\sin\left(\theta - \dfrac{3\pi}{2}\right) = \sin\theta\cos\dfrac{3\pi}{2} - \cos\theta\sin\dfrac{3\pi}{2}$

$= \sin\theta \bullet 0 - \cos\theta \bullet (-1)$

$= \cos\theta$

9. $\cos(\theta + \pi) = \cos\theta\cos\pi - \sin\theta\sin\pi$

$= \cos\theta \bullet (-1) - \sin\theta \bullet 0$

$= -\cos\theta$

11. $\sin(\theta + 2\pi) = \sin\theta\cos 2\pi + \cos\theta\sin 2\pi$

$= \sin\theta \bullet 1 + \cos\theta \bullet 0$

$= \sin\theta$

13. $\cos(75°) = \cos(45° + 30°)$

$= (\cos 45°)(\cos 30°) - (\sin 45°)(\sin 30°)$

$= \dfrac{\sqrt{2}}{2} \bullet \dfrac{\sqrt{3}}{2} - \dfrac{\sqrt{2}}{2} \bullet \dfrac{1}{2}$

$= \dfrac{\sqrt{6} - \sqrt{2}}{4}$

15. $\sin\dfrac{7\pi}{12} = \sin\left(\dfrac{\pi}{3} + \dfrac{\pi}{4}\right)$

$= \sin\dfrac{\pi}{3}\cos\dfrac{\pi}{4} + \sin\dfrac{\pi}{4}\cos\dfrac{\pi}{3}$

$= \dfrac{\sqrt{3}}{2} \bullet \dfrac{\sqrt{2}}{2} + \dfrac{\sqrt{2}}{2} \bullet \dfrac{1}{2}$

$= \dfrac{\sqrt{6} + \sqrt{2}}{4}$

17. $\sin\left(\dfrac{\pi}{4} + s\right) - \sin\left(\dfrac{\pi}{4} - s\right) = \left(\sin\dfrac{\pi}{4}\cos s + \cos\dfrac{\pi}{4}\sin s\right) - \left(\sin\dfrac{\pi}{4}\cos s - \cos\dfrac{\pi}{4}\sin s\right)$

$= \dfrac{\sqrt{2}}{2}\cos s + \dfrac{\sqrt{2}}{2}\sin s - \dfrac{\sqrt{2}}{2}\cos s + \dfrac{\sqrt{2}}{2}\sin s$

$= \sqrt{2}\sin s$

19. $\cos\left(\dfrac{\pi}{3} - \theta\right) - \cos\left(\dfrac{\pi}{3} + \theta\right) = \left(\cos\dfrac{\pi}{3}\cos\theta + \sin\dfrac{\pi}{3}\sin\theta\right) - \left(\cos\dfrac{\pi}{3}\cos\theta - \sin\dfrac{\pi}{3}\sin\theta\right)$

$= \dfrac{1}{2}\cos\theta + \dfrac{\sqrt{3}}{2}\sin\theta - \dfrac{1}{2}\cos\theta + \dfrac{\sqrt{3}}{2}\sin\theta$

$= \sqrt{3}\sin\theta$

21. (a) First we need to compute $\cos \alpha$ and $\sin \beta$. Since the terminal side of α lies in the second quadrant, $\cos \alpha$ is negative and we have:

$$\cos \alpha = -\sqrt{1 - \sin^2 \alpha}$$
$$= -\sqrt{1 - \frac{144}{169}}$$
$$= -\sqrt{\frac{25}{169}}$$
$$= -\frac{5}{13}$$

Since the terminal side of β lies in the fourth quadrant, $\sin \beta$ is negative and we have:

$$\sin \beta = -\sqrt{1 - \cos^2 \beta}$$
$$= -\sqrt{1 - \frac{9}{25}}$$
$$= -\sqrt{\frac{16}{25}}$$
$$= -\frac{4}{5}$$

Thus:

$$\sin (\alpha + \beta) = \sin \alpha \cos \beta + \cos \alpha \sin \beta$$
$$= \frac{12}{13} \cdot \frac{3}{5} - \frac{-5}{13} \cdot \frac{-4}{5}$$
$$= \frac{36}{65} + \frac{20}{65}$$
$$= \frac{56}{65}$$

(b) $$\sin (\alpha - \beta) = \sin \alpha \cos \beta - \cos \alpha \sin \beta$$
$$= \frac{12}{13} \cdot \frac{3}{5} - \frac{-5}{13} \cdot \frac{-4}{5}$$
$$= \frac{36}{65} - \frac{20}{65}$$
$$= \frac{16}{65}$$

(c) $\cos(\alpha + \beta) = \cos\alpha\cos\beta - \sin\alpha\sin\beta$

$$= -\frac{5}{13} \cdot \frac{3}{5} - \frac{12}{13} \cdot \frac{-4}{5}$$

$$= \frac{-15}{65} + \frac{48}{65}$$

$$= \frac{33}{65}$$

(d) $\cos(\alpha - \beta) = \cos\alpha\cos\beta + \sin\alpha\sin\beta$

$$= -\frac{5}{13} \cdot \frac{3}{5} + \frac{12}{13} \cdot \frac{-4}{5}$$

$$= -\frac{15}{65} - \frac{48}{65}$$

$$= -\frac{63}{65}$$

23.   (a)   For $\frac{3\pi}{2} < \theta < 2\pi$, we have:

$$\sin\theta = -\sqrt{1 - \cos^2\theta} = -\sqrt{1 - \frac{144}{169}} = -\frac{5}{13}$$

(b) $\cos 2\theta = \cos(\theta + \theta)$

$$= \cos\theta\cos\theta - \sin\theta\sin\theta$$

$$= \cos^2\theta - \sin^2\theta$$

$$= \frac{144}{169} - \frac{25}{169}$$

$$= \frac{119}{169}$$

25. $\sec s = \frac{5}{4}$ so $\cos s = \frac{4}{5}$ and $\sin s = -\sqrt{1 - \frac{16}{25}} = -\frac{3}{5}$

$\cot t = -1$ so $\cos t = -\frac{\sqrt{2}}{2}$ and $\sin t = \frac{\sqrt{2}}{2}$

Thus, we have:

$$\sin(s - t) = \sin s \cos t - \sin t \cos s$$

$$= -\frac{3}{5} \cdot \frac{-\sqrt{2}}{2} - \frac{\sqrt{2}}{2} \cdot \frac{4}{5}$$

$$= \frac{3\sqrt{2} - 4\sqrt{2}}{10}$$

$$= -\frac{\sqrt{2}}{10}$$

$$\cos (s + t) = \cos s \cos t - \sin s \sin t$$
$$= \frac{4}{5} \cdot \frac{-\sqrt{2}}{2} - \frac{-3}{5} \cdot \frac{\sqrt{2}}{2}$$
$$= \frac{-4\sqrt{2} + 3\sqrt{2}}{10}$$
$$= -\frac{\sqrt{2}}{10}$$

27. $\dfrac{\sin (s + t)}{\cos s \cos t} = \dfrac{\sin s \cos t + \cos s \sin t}{\cos s \cos t}$

$$= \frac{\sin s}{\cos s} + \frac{\sin t}{\cos t}$$
$$= \tan s + \tan t$$

29. $\cos (A - B) - \cos (A + B)$
$$= (\cos A \cos B + \sin A \sin B) - (\cos A \cos B - \sin A \sin B)$$
$$= \cos A \cos B + \sin A \sin B - \cos A \cos B + \sin A \sin B$$
$$= 2 \sin A \sin B$$

31. $\cos (A + B) \cos (A - B) = (\cos A \cos B - \sin A \sin B)(\cos A \cos B + \sin A \sin B)$
$$= (\cos A \cos B)^2 - (\sin A \sin B)^2$$
$$= \cos^2 A \cos^2 B - \sin^2 A \sin^2 B$$
$$= \cos^2 A (1 - \sin^2 B) - (1 - \cos^2 A) \sin^2 B$$
$$= \cos^2 A - \cos^2 A \sin^2 B - \sin^2 B + \cos^2 A \sin^2 B$$
$$= \cos^2 A - \sin^2 B$$

33. $\cos (\alpha + \beta) \cos \beta + \sin (\alpha + \beta) \sin \beta$
$$= (\cos \alpha \cos \beta - \sin \alpha \sin \beta) \cos \beta + (\sin \alpha \cos \beta + \cos \alpha \sin \beta) \sin \beta$$
$$= \cos \alpha \cos^2 \beta - \sin \alpha \sin \beta \cos \beta + \sin \alpha \sin \beta \cos \beta + \cos \alpha \sin^2 \beta$$
$$= \cos \alpha \cos^2 \beta + \cos \alpha \sin^2 \beta$$
$$= \cos \alpha (\cos^2 \beta + \sin^2 \beta)$$
$$= \cos \alpha$$

35. (a)   We complete the table:

t	1	2	3	4
f(t)	1.5	1.5	1.5	1.5

(b)   Conjecture: $f(t) = 1.5$
To prove this, we first simplify the expressions:

$$\cos\left(t + \frac{2\pi}{3}\right) = \cos t \cos \frac{2\pi}{3} - \sin t \sin \frac{2\pi}{3}$$

$$= -\frac{1}{2}\cos t - \frac{\sqrt{3}}{2}\sin t$$

$$\cos\left(t - \frac{2\pi}{3}\right) = \cos t \cos \frac{2\pi}{3} + \sin t \sin \frac{2\pi}{3}$$

$$= -\frac{1}{2}\cos t + \frac{\sqrt{3}}{2}\sin t$$

So:

$$\cos^2\left(t + \frac{2\pi}{3}\right) = \left(-\frac{1}{2}\cos t - \frac{\sqrt{3}}{2}\sin t\right)^2$$

$$= \frac{1}{4}\cos^2 t + \frac{\sqrt{3}}{2}\sin t \cos t + \frac{3}{4}\sin^2 t$$

$$\cos^2\left(t - \frac{2\pi}{3}\right) = \left(-\frac{1}{2}\cos t + \frac{\sqrt{3}}{2}\sin t\right)^2$$

$$= \frac{1}{4}\cos^2 t - \frac{\sqrt{3}}{2}\sin t \cos t + \frac{3}{4}\sin^2 t$$

Thus:

$$f(t) = \cos^2 t + \left(\frac{1}{4}\cos^2 t + \frac{\sqrt{3}}{2}\sin t \cos t + \frac{3}{4}\sin^2 t\right)$$

$$+ \left(\frac{1}{4}\cos^2 t - \frac{\sqrt{3}}{2}\sin t \cos t + \frac{3}{4}\sin^2 t\right)$$

$$= \frac{3}{2}\cos^2 t + \frac{3}{2}\sin^2 t$$

$$= \frac{3}{2}(\cos^2 t + \sin^2 t)$$

$$= \frac{3}{2}$$

37.   When $f(\theta) = \sin \theta$, then $f(\theta + h) = \sin(\theta + h) = \sin \theta \cos h + \cos \theta \sin h$
So $f(\theta + h) - f(\theta) = \sin \theta (\cos h - 1) + \cos \theta \sin h$

Thus $\dfrac{f(\theta + h) - f(\theta)}{h} = \sin \theta \bullet \dfrac{\cos h - 1}{h} + \cos \theta \bullet \dfrac{\sin h}{h}$

39.   Consider $\dfrac{\sin(A - B)}{\cos A \cos B} = \dfrac{\sin A \cos B - \sin B \cos A}{\cos A \cos B} = \tan A - \tan B$
Hence the given expression is equivalent to:

$$\tan \alpha - \tan \beta + \tan \beta - \tan \gamma + \tan \gamma - \tan \alpha = 0$$

41. Since $a^2 + b^2 = 1$ and $c^2 + d^2 = 1$, then $-1 \leq a \leq 1$ and $-1 \leq c \leq 1$.
     So, choosing θ and ϕ such that $a = \cos \theta$, $c = \cos \phi$, we have:

$$b^2 = 1 - a^2 = 1 - \cos^2\theta = \sin^2\theta$$
$$d^2 = 1 - c^2 = 1 - \cos^2\phi = \sin^2\phi$$

and thus $b = \sin \theta$ and $d = \sin \phi$. Thus:

$$\left| ac + bd \right| = \left| \cos \theta \cos \phi + \sin \theta \sin \phi \right| = \left| \cos (\theta - \phi) \right| \leq 1$$

43. (a)   Using $\triangle ABH$, $\cos (\alpha + \beta) = \dfrac{AB}{1}$, so $\cos (\alpha + \beta) = AB$

     (b)   Using $\triangle ACF$, $\cos \alpha = \dfrac{AC}{AF} = \dfrac{AC}{\cos \beta}$ using #42 (e),

           so $AC = \cos \alpha \cos \beta$

     (c)   Using $\triangle EFH$, $\sin (\angle EHF) = \dfrac{EF}{HF}$. But $\angle EHF = \alpha$ from #42 (c), and

           $HF = \sin \beta$ from #42 (b), so $\sin \alpha = \dfrac{EF}{\sin \beta}$, and thus $EF = \sin \alpha \sin \beta$

     (d) $AB = AC - BC$
           $\cos (\alpha + \beta) = \cos \alpha \cos \beta - \sin \alpha \sin \beta$ from the above three steps

8.4 Further Identities

1.   (a) $\tan \theta = \dfrac{3}{4}$ and $\tan t = \dfrac{7}{24}$, so:

$$\tan (\theta + t) = \frac{\tan \theta + \tan t}{1 - \tan \theta \tan t}$$

$$= \frac{\dfrac{3}{4} + \dfrac{7}{24}}{1 - \dfrac{3}{4} \cdot \dfrac{7}{24}}$$

$$= \frac{\dfrac{25}{24}}{\dfrac{25}{32}}$$

$$= \frac{4}{3}$$

(b) $\tan(\theta - t) = \dfrac{\tan\theta - \tan t}{1 + \tan\theta \tan t}$

$= \dfrac{\dfrac{3}{4} - \dfrac{7}{24}}{1 + \dfrac{3}{4} \bullet \dfrac{7}{24}}$

$= \dfrac{\dfrac{11}{24}}{\dfrac{39}{32}}$

$= \dfrac{44}{117}$

3.   (a) $\tan\theta = \dfrac{3}{4}$ and $\tan\dfrac{\pi}{4} = 1$, so:

$\tan\left(\theta + \dfrac{\pi}{4}\right) = \dfrac{\tan\theta + \tan\dfrac{\pi}{4}}{1 - \tan\theta\tan\dfrac{\pi}{4}}$

$= \dfrac{\dfrac{3}{4} + 1}{1 - \dfrac{3}{4} \bullet 1}$

$= \dfrac{\dfrac{7}{4}}{\dfrac{1}{4}}$

$= 7$

(b) $\tan\left(\theta - \dfrac{\pi}{4}\right) = \dfrac{\tan\theta - \tan\dfrac{\pi}{4}}{1 + \tan\theta\tan\dfrac{\pi}{4}}$

$= \dfrac{\dfrac{3}{4} - 1}{1 + \dfrac{3}{4} \bullet 1}$

$= \dfrac{-\dfrac{1}{4}}{\dfrac{7}{4}}$

$= -\dfrac{1}{7}$

5.　(a)　$\sin\theta = \dfrac{3}{5}$ and $\cos\theta = \dfrac{4}{5}$, so:

$$\begin{aligned}
\sin 2\theta &= 2\sin\theta\cos\theta \\
&= 2 \cdot \dfrac{3}{5} \cdot \dfrac{4}{5} \\
&= \dfrac{24}{25}
\end{aligned}$$

(b)　$$\begin{aligned}
\cos 2\theta &= \cos^2\theta - \sin^2\theta \\
&= \left(\dfrac{4}{5}\right)^2 - \left(\dfrac{3}{5}\right)^2 \\
&= \dfrac{16}{25} - \dfrac{9}{25} \\
&= \dfrac{7}{25}
\end{aligned}$$

(c)　$\tan\theta = \dfrac{3}{4}$, so:

$$\begin{aligned}
\tan 2\theta &= \dfrac{2\tan\theta}{1 - \tan^2\theta} \\[2mm]
&= \dfrac{2 \cdot \dfrac{3}{4}}{1 - \left(\dfrac{3}{4}\right)^2} \\[2mm]
&= \dfrac{\dfrac{3}{2}}{\dfrac{7}{16}} \\[2mm]
&= \dfrac{24}{7}
\end{aligned}$$

Note: An easier approach, after doing (a) and (b), would be to say:

$$\tan 2\theta = \dfrac{\sin 2\theta}{\cos 2\theta} = \dfrac{\dfrac{24}{25}}{\dfrac{7}{25}} = \dfrac{24}{7}$$

7.   (a) $\sin \beta = \frac{4}{5}$ and $\cos \beta = \frac{3}{5}$, so:

$$\sin 2\beta = 2 \sin \beta \cos \beta = 2 \cdot \frac{4}{5} \cdot \frac{3}{5} = \frac{24}{25}$$

(b) $\cos 2\beta = \cos^2 \beta - \sin^2 \beta = \left(\frac{3}{5}\right)^2 - \left(\frac{4}{5}\right)^2 = \frac{9}{25} - \frac{16}{25} = -\frac{7}{25}$

(c) $\tan 2\beta = \dfrac{\sin 2\beta}{\cos 2\beta} = \dfrac{\frac{24}{25}}{-\frac{7}{25}} = \dfrac{-24}{7}$

Note: We could also have used the double-angle formula.

9.   (a) $\sin \frac{\theta}{2}$ is positive and $\cos \theta = \frac{4}{5}$, so:

$$\sin \frac{\theta}{2} = \sqrt{\frac{1 - \cos \theta}{2}}$$

$$= \sqrt{\frac{1 - \frac{4}{5}}{2}}$$

$$= \sqrt{\frac{1}{10}}$$

$$= \frac{\sqrt{10}}{10}$$

(b) $\cos \frac{\theta}{2}$ is positive and $\cos \theta = \frac{4}{5}$, so:

$$\cos \frac{\theta}{2} = \sqrt{\frac{1 + \cos \theta}{2}}$$

$$= \sqrt{\frac{1 + \frac{4}{5}}{2}}$$

$$= \sqrt{\frac{9}{10}}$$

$$= \frac{3\sqrt{10}}{10}$$

(c) $\sin \theta = \dfrac{3}{5}$ and $\cos \theta = \dfrac{4}{5}$, so:

$$\tan \frac{\theta}{2} = \frac{\sin \theta}{1 + \cos \theta} = \frac{\dfrac{3}{5}}{1 + \dfrac{4}{5}} = \frac{3}{9} = \frac{1}{3}$$

Note: We could also have computed this directly after parts (a) and (b), as:

$$\tan \frac{\theta}{2} = \frac{\sin \dfrac{\theta}{2}}{\cos \dfrac{\theta}{2}} = \frac{\dfrac{\sqrt{10}}{10}}{\dfrac{3\sqrt{10}}{10}} = \frac{1}{3}$$

11.   (a) $\sin \dfrac{\beta}{2}$ is positive and $\cos \beta = \dfrac{3}{5}$, so:

$$\sin \frac{\beta}{2} = \sqrt{\frac{1 - \cos \beta}{2}}$$

$$= \sqrt{\frac{1 - \dfrac{3}{5}}{2}}$$

$$= \sqrt{\frac{1}{5}}$$

$$= \frac{\sqrt{5}}{5}$$

(b) $\cos \dfrac{\beta}{2}$ is positive and $\cos \beta = \dfrac{3}{5}$, so:

$$\cos \frac{\beta}{2} = \sqrt{\frac{1 + \cos \beta}{2}}$$

$$= \sqrt{\frac{1 + \dfrac{3}{5}}{2}}$$

$$= \sqrt{\frac{4}{5}}$$

$$= \frac{2\sqrt{5}}{5}$$

(c) $\tan \dfrac{\beta}{2} = \dfrac{\sin \dfrac{\beta}{2}}{\cos \dfrac{\beta}{2}} = \dfrac{\dfrac{\sqrt{5}}{5}}{\dfrac{2\sqrt{5}}{5}} = \dfrac{1}{2}$

13.   We first draw a reference triangle in the second quadrant:

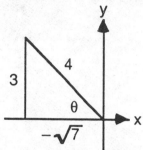

(a) $\sin 2\theta = 2 \sin \theta \cos \theta = 2 \cdot \dfrac{3}{4} \cdot \dfrac{-\sqrt{7}}{4} = -\dfrac{3\sqrt{7}}{8}$

(b) $\cos 2\theta = \cos^2\theta - \sin^2\theta$

$= \left(-\dfrac{\sqrt{7}}{4}\right)^2 - \left(\dfrac{3}{4}\right)^2$

$= \dfrac{7}{16} - \dfrac{9}{16}$

$= -\dfrac{1}{8}$

(c)   Since $\dfrac{\pi}{4} < \dfrac{\theta}{2} < \dfrac{\pi}{2}$, then $\sin \dfrac{\theta}{2}$ is positive:

$\sin \dfrac{\theta}{2} = \sqrt{\dfrac{1 - \cos \theta}{2}}$

$= \sqrt{\dfrac{1 - \left(-\dfrac{\sqrt{7}}{4}\right)}{2}}$

$= \sqrt{\dfrac{4 + \sqrt{7}}{8}}$

$= \dfrac{\sqrt{8 + 2\sqrt{7}}}{4}$

(d)   Since $\dfrac{\pi}{4} < \dfrac{\theta}{2} < \dfrac{\pi}{2}$, then $\cos\dfrac{\theta}{2}$ is positive:

$$\cos\frac{\theta}{2} = \sqrt{\frac{1 + \cos\theta}{2}}$$

$$= \sqrt{\frac{1 - \dfrac{\sqrt{7}}{4}}{2}}$$

$$= \sqrt{\frac{4 - \sqrt{7}}{8}}$$

$$= \frac{\sqrt{8 - 2\sqrt{7}}}{4}$$

15.   We first draw a reference triangle in the third quadrant:

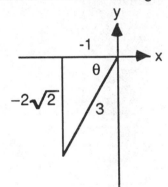

(a) $\sin 2\theta = 2\sin\theta\cos\theta = 2 \cdot \dfrac{-2\sqrt{2}}{3} \cdot \dfrac{-1}{3} = \dfrac{4\sqrt{2}}{9}$

(b) $\cos 2\theta = \cos^2\theta - \sin^2\theta$

$$= \left(-\frac{1}{3}\right)^2 - \left(-\frac{2\sqrt{2}}{3}\right)^2$$

$$= \frac{1}{9} - \frac{8}{9}$$

$$= -\frac{7}{9}$$

(c)   Since $\frac{\pi}{2} < \frac{\theta}{2} < \frac{3\pi}{4}$, then $\sin \frac{\theta}{2}$ is positive:

$$\sin \frac{\theta}{2} = \sqrt{\frac{1 - \cos \theta}{2}}$$

$$= \sqrt{\frac{1 - \left(-\frac{1}{3}\right)}{2}}$$

$$= \sqrt{\frac{2}{3}}$$

$$= \frac{\sqrt{6}}{3}$$

(d)   Since $\frac{\pi}{2} < \frac{\theta}{2} < \frac{3\pi}{4}$, then $\cos \frac{\theta}{2}$ is negative:

$$\cos \frac{\theta}{2} = -\sqrt{\frac{1 + \cos \theta}{2}}$$

$$= -\sqrt{\frac{1 - \frac{1}{3}}{2}}$$

$$= -\sqrt{\frac{1}{3}}$$

$$= -\frac{\sqrt{3}}{3}$$

17.   (a)   Since $0 < \frac{\pi}{12} < \frac{\pi}{2}$, then:

$$\sin \frac{\pi}{12} = \sqrt{\frac{1 - \cos \frac{\pi}{6}}{2}} = \sqrt{\frac{1 - \frac{\sqrt{3}}{2}}{2}} = \frac{\sqrt{2 - \sqrt{3}}}{2}$$

(b)   Since $0 < \frac{\pi}{12} < \frac{\pi}{2}$, then:

$$\cos \frac{\pi}{12} = \sqrt{\frac{1 + \cos \frac{\pi}{6}}{2}} = \sqrt{\frac{1 + \frac{\sqrt{3}}{2}}{2}} = \frac{\sqrt{2 + \sqrt{3}}}{2}$$

(c) $\tan \dfrac{\pi}{12} = \dfrac{\sin \dfrac{\pi}{6}}{1 + \cos \dfrac{\pi}{6}}$

$= \dfrac{\dfrac{1}{2}}{1 + \dfrac{\sqrt{3}}{2}}$

$= \dfrac{1}{2 + \sqrt{3}} \cdot \dfrac{2 - \sqrt{3}}{2 - \sqrt{3}}$

$= \dfrac{2 - \sqrt{3}}{4 - 3}$

$= 2 - \sqrt{3}$

Note: We could also use (a) and (b), as follows:

$\tan \dfrac{\pi}{12} = \dfrac{\sin \dfrac{\pi}{12}}{\cos \dfrac{\pi}{12}}$

$= \dfrac{\dfrac{\sqrt{2 - \sqrt{3}}}{2}}{\dfrac{\sqrt{2 + \sqrt{3}}}{2}}$

$= \dfrac{\sqrt{2 - \sqrt{3}}}{\sqrt{2 + \sqrt{3}}} \cdot \dfrac{\sqrt{2 + \sqrt{3}}}{\sqrt{2 + \sqrt{3}}}$

$= \dfrac{\sqrt{4 - 3}}{2 + \sqrt{3}} \cdot \dfrac{2 - \sqrt{3}}{2 - \sqrt{3}}$

$= \dfrac{2 - \sqrt{3}}{4 - 3}$

$= 2 - \sqrt{3}$

Since using the identity results in less algebraic simplification, we will use that approach.

19.   (a)   Since $90° < 105° < 180°$, then:

$\sin 105° = \sqrt{\dfrac{1 - \cos 210°}{2}} = \sqrt{\dfrac{1 - \left(-\dfrac{\sqrt{3}}{2}\right)}{2}} = \dfrac{\sqrt{2 + \sqrt{3}}}{2}$

(b)   Since $90° < 105° < 180°$, then:

$\cos 105° = -\sqrt{\dfrac{1 + \cos 210°}{2}} = -\sqrt{\dfrac{1 - \dfrac{\sqrt{3}}{2}}{2}} = -\dfrac{\sqrt{2 - \sqrt{3}}}{2}$

(c) $\tan 105° = \dfrac{\sin 210°}{1 + \cos 210°}$

$= \dfrac{-\dfrac{1}{2}}{1 - \dfrac{\sqrt{3}}{2}}$

$= -\dfrac{1}{2 - \sqrt{3}} \cdot \dfrac{2 + \sqrt{3}}{2 + \sqrt{3}}$

$= -\dfrac{2 + \sqrt{3}}{4 - 3}$

$= -2 - \sqrt{3}$

21.   We draw a triangle in the first quadrant:

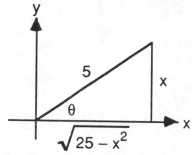

We now apply the double angle formulas:

$\sin 2\theta = 2 \sin \theta \cos \theta$

$= 2 \left(\dfrac{x}{5}\right) \left(\dfrac{\sqrt{25 - x^2}}{5}\right)$

$= \dfrac{2x\sqrt{25 - x^2}}{25}$

$\cos 2\theta = \cos^2\theta - \sin^2\theta$

$= \left(\dfrac{\sqrt{25 - x^2}}{5}\right)^2 - \left(\dfrac{x}{5}\right)^2$

$= \dfrac{25 - x^2}{5} - \dfrac{x^2}{25}$

$= \dfrac{25 - 2x^2}{25}$

23. We draw a triangle in the first quadrant:

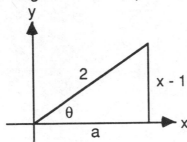

First, we find side a:
$$a^2 + (x - 1)^2 = 4$$
$$a^2 + x^2 - 2x + 1 = 4$$
$$a^2 = 3 + 2x - x^2$$
$$a = \sqrt{3 + 2x - x^2}$$

We now apply the double-angle formulas:
$$\sin 2\theta = 2 \sin \theta \cos \theta$$
$$= 2 \left(\frac{x - 1}{2} \right) \left(\frac{\sqrt{3 + 2x - x^2}}{2} \right)$$
$$= \frac{(x - 1)\sqrt{3 + 2x - x^2}}{2}$$

$$\cos 2\theta = \cos^2\theta - \sin^2\theta$$
$$= \left(\frac{\sqrt{3 + 2x - x^2}}{2} \right)^2 - \left(\frac{x - 1}{2} \right)^2$$
$$= \frac{3 + 3x - x^2}{4} - \frac{x^2 - 2x + 1}{4}$$
$$= \frac{2 + 4x - 2x^2}{4}$$
$$= \frac{1 + 2x - x^2}{2}$$

25. $\sin^4\theta = (\sin^2\theta)^2$

$$= \left(\frac{1 - \cos 2\theta}{2}\right)^2$$

$$= \frac{1 - 2\cos 2\theta + (\cos 2\theta)^2}{4}$$

$$= \frac{1 - 2\cos 2\theta + \dfrac{1 + \cos 4\theta}{2}}{4}$$

$$= \frac{2 - 4\cos 2\theta + 1 + \cos 4\theta}{8}$$

$$= \frac{3 - 4\cos 2\theta + \cos 4\theta}{8}$$

27. $\sin^4\dfrac{\theta}{2} = \left(\sin^2\dfrac{\theta}{2}\right)^2$

$$= \left(\frac{1 - \cos \theta}{2}\right)^2$$

$$= \frac{1 - 2\cos \theta + \cos^2\theta}{4}$$

$$= \frac{1 - 2\cos \theta + \dfrac{1 + \cos 2\theta}{2}}{4}$$

$$= \frac{2 - 4\cos \theta + 1 + \cos 2\theta}{8}$$

$$= \frac{3 - 4\cos \theta + \cos 2\theta}{8}$$

29. (a) $\cos 2\theta = \cos(\theta + \theta)$

$$= \cos \theta \cos \theta - \sin \theta \sin \theta$$

$$= \cos^2\theta - \sin^2\theta$$

(b) $\tan 2\theta = \tan(\theta + \theta)$

$$= \frac{\tan \theta + \tan \theta}{1 - \tan \theta \tan \theta}$$

$$= \frac{2 \tan \theta}{1 - \tan^2\theta}$$

31. $\dfrac{1 - \tan^2 s}{1 + \tan^2 s} \cdot \dfrac{\cos^2 s}{\cos^2 s}$

$$= \dfrac{\cos^2 s - \sin^2 s}{\cos^2 s + \sin^2 s}$$

$$= \cos^2 s - \sin^2 s$$

$$= \cos 2s$$

33. $\cos \theta = \cos \left[2 \left(\dfrac{\theta}{2} \right) \right]$

$$= \cos^2 \dfrac{\theta}{2} - \sin^2 \dfrac{\theta}{2}$$

$$= \cos^2 \dfrac{\theta}{2} - \left(1 - \cos^2 \dfrac{\theta}{2} \right)$$

$$= 2 \cos^2 \dfrac{\theta}{2} - 1$$

35. $\dfrac{1}{8} (3 - 4 \cos 2\theta + \cos 4\theta)$

$$= \dfrac{1}{8} (3 - 4 \cos 2\theta + \cos^2 2\theta - \sin^2 2\theta)$$

$$= \dfrac{1}{8} (3 - 4 \cos 2\theta + 2 \cos^2 2\theta - 1)$$

$$= \dfrac{1}{8} (2 - 4 \cos 2\theta + 2 \cos^2 2\theta)$$

$$= \dfrac{1}{4} (\cos^2 2\theta - 2 \cos 2\theta + 1)$$

$$= \dfrac{1}{4} (\cos 2\theta - 1)^2$$

$$= \dfrac{1}{4} (\cos^2 \theta - \sin^2 \theta - 1)^2$$

$$= \dfrac{1}{4} (\cos^2 \theta - \sin^2 \theta - \sin^2 \theta - \cos^2 \theta)^2$$

$$= \dfrac{1}{4} (-2 \sin^2 \theta)^2$$

$$= \sin^4 \theta$$

37. $\dfrac{2 \tan \theta}{1 + \tan^2 \theta}$

$$= \dfrac{2 \sin \theta}{\cos \theta \left(1 + \dfrac{\sin^2 \theta}{\cos^2 \theta} \right)}$$

$$= \dfrac{2 \sin \theta \cos \theta}{\cos^2 \theta + \sin^2 \theta}$$

$$= 2 \sin \theta \cos \theta$$

$$= \sin 2\theta$$

39. $\sin 2\theta$ $= 2 \sin \theta \cos \theta$

$= 2 \sin \theta \cos \theta (\sin^2\theta + \cos^2\theta)$

$= 2 \sin^3\theta \cos\theta + 2 \sin \theta \cos^3\theta$

41. $\dfrac{1 + \tan \dfrac{\theta}{2}}{1 - \tan \dfrac{\theta}{2}}$ $= \dfrac{1 + \dfrac{\sin \dfrac{\theta}{2}}{\cos \dfrac{\theta}{2}}}{1 - \dfrac{\sin \dfrac{\theta}{2}}{\cos \dfrac{\theta}{2}}}$

$= \dfrac{\cos \dfrac{\theta}{2} + \sin \dfrac{\theta}{2}}{\cos \dfrac{\theta}{2} - \sin \dfrac{\theta}{2}}$

$= \dfrac{\left[\cos \dfrac{\theta}{2} + \sin \dfrac{\theta}{2}\right]^2}{\cos^2 \dfrac{\theta}{2} - \sin^2 \dfrac{\theta}{2}}$

$= \dfrac{1 + 2 \cos \dfrac{\theta}{2} \sin \dfrac{\theta}{2}}{\cos \theta}$

$= \dfrac{1 + \sin \theta}{\cos \theta}$

$= \tan \theta + \sec \theta$

43. $2 \sin^2 (45° - \theta)$ $= 2 [\sin 45° \cos \theta - \cos 45° \sin \theta]^2$

$= 2 \left(\dfrac{\cos \theta - \sin \theta}{\sqrt{2}}\right)^2$

$= 1 - 2 \cos \theta \sin \theta$

$= 1 - \sin 2\theta$

45. $\tan 2\theta \,(\cot \theta - \tan \theta) = (\tan 2\theta)\left(\dfrac{\cos \theta}{\sin \theta} - \dfrac{\sin \theta}{\cos \theta}\right)$

$= (\tan 2\theta)\left(\dfrac{\cos^2\theta - \sin^2\theta}{\sin \theta \cos \theta}\right)$

$= (2 \tan 2\theta)\left(\dfrac{\cos 2\theta}{\sin 2\theta}\right)$

$= 2$

Hence $\tan 2\theta \cot \theta - 1 = \tan 2\theta \tan \theta + 1$

47. (a) $\sin 2A = 2 \sin A \cos A$
$= 2 \sin (90° - B) \cos (90° - B)$
$= 2 \cos B \sin B$
$= \sin 2B$

(b) $\cos 2A = \cos^2A - \sin^2A$
$= [\cos (90° - B)]^2 - [\sin (90° - B)]^2$
$= (\sin B)^2 - (\cos B)^2$
$= -(\cos^2B - \sin^2B)$
$= -\cos 2B$

Hence $\cos 2A + \cos 2B = 0$

(c) $\sin 3A = \sin (2A + A)$
$= \sin 2A \cos A + \cos 2A \sin A$
$= 2 \sin A \cos^2A + \cos^2A \sin A - \sin^3A$
$= 3 \sin A \cos^2A - \sin^3A$
$= 3\left(\dfrac{a}{c}\right)\left(\dfrac{b}{c}\right)^2 - \left(\dfrac{a}{c}\right)^3$
$= \dfrac{3ab^2 - a^3}{c^3}$

49. $\sin (\alpha + 2\beta) = \sin [(\alpha + \beta) + \beta]$
$= \sin (\alpha + \beta) \cos \beta + \sin \beta \cos (\alpha + \beta)$
$= [\sin \alpha \cos \beta + \sin \beta \cos \alpha] \cos \beta$
$= \sin \alpha \cos^2\beta + \cos \alpha \sin \beta \cos \beta$
$= (\sin \alpha)(1 - \sin^2\beta) + \cos \alpha \sin \beta \cos\beta$
$= \sin \alpha + \sin \beta (\cos \alpha \cos \beta - \sin \alpha \sin \beta)$
$= \sin \alpha + \sin \beta \cos (\alpha + \beta)$
$= \sin \alpha$

51. Because $\sin \theta = \dfrac{a^2 - b^2}{a^2 + b^2}$, $\cos \theta = \sqrt{1 - \left(\dfrac{a^2 - b^2}{a^2 + b^2}\right)^2}$

$$= \sqrt{\dfrac{(a^2 + b^2)^2 - (a^2 - b^2)^2}{(a^2 + b^2)^2}}$$

$$= \sqrt{\dfrac{4a^2b^2}{(a^2 + b^2)^2}}$$

$$= \dfrac{2ab}{a^2 + b^2}$$

Thus $\tan \dfrac{\theta}{2} = \dfrac{\sin \theta}{1 + \cos \theta} = \dfrac{a^2 - b^2}{a^2 + b^2 + 2ab} = \dfrac{a^2 - b^2}{(a + b)^2} = \dfrac{a - b}{a + b}$

53. (a) Since:

$$\cos (A - B) = \cos A \cos B + \sin A \sin B$$
$$\cos (A + B) = \cos A \cos B - \sin A \sin B$$

Then:

$$\cos (A - B) - \cos (A + B) = 2 \sin A \sin B$$

Thus $\sin A \sin B = \dfrac{1}{2} [\cos (A - B) - \cos (A + B)]$

(b) Since:

$$\sin (A + B) = \sin A \cos B + \sin B \cos A$$
$$\sin (A - B) = \sin A \cos B - \sin B \cos A$$

Then:

$$\sin (A + B) + \sin (A - B) = 2 \sin A \cos B$$

Thus $\sin A \cos B = \dfrac{1}{2} [\sin (A + B) + \sin (A - B)]$

(c) It follows from (a) that $\cos (A + B) + \cos (A - B) = 2 \cos A \cos B$, thus

$\cos A \cos B = \dfrac{1}{2} [\cos (A + B) + \cos (A - B)]$

55. (a) $\sin \dfrac{\pi}{4} \cos \dfrac{\pi}{12} = \dfrac{1}{2}\left[\sin \dfrac{4\pi}{12} + \sin \dfrac{2\pi}{12}\right]$

$$= \dfrac{1}{2}\left[\sin \dfrac{\pi}{3} + \sin \dfrac{\pi}{6}\right]$$

$$= \dfrac{1}{2}\left[\dfrac{\sqrt{3}}{2} + \dfrac{1}{2}\right]$$

$$= \dfrac{1}{4}(\sqrt{3} + 1)$$

(b) $2 \sin 82.5° \cos 37.5° = \sin 120° + \sin 45°$

$$= \frac{\sqrt{3}}{2} + \frac{\sqrt{2}}{2}$$

$$= \frac{\sqrt{3} + \sqrt{2}}{2}$$

57. If $A + B = \alpha$ and $A - B = \beta$, then $2A = \alpha + \beta$ and $2B = \alpha - \beta$, so:

$$A = \frac{1}{2}(\alpha + \beta) \text{ and } B = \frac{1}{2}(\alpha - \beta)$$

Therefore:

$$\sin A \cos B = \sin \left(\frac{\alpha + \beta}{2} \right) \cos \left(\frac{\alpha - \beta}{2} \right)$$

$$\sin (A + B) + \sin (A - B) = \sin \alpha + \sin \beta$$

Hence #53 (b) implies: $\sin \alpha + \sin \beta = 2 \sin \left(\frac{\alpha + \beta}{2} \right) \cos \left(\frac{\alpha - \beta}{2} \right)$

59. (a) From #58 (b): $\cos \frac{2\pi}{9} + \cos \frac{\pi}{9} = 2 \cos \frac{\pi}{6} \cos \frac{\pi}{18}$

$$= 2 \left(\frac{\sqrt{3}}{2} \right) \cos \frac{\pi}{18}$$

$$= \sqrt{3} \cos \frac{\pi}{18}$$

(b) From #57 : $\sin 105° + \sin 15° = 2 \sin 60° \cos 45°$

$$= 2 \left(\frac{\sqrt{3}}{2} \right) \left(\frac{\sqrt{2}}{2} \right)$$

$$= \frac{\sqrt{6}}{2}$$

61. $\dfrac{\sin 7\theta - \sin 5\theta}{\cos 7\theta + \cos 5\theta} = \dfrac{2 \cos \frac{12\theta}{2} \sin \frac{2\theta}{2}}{2 \cos \frac{12\theta}{2} \cos \frac{2\theta}{2}}$

$$= \frac{\cos 6\theta \sin \theta}{\cos 6\theta \cos \theta}$$

$$= \tan \theta$$

63. (a) Using $\triangle$ ODC, OD $= \cos \theta$ and DC $= \sin \theta$ (recall that OC $= 1$).

Thus, using $\triangle$ ADC, $\tan \dfrac{\theta}{2} = \dfrac{CD}{AD} = \dfrac{\sin \theta}{1 + \cos \theta}$, since AO $= 1$.

(b) $\tan 15° = \dfrac{\sin 30°}{1 + \cos 30°}$

$= \dfrac{\dfrac{1}{2}}{1 + \dfrac{\sqrt{3}}{2}}$

$= \dfrac{1}{2 + \sqrt{3}} \cdot \dfrac{2 - \sqrt{3}}{2 - \sqrt{3}}$

$= \dfrac{2 - \sqrt{3}}{4 - 3}$

$= 2 - \sqrt{3}$

$\tan \dfrac{\pi}{8} = \dfrac{\sin \dfrac{\pi}{4}}{1 + \cos \dfrac{\pi}{4}}$

$= \dfrac{\dfrac{\sqrt{2}}{2}}{1 + \dfrac{\sqrt{2}}{2}}$

$= \dfrac{\sqrt{2}}{2 + \sqrt{2}} \cdot \dfrac{2 - \sqrt{2}}{2 - \sqrt{2}}$

$= \dfrac{2\sqrt{2} - 2}{4 - 2}$

$= \sqrt{2} - 1$

65. (a) We have:

$$\tan (60° - \theta) = \frac{\tan 60° - \tan \theta}{1 + \tan 60° \tan \theta} = \frac{\sqrt{3} - \tan \theta}{1 + \sqrt{3} \tan \theta}$$

$$\tan (60° + \theta) = \frac{\tan 60° + \tan \theta}{1 - \tan 60° \tan \theta} = \frac{\sqrt{3} + \tan \theta}{1 - \sqrt{3} \tan \theta}$$

So:

$$\tan \theta \, \tan (60° - \theta) \, \tan (60° + \theta) = \frac{(3 - \tan^2 \theta) \tan \theta}{1 - 3\tan^2 \theta}$$

Meanwhile:

$$\tan 3\theta = \tan(2\theta + \theta)$$

$$= \frac{\tan 2\theta + \tan \theta}{1 - \tan \theta \tan 2\theta}$$

$$= \frac{\dfrac{2 \tan \theta}{1 - \tan^2\theta} + \tan \theta}{1 - \tan \theta \left(\dfrac{2 \tan \theta}{1 - \tan^2\theta}\right)}$$

$$= \frac{2 \tan \theta + \tan \theta - \tan^3\theta}{1 - \tan^2\theta - 2 \tan^2\theta}$$

$$= \frac{(3 - \tan^2\theta) \tan \theta}{1 - 3 \tan^2\theta}$$

Hence: $\tan \theta \tan(60° - \theta) \tan(60° + \theta) = \tan 3\theta$

(b) Since $\tan 60° = \sqrt{3}$, then letting $\theta = 20°$ in part (a)   implies
$\tan 20° \tan 40° \tan 80° = \sqrt{3}$

67. (a) $\tan A + \tan B + \tan C = \tan 20° + \tan 50° + \tan 110° \approx -1.1918$

$\tan A \tan B \tan C = \tan 20° \tan 50° \tan 110° \approx -1.1918$
It appears that they both equal each other.

(b) $\tan \alpha + \tan \beta + \tan \gamma = \tan \dfrac{\pi}{10} + \tan \dfrac{3\pi}{10} + \tan \dfrac{3\pi}{5} \approx -1.3764$

$\tan \alpha \tan \beta \tan \gamma = \tan \dfrac{\pi}{10} \tan \dfrac{3\pi}{10} \tan \dfrac{3\pi}{5} \approx -1.3764$
Again, they appear to be equal.

(c) Since:

$$\frac{\tan A + \tan B}{1 - \tan A \tan B} = \tan(A + B)$$

And:

$$\tan(A + B) = -\tan[\pi - (A + B)] = -\tan C \quad \text{(recall } A + B + C = \pi)$$

So:

$$\frac{\tan A + \tan B}{1 - \tan A \tan B} = -\tan C$$

$$\tan A + \tan B = -\tan C + \tan A \tan B \tan C$$

$$\tan A + \tan B + \tan C = \tan A \tan B \tan C$$

8.5 Graphs of the Sine and Cosine Functions

1.   period: 2
      amplitude: 1

3.   period: 4
      amplitude: 6

5.   period: 4
      amplitude: 2

7.   period: 6

      amplitude: $\frac{3}{2}$

9.   (a)   y = 2 sin x
             amplitude: 2; period: 2π; x-intercepts: 0, π, 2π

             high point: $\left(\frac{\pi}{2}, 2\right)$; low point: $\left(\frac{3\pi}{2}, -2\right)$

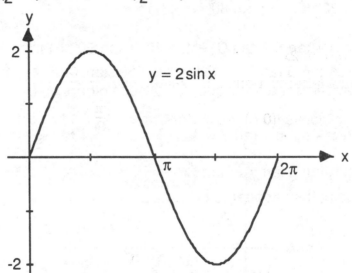

(b) $y = -\sin 2x$

amplitude: 1; period: π; x-intercepts: $0, \dfrac{\pi}{2}, \pi$

high point: $\left(\dfrac{3\pi}{4}, 1\right)$; low point: $\left(\dfrac{\pi}{4}, -1\right)$

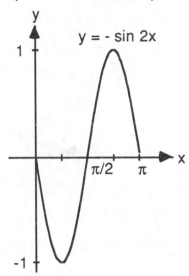

11. (a) $y = \cos 2x$

amplitude: 1; period: π; x-intercepts: $\dfrac{\pi}{4}, \dfrac{3\pi}{4}$

high points: $(0,1)$, $(\pi,1)$; low points: $\left(\dfrac{\pi}{2}, -1\right)$

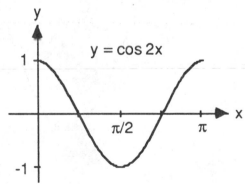

(b) $y = 2 \cos 2x$

amplitude: 2; period: π; x-intercepts: $\dfrac{\pi}{4}$, $\dfrac{3\pi}{4}$

high points: (0,2), (π,2); low points: $\left(\dfrac{\pi}{2}, -2\right)$

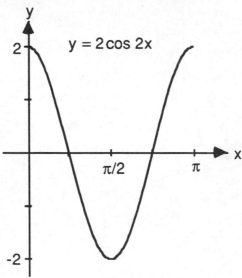

13.   (a) $y = 3 \sin \dfrac{\pi x}{2}$

amplitude: 3; period: 4; x-intercepts: 0, 2, 4
high point: (1,3); low point: (3,-3)

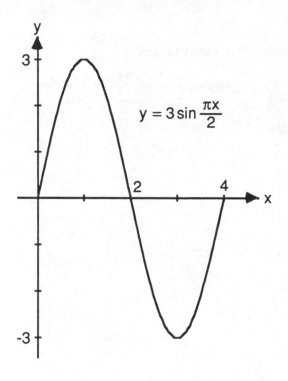

$$y = 3\sin\frac{\pi x}{2}$$

(b) $y = -3\sin\frac{\pi x}{2}$

amplitude: 3; period: 4; x-intercepts: 0,2,4
high point: (3,3); low point: (1,-3)

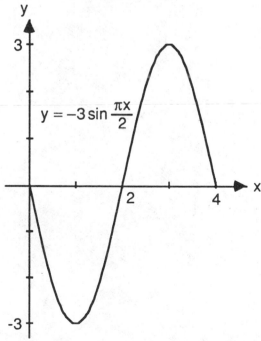

$$y = -3\sin\frac{\pi x}{2}$$

15. (a) $y = \cos 2\pi x$

amplitude: 1; period: 1; x-intercepts: $\frac{1}{4}, \frac{3}{4}$

high points: (0,1), (1,1); low points: $\left(\frac{1}{2}, -1\right)$

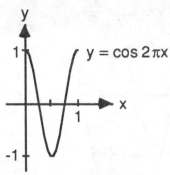

(b) $y = -4\cos 2\pi x$

amplitude: 4; period: 1; x-intercepts: $\frac{1}{4}, \frac{3}{4}$

high point: $\left(\frac{1}{2}, 4\right)$; low points: (0,-4), (1, -4)

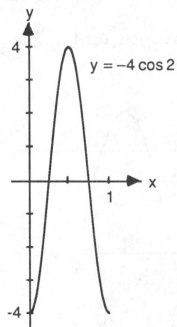

17. $y = 1 + \sin 2x$

amplitude: 1; period: π; x-intercept: $\dfrac{3\pi}{4}$

high point: $\left(\dfrac{\pi}{4}, 2\right)$; low point: $\left(\dfrac{3\pi}{4}, 0\right)$

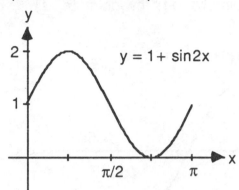

19. $y = 1 - \cos\dfrac{\pi x}{3}$

amplitude: 1; period: 6; x-intercepts: 0, 6
high point: (3,2); low points: (0,0), (6,0)

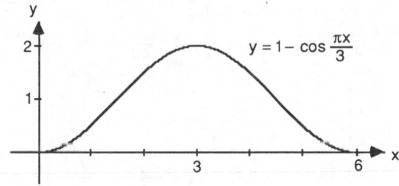

21. $y = \sin\left(2x - \dfrac{\pi}{2}\right)$

amplitude: 1; period: π; phase shift: $\dfrac{\pi}{4}$

x-intercepts: $\dfrac{\pi}{4}, \dfrac{3\pi}{4}, \dfrac{5\pi}{4}$; high point: $\left(\dfrac{\pi}{2}, 1\right)$; low point: $(\pi, -1)$

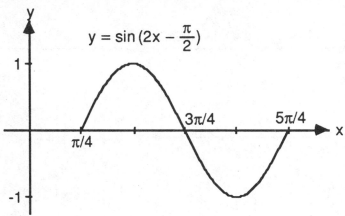

23. $y = \cos(2x - \pi)$

amplitude: 1; period: π; phase shift: $\dfrac{\pi}{2}$

x-intercepts: $\dfrac{3\pi}{4}, \dfrac{5\pi}{4}$; high points: $\left(\dfrac{\pi}{2}, 1\right), \left(\dfrac{3\pi}{2}, 1\right)$; low point: $(\pi, -1)$

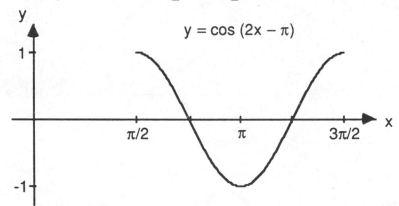

25. $y = 3\sin\left(\dfrac{1}{2}x + \dfrac{\pi}{6}\right)$

amplitude: 3; period: 4π; phase shift: $-\dfrac{\pi}{3}$

x-intercepts: $-\dfrac{\pi}{3}, \dfrac{5\pi}{3}, \dfrac{11\pi}{3}$; high point: $\left(\dfrac{2\pi}{3}, 3\right)$; low point: $\left(\dfrac{8\pi}{3}, -3\right)$

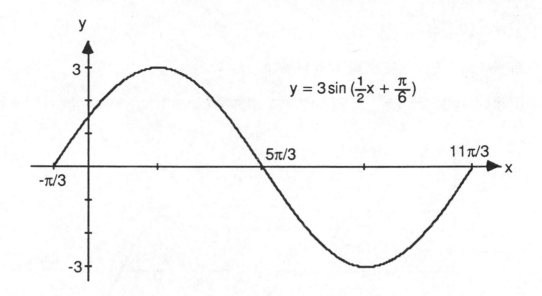

$$y = 3\sin\left(\tfrac{1}{2}x + \tfrac{\pi}{6}\right)$$

27. $y = 4\cos\left(3x - \tfrac{\pi}{4}\right)$

amplitude: 4; period: $\tfrac{2\pi}{3}$; phase shift: $\tfrac{\pi}{12}$

x-intercepts: $\tfrac{\pi}{4}$, $\tfrac{7\pi}{12}$; high points: $\left(\tfrac{\pi}{12}, 4\right)$, $\left(\tfrac{3\pi}{4}, 4\right)$; low point: $\left(\tfrac{5\pi}{12}, -4\right)$

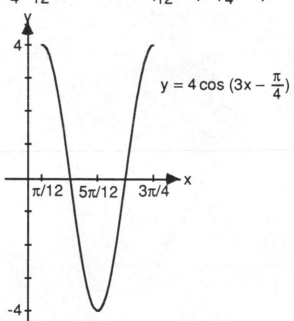

$$y = 4\cos\left(3x - \tfrac{\pi}{4}\right)$$

29. $y = \frac{1}{2} \sin \left(\frac{\pi x}{2} - \pi^2 \right)$

amplitude: $\frac{1}{2}$; period: 4; phase shift: 2π

x-intercepts: 2π, $2\pi + 2$, $2\pi + 4$; high point: $\left(2\pi + 1, \frac{1}{2} \right)$; low point: $\left(2\pi + 3, -\frac{1}{2} \right)$

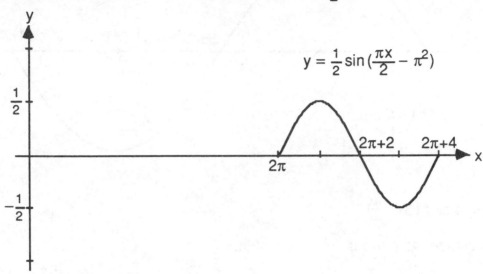

31. $y = 1 - \cos \left(2x - \frac{\pi}{3} \right)$

amplitude: 1; period: π; phase shift: $\frac{\pi}{6}$

x-intercepts: $\frac{\pi}{6}$, $\frac{7\pi}{6}$; high point: $\left(\frac{2\pi}{3}, 2 \right)$; low points: $\left(\frac{\pi}{6}, 0 \right)$, $\left(\frac{7\pi}{6}, 0 \right)$

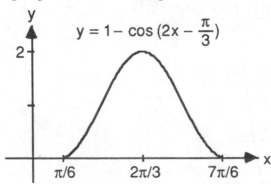

33. (a) Since $\sin \frac{s}{2} = \pm \sqrt{\frac{1 - \cos s}{2}}$, then $\sin x = \pm \sqrt{\frac{1 - \cos 2x}{2}}$

Squaring, we get:

$$\sin^2 x = \frac{1 - \cos 2x}{2}$$

$$\sin^2 x = \frac{1}{2} - \frac{1}{2} \cos 2x$$

(b) amplitude: $\frac{1}{2}$; period: π

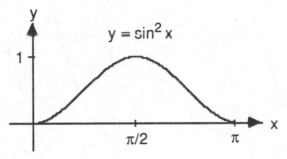

35. $y = \sin x \cos x = \frac{1}{2} \sin 2x$

amplitude: $\frac{1}{2}$; period: π

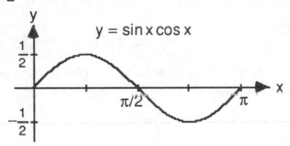

37. (a) Clearly the amplitude is 3. The period is $\dfrac{2\pi}{\dfrac{\pi}{3}} = 6$. For $0 \le t \le 12$,

we get two cycles:

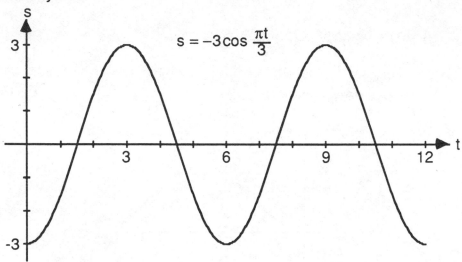

(b) The weight is farthest from the origin when $|s| = 3$. This occurs when $t = 0, 3, 6, 9, 12$ sec.

(c) The weight is positioned at the origin when $s = 0$. This occurs when $t = \dfrac{3}{2}, \dfrac{9}{2}, \dfrac{15}{2}, \dfrac{21}{2}$ sec.

(d) The amplitude here is π, slightly more than 3. The period is 6. For $0 \le t \le 12$, we get two cycles:

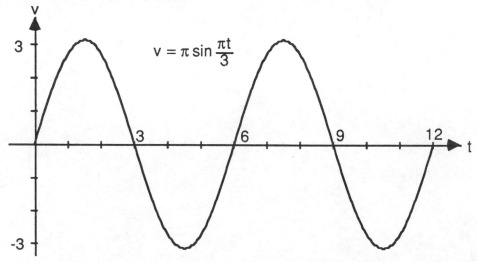

(e)   The velocity is 0 when t = 0, 3, 6, 9, 12 sec. At those values, s is either 3 or -3.

(f)   v < 0 when 3 < t < 6 and 9 < t < 12

(g)   The velocity is greatest at t = $\frac{3}{2}, \frac{15}{2}$, where v ≈ 3.14 ft/sec. The velocity is least at t = $\frac{9}{2}, \frac{21}{2}$, where v ≈ -3.14 ft/sec. At each of these times s = 0.

(h)   We draw the graph:

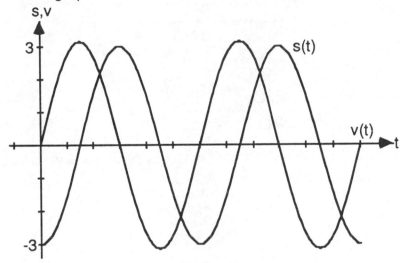

39.   (a)   5 sin (x + δ) = 5 (sin x cos δ + cos x sin δ)

$$= 5\left[\frac{3}{5} \sin x + \frac{4}{5} \cos x\right]$$

= 3 sin x + 4 cos x

(b)   We want to sketch the graph of y = 5 sin (x + δ). The amplitude is 5 and
the period is 2π. Notice that the y-intercept will be 5 sin (0 + δ) = 4. The
phase shift is -δ. Using a calculator, we find that this is approximately
-0.295 π. We draw the graph:

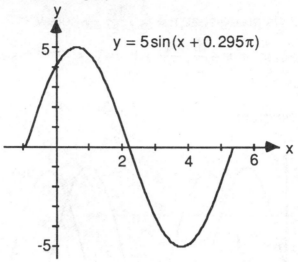

$$y = 5\sin(x + 0.295\pi)$$

8.6 Graphs of the Tangent and the Reciprocal Functions

1.   (a) $y = \tan\left(x + \dfrac{\pi}{4}\right)$

x-intercept: $-\dfrac{\pi}{4}$; y-intercept: 1; asymptotes: $x = -\dfrac{3\pi}{4}$, $x = \dfrac{\pi}{4}$

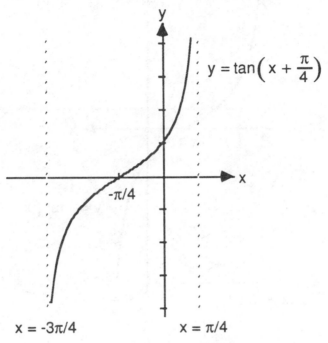

$y = \tan\left(x + \dfrac{\pi}{4}\right)$

$x = -3\pi/4$ $x = \pi/4$

(b) $y = -\tan\left(x + \dfrac{\pi}{4}\right)$

x-intercept: $-\dfrac{\pi}{4}$; y-intercept: -1; asymptotes: $x = -\dfrac{3\pi}{4}$, $x = \dfrac{\pi}{4}$

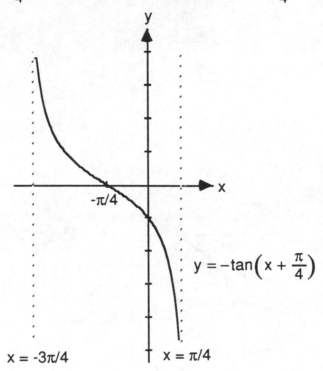

$y = -\tan\left(x + \dfrac{\pi}{4}\right)$

$x = -3\pi/4$

$x = \pi/4$

3.   (a) $y = \tan \dfrac{x}{3}$

x-intercept: 0; y-intercept: 0; asymptotes: $x = -\dfrac{3\pi}{2}$, $x = \dfrac{3\pi}{2}$

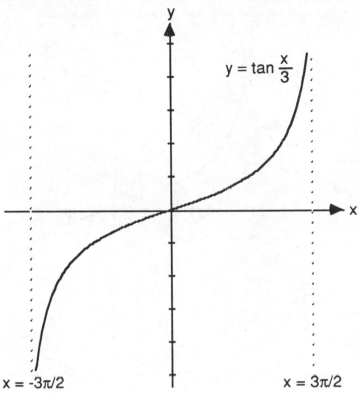

$y = \tan \dfrac{x}{3}$

$x = -3\pi/2$ $x = 3\pi/2$

(b)　$y = -\tan\dfrac{x}{3}$

　　x-intercept: 0; y-intercept: 0; asymptotes: $x = -\dfrac{3\pi}{2}$, $x = \dfrac{3\pi}{2}$

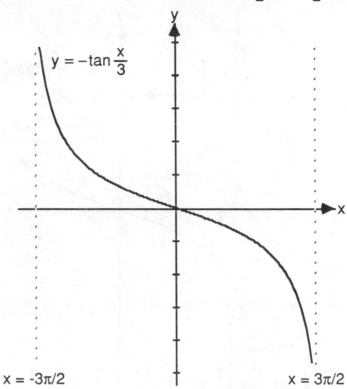

x = -3π/2　　　　　　　　　　　　x = 3π/2

5.　$y = \dfrac{1}{2}\tan\dfrac{\pi x}{2}$

　　x-intercept: 0; y-intercept: 0; asymptotes: $x = -1$, $x = 1$

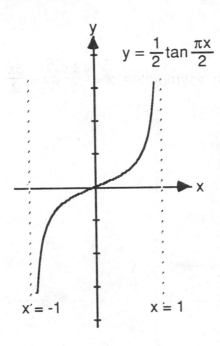

$y = \dfrac{1}{2}\tan\dfrac{\pi x}{2}$

x = -1   x = 1

7. $y = \cot\dfrac{\pi x}{2}$

x-intercept: 1; y-intercept: none; asymptotes: x = 0, x = 2

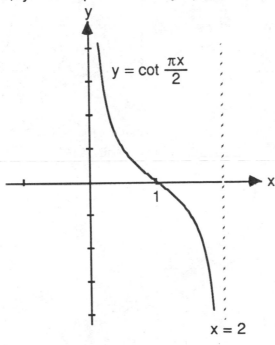

$y = \cot\dfrac{\pi x}{2}$

1

x = 2

9. $y = -\cot\left(x - \frac{\pi}{4}\right)$

x-intercept: $\frac{3\pi}{4}$; y-intercept: 1; asymptotes: $x = \frac{\pi}{4}$, $x = \frac{5\pi}{4}$

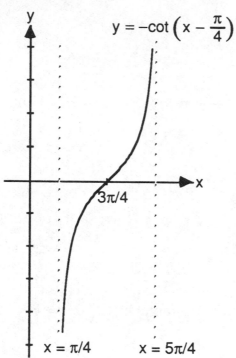

11. $y = \frac{1}{2}\cot 2x$

x-intercept: $\frac{\pi}{4}$; y-intercept: none; asymptotes: $x = 0$, $x = \frac{\pi}{2}$

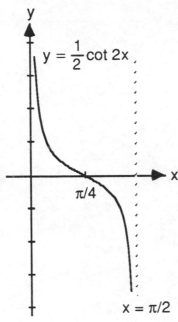

13. $y = \csc\left(x - \dfrac{\pi}{4}\right)$

x-intercept: none; y-intercept: $\sqrt{2}$; asymptotes: $x = -\dfrac{3\pi}{4}$, $x = \dfrac{\pi}{4}$, $x = \dfrac{5\pi}{4}$

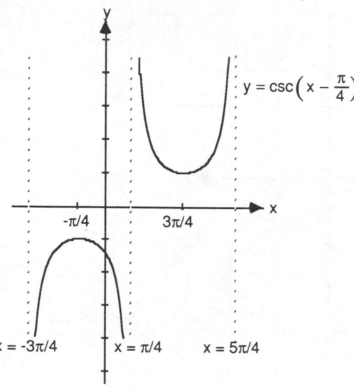

15. $y = -\csc\dfrac{x}{2}$

x-intercept: none; y-intercept: none; asymptotes: $x = -2\pi$, $x = 0$, $x = 2\pi$

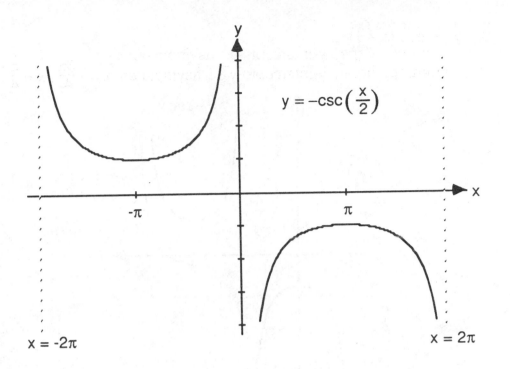

$$y = -\csc\left(\frac{x}{2}\right)$$

$x = -2\pi$ $x = 2\pi$

17. $y = \frac{1}{3}\csc \pi x$

x-intercept: none; y-intercept: none; asymptotes: $x = -1$, $x = 0$, $x = 1$

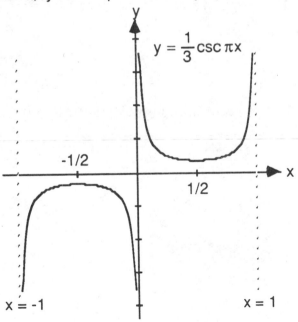

$$y = \frac{1}{3}\csc \pi x$$

$x = -1$ $x = 1$

19. $y = -\sec x$

x-intercept: none; y-intercept: -1; asymptotes: $x = -\dfrac{\pi}{2}$, $x = \dfrac{\pi}{2}$, $x = \dfrac{3\pi}{2}$

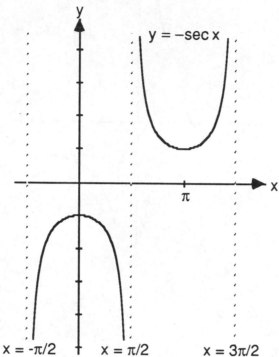

21. $y = \sec(x - \pi)$

x-intercept: none; y-intercept: -1; asymptotes: $x = \dfrac{\pi}{2}$, $x = \dfrac{3\pi}{2}$, $x = \dfrac{5\pi}{2}$

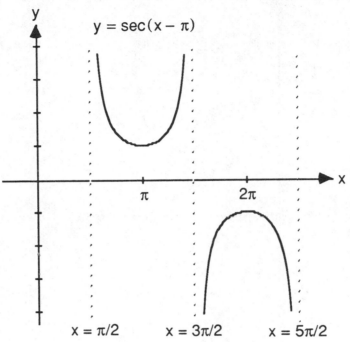

23. $y = 3 \sec \dfrac{\pi x}{2}$

x-intercept: none; y-intercept: 3; asymptotes: x = -1, x = 1, x = 3

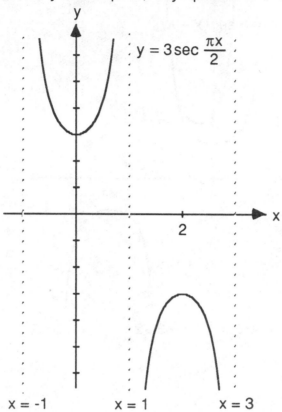

25. $y = 2 \csc \left(2x + \dfrac{\pi}{3}\right) = 2 \csc \left(2 \left(x + \dfrac{\pi}{6}\right)\right)$

period: π; phase shift: $-\dfrac{\pi}{6}$

x-intercept: none; y-intercept: $\dfrac{4\sqrt{3}}{3}$; asymptotes: $x = -\dfrac{2\pi}{3}$, $x = -\dfrac{\pi}{6}$, $x = \dfrac{\pi}{3}$

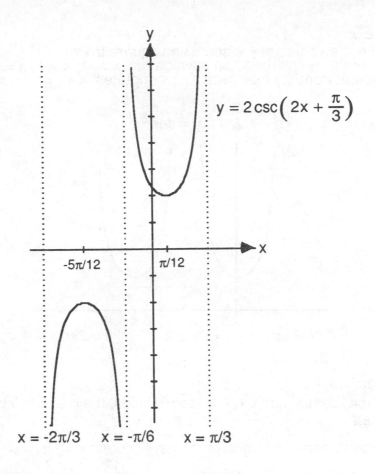

$$y = 2\csc\left(2x + \frac{\pi}{3}\right)$$

-5π/12   π/12

x = -2π/3   x = -π/6   x = π/3

27. y = |tan x|
    We simply take y = tan x and take the absolute value of all y-coordinates.

    x-intercept: 0; y-intercept: 0; asymptotes: $x = -\frac{\pi}{2}$, $x = \frac{\pi}{2}$

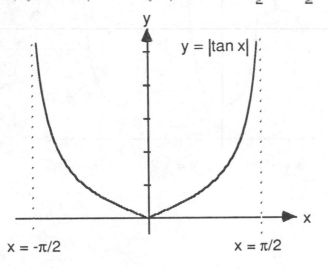

y = |tan x|

x = -π/2   x = π/2

29. (a) $y = \sec^2 x$

We take the values of $y = \sec x$ and square them:

x-intercept: none; y-intercept: 1; asymptotes: $x = -\dfrac{\pi}{2}$, $x = \dfrac{\pi}{2}$, $x = \dfrac{3\pi}{2}$

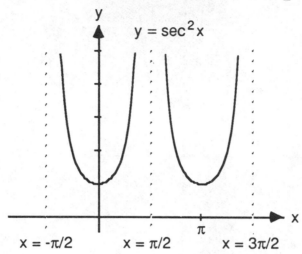

(b) $y = \tan^2 x + 1$

Since the identity $\tan^2 x + 1 = \sec^2 x$ holds, the graph will be the same as in (a).

x-intercept: none; y-intercept: 1; asymptotes: $x = -\dfrac{\pi}{2}$, $x = \dfrac{\pi}{2}$, $x = \dfrac{3\pi}{2}$

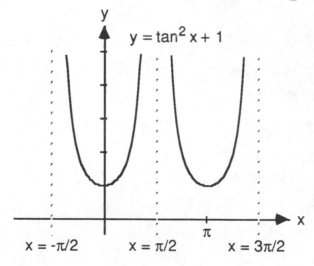

31. (a) $\dfrac{\cos x - \cos 2x}{\sin x + \sin 2x}$

$$= \dfrac{\cos x - (2\cos^2 x - 1)}{\sin x + 2\sin x \cos x}$$

$$= \dfrac{-(2\cos^2 x - \cos x - 1)}{\sin x \,(2\cos x + 1)}$$

$$= \dfrac{-(2\cos x + 1)(\cos x - 1)}{\sin x \,(2\cos x + 1)}$$

$$= \dfrac{1 - \cos x}{\sin x}$$

$$= \tan \dfrac{x}{2}$$

(b) By your own work in (a), the period will be the same as that for

$y = \tan \dfrac{x}{2}$, which is $\dfrac{\pi}{\frac{1}{2}} = 2\pi$

33. $\tan\left(x - \dfrac{\pi}{2}\right) = \dfrac{\sin\left(x - \dfrac{\pi}{2}\right)}{\cos\left(x - \dfrac{\pi}{2}\right)}$

$$= \dfrac{\sin x \cos \dfrac{\pi}{2} - \cos x \sin \dfrac{\pi}{2}}{\cos x \cos \dfrac{\pi}{2} + \sin x \sin \dfrac{\pi}{2}}$$

$$= \dfrac{\sin x \bullet 0 - \cos x \bullet 1}{\cos x \bullet 0 + \sin x \bullet 1}$$

$$= \dfrac{-\cos x}{\sin x}$$

$$= -\cot x$$

So $\cot x = -\tan\left(x - \dfrac{\pi}{2}\right)$

8.7 Trigonometric Equations

1. For $\theta = \dfrac{\pi}{2}$, $2\cos^2\theta - 3\cos\theta = 2(0)^2 - 3(0) = 0$, so $\theta = \dfrac{\pi}{2}$ is a solution.

3. For $x = \dfrac{3\pi}{4}$, $\tan^2 x - 3\tan x + 2 = (-1)^2 + 3 + 2 = 6$, so $x = \dfrac{3\pi}{4}$ is not a solution.

5. $\sin \theta = \frac{\sqrt{3}}{2}$, so $\theta = \frac{\pi}{3}$ and $\theta = \frac{2\pi}{3}$ are the primary solutions. All solutions will be of the form $\theta = \frac{\pi}{3} + 2\pi k$ or $\theta = \frac{2\pi}{3} + 2\pi k$, where k is any integer.

7. $\sin \theta = -\frac{1}{2}$, so $\theta = \frac{7\pi}{6}$ and $\theta = \frac{11\pi}{6}$ are the primary solutions. All solutions will be of the form $\theta = \frac{7\pi}{6} + 2\pi k$ or $\theta = \frac{11\pi}{6} + 2\pi k$, where k is any integer.

9. $\cos \theta = -1$, so $\theta = \pi$ is the primary solution. All solutions will be of the form $\theta = \pi + 2\pi k$, where k is any integer.

11. $\tan \theta = \sqrt{3}$, so $\theta = \frac{\pi}{3}$ is the primary solution. All solutions will be of the form $\theta = \frac{\pi}{3} + \pi k$, where k is any integer.

13. $\tan x = 0$, so $x = 0$ is the primary solution. All solutions will be of the form $x = 0 + \pi k$, or $x = \pi k$, where k is any integer.

15. $2 \cos^2\theta + \cos \theta = \cos \theta (2 \cos \theta + 1) = 0$, so the primary solutions are the solutions of $\cos \theta = 0$ or $\cos \theta = -\frac{1}{2}$, which are $\theta = \frac{\pi}{2}$, $\theta = \frac{3\pi}{2}$, $\theta = \frac{2\pi}{3}$ or $\theta = \frac{4\pi}{3}$. All solutions will be of the form $\theta = \frac{\pi}{2} + \pi k$, $\theta = \frac{2\pi}{3} + 2\pi k$ or $\theta = \frac{4\pi}{3} + 2\pi k$, where k is any integer.

17. $\cos^2 t \sin t - \sin t = \sin t (\cos^2 t - 1) = 0$, thus $\sin t = 0$ or $\cos t = \pm 1$, thus the primary solutions are $t = 0$ or $t = \pi$. All solutions are of the form $t = \pi k$, where k is any integer.

19. $2 \cos^2 x - \sin x - 1 = 2 (1 - \sin^2 x) - \sin x - 1$
$$= -2 \sin^2 x - \sin x + 1$$
$$= (-2 \sin x + 1)(\sin x + 1)$$
So $\sin x = \frac{1}{2}$ or $\sin x = -1$. Thus the primary solutions are $x = \frac{\pi}{6}$, $x = \frac{5\pi}{6}$ or $x = \frac{3\pi}{2}$. All solutions are of the form $x = \frac{\pi}{6} + 2\pi k$, $x = \frac{5\pi}{6} + 2\pi k$ or $x = \frac{3\pi}{2} + 2\pi k$, where k is any integer.

21. $\sqrt{3}\sin t - \sqrt{1 + \sin^2 t} = 0$ is equivalent to $3\sin^2 t = 1 + \sin^2 t$, so $2\sin^2 t = 1$ and thus $\sin^2 t = \frac{1}{2}$ and $\sin t = \pm\frac{\sqrt{2}}{2}$. This would have primary solutions of $\frac{\pi}{4}, \frac{3\pi}{4}, \frac{5\pi}{4}$, or $\frac{7\pi}{4}$, but $\frac{5\pi}{4}$ and $\frac{7\pi}{4}$ do not work in the original equation. So the primary solutions are $t = \frac{\pi}{4}$ or $t = \frac{3\pi}{4}$. All solutions are of the form $t = \frac{\pi}{4} + 2\pi k$ or $t = \frac{3\pi}{4} + 2\pi k$, where k is any integer.

23. If $\cos 3\theta = 1$, then $3\theta = 2\pi k$ for any integer k. So $\theta = \frac{2\pi k}{3}$. Thus the values of θ in the interval [0°, 360°) are 0°, 120°, and 240°.

25. $\sin 3\theta = -\frac{\sqrt{2}}{2}$, so $3\theta = \frac{5\pi}{4} + 2\pi k$ or $\frac{7\pi}{4} + 2\pi k$. Thus $\theta = \frac{5\pi}{12} + \frac{2\pi k}{3}$ or $\frac{7\pi}{12} + \frac{2\pi k}{3}$. So the primary solutions are 75°, 105°, 195°, 225°, 315°, or 345°.

27. $\sin\theta = \cos\frac{\theta}{2}$, and using the hint $2\sin\frac{\theta}{2}\cos\frac{\theta}{2} = \cos\frac{\theta}{2}$, so $\left(\cos\frac{\theta}{2}\right)\left(2\sin\frac{\theta}{2} - 1\right) = 0$, and $\cos\frac{\theta}{2} = 0$ or $\sin\frac{\theta}{2} = \frac{1}{2}$. We have 60° or 300° as solutions, also when $\cos\frac{\theta}{2} = 0$ we have $\frac{\theta}{2} = 90° + 360°k$ or $270° + 360°k$, so $\theta = 180°$. Combining we have $\theta = 60°, 180°$, or 300°.

29. $\sin 2\theta = \sqrt{3}\cos 2\theta$, hence $\tan 2\theta = \sqrt{3}$ and $2\theta = 60° + 180°k$, so $\theta = 30° + 90°k$. Thus $\theta = 30°, 120°, 210°$, or 300°.

31. $\sin\theta = \frac{1}{4}$, hence $\theta = 14.5°$ or 165.5°

33. $2\tan\theta = -4$, so $\tan\theta = -2$, and thus $\theta = 116.6° + 180°k$, hence $\theta = 116.6°$ or 296.6°

35. $\cos^2 x - \cos x - 1 = 0$, so $\cos x = \frac{1 \pm \sqrt{5}}{2}$. Since $\frac{1 + \sqrt{5}}{2} > 1$, the only solutions are those for which $\cos x = \frac{1 - \sqrt{5}}{2}$, and thus $x = 128.2°$ or 231.8°.

37.   Since tan 3x = tan (2x + x)

$$= \frac{\tan 2x + \tan x}{1 - \tan x \tan 2x}$$

$$= \frac{3 \tan x - \tan^3 x}{1 - 3 \tan^2 x}.$$

So tan 3x - tan x $= \dfrac{2 \tan x + 2 \tan^3 x}{1 - 3 \tan^2 x} = 0$

So 2 tan x (1 + tan²x) = 0, thus tan x = 0 since tan²x + 1 ≠ 0. Thus
x = 0, π.

39. $\cos \dfrac{x}{2} = \pm \sqrt{\dfrac{1 + \cos x}{2}} = 1 + \cos x$. Squaring each side, we get

$\dfrac{1 + \cos x}{2} = 1 + 2 \cos x + \cos^2 x$, thus 1 + cos x = 2 + 4 cos x + 2 cos²x.

So   2 cos²x + 3 cos x + 1 = 0, or (2 cos x + 1)(cos x + 1) = 0, thus

cos x = $-\dfrac{1}{2}$ or cos x = -1, and thus x = $\dfrac{2\pi}{3}, \dfrac{4\pi}{3}$, or π. When checking we find

that x = $\dfrac{4\pi}{3}$ is not a solution, and thus the solutions are x = $\dfrac{2\pi}{3}$ or x = π.

41.   sec 4θ + 2 sin 4θ = 0, so $\dfrac{1}{\cos 4\theta}$ = -2 sin 4θ, or 2 sin 4θ cos 4θ = -1 thus

sin 8θ = -1 and thus 8θ = $\dfrac{3\pi}{2}$ + 2πk, so θ = $\dfrac{3\pi}{16} + \dfrac{k\pi}{4}$, where k is any integer.

43.   sin 5x - sin 3x = 0

$2 \cos \dfrac{5x + 3x}{2} \sin \dfrac{5x - 3x}{2} = 0$

2 cos 4x sin x = 0

cos 4x sin x = 0

cos 4x = 0 or sin x = 0

So 4x = $\dfrac{\pi}{2}, \dfrac{3\pi}{2}, \dfrac{5\pi}{2}, \dfrac{7\pi}{2}, \dfrac{9\pi}{2}, \dfrac{11\pi}{2}, \dfrac{13\pi}{2}, \dfrac{15\pi}{2}$, or x = 0, π, 2π. So the

solutions are x = $\dfrac{\pi}{8}, \dfrac{3\pi}{8}, \dfrac{5\pi}{8}, \dfrac{7\pi}{8}, \dfrac{9\pi}{8}, \dfrac{11\pi}{8}, \dfrac{13\pi}{8}, \dfrac{15\pi}{8}$, 0, π, 2π.

45. $\sin 3x = \cos 2x = \sin\left(\frac{\pi}{2} - 2x\right)$, so:

$$\sin 3x - \sin\left(\frac{\pi}{2} - 2x\right) = 2\cos\left(\frac{x}{2} + \frac{\pi}{4}\right)\sin\left(\frac{5x}{2} - \frac{\pi}{4}\right) = 0$$

Hence $\frac{x}{2} + \frac{\pi}{4} = \frac{\pi}{2}, \frac{3\pi}{2}$, or $\frac{5x}{2} - \frac{\pi}{4} = 0, \pi, 2\pi, 3\pi, 4\pi, 5\pi$. So $\frac{x}{2} = \frac{\pi}{4}, \frac{5\pi}{4}$ and

thus $x = \frac{\pi}{2}, \frac{5\pi}{2}$. Or $\frac{5x}{2} = \frac{\pi}{4}, \frac{5\pi}{4}, \frac{9\pi}{4}, \frac{13\pi}{4}, \frac{17\pi}{4}, \frac{21\pi}{4}$ and thus

$x = \frac{\pi}{10}, \frac{\pi}{2}, \frac{9\pi}{10}, \frac{13\pi}{10}, \frac{17\pi}{10}, \frac{21\pi}{10}$. Now $\frac{5\pi}{2}$ and $\frac{21\pi}{10}$ are not in the interval, so

the solutions are $x = \frac{\pi}{10}, \frac{\pi}{2}, \frac{9\pi}{10}, \frac{13\pi}{10}$, or $\frac{17\pi}{10}$.

47. Since $\cos\left(x - \frac{2\pi}{9}\right) = \sin\left[\frac{\pi}{2} - \left(x - \frac{2\pi}{9}\right)\right] = \sin\left(\frac{13\pi}{18} - x\right)$, then:

$$\sin\left(x + \frac{\pi}{18}\right) - \cos\left(x - \frac{2\pi}{9}\right) = \sin\left(x + \frac{\pi}{18}\right) - \sin\left(\frac{13\pi}{18} - x\right)$$

$$= 2\cos\frac{7\pi}{18}\sin\left(x - \frac{\pi}{3}\right)$$

$$= 0$$

Thus $\sin\left(x - \frac{\pi}{3}\right) = 0$, and $x - \frac{\pi}{3} = 0, \pi$ and thus $x = \frac{\pi}{3}$ or $x = \frac{4\pi}{3}$.

49.
$$4\sin\theta - 3\cos\theta = 2$$
$$4\sin\theta = 3\cos\theta + 2$$
$$16\sin^2\theta = 9\cos^2\theta + 12\cos\theta + 4$$
$$16(1 - \cos^2\theta) = 9\cos^2\theta + 12\cos\theta + 4$$
$$16 - 16\cos^2\theta = 9\cos^2\theta + 12\cos\theta + 4$$
$$25\cos^2\theta + 12\cos\theta - 12 = 0$$

This will not factor, so we use the quadratic formula:

$$\cos\theta = \frac{-12 \pm \sqrt{(12)^2 - 4(25)(-12)}}{2(25)}$$

$$= \frac{-12 \pm \sqrt{1344}}{50}$$

$$= \frac{-12 \pm 8\sqrt{21}}{50}$$

$$= \frac{-6 \pm 4\sqrt{21}}{25}$$

So $\cos\theta = .4932$ or $\cos\theta = -.9732$, and thus $\theta = 60.45°$ (the other solution is not in the required interval.)

51. (a) If sin x cos x = 1, then $\sin^2 x \cos^2 x = 1$, and thus $\sin^2 x (1 - \sin^2 x) = 1$
          thus $\sin^2 x - \sin^4 x = 1$, so $\sin^4 x - \sin^2 x + 1 = 0$.

     (b) Using the quadratic formula:
          $$\sin^2 x = \frac{1 \pm \sqrt{1-4}}{2}$$, which has no solutions.
          Alternately, double both sides of the equation to get
          2 sin x cos x = sin 2x = 2, which is impossible.

8.8 The Inverse Trigonometric Functions

1. $\dfrac{\pi}{3}$

3. $\dfrac{\pi}{3}$

5. $-\dfrac{\pi}{6}$

7. $\dfrac{\pi}{4}$

9. undefined

11. $\dfrac{1}{4}$

13. $\dfrac{3}{4}$

15. $-\dfrac{\pi}{7}$

17. $\dfrac{\pi}{2}$

19. 0

21. If $\theta = \sin^{-1}\frac{4}{5}$, then $\sin\theta = \frac{4}{5}$ and we have the triangle:

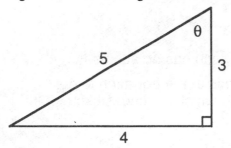

So $\tan\left(\sin^{-1}\frac{4}{5}\right) = \tan\theta = \frac{4}{3}$

23. $\sin(\tan^{-1} 1) = \sin\frac{\pi}{4} = \frac{\sqrt{2}}{2}$

25. We have the triangle:

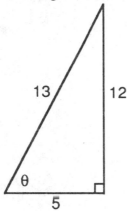

So $\tan\left(\arccos\frac{5}{13}\right) = \tan\theta = \frac{12}{5}$

27. $\cos(\arctan\sqrt{3}) = \cos 60° = \frac{1}{2}$

29. We have the triangle:

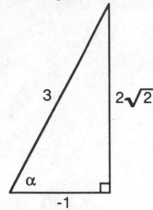

So $\sin\left(\cos^{-1}\left(-\frac{1}{3}\right)\right) = \sin\alpha = \frac{2\sqrt{2}}{3}$

31. (a)   0.84 radians or 48.59°
     (b)   0.84 radians or 48.59°
     (c)   1.26 radians or 72.34°
     (d)   0.90 radians or 51.57°

33. $\sec\left(\cos^{-1}\left(\frac{\sqrt{2}}{2}\right) + \sin^{-1}(-1)\right)$ $= \sec\left(\frac{\pi}{4} - \frac{\pi}{2}\right)$

$= \sec\left(-\frac{\pi}{4}\right)$

$= \dfrac{1}{\cos\left(-\frac{\pi}{4}\right)}$

$= \dfrac{1}{\frac{\sqrt{2}}{2}}$

$= \dfrac{2}{\sqrt{2}}$

$= \sqrt{2}$

35. Let $\theta = \sin^{-1} x$, so we have the triangle:

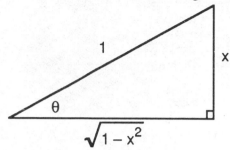

So $\cos (\sin^{-1} x) = \cos \theta = \sqrt{1 - x^2}$

37. Given $\sin \theta = \dfrac{3x}{2}$, we draw the triangle:

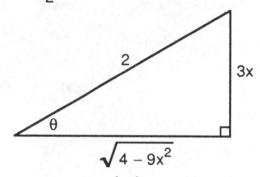

So $\dfrac{\theta}{4} - \sin 2\theta = \dfrac{\sin^{-1}\left(\dfrac{3x}{2}\right)}{4} - 2 \sin \theta \cos \theta$

$= \dfrac{1}{4} \sin^{-1}\left(\dfrac{3x}{2}\right) - 2\left(\dfrac{3x}{2}\right) \cdot \dfrac{\sqrt{4 - 9x^2}}{2}$

$= \dfrac{1}{4} \sin^{-1}\left(\dfrac{3x}{2}\right) - \dfrac{3x\sqrt{4 - 9x^2}}{2}$

39. Given $\tan \theta = \dfrac{x - 1}{2}$, we draw the triangle:

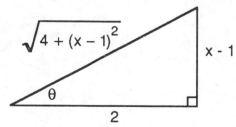

So $\theta - \cos\theta = \tan^{-1}\left(\dfrac{x-1}{2}\right) - \dfrac{2}{\sqrt{4+(x-1)^2}}$

$= \tan^{-1}\left(\dfrac{x-1}{2}\right) - \dfrac{2}{\sqrt{5-2x+x^2}}$

41. Let $\theta = \tan^{-1} 4$, so we have the triangle:

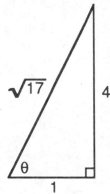

So $\sin(2\tan^{-1} 4)$ $= \sin 2\theta$

$= 2\sin\theta\cos\theta$

$= 4 \cdot \dfrac{4}{\sqrt{17}} \cdot \dfrac{1}{\sqrt{17}}$

$= \dfrac{8}{17}$

43. Let $\alpha = \arccos\dfrac{3}{5}$, so we have the triangle:

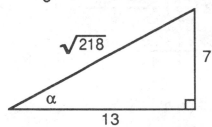

Let $\beta = \arctan \dfrac{7}{13}$, so we have the triangle:

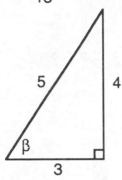

So $\sin \left(\arccos \dfrac{3}{5} - \arctan \dfrac{7}{13} \right) = \sin (\alpha - \beta)$

$$= \sin \alpha \cos \beta - \sin \beta \cos \alpha$$

$$= \dfrac{4}{5} \cdot \dfrac{13}{\sqrt{218}} - \dfrac{7}{\sqrt{218}} \cdot \dfrac{3}{5}$$

$$= \dfrac{31}{5\sqrt{218}}$$

$$= \dfrac{31\sqrt{218}}{1090}$$

45.   Let $A = \tan^{-1} 2$, so we have the triangle:

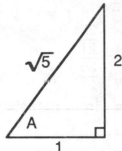

Let B = $\tan^{-1} 3$, so we have the triangle:

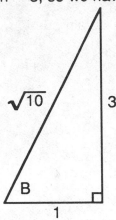

So cos ($\tan^{-1} 2 + \tan^{-1} 3$) = cos (A + B)
$$= \cos A \cos B - \sin A \sin B$$
$$= \frac{1}{\sqrt{5}} \cdot \frac{1}{\sqrt{10}} - \frac{2}{\sqrt{5}} \cdot \frac{3}{\sqrt{10}}$$
$$= -\frac{1}{\sqrt{2}}$$
$$= -\frac{\sqrt{2}}{2}$$

47. Let $\theta = \tan^{-1} \frac{4}{3}$ and $\beta = \tan^{-1} \frac{1}{7}$. Then we have:

$$\tan (\theta - \beta) = \frac{\tan \theta - \tan \beta}{1 + \tan \theta \tan \beta} = \frac{\frac{4}{3} - \frac{1}{7}}{1 + \frac{4}{3} \cdot \frac{1}{7}} = \frac{\frac{25}{21}}{\frac{25}{21}} = 1$$

Thus tan ($\theta - \beta$) = 1. Also, by reasoning that is similar to that used in the solution to #46 we find that $0 < \theta - \beta < \frac{\pi}{2}$, and therefore $\theta - \beta = \frac{\pi}{4}$, as required.

49. Let $\theta = \sin^{-1} x$, with $-1 < x < 1$. Then we have $\sin \theta = x$, where $-\frac{\pi}{2} < \theta < \frac{\pi}{2}$. From the equation $\sin \theta = x$ we obtain $\cos \theta = \pm\sqrt{1 - x^2}$, and since $\cos \theta$ is positive $\left(-\frac{\pi}{2} < \theta < \frac{\pi}{2}\right)$ we have $\cos \theta = \sqrt{1 - x^2}$. Thus we have $\tan \theta = \dfrac{\sin \theta}{\cos \theta} = \dfrac{x}{\sqrt{1 - x^2}}$, and thus $\theta = \tan^{-1} \dfrac{x}{\sqrt{1 - x^2}}$.

Therefore, $\sin^{-1} x = \tan^{-1} \dfrac{x}{\sqrt{1 - x^2}}$, as required.

51. Let $\beta = \tan^{-1} \frac{1}{7}$ and $\theta = \tan^{-1} \frac{1}{3}$. By means of the double angle formula for tangent, we obtain $\tan 2\theta = \frac{3}{4}$. Now we compute:

$$\tan (\beta + 2\theta) = \frac{\tan \beta + \tan 2\theta}{1 - \tan \beta \tan 2\theta} = \frac{\frac{1}{7} + \frac{3}{4}}{1 - \frac{1}{7} \cdot \frac{3}{4}} = 1$$

That is, $\tan (\beta + 2\theta) = 1$. We can conclude from this that $\beta + 2\theta = \frac{\pi}{4}$ if we know $0 < \beta + 2\theta < \frac{\pi}{2}$. Now since $\tan \beta = \frac{1}{7}$ which is less than $\frac{1}{\sqrt{3}}$, we know that $\beta < \frac{\pi}{6}$. Similarly, since $\tan 2\theta = \frac{3}{4} < \frac{\sqrt{3}}{2}$, we know that $2\theta < \frac{\pi}{3}$. Therefore, $\beta + 2\theta$ is less than $\frac{\pi}{6} + \frac{\pi}{3} = \frac{\pi}{2}$. Clearly they are also both positive. In summary, we have $\tan (\beta + 2\theta) = 1$ and $0 < \beta + 2\theta < \frac{\pi}{2}$, which implies that $\beta + 2\theta = \frac{\pi}{4}$. Thus $\tan^{-1} \frac{1}{7} + 2 \tan^{-1} \frac{1}{3} = \frac{\pi}{4}$, as required.

53. Let $\theta = \sin^{-1} x$. Notice that this implies that $-\frac{\pi}{2} < \theta < \frac{\pi}{2}$. Using the equation $\sin \theta = x$, we have $\cos \theta = \pm\sqrt{1 - x^2}$. Since $\cos \theta$ is positive in this interval, then $\cos \theta = \sqrt{1 - x^2}$. Thus:

$$\sin (2 \sin^{-1} x) = \sin 2\theta = 2 \sin \theta \cos \theta = 2x\sqrt{1 - x^2}$$

55. $\tan(\tan^{-1}1 + \tan^{-1}2) = \dfrac{1+2}{1-1(2)} = -3$, and

$\tan(\pi - \tan^{-1}3) = \dfrac{\tan\pi - 3}{1 + 3\tan\pi} = -3$. So we have:

$\qquad \tan^{-1}1 + \tan^{-1}2 + \tan^{-1}3 = \pi + k\pi$ for some k

However we know that all three angles lie in $\left(0, \dfrac{\pi}{2}\right)$, and so their sum must lie in

$\left(0, \dfrac{3\pi}{2}\right)$, and thus k = 0. Hence $\tan^{-1}1 + \tan^{-1}2 + \tan^{-1}3 = \pi$.

57.   (a)   Letting $y = \tan^{-1}x$, then $\tan 2y = \dfrac{2\tan y}{1 - \tan^2 y}$, so:

$\qquad \tan^{-1}[\tan 2y] = \tan^{-1}\left[\dfrac{2\tan y}{1 - \tan^2 y}\right] = \tan^{-1}\left[\dfrac{2x}{1 - x^2}\right]$

$\qquad 2y = 2\tan^{-1}x = \tan^{-1}\left[\dfrac{2x}{1 - x^2}\right]$

(b)   From (a):

$$2\tan^{-1}\dfrac{1}{5} = \tan^{-1}\left[\dfrac{\dfrac{2}{5}}{1 - \dfrac{1}{25}}\right] = \tan^{-1}\dfrac{5}{12}$$

Again applying the formula from (a):

$$4\tan^{-1}\dfrac{1}{5} = 2\tan^{-1}\dfrac{5}{12}$$

$$= \tan^{-1}\left[\dfrac{2 \cdot \dfrac{5}{12}}{1 - \left(\dfrac{5}{12}\right)^2}\right]$$

$$= \tan^{-1}\dfrac{120}{119}$$

(c) $4\tan^{-1}\dfrac{1}{5} - \tan^{-1}\dfrac{1}{239} = \tan^{-1}\dfrac{120}{119} - \tan^{-1}\dfrac{1}{239}$

Using the formula $\tan^{-1}x - \tan^{-1}y = \tan^{-1}\left[\dfrac{x-y}{1+xy}\right]$, proved in a

similar fashion to #45, we have the expression becoming:

$$\tan^{-1}\left[\dfrac{\dfrac{120}{119} - \dfrac{1}{239}}{1 + \dfrac{120}{119} \cdot \dfrac{1}{239}}\right] = \tan^{-1}1 = \dfrac{\pi}{4}$$

Chapter 8 Review Exercises

1. $\dfrac{3\pi}{4} \cdot \dfrac{360°}{2\pi} = 135°$

3. $5\pi \cdot \dfrac{360°}{2\pi} = 900°$

5. $\dfrac{5\pi}{6} \cdot \dfrac{360°}{2\pi} = 150°$

7. $2 \cdot \dfrac{360°}{2\pi} = \dfrac{360°}{\pi}$

9. $360° \cdot \dfrac{2\pi \text{ radians}}{360°} = 2\pi \text{ radians}$

11. $1° \cdot \dfrac{2\pi \text{ radians}}{360°} = \dfrac{\pi}{180} \text{ radians}$

13. $7.5° \cdot \dfrac{2\pi \text{ radians}}{360°} = \dfrac{\pi}{24} \text{ radians}$

15. $\dfrac{1}{\pi}^{°} \cdot \dfrac{2\pi \text{ radians}}{360°} = \dfrac{1}{180} \text{ radians}$

17. $\cos \pi = -1$

19. $\csc \dfrac{2\pi}{3} = \dfrac{1}{\sin \dfrac{2\pi}{3}} = \dfrac{1}{\dfrac{\sqrt{3}}{2}} = \dfrac{2}{\sqrt{3}} = \dfrac{2\sqrt{3}}{3}$

21. $\cot \dfrac{11\pi}{6} = \dfrac{\cos \dfrac{11\pi}{6}}{\sin \dfrac{11\pi}{6}} = \dfrac{\dfrac{\sqrt{3}}{2}}{-\dfrac{1}{2}} = -\sqrt{3}$

23. $\sin \dfrac{\pi}{6} = \dfrac{1}{2}$

25. $\cot \dfrac{5\pi}{4} = 1$

27. $\csc\left(-\dfrac{5\pi}{6}\right) = \dfrac{1}{\sin\left(-\dfrac{5\pi}{6}\right)} = \dfrac{1}{-\dfrac{1}{2}} = -2$

29. $s = r\theta = 16 \cdot \dfrac{\pi}{8}$ cm $= 2\pi$ cm

    $A = \dfrac{1}{2}r^2\theta = \dfrac{1}{2}(16)^2 \cdot \dfrac{\pi}{8}$ cm^2 $= 16\pi$ cm^2

31. $\theta = \dfrac{s}{r} = 1$, so $A = \dfrac{1}{2}r^2\theta = \dfrac{1}{2}(1)^2(1)$ cm^2 $= \dfrac{1}{2}$ cm^2

33. $r = \dfrac{s}{\theta} = \dfrac{4 \text{ cm}}{\dfrac{\pi}{5}} = \dfrac{20}{\pi}$ cm

    $A = \dfrac{1}{2}r^2\theta = \dfrac{1}{2}\left(\dfrac{20}{\pi} \text{ cm}\right)^2 \left(\dfrac{\pi}{5}\right) = \dfrac{1}{2}\left(\dfrac{400}{\pi^2} \text{ cm}^2\right)\left(\dfrac{\pi}{5}\right) = \dfrac{40}{\pi}$ cm^2

35. $s = r\theta$, so $12 = r\theta = r(r + 1)$, hence:
    $$r^2 + r - 12 = 0$$
    $$(r + 4)(r - 3) = 0$$
    So r = 3 cm (since r cannot be negative), and θ = 4 radians.

37. $180° - (40° + 70°) = 70°$, but $70° \cdot \dfrac{\pi}{180°} = \dfrac{7\pi}{18}$ radians

39. $\sin 1 \approx 0.841$

41. $\sin\dfrac{3\pi}{2} = -1.000$

43. $\sin(\sin(0.0123)) \approx 0.012$

45. $\sin^2 1986 + \cos^2 1986 \approx 0.241 + 0.759 = 1.000$

47. $\cos 0.5 \approx 0.878$ while $\cos^2 0.25 \approx 0.939$ and $\sin^2 0.25 \approx 0.061$, so:
    $\cos^2 0.25 - \sin^2 0.25 \approx 0.878 \approx \cos 0.5$

49. $\sqrt{25 - x^2}$ $= \sqrt{25 - 25 \sin^2\theta}$

$= 5\sqrt{1 - \sin^2\theta}$

$= 5\sqrt{\cos^2\theta}$

$= 5\cos\theta$

51. $(x^2 - 100)^{1/2} = (100\sec^2\theta - 100)^{1/2}$

$= 10(\sec^2\theta - 1)^{1/2}$

$= 10(\tan^2\theta)^{1/2}$

$= 10\tan\theta$

53. $(x^2 + 5)^{-1/2} = (5\tan^2\theta + 5)^{-1/2}$

$= \dfrac{\sqrt{5}}{5}(\sec^2\theta)^{-1/2}$

$= \dfrac{\sqrt{5}}{5}\cos\theta$

55. $\sin\theta = \dfrac{3}{5}$, so $\cos\theta = \sqrt{1 - \left(\dfrac{3}{5}\right)^2} = \sqrt{\dfrac{16}{25}} = \dfrac{4}{5}$. Thus:

$$\sin\dfrac{\theta}{2} = \sqrt{\dfrac{1 - \cos\theta}{2}} = \sqrt{\dfrac{1 - \dfrac{4}{5}}{2}} = \sqrt{\dfrac{1}{10}} = \dfrac{\sqrt{10}}{10}$$

57. If $\tan\theta = \dfrac{7}{24}$, then $\cos\theta = \dfrac{24}{25}$ and $\sin\theta = \dfrac{7}{25}$. So:

$\cos 2\theta = \cos^2\theta - \sin^2\theta$

$= \left(\dfrac{24}{25}\right)^2 - \left(\dfrac{7}{25}\right)^2$

$= \dfrac{576 - 49}{625}$

$= \dfrac{527}{625}$

59. $\csc\theta = \dfrac{29}{20}$, so $\sin\theta = \dfrac{20}{29}$ and:

$$\cos\theta = -\sqrt{1 - \left(\dfrac{20}{29}\right)^2} = -\sqrt{1 - \dfrac{400}{841}} = -\dfrac{441}{841} = -\dfrac{21}{29}$$

So $\dfrac{\pi}{2} < \theta < \pi$ and $\cos\dfrac{\theta}{2} = \sqrt{\dfrac{1 + \left(-\dfrac{21}{29}\right)}{2}} = \sqrt{\dfrac{8}{58}} = \dfrac{2\sqrt{29}}{29}$

61. $\sec^2 2\theta = 1 + \tan^2 2\theta = 1 + \left(\dfrac{7}{24}\right)^2 = \dfrac{625}{576}$, hence $\cos^2 2\theta = \dfrac{576}{625}$ and thus

   $\cos 2\theta = -\dfrac{24}{25}$ (note that $\pi < 2\theta < \dfrac{3\pi}{2}$). Thus:

$$1 - 2\sin^2\theta = -\dfrac{24}{25}$$
$$\sin^2\theta = \dfrac{49}{50}$$
$$\sin\theta = \dfrac{7}{5\sqrt{2}} = \dfrac{7\sqrt{2}}{10}$$

63.   Using the hint, we have two congruent shaded regions each with $r = 1$ cm and
   $\theta = \dfrac{\pi}{2}$, and thus the total area is:

$$2 \bullet \dfrac{1}{2} \text{ cm}^2 \left(\dfrac{\pi}{2} - 1\right) = \dfrac{\pi - 2}{2} \text{ cm}^2$$

65.   (a) $\cos 37° + \cos 35° \approx 1.62$ while $\cos 1° + \sin 19° + \sin 17° \approx 1.618$

   (b) $\cos 40° + \cos 32° \approx 1.61$ while $\cos 4° + \sin 22° + \sin 14° \approx 1.614$

   (c) $\cos 42° + \cos 30° \approx 1.61$ while $\cos 6° + \sin 24° + \sin 12° \approx 1.609$

67. $(\sin x + \cos x)^2 + (\sin x - \cos x)^2$
   $= (\sin^2 x + 2\sin x \cos x + \cos^2 x) + (\sin^2 x - 2\sin x \cos x + \cos^2 x)$
   $= 2(\sin^2 x + \cos^2 x)$
   $= 2$

69. $(\cos x + \sin x - 1)(\cos x + \sin x + 1)$
   $= (\cos x + \sin x)^2 - 1$
   $= \cos^2 x + 2\sin x \cos x + \sin^2 x - 1$
   $= 2\sin x \cos x$

71. $(9 - 4\sin x - \cos^2 x)(9 + 4\sin x - \cos^2 x)$
   $= (9 - \cos^2 x)^2 - (4\sin x)^2$
   $= 81 - 18\cos^2 x + \cos^4 x - 16\sin^2 x$
   $= 81 + \cos^4 x - 16 - 2\cos^2 x$
   $= 65 + (1 - \sin^2 x)^2 - 2(1 - \sin^2 x)$
   $= 65 + 1 - 2\sin^2 x + \sin^4 x - 2 + 2\sin^2 x$
   $= 64 + \sin^4 x$

73. $(a \sin x - b \cos x)^2 + (a \cos x + b \sin x)^2$
$\quad = a^2\sin^2x - 2ab \cos x \sin x + b^2\cos^2x + a^2\cos^2x + 2ab \cos x \sin x + b^2\sin^2x$
$\quad = (a^2 + b^2) \sin^2x + (a^2 + b^2) \cos^2x$
$\quad = a^2 + b^2$

75. $\tan A = \dfrac{12}{5}$ implies that $\sin A = \dfrac{12}{13}$ and $\cos A = \dfrac{5}{13}$

$\tan B = \dfrac{3}{4}$ implies that $\sin B = \dfrac{3}{5}$ and $\cos B = \dfrac{4}{5}$

So $\cos (A + B) = \cos A \cos B - \sin A \sin B$
$$= \frac{5}{13} \cdot \frac{4}{5} - \frac{12}{13} \cdot \frac{3}{5}$$
$$= \frac{20}{65} - \frac{36}{65}$$
$$= -\frac{16}{65}$$

77. $\sin (\pi - x) = \sin \pi \cos x - \cos \pi \sin x$
$\qquad\qquad\;\; = 0 (\cos x) - (-1) \sin x$
$\qquad\qquad\;\; = \sin x$

79. $\sin (10° + 80°) = \sin (90°) = 1$

81. $\cos \left(\dfrac{2\pi}{5} + \dfrac{\pi}{10}\right) = \cos \dfrac{5\pi}{10} = \cos \dfrac{\pi}{2} = 0$

83. $2 \sin \dfrac{\pi}{6} \cos x = 2 \cdot \dfrac{1}{2} \cdot \cos x = \cos x$

85. $\tan y = \tan (x + 60°) = \dfrac{\tan x + \sqrt{3}}{1 - \sqrt{3} \tan x}$

$\tan z = \tan (x - 60°) = \dfrac{\tan x - \sqrt{3}}{1 + \sqrt{3} \tan x}$

We will first simplify each of the quantities:
$$\tan x \tan y = \frac{(\tan x)(\tan x + \sqrt{3})}{1 - \sqrt{3} \tan x}$$
$$= \frac{(\tan x)(\tan x + \sqrt{3})(1 + \sqrt{3} \tan x)}{1 - 3 \tan^2x}$$
$$= \frac{\sqrt{3} \tan^3x + 4 \tan^2x + \sqrt{3} \tan x}{1 - 3 \tan^2x}$$

$$\tan y \tan z = \frac{\tan x + \sqrt{3}}{1 - \sqrt{3} \tan x} \cdot \frac{\tan x - \sqrt{3}}{1 + \sqrt{3} \tan x}$$

$$= \frac{\tan^2 x - 3}{1 - 3 \tan^2 x}$$

$$\tan x \tan z = \frac{(\tan x)(\tan x - \sqrt{3})}{1 + \sqrt{3} \tan x}$$

$$= \frac{(\tan x)(\tan x - \sqrt{3})(1 - \sqrt{3} \tan x)}{1 - 3 \tan^2 x}$$

$$= \frac{-\sqrt{3} \tan^3 x + 4 \tan^2 x - \sqrt{3} \tan x}{1 - 3 \tan^2 x}$$

Adding these three quantities and combining like terms, we get:

$$\frac{8 \tan^2 x + \tan^2 x - 3}{1 - 3 \tan^2 x} = \frac{9 \tan^2 x - 3}{1 - 3 \tan^2 x}$$

$$= \frac{3(3 \tan^2 x - 1)}{-1(3 \tan^2 x - 1)}$$

$$= -3$$

87. $\sin (x + y + z)$

$= \sin (x + y) \cos z + \sin z \cos (x + y)$

$= \cos z (\sin x \cos y + \sin y \cos x) + \sin z (\cos x \cos y - \sin x \sin y)$

$= \dfrac{15}{17} \cdot \dfrac{3}{5} \cdot \dfrac{12}{13} + \dfrac{15}{17} \cdot \dfrac{5}{13} \cdot \dfrac{4}{5} + \dfrac{8}{17} \cdot \dfrac{4}{5} \cdot \dfrac{12}{13} - \dfrac{8}{17} \cdot \dfrac{3}{5} \cdot \dfrac{5}{13}$

$= \dfrac{540 + 300 + 384 - 120}{1105}$

$= \dfrac{1104}{1105}$

89.   A = 4 and B =1, so the equation is $y = 4 \sin x$

91.   A = -2 and $\dfrac{2\pi}{B} = \dfrac{\pi}{2}$, so B = 4. So the equation is y = -2 cos 4x.

93.   Since $\sqrt{2} = A \sin \left(\dfrac{3\pi}{2} - \pi \right) = A \sin \dfrac{\pi}{2} = A$, then the amplitude is $\sqrt{2}$.

95. $y = -3 \cos 4x$

x-intercepts: $\dfrac{\pi}{8}, \dfrac{3\pi}{8}$; high point: $\left(\dfrac{\pi}{4}, 3\right)$; low points: $(0,-3)$, $\left(\dfrac{\pi}{2}, -3\right)$

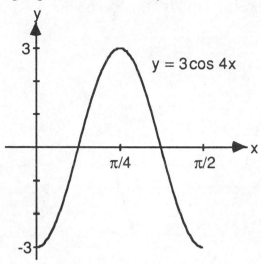

$y = 3\cos 4x$

97. $y = 2 \sin\left(\dfrac{\pi x}{2} - \dfrac{\pi}{4}\right)$

x-intercepts: $\dfrac{1}{2}, \dfrac{5}{2}, \dfrac{9}{2}$; high point: $\left(\dfrac{3}{2}, 2\right)$; low point: $\left(\dfrac{7}{2}, -2\right)$

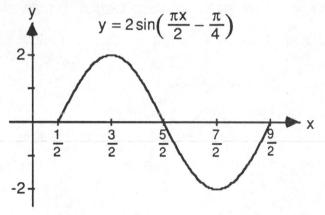

$y = 2\sin\left(\dfrac{\pi x}{2} - \dfrac{\pi}{4}\right)$

99. $y = 3\cos\left(\dfrac{\pi x}{3} - \dfrac{\pi}{3}\right)$

x-intercepts: $\dfrac{5}{2}, \dfrac{9}{2}$; high points: (1,3), (7,3); low point: (4,-3)

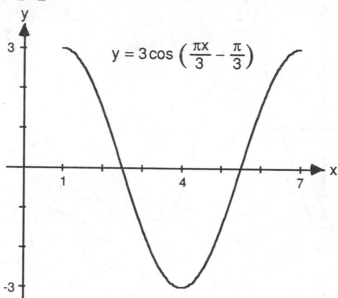

101. $y = -\cos 2x \sin 2x = -\dfrac{1}{2}\sin 4x$ by the double angle identity

x-intercepts: $0, \dfrac{\pi}{4}, \dfrac{\pi}{2}$; high point: $\left(\dfrac{3\pi}{8}, \dfrac{1}{2}\right)$; low point: $\left(\dfrac{\pi}{8}, -\dfrac{1}{2}\right)$

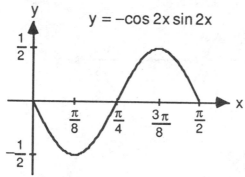

103. (a) $y = \tan \dfrac{\pi x}{4}$

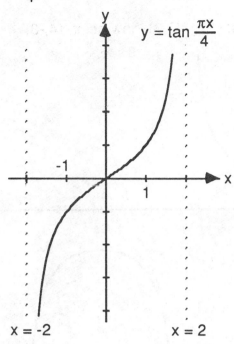

(b) $y = \cot \dfrac{\pi x}{4}$

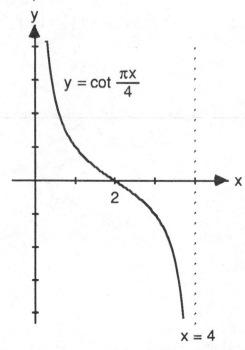

105. (a) $y = 3 \sec \dfrac{x}{4}$

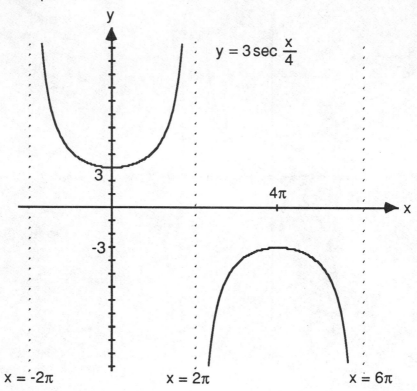

$y = 3 \sec \dfrac{x}{4}$

(b) $y = 3 \csc \dfrac{x}{4}$

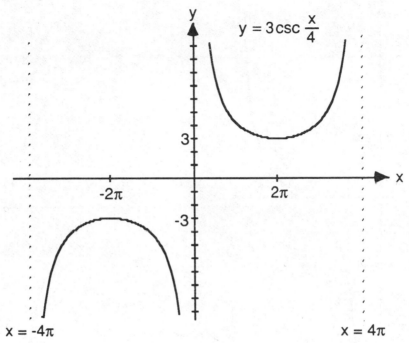

107. $y = \tan(x - 2)$

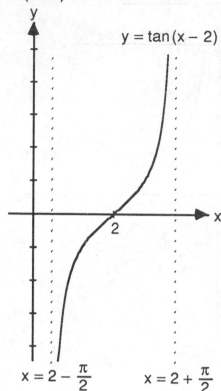

$y = \tan(x - 2)$

$x = 2 - \dfrac{\pi}{2}$ $x = 2 + \dfrac{\pi}{2}$

109. $\cot(x + y) = \dfrac{1}{\tan(x+y)}$

$\quad\quad = \dfrac{1 - \tan x \tan y}{\tan x + \tan y} \cdot \dfrac{\cot x \cot y}{\cot x \cot y}$

$\quad\quad = \dfrac{\cot x \cot y - 1}{\cot y + \cot x}$

111. $\dfrac{2 \tan x}{1 + \tan^2 x} \cdot \dfrac{\cos^2 x}{\cos^2 x} \quad = \dfrac{2 \sin x \cos x}{\cos^2 x + \sin^2 x}$

$\quad\quad\quad\quad\quad\quad\quad = 2 \sin x \cos x$

$\quad\quad\quad\quad\quad\quad\quad = \sin 2x$

113. Using the result from exercise #112, we have:

$\dfrac{\sin(x+y)\sin(x-y)}{\cos^2 x \cos^2 y} \quad = \dfrac{\sin^2 x \cos^2 y - \cos^2 x \sin^2 y}{\cos^2 x \cos^2 y}$

$\quad\quad\quad\quad\quad = \dfrac{\sin^2 x}{\cos^2 x} - \dfrac{\sin^2 y}{\cos^2 y}$

$\quad\quad\quad\quad\quad = \tan^2 x - \tan^2 y$

115. $\sin x \left(\tan \dfrac{x}{2} + \cot \dfrac{x}{2}\right) = \sin x \left[\dfrac{\sin x}{1 + \cos x} + \dfrac{1 + \cos x}{\sin x}\right]$

$$= \sin x \left[\dfrac{\sin^2 x + 1 + 2\cos x + \cos^2 x}{(\sin x)(1 + \cos x)}\right]$$

$$= \sin x \left[\dfrac{2 + 2\cos x}{\sin x (1 + \cos x)}\right]$$

$$= 2$$

117. Since $\tan\left(\dfrac{\pi}{4} - x\right) = \dfrac{\tan \dfrac{\pi}{4} - \tan x}{1 + \tan x \tan \dfrac{\pi}{4}} = \dfrac{1 - \tan x}{1 + \tan x}$

Then combined with the result from exercise #116:

$$\tan\left(\dfrac{\pi}{4} + x\right) - \tan\left(\dfrac{\pi}{4} - x\right) = \dfrac{1 + \tan x}{1 - \tan x} - \dfrac{1 - \tan x}{1 + \tan x}$$

$$= \dfrac{4 \tan x}{1 - \tan^2 x}$$

$$= 2 \tan 2x$$

119. $2 \sin\left(\dfrac{\pi}{4} - \dfrac{x}{2}\right) \cos\left(\dfrac{\pi}{4} - \dfrac{x}{2}\right) = \sin\left(\dfrac{\pi}{2} - x\right)$ by using the double-angle identity for sine, and this is equal to $\cos x$.

121. $\dfrac{\cos x + \sin x}{\cos x - \sin x} = \dfrac{(\cos x + \sin x)^2}{\cos^2 x - \sin^2 x}$

$$= \dfrac{\cos^2 x + 2 \sin x \cos x + \sin^2 x}{\cos 2x}$$

$$= \dfrac{1 + \sin 2x}{\cos 2x}$$

$$= \dfrac{1}{\cos 2x} + \dfrac{\sin 2x}{\cos 2x}$$

$$= \tan 2x + \sec 2x$$

123. $2 \sin x + \sin 2x = 2 \sin x + 2 \sin x \cos x$

$$= 2 \sin x (1 + \cos x)$$

$$= \dfrac{2 \sin x (1 - \cos^2 x)}{1 - \cos x}$$

$$= \dfrac{2 \sin^3 x}{1 - \cos x}$$

125. $\dfrac{1 - \cos x + \sin x}{1 + \cos x + \sin x}$

$$= \dfrac{(1 + \sin x)^2 - \cos^2 x}{[(1 + \sin x) + \cos x]^2}$$

$$= \dfrac{1 + 2\sin x + \sin^2 x - \cos^2 x}{(1 + 2\sin x + \sin^2 x) + 2\cos x\,(1 + \sin x) + \cos^2 x}$$

$$= \dfrac{2\sin x + 2\sin^2 x}{2 + 2\sin x + 2\cos x\,(1 + \sin x)}$$

$$= \dfrac{2\sin x\,(1 + \sin x)}{2\,(1 + \sin x) + 2\cos x\,(1 + \sin x)}$$

$$= \dfrac{\sin x}{1 + \cos x}$$

$$= \tan\dfrac{x}{2}$$

127. $\sin(x + y)\cos y - \cos(x + y)\sin y = \sin[(x + y) - y)] = \sin x$

129. $\dfrac{1 - \tan^2\dfrac{x}{2}}{1 + \tan^2\dfrac{x}{2}} \quad = \dfrac{\cos^2\dfrac{x}{2} - \sin^2\dfrac{x}{2}}{\cos^2\dfrac{x}{2} + \sin^2\dfrac{x}{2}}$

$$= \cos^2\dfrac{x}{2} - \sin^2\dfrac{x}{2}$$

$$= \cos 2\bullet\dfrac{x}{2}$$

$$= \cos x$$

131. $\sin 4x = 2\sin 2x\cos 2x$

$$= 2(2\sin x\cos x)(\cos^2 x - \sin^2 x)$$

$$= 4\sin x\cos x\,(1 - 2\sin^2 x)$$

$$= 4\sin x\cos x - 8\sin^3 x\cos x$$

133. $\sin 5x = \sin 4x\cos x + \cos 4x\sin x$

$$= (4\sin x\cos^2 x - 8\sin^3 x\cos^2 x) + (8\sin x\cos^4 x - 8\sin x\cos^2 x + \sin x)$$

$$= -4\sin x\cos^2 x - 8\sin^3 x\cos^2 x + 8\sin x\cos^4 x + \sin x$$

$$= -4\sin x\,(1 - \sin^2 x) - 8\sin^3 x\,(1 - \sin^2 x) + 8\sin x\,(1 - \sin^2 x)^2 + \sin x$$

$$= -4\sin x + 4\sin^3 x - 8\sin^3 x + 8\sin^5 x + 8\sin x - 16\sin^3 x + 8\sin^5 x + \sin x$$

$$= 16\sin^5 x - 20\sin^3 x + 5\sin x$$

135. $\sin 80° - \sin 20° = 2\cos 50°\sin 30°$

$$= 2\,(\cos 50°)\dfrac{1}{2}$$

$$= \cos 50°$$

137. $\dfrac{\cos x - \cos 3x}{\sin x + \sin 3x}$ $= \dfrac{-2\sin 2x\,\sin(-x)}{2\sin 2x\,\cos x}$

$= \dfrac{2\sin 2x\,\sin x}{2\sin 2x\,\cos x}$

$= \tan x$

139. $\sin\dfrac{5\pi}{12} + \sin\dfrac{\pi}{12} = 2\sin\dfrac{\pi}{4}\cos\dfrac{\pi}{6}$

$= 2\cdot\dfrac{\sqrt{2}}{2}\cdot\dfrac{\sqrt{3}}{2}$

$= \dfrac{\sqrt{6}}{2}$

141. $\dfrac{\cos 3y + \cos(2x - 3y)}{\sin 3y + \sin(2x - 3y)} = \dfrac{2\cos x\,\cos(3y - x)}{2\sin x\,\cos(3y - x)} = \cot x$

143. $\dfrac{\sin 40° - \sin 20°}{\cos 20° - \cos 40°} = \dfrac{2\cos 30°\,\sin 10°}{2\sin 30°\,\sin 10°} = \cot 30° = \sqrt{3}$

While $\dfrac{\sin 10° - \sin 50°}{\cos 50° - \cos 10°} = \dfrac{2\cos 30°\,\sin(-20°)}{-2\sin 30°\,\sin 20°} = \cot 30° = \sqrt{3}$

Hence $\dfrac{\sin 40° - \sin 20°}{\cos 20° - \cos 40°} = \dfrac{\sin 10° - \sin 50°}{\cos 50° - \cos 10°}$

145. $\tan^2 x - 3 = 0$, so $\tan^2 x = 3$ and $\tan x = \pm\sqrt{3}$. If $\tan x = \sqrt{3}$ then $x = \dfrac{\pi}{3}$ or $\dfrac{4\pi}{3}$ while if $\tan x = -\sqrt{3}$ then $x = \dfrac{2\pi}{3}$ or $\dfrac{5\pi}{3}$. So the solutions are $x = \dfrac{\pi}{3}, \dfrac{2\pi}{3}, \dfrac{4\pi}{3}$, or $\dfrac{5\pi}{3}$.

147. Squaring $1 + \sin x = \cos x$ yields $1 + 2\sin x + \sin^2 x = \cos^2 x$, and thus $1 + 2\sin^2 x + 2\sin x = 1$ so $2\sin x(1 + \sin x) = 0$. So $\sin x = 0$ or $\sin x = -1$, thus $x = 0, \pi$, or $\dfrac{3\pi}{2}$. When checking we find $x = \pi$ is not a solution, so the solutions are $x = 0$ and $\dfrac{3\pi}{2}$.

149. $\sin x - \cos 2x + 1 = 0$, thus $\sin x - \cos^2 x + \sin^2 x + 1 = 0$, which simplifies to $2\sin^2 x + \sin x = 0$. Thus $\sin x(1 + 2\sin x) = 0$. So $\sin x = 0$ or $\sin x = -\dfrac{1}{2}$, and thus the solutions are $x = 0, \pi, \dfrac{7\pi}{6}$, or $\dfrac{11\pi}{6}$.

151. $3 \csc x - 4 \sin x = 0$

$$3 \csc x = 4 \sin x$$

$$\sin^2 x = \frac{3}{4}$$

$$\sin x = \pm \frac{\sqrt{3}}{2}$$

So the solutions are $x = \frac{\pi}{3}, \frac{2\pi}{3}, \frac{4\pi}{3},$ or $\frac{5\pi}{3}$.

153. $2 \sin^4 x - 3 \sin^2 x + 1 = 0$

$$(2 \sin^2 x - 1)(\sin^2 x - 1) = 0$$

$$\sin^2 x = \frac{1}{2} \text{ or } \sin^2 x = 1$$

$$\sin x = \pm \frac{\sqrt{2}}{2} \text{ or } \sin x = \pm 1$$

So the solutions are $x = \frac{\pi}{4}, \frac{\pi}{2}, \frac{3\pi}{4}, \frac{5\pi}{4}, \frac{3\pi}{2},$ or $\frac{7\pi}{4}$.

155. $\sin^4 x + \cos^4 x = (1 - \cos^2 x)^2 + \cos^4 x = \frac{5}{8}$

$2 \cos^4 x - 2 \cos^2 x + \frac{3}{8} = 0$, therefore $\cos^2 x = \frac{2 \pm \sqrt{4 - 3}}{4} = \frac{3}{4}$ or $\frac{1}{4}$

So $\cos x = \pm \frac{\sqrt{3}}{2}$ or $\cos x = \pm \frac{1}{2}$

So the solutions are $x = \frac{\pi}{6}, \frac{\pi}{3}, \frac{2\pi}{3}, \frac{5\pi}{6}, \frac{7\pi}{6}, \frac{4\pi}{3}, \frac{5\pi}{3},$ or $\frac{11\pi}{6}$.

157. $\cot x + \csc x + \sec x = \tan x$

$$\frac{\cos x}{\sin x} + \frac{1}{\sin x} + \frac{1}{\cos x} = \frac{\sin x}{\cos x}$$

Multiplying each side of the equation by $\sin x \cos x$, we get:

$$\cos^2 x + \cos x + \sin x = \sin^2 x$$

$$\cos^2 x - \sin^2 x + \cos x + \sin x = 0$$

$$(\cos x + \sin x)(\cos x - \sin x + 1) = 0$$

$$\cos x + \sin x = 0 \text{ or } \cos x - \sin x + 1 = 0$$

So $\tan x = -1$, thus $x = \frac{3\pi}{4}$ or $\frac{7\pi}{4}$. Or $\sin x - \cos x = 1$, which has solutions $x = \frac{x}{2}, \pi$. So the solutions are $x = \frac{\pi}{2}, \frac{3\pi}{4}, \pi, \frac{7\pi}{4}$.

159.
$$a \sin x + b \cos x = a \csc x + b \sec x$$
$$a \sin^2 x \cos x + b \cos^2 x \sin x = a \cos x + b \sin x$$
$$a \cos x (1 - \sin^2 x) + b \sin x (1 - \cos^2 x) = 0$$
$$a \cos^3 x + b \sin^3 x = 0$$

$$\tan^3 x = -\frac{a}{b}, \text{ thus } \tan x = -\sqrt[3]{\frac{a}{b}}$$

161. $\cos^{-1}\left(-\frac{\sqrt{2}}{2}\right) = \frac{3\pi}{4}$

163. $\sin^{-1} 0 = 0$

165. $\arctan \sqrt{3} = \frac{\pi}{3}$

167. $\tan^{-1}(-1) = -\frac{\pi}{4}$

169. $\sin(\sin^{-1} 1) = 1$

171. $\sin\left[\arccos\left(-\frac{1}{2}\right)\right] = \sin\frac{2\pi}{3} = \frac{\sqrt{3}}{2}$

173. $\cot\left(\cos^{-1}\frac{1}{2}\right) = \cot\frac{\pi}{3} = \frac{\sqrt{3}}{3}$

175. $\sin\left(\frac{3\pi}{2} + \arccos\frac{3}{5}\right) = -\cos\left(\arccos\frac{3}{5}\right) = -\frac{3}{5}$

177. $\sin\left(2 \sin^{-1}\frac{4}{5}\right) = 2 \sin\left(\sin^{-1}\frac{4}{5}\right) \cos\left(\sin^{-1}\frac{4}{5}\right)$

$$= 2 \cdot \frac{4}{5} \cdot \frac{3}{5}$$

$$= \frac{24}{25}$$

179. $\sin^{-1}\left(\sin\frac{\pi}{7}\right) = \frac{\pi}{7}$

181. $\sin\left(\arctan\frac{1}{2} + \arctan\frac{1}{3}\right)$

$= \sin\left(\arctan\frac{1}{2}\right)\cos\left(\arctan\frac{1}{3}\right) + \cos\left(\arctan\frac{1}{2}\right)\sin\left(\arctan\frac{1}{3}\right)$

$= \frac{1}{\sqrt{5}}\cdot\frac{3}{\sqrt{10}} + \frac{2}{\sqrt{5}}\cdot\frac{1}{\sqrt{10}}$

$= \frac{5}{\sqrt{50}}$

$= \frac{1}{\sqrt{2}}$

$= \frac{\sqrt{2}}{2}$

183. $\tan(\tan^{-1}x + \tan^{-1}y) = \dfrac{\tan(\tan^{-1}x) + \tan(\tan^{-1}y)}{1 - \tan(\tan^{-1}x)\tan(\tan^{-1}y)} = \dfrac{x+y}{1-xy}$

185. Set up the triangle:

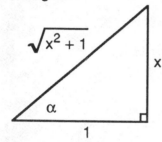

So $\sin(2\arctan x) = \sin 2\alpha$

$= 2\sin\alpha\cos\alpha$

$= 2\cdot\dfrac{x}{\sqrt{x^2+1}}\cdot\dfrac{1}{\sqrt{x^2+1}}$

$= \dfrac{2x}{x^2+1}$

187. Using the triangle:

$$\sin\left[\frac{1}{2}\sin^{-1}(x^2)\right] = \sin\frac{A}{2}$$

$$= \sqrt{\frac{1-\cos A}{2}}$$

$$= \sqrt{\frac{1-\sqrt{1-x^4}}{2}}$$

189. Since $\sin\left(\frac{\pi}{4} - \arcsin\frac{\sqrt{82}}{82}\right)$

$$= \frac{\sqrt{2}}{2}\left(\cos\left(\sin^{-1}\frac{\sqrt{82}}{82}\right)\right) - \frac{\sqrt{2}}{2}\cdot\frac{\sqrt{82}}{82}$$

$$= \frac{\sqrt{2}}{2}\sqrt{1-\frac{1}{82}} - \frac{\sqrt{41}}{82}$$

$$= \frac{9\sqrt{2}}{2\sqrt{82}} - \frac{\sqrt{41}}{82}$$

$$= \frac{8\sqrt{41}}{82}$$

$$= \frac{4\sqrt{41}}{41}$$

Then $\frac{\pi}{4} - \arcsin\frac{\sqrt{82}}{82} = \arcsin\frac{4\sqrt{41}}{41}$, and thus $\arcsin\frac{4\sqrt{41}}{41} + \arcsin\frac{\sqrt{82}}{82} = \frac{\pi}{4}$

191. (a) $\cos 20° \cos 40° \cos 60° \cos 80° = 0.0625$

(b)   Since $\cos 40° \cos 80° = \frac{1}{2}(\cos 120° + \cos 40°) = \frac{1}{2}\left(\cos 40° - \frac{1}{2}\right)$
Then:

$$\cos 20° \cos 40° \cos 80° = \frac{1}{2}\left(\cos 20° \cos 40° - \frac{1}{2}\cos 20°\right)$$

$$= \frac{1}{2}\left[\frac{1}{2}(\cos 60° + \cos 20°) - \frac{1}{2}\cos 20°\right]$$

$$= \frac{1}{2} \cdot \frac{1}{4}$$

$$= \frac{1}{8}$$

Finally $\cos 20° \cos 40° \cos 60° \cos 80° = \frac{1}{8}\cos 60° = \frac{1}{16} = 0.0625$

CHAPTER 9
ADDITIONAL TOPICS IN TRIGONOMETRY

9.1 The Law of Sines and the Law of Cosines

1. We draw the triangle:

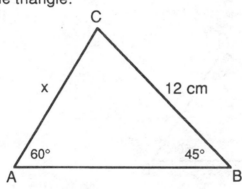

$$\frac{\sin 45°}{x} = \frac{\sin 60°}{12}$$

Thus:

$$x = 12 \cdot \frac{\sin 45°}{\sin 60°} = 12 \cdot \frac{\sqrt{2}}{2} \cdot \frac{2}{\sqrt{3}} = \frac{12\sqrt{2}}{\sqrt{3}} = 4\sqrt{6} \ \text{cm}$$

3.   We draw the triangle:

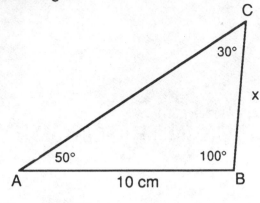

$$\frac{\sin 50°}{x} = \frac{\sin 30°}{10}$$

Thus:

$$x = \frac{10 \sin 50°}{\sin 30°} = \frac{10 \sin 50°}{\frac{1}{2}} = 20 \sin 50° \text{ cm}$$

5.   We draw a triangle:

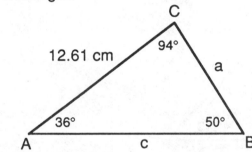

$$\frac{\sin 36°}{a} = \frac{\sin 50°}{12.61}$$

Thus:

$$a = \frac{12.61 \sin 36°}{\sin 50°} \approx 9.7 \text{ cm}$$

$$\frac{\sin 94°}{c} = \frac{\sin 50°}{12.61}$$

Thus:

$$c = \frac{12.61 \sin 94°}{\sin 50°} \approx 16.4 \text{ cm}$$

7.   We draw a triangle:

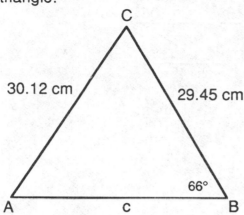

$$\frac{\sin A}{29.45 \text{ cm}} = \frac{\sin 66°}{30.12 \text{ cm}}$$

Thus:

$$\sin A = \frac{29.45 \sin 66°}{30.12} \approx 0.8932, \text{ so } A \approx 63.3°$$

Then C = 180° - 66° - 63.3° ≈ 50.7°

$$\frac{\sin 50.7°}{c} = \frac{\sin 66°}{30.12}$$

Thus:

$$c = \frac{30.12 \sin 50.7°}{\sin 66°} \approx 25.5 \text{ cm}$$

9.   (a)   Since the reference angle is 45° and the angle belongs to a triangle, then:

$$\angle B = 45° \text{ or } 135°$$

(b)   Reference: 30°, quadrant: II; hence:

$$\angle A = 150°$$

(c)   Quadrants: I or II, reference: ≈ 14.5°, so

$$\angle D = 14.5° \text{ or } 165.5°$$

11.   (a) $\dfrac{\sin A}{\sqrt{2}} = \dfrac{\sin 30°}{1}$ hence $\sin A = \sqrt{2} \sin 30° = \dfrac{\sqrt{2}}{2}$

(b)   Hence A has a reference angle 45°, and so A = 45° or 135°

(c)   If $A = 45°$, $B = 30°$, $a = \sqrt{2}$, $b = 1$, then:

$$C = 105° \text{ and } \frac{\sin 45°}{\sqrt{2}} = \frac{\sin 105°}{c}$$

Hence $c = \dfrac{\sqrt{2} \sin 105°}{\sin 45°} = \dfrac{\sqrt{2} \sin 75°}{\sin 45°} \approx 1.93$

(d)   If $A = 135°$, $B = 30°$, $a = \sqrt{2}$, $b = 1$, then:

$$C = 15° \text{ and } \frac{\sin 30°}{1} = \frac{\sin 15°}{c}$$

Hence $c = \dfrac{\sin 15°}{\sin 30°} \approx 0.52$

13. $\dfrac{\sin 20°}{2} = \dfrac{\sin 100°}{a} = \dfrac{\sin 50°}{b}$

$\dfrac{\sin 70°}{c} = \dfrac{\sin 95°}{b} = \dfrac{\sin 15°}{d}$

Hence:

$a = \dfrac{2 \sin 110°}{\sin 20°} = \dfrac{2 \sin 70°}{\sin 20°}$

$b = \dfrac{2 \sin 50°}{\sin 20°}$

$c = \dfrac{b \sin 70°}{\sin 95°} = \dfrac{2 \sin 50° \sin 70°}{\sin 20° \sin 85°}$

$d = \dfrac{b \sin 15°}{\sin 95°} = \dfrac{2 \sin 50° \sin 15°}{\sin 20° \sin 85°}$

15.   (a) $x^2 = (15)^2 + (9)^2 - 2\,(9)\,(15) \cos 120° \text{ cm}^2$

$= 306 - 270 \left(-\dfrac{1}{2}\right)$

$= 441 \text{ cm}^2$

$x = \sqrt{441 \text{ cm}^2} = 21 \text{ cm}$

(b) $x^2 = 4^2 + 4^2 - 2\,(4)\,(4) \cos 85° \text{ in.}^2$

$\approx 29.2 \text{ in.}^2$

$x \approx 5.4 \text{ in.}$

17. $a = 6$, $b = 7$, $c = 10$, so:

$6^2 = 7^2 + 10^2 - 2\,(7)\,(10) \cos A, \text{ so } \cos A = \dfrac{113}{140}$

$7^2 = 6^2 + 10^2 - 2\,(6)\,(10) \cos B, \text{ so } \cos B = \dfrac{87}{120} = \dfrac{29}{40}$

$10^2 = 6^2 + 7^2 - 2\,(6)\,(7) \cos C, \text{ so } \cos C = -\dfrac{15}{84} = -\dfrac{5}{28}$

19. We first draw the figure:

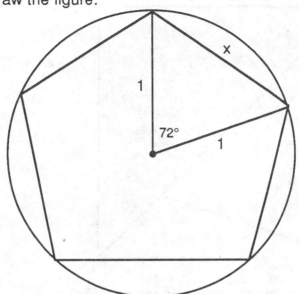

We apply the law of cosines to find x:

$$x^2 = 1^2 + 1^2 - 2\,(1)\,(1)\cos 72°$$
$$= 2 - 2\cos 72°$$
$$\approx 2 - .6180$$
$$\approx 1.382$$

$x \approx \sqrt{1.38} \approx 1.18$ and 5x, the perimeter of the pentagon, is 5.9 units.

21. (a) $a = \sqrt{(6.1)^2 + (3.2)^2 - 2\,(6.1)\,(3.2)\cos 40°}$ cm $\approx$ 4.2 cm

(b) $\dfrac{\sin C}{3.2} = \dfrac{\sin 40°}{4.2}$ so $\sin C = \dfrac{3.2}{4.2}\sin 40° \approx .49$

Then $C \approx 29.3°$

(c)   Hence $\angle B = 180° - 40° - 29.3° \approx 110.7°$

23.   We draw the figure:

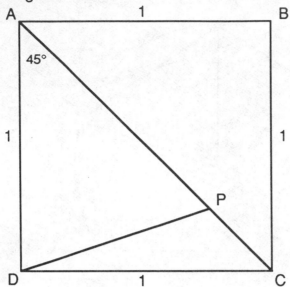

AP = 1, so applying the law of cosines to triangle APD:

$$(PD)^2 = 1^2 + 1^2 - 2 (1) (1) \cos 45° = 2 - 2 \cdot \frac{\sqrt{2}}{2} = 2 - \sqrt{2}$$

Hence PD = $\sqrt{2 - \sqrt{2}}$

25.   (a)   Using the law of cosines, we have:

$$(m^2 + n^2 + mn)^2 = (2mn + n^2)^2 + (m^2 - n^2)^2 - 2(2mn + n^2)(m^2 - n^2)\cos C$$

After carrying out the indicated squaring operations, and then   combining like terms, the equation becomes:

$$2m^3n - 2mn^3 + m^2n^2 - n^4 = -2(2mn + n^2)(m^2 - n^2) \cos C$$
$$2mn(m^2 - n^2) + n^2(m^2 - n^2) = -2(2mn + n^2)(m^2 - n^2) \cos C$$
$$(m^2 - n^2)(2mn + n^2) = -2(2mn + n^2)(m^2 - n^2) \cos C$$

Therefore $\cos C = -\frac{1}{2}$, and consequently C = 120°

(b)   Let m = 2 and n = 1. Then by means of the expressions in part (a), we obtain a = 5, b = 3, c = 7.

27. We draw the figure:

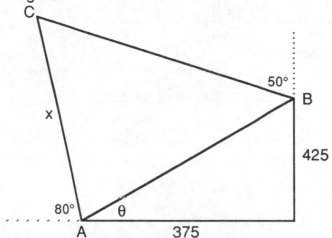

$$AB = \sqrt{(375)^2 + (425)^2} \approx 566.8 \text{ ft}$$

$$\tan \theta = \frac{425}{375}, \text{ so } \theta = 48.6°$$

$$\angle CAB = 180° - 80° - 48.6° = 51.4°$$

$$\angle ABC = 180° - 50° - (90° - 48.6°) = 88.6°$$

$$\angle ACB = 180° - 51.4° - 88.6° = 40°$$

Hence:

$$\frac{\sin 40°}{566.8} = \frac{\sin 88.6°}{x}$$

So:

$$x = \frac{566.8 \sin 88.6°}{\sin 40°} \approx 881.5 \text{ ft}$$

29. $\cos (180° - A) = \dfrac{\text{adjacent}}{\text{hypotenuse}} = \dfrac{u}{b}$. Therefore:

$$u = b \cos (180° - A) = b(- \cos A) = -b \cos A$$

Thus we have:

$$u = - b \cos A$$

$$-u = b \cos A$$

This shows that the x-coordinate of C is b cos A, as required.
Similarly, we have:

$$\sin (180° - A) = \frac{\text{opposite}}{\text{hypotenuse}} = \frac{v}{b}$$

Therefore:

$$v = b \sin (180° - A) = b \sin A$$

This shows the y-coordinate of C is b sin A, as required.

31. Following the hint that is given, we obtain the two equations:

$$\lambda^2 = a^2 + d^2 - 2ad \cos(180° - \theta) \quad (1)$$

$$\lambda^2 = b^2 + c^2 - 2bc \cos \theta \quad (2)$$

Equation (1) can be rewritten:

$$\lambda^2 = a^2 + d^2 + 2ad \cos \theta$$

Upon solving this last equation for $\cos \theta$, we obtain:

$$\cos \theta = \frac{\lambda^2 - a^2 - d^2}{2ad}$$

Now we use this expression for $\cos \theta$ in equation (2) to obtain:

$$\lambda^2 = b^2 + c^2 - 2bc \left(\frac{\lambda^2 - a^2 - d^2}{2ad} \right)$$

$$\lambda^2 ad = b^2 ad + c^2 ad - bc\lambda^2 + a^2 bc + bcd^2$$

$$\lambda^2(ad + bc) = b^2 ad + c^2 ad + a^2 bc + d^2 bc$$

$$\lambda^2(ad + bc) = (c^2 ad + a^2 bc) + (b^2 ad + d^2 bc)$$

$$\lambda^2(ad + bc) = ac(cd + ab) + bd(ad + cd)$$

$$\lambda^2(ad + bc) = (ab + cd)(ac + bd)$$

$$\lambda^2 = \frac{(ab + cd)(ac + bd)}{ad + bc}$$

33. (a) We draw the figure:

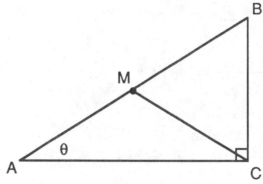

Using the law of cosines and triangle ACM, we have:

$$(CM)^2 = (AC)^2 + (AM)^2 - 2(AM)(AC) \cos \theta$$

But $AM = \dfrac{1}{2}(AB)$ and $\cos \theta = \dfrac{AC}{AB}$, so:

$$(CM)^2 = (AC)^2 + \frac{1}{4}(AB)^2 - 2 \left(\frac{1}{2} AB \right)(AC) \left(\frac{AC}{AB} \right)$$

$$(CM)^2 = (AC)^2 + \frac{1}{4}(AB)^2 - (AC)^2$$

$$(CM)^2 = \frac{1}{4}(AB)^2$$

This is the desired result.

(b)   We draw the figure:

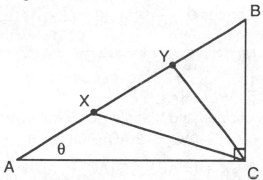

Using the law of cosines and triangle ACX, we have:

$$(CX)^2 = (AC)^2 + (AX)^2 - 2(AC)(AX) \cos \theta$$

$$= (AC)^2 + \left(\tfrac{1}{3} AB\right)^2 - 2 (AC) \left(\tfrac{1}{3} AB\right) \left(\tfrac{AC}{AB}\right)$$

$$= \tfrac{1}{3}(AC)^2 + \tfrac{1}{9}(AB)^2$$

Using the law of cosines and triangle ACY, we have:

$$(CY)^2 = (AC)^2 + (AY)^2 - 2(AC)(AY) \cos \theta$$

$$= (AC)^2 + \left(\tfrac{2}{3} AB\right)^2 - 2 (AC) \left(\tfrac{2}{3} AB\right)\left(\tfrac{AC}{AB}\right)$$

$$= -\tfrac{1}{3}(AC)^2 + \tfrac{4}{9}(AB)^2$$

Thus:

$$(CX)^2 + (CY)^2 = \tfrac{5}{9}(AB)^2$$

This is the desired result.

(c)   We draw the figure:

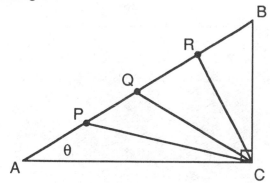

Using the law of cosines and triangle ACP, we have:

$$(CP)^2 = (AC)^2 + (AP)^2 - 2(AC)(AP)\cos\theta$$

$$= (AC)^2 + \left(\frac{1}{4}AB\right)^2 - 2(AC)\left(\frac{1}{4}AB\right)\left(\frac{AC}{AB}\right)$$

$$= (AC)^2 + \frac{1}{16}(AB)^2 - \frac{1}{2}(AC)^2$$

$$= \frac{1}{2}(AC)^2 + \frac{1}{16}(AB)^2$$

Using the law of cosines and triangle ACQ, we have:

$$(CQ)^2 = (AC)^2 + (AQ)^2 - 2(AC)(AQ)\cos\theta$$

$$= (AC)^2 + \left(\frac{1}{2}AB\right)^2 - 2(AC)\left(\frac{1}{2}AB\right)\left(\frac{AC}{AB}\right)$$

$$= (AC)^2 + \frac{1}{4}(AB)^2 - (AC)^2$$

$$= \frac{1}{4}(AB)^2$$

Using the law of cosines and triangle ACR, we have:

$$(CR)^2 = (AC)^2 + (AR)^2 - 2(AC)(AR)\cos\theta$$

$$= (AC)^2 + \left(\frac{3}{4}AB\right)^2 - 2(AC)\left(\frac{3}{4}AB\right)\left(\frac{AC}{AB}\right)$$

$$= (AC)^2 + \frac{9}{16}(AB)^2 - \frac{3}{2}(AC)^2$$

$$= -\frac{1}{2}(AC)^2 + \frac{9}{16}(AB)^2$$

Adding these results, we have:

$$(CP)^2 + (CQ)^2 + (CR)^2 = \frac{7}{8}(AB)^2$$

9.2 Vectors in the Plane, Part 1: A Geometric Approach

Note: Bold face will be used to represent vectors.

1.   We graph the vector:

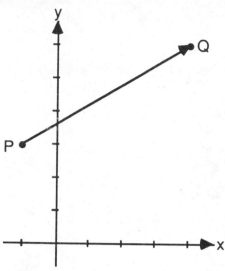

The magnitude is given by:

$$|\mathbf{PQ}| = \sqrt{(4 - (-1))^2 + (6 - 3)^2} = \sqrt{25 + 9} = \sqrt{34}$$

3.   We graph the vector:

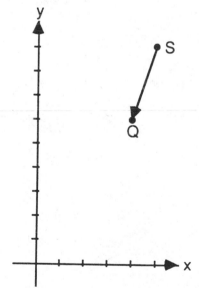

The magnitude is given by:

$$|\mathbf{SQ}| = \sqrt{(4 - 5)^2 + (6 - 9)^2} = \sqrt{1 + 9} = \sqrt{10}$$

5.   We graph the vector:

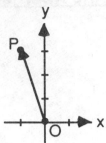

The magnitude is given by:
$$|\mathbf{OP}| = \sqrt{(-1-0)^2 + (3-0)^2} = \sqrt{1+9} = \sqrt{10}$$

7.   We graph the vector sum:

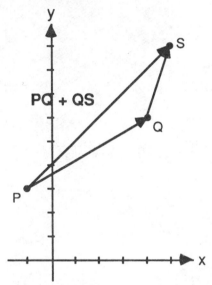

The magnitude is given by:
$$|\mathbf{PQ} + \mathbf{QS}| = |\mathbf{PS}| = \sqrt{(5-(-1))^2 + (9-3)^2} = \sqrt{36+36} = 6\sqrt{2}$$

9.   We graph the vector sum:

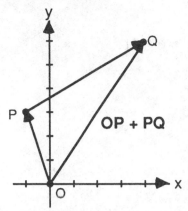

The magnitude is given by:

$$|OP + PQ| = |OQ| = \sqrt{(4-0)^2 + (6-0)^2} = \sqrt{16 + 36} = 2\sqrt{13}$$

11.   We graph the vector sum:

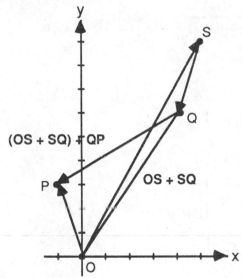

The magnitude is given by:

$$|(OS + SQ) + QP| = |OQ + QP|$$
$$= |OP|$$
$$= \sqrt{(-1-0)^2 + (3-0)^2}$$
$$= \sqrt{1 + 9}$$
$$= \sqrt{10}$$

13.   We graph the vector sum:

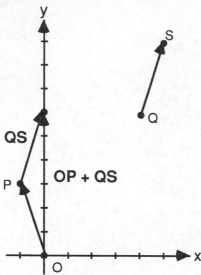

The magnitude is given by:
$$|\mathbf{OP} + \mathbf{QS}| = \sqrt{(0-0)^2 + (6-0)^2} = \sqrt{0 + 36} = 6$$

15.   We graph the vector sum:

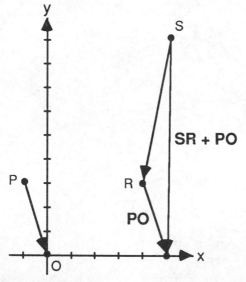

The magnitude is given by:
$$|\mathbf{SR} + \mathbf{PO}| = \sqrt{(5-5)^2 + (9-0)^2} = \sqrt{0 + 81} = 9$$

17. We graph the vector sum:

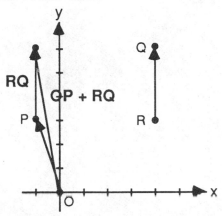

The magnitude is given by:
$$|\mathbf{OP} + \mathbf{RQ}| = \sqrt{(-1 - 0)^2 + (6 - 0)^2} = \sqrt{1 + 36} = \sqrt{37}$$

19. We graph the vector sum:

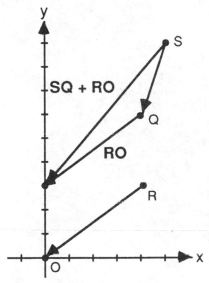

The magnitude is given by:
$$|\mathbf{SQ} + \mathbf{RO}| = \sqrt{(5 - 0)^2 + (9 - 3)^2} = \sqrt{25 + 36} = \sqrt{61}$$

21.   We graph the vector sum:

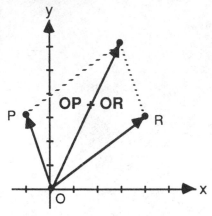

The magnitude is given by:
$$|\mathbf{OP + OR}| = \sqrt{(3 - 0)^2 + (6 - 0)^2} = \sqrt{9 + 36} = 3\sqrt{5}$$

23.   We graph the vector sum:

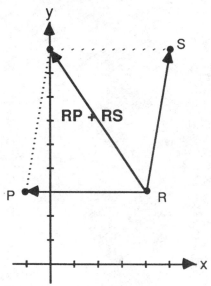

The magnitude is given by:
$$|\mathbf{RP + RS}| = \sqrt{(0 - 4)^2 + (9 - 3)^2} = \sqrt{16 + 36} = 2\sqrt{13}$$

25. We graph the vector sum:

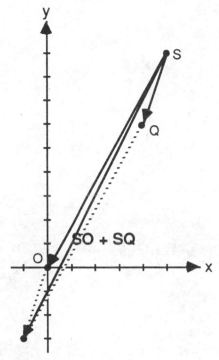

The magnitude is given by:

$$|\mathbf{SO} + \mathbf{SQ}| = \sqrt{(-1 - 5)^2 + (-3 - 9)^2} = \sqrt{36 + 144} = 6\sqrt{5}$$

27. We draw the figure:

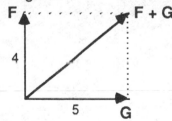

$$|\mathbf{F} + \mathbf{G}| = \sqrt{4^2 + 5^2} = \sqrt{16 + 25} = \sqrt{41} \text{ N}$$

$$\theta = \tan^{-1} \frac{4}{5} \approx 38.7°$$

29.   We draw the figure:

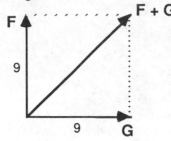

$$|F + G| = \sqrt{9^2 + 9^2} = 9\sqrt{2} \text{ N}$$

$$\theta = \tan^{-1}\frac{9}{9} = \tan^{-1} 1 = 45°$$

31.   We draw the figure:

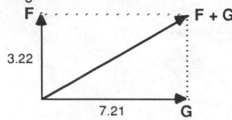

$$|F + G| = \sqrt{3.22^2 + 7.21^2} = \sqrt{62.3525} \approx 7.90 \text{ N}$$

$$\theta = \tan^{-1}\frac{3.22}{7.21} \approx 24.1°$$

33.   We draw the parallelogram:

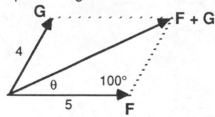

Let $d = |F + G|$. Then using the law of cosines:

$$d^2 = 5^2 + 4^2 - 2\,(5)\,(4)\cos 100°$$

$$d^2 = 41 - 40\cos 100°$$

$$d = \sqrt{41 - 40\cos 100°} \approx 6.92 \text{ N}$$

We find θ by the law of sines:

$$\frac{\sin\theta}{4} = \frac{\sin 100°}{d}$$

$$\sin\theta = \frac{4\sin 100°}{\sqrt{41 - 40\cos 100°}} \approx 0.5689$$

$$\theta \approx 34.67°$$

35. We draw the parallelogram:

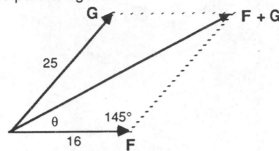

Let d $= |\mathbf{F} + \mathbf{G}|$. Then using the law of cosines:

$$d^2 = 16^2 + 25^2 - 2\,(16)\,(25)\,\cos 145°$$
$$d^2 = 881 - 800\,\cos 145°$$
$$d = \sqrt{881 - 800\,\cos 145°} \approx 39.20\ N$$

We find θ by the law of sines:

$$\frac{\sin\theta}{25} = \frac{\sin 145°}{d}$$

$$\sin\theta = \frac{25\,\sin 145°}{\sqrt{881 - 800\,\cos 145°}} \approx 0.3658$$

$$\theta \approx 21.46°$$

37. We draw the parallelogram:

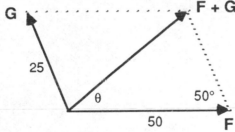

Let d $= |\mathbf{F} + \mathbf{G}|$. Then using the law of cosines:

$$d^2 = 50^2 + 25^2 - 2\,(50)\,(25)\,\cos 50°$$
$$d^2 = 3125 - 2500\,\cos 50°$$
$$d = \sqrt{3125 - 2500\,\cos 50°} \approx 38.96\ N$$

We find θ by the law of sines:

$$\frac{\sin\theta}{25} = \frac{\sin 50°}{d}$$

$$\sin\theta = \frac{25\,\sin 50°}{\sqrt{3125 - 2500\,\cos 50°}} \approx 0.4915$$

$$\theta \approx 29.44°$$

39. $V_x = 16 \cos 30° \approx 13.86$ cm/sec
     $V_y = 16 \sin 30° = 8$ cm/sec

41. $F_x = 14 \cos 75° \approx 3.62$ N
     $F_y = 14 \sin 75° \approx 13.52$ N

43. $V_x = 1 \cos 135° \approx -0.71$ cm/sec
     $V_y = 1 \sin 135° \approx 0.71$ cm/sec

45. $F_x = 1.25 \cos 145° \approx -1.02$ N
     $F_y = 1.25 \sin 145° \approx 0.72$ N

47. We draw the vectors:

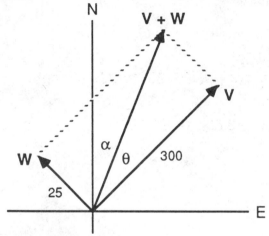

Let θ be the drift angle. Then:
$$\tan \theta = \frac{25}{300} = \frac{1}{12}$$
$$\theta = \tan^{-1} \frac{1}{12} \approx 4.76°$$
The ground speed is given by:
$$|V + W| = \sqrt{25^2 + 300^2} = \sqrt{90625} \approx 301.04 \text{ mph}$$
Let α be the bearing. Then:
$$\alpha = 30° - \theta \approx 30° - 4.76° \approx 25.24°$$

49. We draw the vectors:

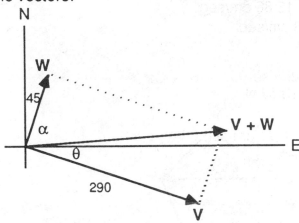

Let θ be the drift angle. Then:

$$\tan \theta = \frac{45}{290} = \frac{9}{58}$$

$$\theta = \tan^{-1} \frac{9}{58} \approx 8.82°$$

The ground speed is given by:

$$|\mathbf{V} + \mathbf{W}| = \sqrt{290^2 + 45^2} = \sqrt{86125} \approx 293.47 \text{ mph}$$

Let α be the bearing. Then:

$$\alpha = 100° - \theta \approx 100° - 8.82° \approx 91.18°$$

51. We draw a figure:

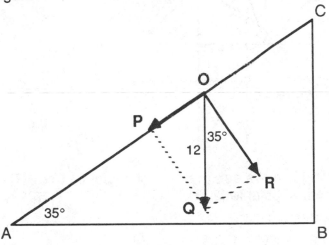

∠QOR = 35° since it is complementary to ∠POQ, but ∠POQ ≈ ∠ACB.

So: $|\mathbf{OR}| = 12 \cos 35° \approx 9.83 \text{ lb}$

$|\mathbf{OP}| = 12 \sin 35° \approx 6.88 \text{ lb}$

53.   Using the same approach as in #51, we have:

perpendicular: 12 cos 10° ≈ 11.82 lb

parallel: 12 sin 10° ≈ 2.08 lb

55.   (a)   We draw the vector sum (A + B) + C:

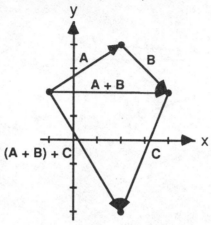

From the diagram, we see that the initial point of (A + B) + C is (-1,2) and the terminal point is (2,-3).

(b)   We draw the vector sum A + (B + C):

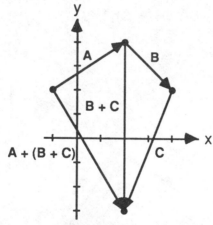

From the diagram, we see that the initial point of A + (B + C) is (-1,2) and the terminal point is (2,-3).

9.3 Vectors in the Plane, Part 2: An Algebraic Approach

1. $|\langle 4, 3 \rangle| = \sqrt{4^2 + 3^2} = \sqrt{25} = 5$

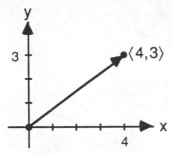

3. $|\langle -4, 2 \rangle| = \sqrt{(-4)^2 + 2^2} = \sqrt{20} = 2\sqrt{5}$

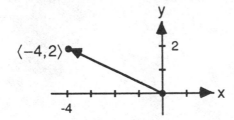

5. $\left|\left\langle \dfrac{3}{4}, -\dfrac{1}{2} \right\rangle\right| = \sqrt{\left(\dfrac{3}{4}\right)^2 + \left(-\dfrac{1}{2}\right)^2} = \sqrt{\dfrac{9}{16} + \dfrac{1}{4}} = \dfrac{\sqrt{13}}{4}$

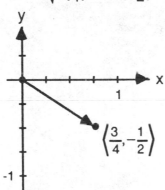

7. $\mathbf{PQ} = \langle\, 3 - 2\, ,\, 7 - 3\, \rangle = \langle 1, 4 \rangle$

9. $\mathbf{PQ} = \langle\, -3 - (-2)\, ,\, -2 - (-3)\, \rangle = \langle -3 + 2,\, -2 + 3 \rangle = \langle -1, 1 \rangle$

11. $\mathbf{PQ} = \langle\, 3 - (-5)\, ,\, -4 - 1\, \rangle = \langle 3 + 5,\, -5 \rangle = \langle 8, -5 \rangle$

13. $\mathbf{a} + \mathbf{b} = \langle 2 + 5\, ,\, 3 + 4 \rangle = \langle 7, 7 \rangle$

15. $2a + 4b = \langle 4, 6 \rangle + \langle 20, 16 \rangle = \langle 24, 22 \rangle$

17. $b + c = \langle 5 + 6, 4 - 1 \rangle = \langle 11, 3 \rangle$, so:
$$|b + c| = \sqrt{11^2 + 3^2} = \sqrt{130}$$

19. $a + c = \langle 2 + 6, 3 - 1 \rangle = \langle 8, 2 \rangle$, so:
$$|a + c| = \sqrt{8^2 + 2^2} = \sqrt{68} = 2\sqrt{17}$$
$$|a| = \sqrt{2^2 + 3^2} = \sqrt{13}$$
$$|c| = \sqrt{6^2 + (-1)^2} = \sqrt{37}$$
So $|a + c| - |a| - |c| = 2\sqrt{17} - \sqrt{13} - \sqrt{37}$

21. $b + c = \langle 5 + 6, 4 - 1 \rangle = \langle 11,3 \rangle$, so:
$$a + (b + c) = \langle 2,3 \rangle + \langle 11,3 \rangle = \langle 13,6 \rangle$$

23. $3a + 4a = \langle 6,9 \rangle + \langle 8,12 \rangle = \langle 14,21 \rangle$

25. $a - b = \langle 2,3 \rangle - \langle 5,4 \rangle = \langle -3, -1 \rangle$

27. $3b - 4d = \langle 15,12 \rangle - \langle -8,0 \rangle = \langle 15 + 8, 12 - 0 \rangle = \langle 23,12 \rangle$

29. $b + c = \langle 11,3 \rangle$, so:
$$a - (b + c) = \langle 2,3 \rangle - \langle 11,3 \rangle = \langle -9,0 \rangle$$

31. $c + d = \langle 4, -1 \rangle$ and $c - d = \langle 8, -1 \rangle$, while:
$$|c + d| = \sqrt{16 + 1} = \sqrt{17} \text{ and } |c - d| = \sqrt{64 + 1} = \sqrt{65}$$
So:
$$|c + d|^2 - |c - d|^2 = 17 - 65 = -48$$

33. $\langle 3,8 \rangle = \langle 3,0 \rangle + \langle 0,8 \rangle = 3i + 8j$

35. $\langle -8,-6 \rangle = \langle -8,0 \rangle + \langle 0,-6 \rangle = -8i - 6j$

37. $3 \langle 5,3 \rangle + 2 \langle 2,7 \rangle = 3(5i + 3j) + 2(2i + 7j)$
$$= 15i + 9j + 4i + 14j$$
$$= 19i + 23j$$

39. $i + j = \langle 1,1 \rangle$

41. $5i - 4j = \langle 5, -4 \rangle$

43. $|\langle 4,8 \rangle| = \sqrt{4^2 + 8^2} = \sqrt{80} = 4\sqrt{5}$, so a unit vector would be given by:

$$\frac{1}{4\sqrt{5}} \langle 4,8 \rangle = \left\langle \frac{1}{\sqrt{5}}, \frac{2}{\sqrt{5}} \right\rangle = \left\langle \frac{\sqrt{5}}{5}, \frac{2\sqrt{5}}{5} \right\rangle$$

45. $|\langle 6,-3 \rangle| = \sqrt{6^2 + (-3)^2} = \sqrt{45} = 3\sqrt{5}$, so a unit vector would be given by:

$$\frac{1}{3\sqrt{5}} \langle 6,-3 \rangle = \left\langle \frac{2}{\sqrt{5}}, \frac{-1}{\sqrt{5}} \right\rangle = \left\langle \frac{2\sqrt{5}}{5}, \frac{-\sqrt{5}}{5} \right\rangle$$

47. $|8i - 9j| = \sqrt{8^2 + (-9)^2} = \sqrt{145}$, so a unit vector would be given by:

$$\frac{1}{\sqrt{145}}(8i - 9j) = \frac{8}{\sqrt{145}}i - \frac{9}{\sqrt{145}}j = \frac{8\sqrt{145}}{145}i - \frac{9\sqrt{145}}{145}j$$

49. $u_1 = \cos\frac{\pi}{6} = \frac{\sqrt{3}}{2}$, $u_2 = \sin\frac{\pi}{6} = \frac{1}{2}$

51. $u_1 = \cos\frac{2\pi}{3} = -\frac{1}{2}$, $u_2 = \sin\frac{2\pi}{3} = \frac{\sqrt{3}}{2}$

53. $u_1 = \cos\frac{5\pi}{6} = -\frac{\sqrt{3}}{2}$, $u_2 = \sin\frac{5\pi}{6} = \frac{1}{2}$

55. property 1

$$\begin{aligned}
\mathbf{u} + (\mathbf{v} + \mathbf{w}) &= \langle u_1, u_2 \rangle + \left(\langle v_1, v_2 \rangle + \langle w_1, w_2 \rangle \right) \\
&= \langle u_1, u_2 \rangle + \langle v_1 + w_1, v_2 + w_2 \rangle \\
&= \langle u_1 + v_1 + w_1, u_2 + v_2 + w_2 \rangle \\
&= \langle u_1 + v_1, u_2 + v_2 \rangle + \langle w_1, w_2 \rangle \\
&= \left(\langle u_1, u_2 \rangle + \langle v_1, v_2 \rangle \right) + \langle w_1, w_2 \rangle \\
&= (\mathbf{u} + \mathbf{v}) + \mathbf{w}
\end{aligned}$$

property 2

$$\begin{aligned}
\mathbf{0} + \mathbf{v} &= \langle 0,0 \rangle + \langle v_1, v_2 \rangle \\
&= \langle 0 + v_1, 0 + v_2 \rangle \\
&= \langle v_1 + 0, v_2 + 0 \rangle \\
&= \langle v_1, v_2 \rangle + \langle 0,0 \rangle \\
&= \mathbf{v} + \mathbf{0}
\end{aligned}$$

$$\mathbf{v} + \mathbf{0} = \langle v_1, v_2 \rangle + \langle 0, 0 \rangle$$
$$= \langle v_1 + 0, v_2 + 0 \rangle$$
$$= \langle v_1, v_2 \rangle$$
$$= \mathbf{v}$$

57. property 5

$$a(\mathbf{u} + \mathbf{v}) = a(\langle u_1, u_2 \rangle + \langle v_1, v_2 \rangle)$$
$$= a\langle u_1 + v_1, u_2 + v_2 \rangle$$
$$= \langle a(u_1 + v_1), a(u_2 + v_2) \rangle$$
$$= \langle au_1 + av_1, au_2 + av_2 \rangle$$
$$= \langle au_1, au_2 \rangle + \langle av_1, av_2 \rangle$$
$$= a\langle u_1, u_2 \rangle + a\langle v_1, v_2 \rangle$$
$$= a\mathbf{u} + a\mathbf{v}$$

property 6

$$(a + b)\mathbf{v} = (a + b)\langle v_1, v_2 \rangle$$
$$= \langle (a + b)v_1, (a + b)v_2 \rangle$$
$$= \langle av_1 + bv_1, av_2 + bv_2 \rangle$$
$$= \langle av_1, av_2 \rangle + \langle bv_1, bv_2 \rangle$$
$$= a\langle v_1, v_2 \rangle + b\langle v_1, v_2 \rangle$$
$$= a\mathbf{v} + b\mathbf{v}$$

59. (a) $$|\mathbf{PQ}| = |\langle x_2 - x_1, y_2 - y_1 \rangle|$$
$$= \sqrt{(x_2 - x_1)^2 + (y_2 - y_1)^2}$$
$$= \sqrt{x_2^2 - 2x_1x_2 + x_1^2 + y_2^2 - 2y_1y_2 + y_1^2}$$
$$= \sqrt{(x_1^2 + y_1^2) + (x_2^2 + y_2^2) - 2(x_1x_2 + y_1y_2)}$$
$$= \sqrt{|\mathbf{OP}|^2 + |\mathbf{OQ}|^2 - 2(x_1x_2 + y_1y_2)}$$

Squaring each side obtains the required result.

(b)   This is merely a restatement of the law of cosines for angle θ.

(c)   We have:

$$|\mathbf{OP}|^2 + |\mathbf{OQ}|^2 - 2(x_1x_2 + y_1y_2) = |\mathbf{OP}|^2 + |\mathbf{OQ}|^2 - 2|\mathbf{OP}||\mathbf{OQ}|\cos\theta$$
$$-2(x_1x_2 + y_1y_2) = -2|\mathbf{OP}||\mathbf{OQ}|\cos\theta$$
$$x_1x_2 + y_1y_2 = |\langle x_1, y_1 \rangle||\langle x_2, y_2 \rangle|\cos\theta$$

Dividing by $|\langle x_1, y_1 \rangle||\langle x_2, y_2 \rangle|$ yields the required result.

9.4 **Introduction to Polar Coordinates**

1.   (a) $x = 3 \cos \dfrac{2\pi}{3} = 3\left(-\dfrac{1}{2}\right) = -\dfrac{3}{2}$

$y = 3 \sin \dfrac{2\pi}{3} = 3\left(\dfrac{\sqrt{3}}{2}\right) = \dfrac{3\sqrt{3}}{2}$

So the rectangular coordinates are $\left(-\dfrac{3}{2}, \dfrac{3\sqrt{3}}{2}\right)$

(b) $x = 4 \cos \dfrac{11\pi}{6} = 4\left(\dfrac{\sqrt{3}}{2}\right) = 2\sqrt{3}$

$y = 4 \sin \dfrac{11\pi}{6} = 4\left(-\dfrac{1}{2}\right) = -2$

So the rectangular coordinates are $(2\sqrt{3}, -2)$

(c) $x = 4 \cos \left(-\dfrac{\pi}{6}\right) = 4\left(\dfrac{\sqrt{3}}{2}\right) = 2\sqrt{3}$

$y = 4 \sin \left(-\dfrac{\pi}{6}\right) = 4\left(-\dfrac{1}{2}\right) = -2$

So the rectangular coordinates are $(2\sqrt{3}, -2)$

3.   (a) $x = 1 \cos \dfrac{\pi}{2} = 1(0) = 0$

$y = 1 \sin \dfrac{\pi}{2} = 1(1) = 1$

So the rectangular coordinates are $(0,1)$

(b) $x = 1 \cos \dfrac{5\pi}{2} = 1(0) = 0$

$y = 1 \sin \dfrac{5\pi}{2} = 1(1) = 1$

So the rectangular coordinates are $(0,1)$

(c) $x = 1 \cos \frac{\pi}{8} = 1 \left(\sqrt{\frac{1 + \frac{\sqrt{2}}{2}}{2}} \right) = \sqrt{\frac{2 + \sqrt{2}}{4}} = \frac{\sqrt{2 + \sqrt{2}}}{2}$

$y = 1 \sin \frac{\pi}{8} = 1 \left(\sqrt{\frac{1 - \frac{\sqrt{2}}{2}}{2}} \right) = \sqrt{\frac{2 - \sqrt{2}}{4}} = \frac{\sqrt{2 - \sqrt{2}}}{2}$

So the rectangular coordinates are $\left(\dfrac{\sqrt{2 + \sqrt{2}}}{2}, \dfrac{\sqrt{2 - \sqrt{2}}}{2} \right)$

5. We have:

$r^2 = 1 + 1 = 2$, so $r = \sqrt{2}$

$\theta = \tan^{-1} \left(\dfrac{-1}{-1} \right) + \pi = \dfrac{\pi}{4} + \pi = \dfrac{5\pi}{4}$

So the polar form is $\left(\sqrt{2}, \dfrac{5\pi}{4} \right)$

7. Multplying by r, we have:

$$r^2 = 2r \cos \theta$$
$$x^2 + y^2 = 2x$$
$$x^2 - 2x + y^2 = 0$$
$$(x - 1)^2 + y^2 = 1$$

9. $\sqrt{x^2 + y^2} = \dfrac{y}{x}$

$$x^2 + y^2 = \dfrac{y^2}{x^2}$$
$$x^4 + x^2 y^2 = y^2$$
$$x^4 + x^2 y^2 - y^2 = 0$$

11. Using the double-angle identity, we have:

$r = 3(\cos^2 \theta - \sin^2 \theta)$

Multplying by r^2:

$$r^3 = 3(r^2 \cos^2 \theta - r^2 \sin^2 \theta)$$
$$(x^2 + y^2)^{3/2} = 3(x^2 - y^2)$$
$$(x^2 + y^2)^3 = 9(x^2 - y^2)^2$$

Multiplying out parentheses yields:

$$x^6 + 3x^4 y^2 + 3x^2 y^4 + y^6 = 9x^4 - 18x^2 y^2 + 9y^4$$
$$x^6 - 9x^4 + 3x^4 y^2 + 18x^2 y^2 + 3x^2 y^4 - 9y^4 + y^6 = 0$$

13. Multiplying each side by $2 - \sin^2\theta$ yields:
$$2r^2 - r^2\sin^2\theta = 8$$
$$2(x^2 + y^2) - y^2 = 8$$
$$2x^2 + 2y^2 - y^2 = 8$$
$$2x^2 + y^2 = 8$$
$$\frac{x^2}{4} + \frac{y^2}{8} = 1$$

15. Multplying out parentheses yields:
$$r\cos\theta + 2r\sin\theta = 1$$
$$x + 2y = 1$$

17. $3r\cos\theta - 4r\sin\theta = 2$
$$r(3\cos\theta - 4\sin\theta) = 2$$
$$r = \frac{2}{3\cos\theta - 4\sin\theta}$$

19. $r^2\sin^2\theta = r^3\cos^3\theta$
$$\sin^2\theta = r\cos^3\theta$$
$$r = \frac{\sin^2\theta}{\cos^3\theta}$$
$$r = \tan^2\theta\sec\theta$$

21. $2(r\cos\theta)(r\sin\theta) = 1$
$$r^2(2\sin\theta\cos\theta) = 1$$
$$r^2\sin 2\theta = 1$$
$$r^2 = \frac{1}{\sin 2\theta}$$
$$r^2 = \csc 2\theta$$

23. $9r^2\cos^2\theta + r^2\sin^2\theta = 9$
$$r^2(9\cos^2\theta + \sin^2\theta) = 9$$
$$r^2 = \frac{9}{9\cos^2\theta + \sin^2\theta}$$

25. To help gain familiarity with polar equations, it may help to convert to rectangular form. Multiplying by r, we have:

$$r^2 = 3r \cos \theta$$
$$x^2 + y^2 = 3x$$
$$x^2 - 3x + y^2 = 0$$
$$\left(x - \frac{3}{2}\right)^2 + y^2 = \frac{9}{4}$$

This is a circle of radius $\frac{3}{2}$ centered at $\left(\frac{3}{2}, 0\right)$:

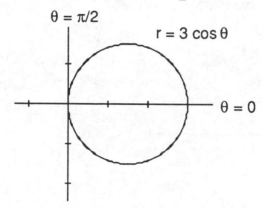

27. Converting to rectangular form does not help here, so we plot points directly:

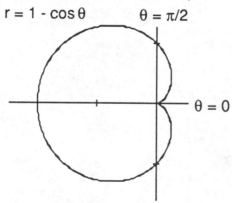

29.   Again we plot points in polar form, noting that ±r values are the same and that $0 \leq \theta \leq \frac{\pi}{2}$ or $\pi \leq \theta \leq \frac{3\pi}{2}$:

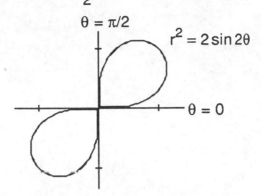

31.   Converting to rectangular coordinates:
$$r^2 = 1$$
$$x^2 + y^2 = 1$$
This is a circle of radius 1 centered at the origin:

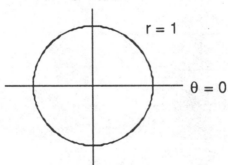

33.   We graph in polar coordinates, noting ±r values:

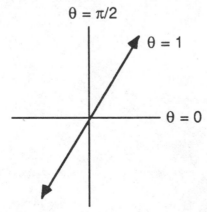

35.   We graph in polar coordinates:

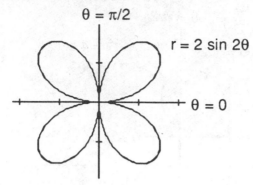

37.   We graph in polar coordinates:

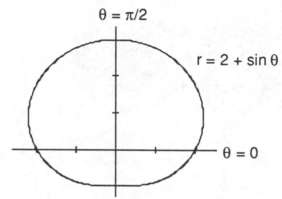

39.   We graph in polar coordinates:

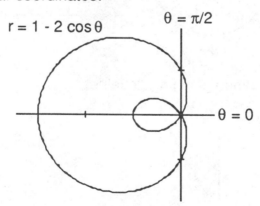

41. We graph in polar coordinates, noting symmetry of ±r values:

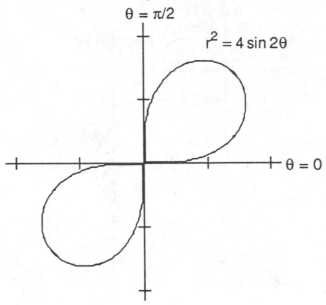

43. We graph in polar coordinates:

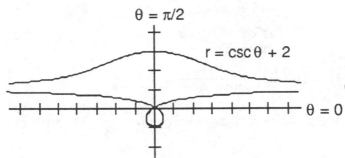

45. To aid in graphing, we convert to rectangular coordinates:

$$r = \frac{1}{\cos^2 \frac{\theta}{2}}$$

$$r = \frac{2}{1 + \cos \theta}$$

$$r + r \cos \theta = 2$$

$$\sqrt{x^2 + y^2} + x = 2$$

$$\sqrt{x^2 + y^2} = 2 - x$$

$$x^2 + y^2 = 4 - 4x + x^2$$

$$y^2 = -4(x - 1)$$

This is a parabola, opening to the left, with vertex (1,0):

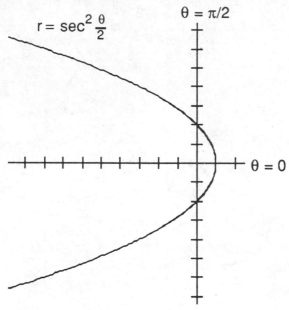

47.   We first multiply by r:

$$r^2 = ar\cos\theta + br\sin\theta$$
$$x^2 + y^2 = ax + by$$
$$x^2 - ax + y^2 - by = 0$$
$$\left(x - \frac{a}{2}\right)^2 + \left(y - \frac{b}{2}\right)^2 = \frac{a^2 + b^2}{4}$$

This is the equation of a circle with center $\left(\frac{a}{2}, \frac{b}{2}\right)$ and radius $\frac{\sqrt{a^2 + b^2}}{2}$.

49.   We multiply by 1 - a cos θ to get:

$$r - ar\cos\theta = ab$$
$$\sqrt{x^2 + y^2} - ax = ab$$
$$\sqrt{x^2 + y^2} = a(x + b)$$
$$x^2 + y^2 = a^2(x + b)^2$$
$$x^2 + y^2 = a^2x^2 + 2a^2bx + a^2b^2$$
$$x^2 - a^2x^2 + y^2 - 2a^2bx - a^2b^2 = 0$$
$$(1 - a^2)x^2 + y^2 - 2a^2bx - a^2b^2 = 0$$

51. (a) $F_1P = \sqrt{(x + k)^2 + y^2}$ and $F_2P = \sqrt{(x - k)^2 + y^2}$, so the equation becomes:

$$\sqrt{(x + k)^2 + y^2}\ \sqrt{(x - k)^2 + y^2} = k^2$$
$$\sqrt{(x^2 + k^2 + y^2)^2 - (2kx)^2} = k^2$$
$$(x^2 + y^2)^2 + 2k^2(x^2 + y^2) + k^4 - 4k^2x^2 = k^4$$
$$(x^2 + y^2)^2 = 2k^2(x^2 - y^2)$$

(b) Substituting, we have:

$$r^4 = 2k^2 (r^2\cos^2\theta - r^2\sin^2\theta)$$
$$r^2 = 2k^2 (\cos^2\theta - \sin^2\theta)$$
$$r^2 = 2k^2 \cos 2\theta$$

(c) We graph in polar form:

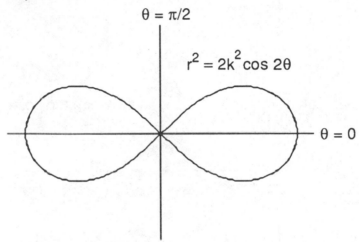

$\theta = \pi/2$

$r^2 = 2k^2 \cos 2\theta$

$\theta = 0$

9.5 Trigonometric Form for Complex Numbers

1. The complex number $4 + 2i$ is identified with the point $(4,2)$:

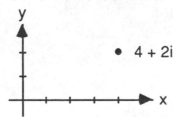

y

• $4 + 2i$

x

3.   The complex number -5 + i is identified with the point (-5,1):

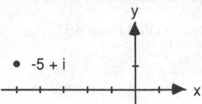

5.   The complex number 1 - 4i is identified with the point (1,-4):

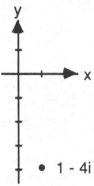

7.   The complex number -i, or 0 - 1i, is identified with the point (0,-1):

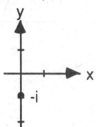

9. $2\left[\cos\dfrac{\pi}{4} + i\sin\dfrac{\pi}{4}\right] = 2\left[\dfrac{\sqrt{2}}{2} + \dfrac{\sqrt{2}}{2}i\right] = \sqrt{2} + \sqrt{2}\,i$

11. $4\left[\cos\dfrac{5\pi}{6} + i\sin\dfrac{5\pi}{6}\right] = 4\left[-\dfrac{\sqrt{3}}{2} + \dfrac{1}{2}i\right] = -2\sqrt{3} + 2i$

13. $\sqrt{2}\,[\cos 225° + i\sin 225°] = \sqrt{2}\left[-\dfrac{\sqrt{2}}{2} - \dfrac{\sqrt{2}}{2}i\right] = -1 - i$

15. $\sqrt{3}\left[\cos\dfrac{\pi}{2} + i\sin\dfrac{\pi}{2}\right] = \sqrt{3}\,(0 + 1i) = \sqrt{3}\,i$

17. We use the hint to find cos 75° and sin 75°:

$$\cos 75° = \cos(30° + 45°)$$
$$= \cos 30° \cos 45° - \sin 30° \sin 45°$$
$$= \frac{\sqrt{3}}{2} \cdot \frac{\sqrt{2}}{2} - \frac{1}{2} \cdot \frac{\sqrt{2}}{2}$$
$$= \frac{\sqrt{6} - \sqrt{2}}{4}$$

$$\sin 75° = \sin(30° + 45°)$$
$$= \sin 30° \cos 45° + \cos 30° \sin 45°$$
$$= \frac{1}{2} \cdot \frac{\sqrt{2}}{2} + \frac{\sqrt{3}}{2} \cdot \frac{\sqrt{2}}{2}$$
$$= \frac{\sqrt{6} + \sqrt{2}}{4}$$

So $\quad 4[\cos 75° + i \sin 75°] = 4\left[\frac{\sqrt{6} - \sqrt{2}}{4} + \frac{\sqrt{6} + \sqrt{2}}{4} i\right]$
$$= (\sqrt{6} - \sqrt{2}) + (\sqrt{6} + \sqrt{2})i$$

19. Here $a = \frac{\sqrt{3}}{2}$ and $b = \frac{1}{2}$, so $r = \sqrt{a^2 + b^2} = \sqrt{\frac{3}{4} + \frac{1}{4}} = 1$.

We now find θ such that $\cos \theta = \frac{a}{r} = \frac{\sqrt{3}}{2}$ and $\sin \theta = \frac{b}{r} = \frac{1}{2}$.

Such a θ is $\theta = \frac{\pi}{6}$. Thus $\frac{\sqrt{3}}{2} + \frac{1}{2} i = \cos \frac{\pi}{6} + i \sin \frac{\pi}{6}$.

21. Here $a = -1$ and $b = \sqrt{3}$, so $r = \sqrt{a^2 + b^2} = \sqrt{1 + 3} = \sqrt{4} = 2$.

We now find θ such that $\cos \theta = \frac{a}{r} = -\frac{1}{2}$ and $\sin \theta = \frac{b}{r} = \frac{\sqrt{3}}{2}$.

Such a θ is $\theta = \frac{2\pi}{3}$. Thus $-1 + \sqrt{3} i = 2\left[\cos \frac{2\pi}{3} + i \sin \frac{2\pi}{3}\right]$

23. Here $a = -2\sqrt{3}$ and $b = -2$, so $r = \sqrt{a^2 + b^2} = \sqrt{12 + 4} = \sqrt{16} = 4$.

We now find θ such that $\cos \theta = \frac{a}{r} = -\frac{2\sqrt{3}}{4} = -\frac{\sqrt{3}}{2}$ and

$\sin \theta = \frac{b}{r} = -\frac{2}{4} = -\frac{1}{2}$. Such a θ is $\theta = \frac{7\pi}{6}$.

Thus $-2\sqrt{3} - 2i = 4\left[\cos \frac{7\pi}{6} + i \sin \frac{7\pi}{6}\right]$

25. Here $a = 0$ and $b = -6$, so $r = \sqrt{a^2 + b^2} = \sqrt{0 + 36} = 6$. We now find θ such that $\cos\theta = \dfrac{a}{r} = \dfrac{0}{6} = 0$ and $\sin\theta = \dfrac{b}{r} = -\dfrac{6}{6} = -1$. Such a θ is $\theta = \dfrac{3\pi}{2}$. Thus $-6i = 6\left[\cos\dfrac{3\pi}{2} + i\sin\dfrac{3\pi}{2}\right]$.

27. Here $a = \dfrac{\sqrt{3}}{4}$ and $b = -\dfrac{1}{4}$, so $r = \sqrt{a^2 + b^2} = \sqrt{\dfrac{3}{16} + \dfrac{1}{16}} = \sqrt{\dfrac{1}{4}} = \dfrac{1}{2}$.

We now find θ such that $\cos\theta = \dfrac{a}{r} = \dfrac{\frac{\sqrt{3}}{4}}{\frac{1}{2}} = \dfrac{\sqrt{3}}{2}$ and $\sin\theta = \dfrac{b}{r} = \dfrac{-\frac{1}{4}}{\frac{1}{2}} = -\dfrac{1}{2}$.

Such a θ is $\theta = \dfrac{11\pi}{6}$. Thus $\dfrac{\sqrt{3}}{4} - \dfrac{1}{4}i = \dfrac{1}{2}\left[\cos\dfrac{11\pi}{6} + i\sin\dfrac{11\pi}{6}\right]$.

29. $2\left[\cos 22° + i\sin 22°\right] \bullet 3\left[\cos 38° + i\sin 38°\right] = 6\left[\cos 60° + i\sin 60°\right]$
$$= 6\left(\dfrac{1}{2} + \dfrac{\sqrt{3}}{2}i\right)$$
$$= 3 + 3\sqrt{3}\,i$$

31. $\sqrt{2}\left[\cos\dfrac{\pi}{3} + i\sin\dfrac{\pi}{3}\right] \bullet \sqrt{2}\left[\cos\dfrac{4\pi}{3} + i\sin\dfrac{4\pi}{3}\right] = 2\left[\cos\dfrac{5\pi}{3} + i\sin\dfrac{5\pi}{3}\right]$
$$= 2\left(\dfrac{1}{2} - \dfrac{\sqrt{3}}{2}i\right)$$
$$= 1 - \sqrt{3}\,i$$

33. $3\left[\cos\dfrac{\pi}{7} + i\sin\dfrac{\pi}{7}\right] \bullet \sqrt{2}\left[\cos\dfrac{\pi}{7} + i\sin\dfrac{\pi}{7}\right] = 3\sqrt{2}\left[\cos\dfrac{2\pi}{7} + i\sin\dfrac{2\pi}{7}\right]$

35. $6\left[\cos 50° + i\sin 50°\right] \div 2\left[\cos 5° + i\sin 5°\right] = 3\left[\cos 45° + i\sin 45°\right]$
$$= 3\left(\dfrac{\sqrt{2}}{2} + \dfrac{\sqrt{2}}{2}i\right)$$
$$= \dfrac{3\sqrt{2}}{2} + \dfrac{3\sqrt{2}}{2}i$$

37. $2^{4/3}\left[\cos\dfrac{5\pi}{12} + i\sin\dfrac{5\pi}{12}\right] \div 2^{1/3}\left[\cos\dfrac{\pi}{4} + i\sin\dfrac{\pi}{4}\right] = 2\left[\cos\dfrac{\pi}{6} + i\sin\dfrac{\pi}{6}\right]$
$$= 2\left(\dfrac{\sqrt{3}}{2} + \dfrac{1}{2}i\right)$$
$$= \sqrt{3} + i$$

39. $\left[\cos \dfrac{2\pi}{5} + i \sin \dfrac{2\pi}{5}\right] \div \left[\cos \dfrac{2\pi}{5} + i \sin \dfrac{2\pi}{5}\right]$

$$= \cos 0 + i \sin 0$$
$$= 1 + 0i$$
$$= 1$$

41. $\left[3\left(\cos \dfrac{\pi}{3} + i \sin \dfrac{\pi}{3}\right)\right]^5 = 3^5\left[\cos \dfrac{5\pi}{3} + i \sin \dfrac{5\pi}{3}\right]$

$$= 243\left(\dfrac{1}{2} - \dfrac{\sqrt{3}}{2}i\right)$$
$$= \dfrac{243}{2} - \dfrac{243\sqrt{3}}{2}i$$

43. $\left[\dfrac{1}{2}\left(\cos \dfrac{\pi}{24} + i \sin \dfrac{\pi}{24}\right)\right]^6 = \left(\dfrac{1}{2}\right)^6\left[\cos \dfrac{\pi}{4} + i \sin \dfrac{\pi}{4}\right]$

$$= \dfrac{1}{64}\left(\dfrac{\sqrt{2}}{2} + \dfrac{\sqrt{2}}{2}i\right)$$
$$= \dfrac{\sqrt{2}}{128} + \dfrac{\sqrt{2}}{128}i$$

45. $\left[2^{1/5}(\cos 63° + i \sin 63°)\right]^{10} = (2^{1/5})^{10}[\cos 630° + i \sin 630°]$

$$= 4(0 - 1i)$$
$$= -4i$$

47. $2[\cos 200° + i \sin 200°] \cdot \sqrt{2}[\cos 20° + i \sin 20°] \cdot \dfrac{1}{2}[\cos 5° + i \sin 5°]$

$$= \dfrac{2\sqrt{2}}{2}[\cos 225° + i \sin 225°]$$
$$= \sqrt{2}\left(-\dfrac{\sqrt{2}}{2} - \dfrac{\sqrt{2}}{2}i\right)$$
$$= -1 - i$$

49. Since $\dfrac{1}{2} - \dfrac{\sqrt{3}}{2}i = \cos \dfrac{5\pi}{3} + i \sin \dfrac{5\pi}{3}$, then:

$$\left(\dfrac{1}{2} - \dfrac{\sqrt{3}}{2}i\right)^5 = \cos \dfrac{25\pi}{3} + i \sin \dfrac{25\pi}{3} = \dfrac{1}{2} + \dfrac{\sqrt{3}}{2}i$$

51.   Since $-2 - 2i = 2\sqrt{2}\left(-\dfrac{\sqrt{2}}{2} - \dfrac{\sqrt{2}}{2}i\right) = 2\sqrt{2}\left[\cos\dfrac{5\pi}{4} + i\sin\dfrac{5\pi}{4}\right]$, then:

$$(-2 - 2i)^5 = (2\sqrt{2})^5\left[\cos\dfrac{25\pi}{4} + i\sin\dfrac{25\pi}{4}\right]$$

$$= 128\sqrt{2}\left(\dfrac{\sqrt{2}}{2} + \dfrac{\sqrt{2}}{2}i\right)$$

$$= 128 + 128i$$

53.   Since $-2\sqrt{3} - 2i = 4\left(-\dfrac{\sqrt{3}}{2} - \dfrac{1}{2}i\right) = 4\left[\cos\dfrac{7\pi}{6} + i\sin\dfrac{7\pi}{6}\right]$, then:

$$(-2\sqrt{3} - 2i)^4 = 4^4\left[\cos\dfrac{14\pi}{3} + i\sin\dfrac{14\pi}{3}\right]$$

$$= 256\left(-\dfrac{1}{2} + \dfrac{\sqrt{3}}{2}i\right)$$

$$= -128 + 128\sqrt{3}\,i$$

55.   We write $-27i = 27(0 - 1i) = 27\left[\cos\dfrac{3\pi}{2} + i\sin\dfrac{3\pi}{2}\right]$.

Now let $z = r(\cos\theta + i\sin\theta)$ denote a cube root of $-27i$. Then:

$$z^3 = r^3(\cos 3\theta + i\sin 3\theta) = 27\left[\cos\dfrac{3\pi}{2} + i\sin\dfrac{3\pi}{2}\right]$$

Then $r^3 = 27$ so $r = 3$, and $3\theta = \dfrac{3\pi}{2} + 2\pi k$, so $\theta = \dfrac{\pi}{2} + \dfrac{2\pi}{3}k$

When $k = 0$, we have: $z_1 = 3\left[\cos\dfrac{\pi}{2} + i\sin\dfrac{\pi}{2}\right] = 3(0 + i) = 3i$

When $k = 1$, we have: $z_2 = 3\left[\cos\dfrac{7\pi}{6} + i\sin\dfrac{7\pi}{6}\right]$

$$= 3\left(-\dfrac{\sqrt{3}}{2} - \dfrac{1}{2}i\right)$$

$$= -\dfrac{3\sqrt{3}}{2} - \dfrac{3}{2}i$$

When $k = 2$, we have: $z_3 = 3\left[\cos\dfrac{11\pi}{6} + i\sin\dfrac{11\pi}{6}\right]$

$$= 3\left(\dfrac{\sqrt{3}}{2} - \dfrac{1}{2}i\right)$$

$$= \dfrac{3\sqrt{3}}{2} - \dfrac{3}{2}i$$

So the cube roots are $3i$, $-\dfrac{3\sqrt{3}}{2} - \dfrac{3}{2}i$, and $\dfrac{3\sqrt{3}}{2} - \dfrac{3}{2}i$

57. We write $1 = 1(1 + 0i) = 1[\cos 0 + i \sin 0]$. Now let $z = r(\cos \theta + i \sin \theta)$ denote an eighth root of 1. Then:
$$z^8 = r^8(\cos 8\theta + i \sin 8\theta) = 1[\cos 0 + i \sin 0]$$

Then $r^8 = 1$ so $r = 1$, and $8\theta = 0 + 2\pi k$, so $\theta = 0 + \dfrac{\pi}{4}k$.

When $k = 0$, we have: $z_1 = 1[\cos 0 + i \sin 0] = 1(1 + 0i) = 1$

When $k = 1$, we have: $z_2 = 1\left[\cos\dfrac{\pi}{4} + i \sin\dfrac{\pi}{4}\right]$

$$= 1\left(\dfrac{\sqrt{2}}{2} + \dfrac{\sqrt{2}}{2}i\right)$$

$$= \dfrac{\sqrt{2}}{2} + \dfrac{\sqrt{2}}{2}i$$

When $k = 2$, we have: $z_3 = 1\left[\cos\dfrac{\pi}{2} + i \sin\dfrac{\pi}{2}\right] = 1(0 + i) = i$

When $k = 3$, we have: $z_4 = 1\left[\cos\dfrac{3\pi}{4} + i \sin\dfrac{3\pi}{4}\right] = -\dfrac{\sqrt{2}}{2} + \dfrac{\sqrt{2}}{2}i$

When $k = 4$, we have: $z_5 = 1[\cos \pi + i \sin \pi] = -1 + 0i = -1$

When $k = 5$, we have: $z_6 = 1\left[\cos\dfrac{5\pi}{4} + i \sin\dfrac{5\pi}{4}\right] = -\dfrac{\sqrt{2}}{2} - \dfrac{\sqrt{2}}{2}i$

When $k = 6$, we have: $z_7 = 1\left[\cos\dfrac{3\pi}{2} + i \sin\dfrac{3\pi}{2}\right] = 0 - i = -i$

When $k = 7$, we have: $z_8 = 1\left[\cos\dfrac{7\pi}{4} + i \sin\dfrac{7\pi}{4}\right] = \dfrac{\sqrt{2}}{2} - \dfrac{\sqrt{2}}{2}i$

So the eighth roots of 1 are $1, \dfrac{\sqrt{2}}{2} + \dfrac{\sqrt{2}}{2}i, i, -\dfrac{\sqrt{2}}{2} + \dfrac{\sqrt{2}}{2}i, -1, -\dfrac{\sqrt{2}}{2} - \dfrac{\sqrt{2}}{2}i, -i,$ and $\dfrac{\sqrt{2}}{2} - \dfrac{\sqrt{2}}{2}i$.

59. We write $64 = 64(1 + 0i) = 64[\cos 0 + i \sin 0]$. Now let $z = r(\cos \theta + i \sin \theta)$ denote a cube root of 64. Then:
$$z^3 = r^3[\cos 3\theta + i \sin 3\theta] = 64[\cos 0 + i \sin 0]$$

Then $r^3 = 64$ so $r = 4$, and $3\theta = 0 + 2\pi k$, so $\theta = 0 + \dfrac{2\pi}{3}k$.

When $k = 0$, we have: $z_1 = 4[\cos 0 + i \sin 0] = 4(1 + 0i) = 4$

When $k = 1$, we have: $z_2 = 4\left[\cos\dfrac{2\pi}{3} + i \sin\dfrac{2\pi}{3}\right]$

$$= 4\left(-\dfrac{1}{2} + \dfrac{\sqrt{3}}{2}i\right)$$

$$= -2 + 2\sqrt{3}\,i$$

When k = 2, we have: $z_3 = 4\left[\cos\dfrac{4\pi}{3} + i\sin\dfrac{4\pi}{3}\right]$

$$= 4\left(-\dfrac{1}{2} - \dfrac{\sqrt{3}}{2}i\right)$$

$$= -2 - 2\sqrt{3}\,i$$

So the cube roots of 64 are 4, -2 + 2$\sqrt{3}$ i, and -2 - 2$\sqrt{3}$ i.

61. We write 729 = 729 (1 + 0i) = 729 [cos 0 + i sin 0] . Now let
z = r (cos θ + i sin θ) denote a sixth root of 729. Then:

$$z^6 = r^6[\cos 6\theta + i\ \sin 6\theta] = 729\,[\cos 0 + i\sin 0]$$

Then $r^6 = 729$ so r = 3, and 6θ = 0 + 2πk, so $\theta = 0 + \dfrac{\pi}{3}k$.

When k = 0, we have: $z_1 = 3\,[\cos 0 + i\sin 0] = 3(1 + 0i) = 3$

When k = 1, we have: $z_2 = 3\left[\cos\dfrac{\pi}{3} + i\sin\dfrac{\pi}{3}\right]$

$$= 3\left(\dfrac{1}{2} + \dfrac{\sqrt{3}}{2}i\right)$$

$$= \dfrac{3}{2} + \dfrac{3\sqrt{3}}{2}i$$

When k = 2, we have: $z_3 = 3\left[\cos\dfrac{2\pi}{3} + i\sin\dfrac{2\pi}{3}\right]$

$$= 3\left(-\dfrac{1}{2} + \dfrac{\sqrt{3}}{2}i\right)$$

$$= -\dfrac{3}{2} + \dfrac{3\sqrt{3}}{2}i$$

When k = 3, we have: $z_4 = 3\,[\cos \pi + i\sin \pi] = 3(-1 + 0i) = -3$

When k = 4, we have: $z_5 = 3\left[\cos\dfrac{4\pi}{3} + i\sin\dfrac{4\pi}{3}\right]$

$$= 3\left(-\dfrac{1}{2} - \dfrac{\sqrt{3}}{2}i\right)$$

$$= -\dfrac{3}{2} - \dfrac{3\sqrt{2}}{2}i$$

When k = 5, we have: $z_6 = 3\left[\cos\dfrac{5\pi}{3} + i\sin\dfrac{5\pi}{3}\right]$

$$= 3\left(\dfrac{1}{2} - \dfrac{\sqrt{3}}{2}i\right)$$

$$= \dfrac{3}{2} - \dfrac{3\sqrt{3}}{2}i$$

So the sixth roots of 729 are $3, \frac{3}{2} + \frac{3\sqrt{3}}{2} i, -\frac{3}{2} + \frac{3\sqrt{3}}{2} i, -3, -\frac{3}{2} - \frac{3\sqrt{3}}{2} i,$

and $\frac{3}{2} - \frac{3\sqrt{3}}{2} i$.

63. $7 - 7i = 7\sqrt{2}\left(\frac{1}{\sqrt{2}} - \frac{1}{\sqrt{2}}i\right) = 7\sqrt{2}\left[\cos\frac{7\pi}{4} + i\sin\frac{7\pi}{4}\right]$. So:

$$(7 - 7i)^8 = (7\sqrt{2})^8[\cos 14\pi + i\sin 14\pi]$$
$$= (7^8)(2^4)(1 + 0i)$$
$$= 92,236,816$$

65.   We have $i = 1\left[\cos\frac{\pi}{2} + i\sin\frac{\pi}{2}\right]$. Now let z be a fifth root of i, where

$z = r(\cos\theta + i\sin\theta)$. Then:

$$z^5 = r^5[\cos 5\theta + i\sin 5\theta] = 1\left[\cos\frac{\pi}{2} + i\sin\frac{\pi}{2}\right]$$

So $r^5 = 1$, thus r = 1, and $5\theta = \frac{\pi}{2} + 2\pi k = 90° + 360°k$, so $\theta = 18° + 72°k$

When k = 0: $z_1 = 1[\cos 18° + i\sin 18°] = 0.95 + 0.31i$
When k = 1: $z_2 = 1[\cos 90° + i\sin 90°] = i$
When k = 2: $z_3 = 1[\cos 162° + i\sin 162°] = -0.95 + 0.31i$
When k = 3: $z_4 = 1[\cos 234° + i\sin 234°] = -0.59 - 0.81i$
When k = 4: $z_5 = 1[\cos 306° + i\sin 306°] = 0.59 - 0.81i$
So the fifth roots of i are 0.95 + 0.31i, i, -0.95 + 0.31i, -0.59 - 0.81i, and
0.59 - 0.81i. Each of the real and imaginary parts here has been rounded off to
two decimal places.

67.   We write $8 - 8\sqrt{3} i = 16\left(\frac{1}{2} - \frac{\sqrt{3}}{2}i\right) = 16\left[\cos\frac{5\pi}{3} + i\sin\frac{5\pi}{3}\right]$. Now let

$z = r(\cos\theta + i\sin\theta)$ denote a fourth root of $8 - 8\sqrt{3} i$. Then:

$$z^4 = r^4[\cos 4\theta + i\sin 4\theta] = 16\left[\cos\frac{5\pi}{3} + i\sin\frac{5\pi}{3}\right]$$

Then $r^4 = 16$ so r = 2, and $4\theta = \frac{5\pi}{3} + 2\pi k$, so $\theta = \frac{5\pi}{12} + \frac{\pi}{2}k$.

When k = 0, we have: $z_1 = 2\left[\cos\frac{5\pi}{12} + i\sin\frac{5\pi}{12}\right]$

$$= 2\left[\frac{\sqrt{6} - \sqrt{2}}{4} + \frac{\sqrt{6} + \sqrt{2}}{4}i\right]$$

(using the addition formulas)

$$= \frac{\sqrt{6} - \sqrt{2}}{2} + \frac{\sqrt{6} + \sqrt{2}}{2}i$$

When k = 1, we have: $z_2 = 2\left[\cos\dfrac{11\pi}{12} + i\sin\dfrac{11\pi}{12}\right]$

$= 2\left[\dfrac{-\sqrt{2} - \sqrt{6}}{4} + \dfrac{\sqrt{6} - \sqrt{2}}{4}\,i\right]$

$= \dfrac{-\sqrt{2} - \sqrt{6}}{2} + \dfrac{\sqrt{6} - \sqrt{2}}{2}\,i$

When k = 2, we have: $z_3 = 2\left[\cos\dfrac{17\pi}{12} + i\sin\dfrac{17\pi}{12}\right]$

$= 2\left[\dfrac{\sqrt{2} - \sqrt{6}}{4} + \dfrac{-\sqrt{2} - \sqrt{6}}{4}\,i\right]$

$= \dfrac{\sqrt{2} - \sqrt{6}}{2} - \dfrac{\sqrt{2} + \sqrt{6}}{2}\,i$

When k = 3, we have: $z_4 = 2\left[\cos\dfrac{23\pi}{12} + i\sin\dfrac{23\pi}{12}\right]$

$= 2\left[\dfrac{\sqrt{2} + \sqrt{6}}{4} + \dfrac{\sqrt{2} - \sqrt{6}}{4}\,i\right]$

$= \dfrac{\sqrt{2} + \sqrt{6}}{2} + \dfrac{\sqrt{2} - \sqrt{6}}{2}\,i$

So the fourth roots of $8 - 8\sqrt{3}$ are $\dfrac{\sqrt{6} - \sqrt{2}}{2} + \dfrac{\sqrt{6} + \sqrt{2}}{2}\,i$,

$\dfrac{-\sqrt{2} - \sqrt{6}}{2} + \dfrac{\sqrt{6} - \sqrt{2}}{2}\,i$, $\dfrac{\sqrt{2} - \sqrt{6}}{2} + \dfrac{-\sqrt{2} - \sqrt{6}}{2}\,i$, and $\dfrac{\sqrt{2} + \sqrt{6}}{2} + \dfrac{\sqrt{2} - \sqrt{6}}{2}\,i$.

Note: If you used half-angle formulas, your answers, though identical in value, may "look" vastly different. Those answers (which are correct) are $\sqrt{2 - \sqrt{3}} + i\sqrt{2 + \sqrt{3}}$, $-\sqrt{2 + \sqrt{3}} + i\sqrt{2 - \sqrt{3}}$, $-\sqrt{2 - \sqrt{3}} - i\sqrt{2 + \sqrt{3}}$, and $\sqrt{2 + \sqrt{3}} - i\sqrt{2 - \sqrt{3}}$

69. (a)   Let $z = r(\cos\theta + i\sin\theta)$, so $z^3 = r^3(\cos 3\theta + i\sin 3\theta)$.

Since $1 = 1(\cos 0 + i\sin 0)$, we have $r^3 = 1$ so $r = 1$, and

$3\theta = 0 + 2\pi k$, so $\theta = 0 + \dfrac{2\pi}{3}k$.

When k = 0: $z_1 = 1[\cos 0 + i\sin 0] = 1(1 + 0i) = 1$

When k = 1: $z_2 = 1\left[\cos\dfrac{2\pi}{3} + i\sin\dfrac{2\pi}{3}\right]$

$= 1\left(-\dfrac{1}{2} + \dfrac{\sqrt{3}}{2}\,i\right)$

$= -\dfrac{1}{2} + \dfrac{\sqrt{3}}{2}\,i$

When $k = 2$: $\quad z_3 = 1\left[\cos\dfrac{4\pi}{3} + i\sin\dfrac{4\pi}{3}\right]$

$$= 1\left(-\dfrac{1}{2} - \dfrac{\sqrt{3}}{2}i\right)$$

$$= -\dfrac{1}{2} - \dfrac{\sqrt{3}}{2}i$$

So the cube roots of 1 are 1, $-\dfrac{1}{2} + \dfrac{\sqrt{3}}{2}i$, and $-\dfrac{1}{2} - \dfrac{\sqrt{3}}{2}i$.

(b) $\quad z_1 + z_2 + z_3 = 1 + \left(-\dfrac{1}{2} + \dfrac{\sqrt{3}}{2}i\right) + \left(-\dfrac{1}{2} - \dfrac{\sqrt{3}}{2}i\right) = 0 + 0i = 0$

$z_1 z_2 = 1\left[\cos\dfrac{2\pi}{3} + i\sin\dfrac{2\pi}{3}\right]$

$\quad = -\dfrac{1}{2} + \dfrac{\sqrt{3}}{2}i$ (Note this is z_3)

$z_2 z_3 = 1\left[\cos 2\pi + i\sin 2\pi\right]$

$\quad = 1$ (Note this is z_1)

$z_3 z_1 = 1\left[\cos\dfrac{4\pi}{3} + i\sin\dfrac{4\pi}{3}\right]$

$\quad = -\dfrac{1}{2} - \dfrac{\sqrt{3}}{2}i$ (Note this is z_2)

So $z_1 z_2 + z_2 z_3 + z_3 z_1 = z_1 + z_2 + z_3 = 0$

71. $\left[\dfrac{-1 + i\sqrt{3}}{2}\right]^5 = \left[-\dfrac{1}{2} + \dfrac{\sqrt{3}}{2}i\right]^5$

$\quad = \left[\cos\dfrac{2\pi}{3} + i\sin\dfrac{2\pi}{3}\right]^5$

$\quad = \cos\dfrac{10\pi}{3} + i\sin\dfrac{10\pi}{3}$

$\quad = -\dfrac{1}{2} - \dfrac{\sqrt{3}}{2}i$

$\left[\dfrac{-1 - i\sqrt{3}}{2}\right]^5 = \left[-\dfrac{1}{2} - \dfrac{\sqrt{3}}{2}i\right]^5$

$\quad = \left[\cos\dfrac{4\pi}{3} + i\sin\dfrac{4\pi}{3}\right]^5$

$\quad = \cos\dfrac{20\pi}{3} + i\sin\dfrac{20\pi}{3}$

$\quad = -\dfrac{1}{2} + \dfrac{\sqrt{3}}{2}i$

So $\left[\dfrac{-1 + i\sqrt{3}}{2}\right]^5 + \left[\dfrac{-1 - i\sqrt{3}}{2}\right]^5 = \left(-\dfrac{1}{2} - \dfrac{\sqrt{3}}{2}i\right) + \left(-\dfrac{1}{2} + \dfrac{\sqrt{3}}{2}i\right) = -1$

73. $(\cos \theta + i \sin \theta)(\cos \theta - i \sin \theta) = \cos^2\theta - i^2 \sin^2\theta$

$$= \cos^2\theta + \sin^2\theta, \text{ since } i^2 = -1$$

$$= 1$$

75.   Using the hint, we have:

$$\frac{r (\cos \alpha + i \sin \alpha)}{R (\cos \beta + i \sin \beta)} \cdot \frac{(\cos \beta - i \sin \beta)}{(\cos \beta - i \sin \beta)}$$

$$= \frac{r (\cos \alpha \cos \beta + i \sin \alpha \cos \beta - i \cos \alpha \sin \beta - i^2 \sin \alpha \sin \beta)}{R (\cos^2\beta - i^2 \sin^2\beta)}$$

$$= \frac{r [(\cos \alpha \cos \beta + \sin\alpha \sin \beta) + i (\sin \alpha \cos \beta - \cos \alpha \sin \beta)]}{R (\cos^2\beta + \sin^2\beta)}$$

Using the difference identities for sine and cosine:

$$= \frac{r [\cos (\alpha - \beta) + i \sin (\alpha - \beta)]}{R}$$

$$= \frac{r}{R} [\cos (\alpha - \beta) + i \sin (\alpha - \beta)]$$

77.   Using the hint, $\dfrac{1}{z} = \dfrac{1 (\cos 0 + i \sin 0)}{r (\cos \theta + i \sin \theta)}$

$$= \frac{1}{r} [\cos (0 - \theta) + i \sin (0 - \theta)] \quad \text{by exercise #75}$$

$$= \frac{1}{r} [\cos (-\theta) + i \sin (-\theta)]$$

$$= \frac{1}{r} (\cos \theta - i \sin \theta)$$

since $\cos (-\theta) = \cos \theta$ and $\sin (-\theta) = - \sin \theta$

This proves the desired result.

Chapter 9 Review Exercises

1. We draw the triangle:

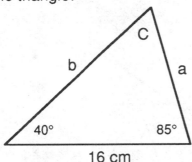

$\angle C = 180° - 40° - 85° = 55°$
Using the law of sines:
$$\frac{\sin 40°}{a} = \frac{\sin 55°}{16} \text{ , so } a = \frac{16 \sin 40°}{\sin 55°} \approx 12.6 \text{ cm}$$
Using the law of sines:
$$\frac{\sin 85°}{b} = \frac{\sin 55°}{16} \text{ , so } b = \frac{16 \sin 85°}{\sin 55°} \approx 19.5 \text{ cm}$$

3. (a)   We draw the triangle:

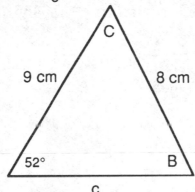

Using the law of sines:
$$\frac{\sin B}{9} = \frac{\sin 52°}{8} \text{ , so } \sin B = \frac{9 \sin 52°}{8} \approx .8865$$

Thus $\angle B \approx 62.4°$

$\angle C \approx 180° - 52° - 62.4° \approx 65.6°$
Using the law of sines:
$$\frac{\sin 65.6°}{c} = \frac{\sin 52°}{8} \text{ , so } c = \frac{8 \sin 65.6°}{\sin 52°} \approx 9.2 \text{ cm}$$

(b)   sin B $\approx$ .8865, thus $\angle B \approx$ 117.6°

$\angle C = 180° - 52° - 117.6° \approx$ 10.4°

Using the law of sines:

$$\frac{\sin 10.4°}{c} = \frac{\sin 52°}{8}, \text{ so } c = \frac{8 \sin 10.4°}{\sin 52°} \approx 1.8 \text{ cm}$$

5.   We draw the triangle:

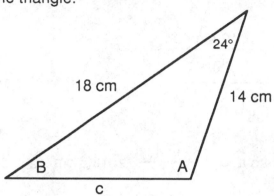

Using the law of cosines:

$c^2 = 18^2 + 14^2 - 2 (18) (14) \cos 24°$, so $c \approx 7.7$ cm

Using the law of sines:

$$\frac{\sin A}{18} = \frac{\sin 24°}{7.7}, \text{ so } \sin A = \frac{18 \sin 24°}{7.7} \approx 0.9486, \text{ thus either}$$

$\angle A \approx 71.5°$ or $\angle A \approx 108.5°$

If $\angle A = 71.5°$, then $\angle B = 180° - 24° - 71.5° \approx 84.5°$. But this is impossible since $\angle B < \angle A$. If $\angle A = 108.5°$, then $\angle B = 180° - 24° - 108.5° \approx 47.5°$

7.   We draw the triangle:

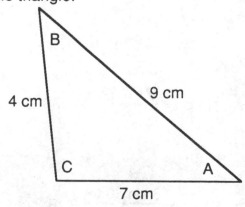

Using the law of cosines:

$9^2 = 4^2 + 7^2 - 2\,(4)\,(7)\cos C$, so $\cos C \approx -.2857$, thus $C \approx 106.6°$

Using the law of sines:

$\dfrac{\sin 106.6°}{9} = \dfrac{\sin B}{7}$, so $\sin B = \dfrac{7 \sin 106.6°}{9} \approx .7454$,

thus $B \approx 48.2°$

$\angle A \approx 180° - 106.6° - 48.2° \approx 25.2°$

9. $\dfrac{\sin 50°}{BE} = \dfrac{\sin 86°}{12}$, so $BE = \dfrac{12 \sin 50°}{\sin 86°} \approx 9.21$ cm

11.   Area $= \dfrac{1}{2}(12\text{ cm})(BE \sin 36°)$

$= \dfrac{1}{2}(12\text{ cm})(9.21\text{ cm})(\sin 36°)$

≈ 32.48 cm^2

13.   Area $= \dfrac{1}{2}(12\text{ cm})(BD \sin 44°)$

$= \dfrac{1}{2}(12\text{ cm})(13.25\text{ cm})(\sin 44°)$

≈ 55.23 cm^2

15. $CD = \sqrt{(BC)^2 + (BD)^2 - 2(BC)(BD)\cos 36°}$

$= \sqrt{319.56 - 318 \cos 36°}$

≈ 7.89 cm

17. $\dfrac{\sin 80°}{AC} = \dfrac{\sin 50°}{12}$, so $AC = \dfrac{12 \sin 80°}{\sin 50°} \approx 15.43$ cm

19.   We re-draw the figure:

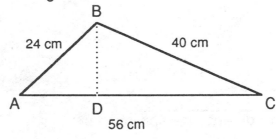

We use the law of cosines to find $\angle ABC$:

$$56^2 = 40^2 + 24^2 - 2\,(40)\,(24)\cos(\angle ABC)$$
$$-0.5 = \cos(\angle ABC)$$
$$\angle ABC = 120°$$

We now use the law of sines to find $\angle A$:

$$\frac{\sin A}{40} = \frac{\sin 120°}{56}, \text{ so } \sin A \approx 0.6186, \text{ thus } A \approx 38.21°$$

Then $\angle ADB \approx 180° - 60° - 38.21° \approx 81.79°$. We find BD by the law of sines:

$$\frac{\sin 81.79°}{24} = \frac{\sin 38.21°}{BD}, \text{ so } BD = \frac{24 \sin 38.21°}{\sin 81.79°} \approx 15 \text{ cm}$$

21. We re-draw the figure:

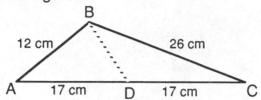

Using the law of cosines we find $\angle A$:

$$26^2 = 12^2 + 34^2 - 2\,(12)\,(34)\cos A$$
$$\cos A \approx 0.7647$$
$$A \approx 40.12°$$

We can now find BD by using the law of cosines (on $\triangle$ ADB):

$$(BD)^2 = 12^2 + 17^2 - 2\,(12)\,(17)\cos 40.12°$$
$$(BD)^2 = 121$$
$$BD = 11 \text{ cm}$$

23. We draw a figure:

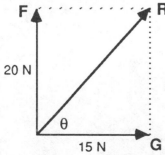

The resultant has a magnitude and direction given by:

$$|\mathbf{R}| = \sqrt{15^2 + 20^2} = \sqrt{625} = 25 \text{ N}$$
$$\theta = \tan^{-1}\frac{20}{15} \approx 53.1°$$

25. $\mathbf{v}_x = 50\cos 35° \approx 41.0$ cm/sec

$\mathbf{v}_y = 50\sin 35° \approx 28.7$ cm/sec

27. We draw the figure:

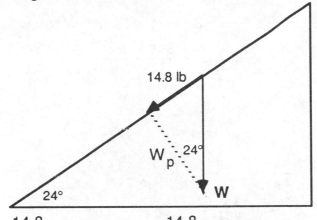

$\tan 24° = \dfrac{14.8}{|\mathbf{W}_p|}$, so $|\mathbf{W}_p| = \dfrac{14.8}{\tan 24°} \approx 33.2$ lb

$\sin 24° = \dfrac{14.8}{|\mathbf{W}|}$, so $|\mathbf{W}| = \dfrac{14.8}{\sin 24°} \approx 36.4$ lb

29. $|\langle 2,6\rangle| = \sqrt{2^2 + 6^2} = \sqrt{40}$ and $|\langle -5,b\rangle| = \sqrt{(-5)^2 + b^2} = \sqrt{b^2 + 25}$
We find b by solving the equation:

$$\sqrt{b^2 + 25} = \sqrt{40}$$
$$b^2 + 25 = 40$$
$$b^2 = 15$$
$$b - \pm\sqrt{15}$$

31. $\mathbf{a} + \mathbf{b} = \langle 3,5\rangle + \langle 7,4\rangle = \langle 10,9\rangle$

33. $3\mathbf{c} + 2\mathbf{a} = 3\langle 2,-1\rangle + 2\langle 3,5\rangle$
$= \langle 6,-3\rangle + \langle 6,10\rangle$
$= \langle 12,7\rangle$

35. $\mathbf{b} + \mathbf{d} = \langle 7,7\rangle$ and $\mathbf{b} - \mathbf{d} = \langle 7,1\rangle$, so:
$$|\mathbf{b} + \mathbf{d}|^2 - |\mathbf{b} - \mathbf{d}|^2 = (7^2 + 7^2) - (7^2 + 1^2) = 98 - 50 = 48$$

37. $(\mathbf{a} + \mathbf{b}) + \mathbf{c} = \langle 10,9\rangle + \langle 2,-1\rangle = \langle 12,8\rangle$

39. $(\mathbf{a} - \mathbf{b}) - \mathbf{c} = \langle -4,1\rangle - \langle 2,-1\rangle = \langle -6,2\rangle$

41. $\mathbf{4c + 2a - 3b} = \langle 8,-4 \rangle + \langle 6,10 \rangle - \langle 21,12 \rangle = \langle -7,-6 \rangle$

43. $\langle 7,-6 \rangle = 7\mathbf{i} - 6\mathbf{j}$

45. $|\langle 6,4 \rangle| = \sqrt{36 + 16} = \sqrt{52} = 2\sqrt{13}$, so such a unit vector would be:

$$\frac{1}{2\sqrt{13}} \langle 6,4 \rangle = \left\langle \frac{3}{\sqrt{13}}, \frac{2}{\sqrt{13}} \right\rangle = \left\langle \frac{3\sqrt{13}}{13}, \frac{2\sqrt{13}}{13} \right\rangle$$

47. $u_1 = \cos\dfrac{\pi}{12}$

$= \cos\left(\dfrac{\pi}{3} - \dfrac{\pi}{4}\right)$

$= \cos\dfrac{\pi}{3}\cos\dfrac{\pi}{4} + \sin\dfrac{\pi}{3}\sin\dfrac{\pi}{4}$

$= \dfrac{1}{2} \cdot \dfrac{\sqrt{2}}{2} + \dfrac{\sqrt{3}}{2} \cdot \dfrac{\sqrt{2}}{2}$

$= \dfrac{\sqrt{6} + \sqrt{2}}{4}$

$u_2 = \sin\dfrac{\pi}{12}$

$= \sin\left(\dfrac{\pi}{3} - \dfrac{\pi}{4}\right)$

$= \sin\dfrac{\pi}{3}\cos\dfrac{\pi}{4} - \cos\dfrac{\pi}{3}\sin\dfrac{\pi}{4}$

$= \dfrac{\sqrt{3}}{2} \cdot \dfrac{\sqrt{2}}{2} - \dfrac{1}{2} \cdot \dfrac{\sqrt{2}}{2}$

$= \dfrac{\sqrt{6} - \sqrt{2}}{4}$

49. (a)   We graph in polar coordinates:

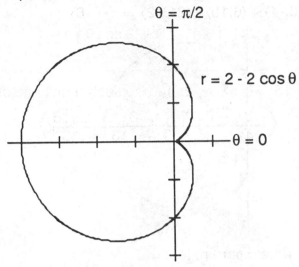

$\theta = \pi/2$

$r = 2 - 2\cos\theta$

$\theta = 0$

(b)   We graph in polar coordinates:

$\theta = \pi/2$

$r = 2 - 2\sin\theta$

$\theta = 0$

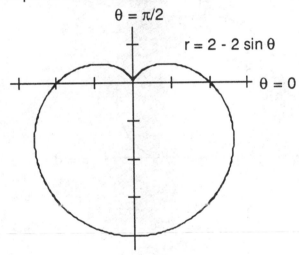

51.   (a)   We graph in polar coordinates:

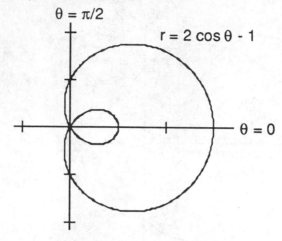

(b)   We graph in polar coordinates:

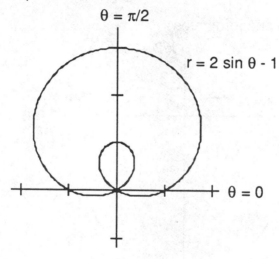

53.   (a)   We graph in polar coordinates:

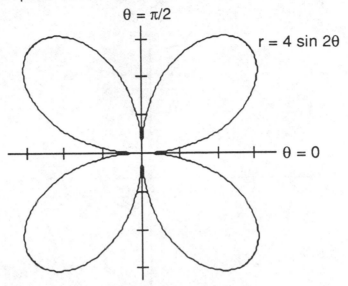

(b)   We graph in polar coordinates:

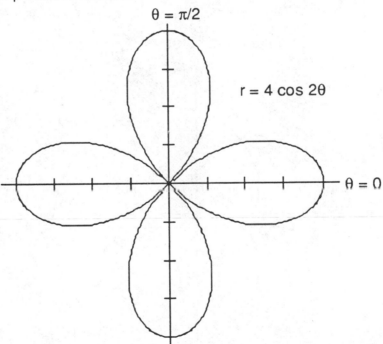

55. (a)   We graph in polar coordinates:

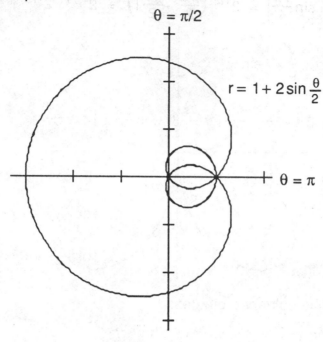

$$r = 1 + 2\sin\frac{\theta}{2}$$

(b)   We graph in polar coordinates:

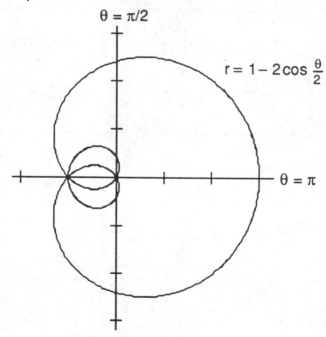

$$r = 1 - 2\cos\frac{\theta}{2}$$

57. $3\left[\cos\dfrac{\pi}{3} + i\sin\dfrac{\pi}{3}\right] = 3\left(\dfrac{1}{2} + \dfrac{\sqrt{3}}{2}i\right) = \dfrac{3}{2} + \dfrac{3\sqrt{3}}{2}i$

59. $2^{1/4}\left[\cos\dfrac{7\pi}{4} + i\sin\dfrac{7\pi}{4}\right] = 2^{1/4}\left(\dfrac{\sqrt{2}}{2} - \dfrac{\sqrt{2}}{2}i\right) = 2^{-1/4} - 2^{-1/4}i$

61. $\dfrac{1}{2} + \dfrac{\sqrt{3}}{2}i = 1\left[\cos\dfrac{\pi}{3} + i\sin\dfrac{\pi}{3}\right]$

63. $-3\sqrt{2} - 3\sqrt{2}\,i = 6\left(-\dfrac{\sqrt{2}}{2} - \dfrac{\sqrt{2}}{2}i\right) = 6\left[\cos\dfrac{5\pi}{4} + i\sin\dfrac{5\pi}{4}\right]$

65. $5\left[\cos\dfrac{\pi}{7} + i\sin\dfrac{\pi}{7}\right] \cdot 2\left[\cos\dfrac{3\pi}{28} + i\sin\dfrac{3\pi}{28}\right] = 10\left[\cos\dfrac{7\pi}{28} + i\sin\dfrac{7\pi}{28}\right]$

$$= 10\left[\cos\dfrac{\pi}{4} + i\sin\dfrac{\pi}{4}\right]$$

$$= 10\left(\dfrac{\sqrt{2}}{2} + \dfrac{\sqrt{2}}{2}i\right)$$

$$= 5\sqrt{2} + 5\sqrt{2}\,i$$

67. $8\left[\cos\dfrac{\pi}{12} + i\sin\dfrac{\pi}{12}\right] \div 4\left[\cos\dfrac{\pi}{3} + i\sin\dfrac{\pi}{3}\right]$

$$= 2\left[\cos\left(-\dfrac{3\pi}{12}\right) + i\sin\left(-\dfrac{3\pi}{12}\right)\right]$$

$$= 2\left[\cos\left(-\dfrac{\pi}{4}\right) + i\sin\left(-\dfrac{\pi}{4}\right)\right]$$

$$= 2\left(\dfrac{\sqrt{2}}{2} - \dfrac{\sqrt{2}}{2}i\right)$$

$$= \sqrt{2} - \sqrt{2}\,i$$

69. $\left[\cos\dfrac{\pi}{9} + i\sin\dfrac{\pi}{9}\right] \cdot 3\left[\cos\dfrac{4\pi}{9} + i\sin\dfrac{4\pi}{9}\right] = 3\left[\cos\dfrac{5\pi}{9} + i\sin\dfrac{5\pi}{9}\right]$

71. $\left[3^{1/4}\left(\cos\dfrac{\pi}{36} + i\sin\dfrac{\pi}{36}\right)\right]^{12} = 3^3\left[\cos\dfrac{12\pi}{36} + i\sin\dfrac{12\pi}{36}\right]$

$$= 27\left[\cos\dfrac{\pi}{3} + i\sin\dfrac{\pi}{3}\right]$$

$$= 27\left(\dfrac{1}{2} + \dfrac{\sqrt{3}}{2}i\right)$$

$$= \dfrac{27}{2} + \dfrac{27\sqrt{3}}{2}i$$

73. Since $\sqrt{3} + i = 2\left(\frac{\sqrt{3}}{2} + \frac{1}{2}i\right) = 2\left[\cos\frac{\pi}{6} + i\sin\frac{\pi}{6}\right]$, then:

$$(\sqrt{3} + i)^{10} = \left[2\left(\cos\frac{\pi}{6} + i\sin\frac{\pi}{6}\right)\right]^{10}$$

$$= 2^{10}\left[\cos\frac{5\pi}{3} + i\sin\frac{5\pi}{3}\right]$$

$$= 2^{10}\left(\frac{1}{2} - \frac{\sqrt{3}}{2}i\right)$$

$$= 2^9 - 2^9\sqrt{3}\,i$$

$$= 512 - 512\sqrt{3}\,i$$

75. Let $z = r(\cos\theta + i\sin\theta)$ and $1 = 1[\cos 0 + i\sin 0]$, so:

$$z^6 = r^6(\cos 6\theta + i\sin 6\theta) = 1(\cos 0 + i\sin 0)$$

Thus $r = 1$ and $6\theta = 0 + 2\pi k$, so $\theta = 0 + \frac{\pi}{3}k$.

When $k = 0$: $z_1 = 1[\cos 0 + i\sin 0] = 1(1 + 0i) = 1$

When $k = 1$: $z_2 = 1\left[\cos\frac{\pi}{3} + i\sin\frac{\pi}{3}\right] = \frac{1}{2} + \frac{\sqrt{3}}{2}i$

When $k = 2$: $z_3 = 1\left[\cos\frac{2\pi}{3} + i\sin\frac{2\pi}{3}\right] = -\frac{1}{2} + \frac{\sqrt{3}}{2}i$

When $k = 3$: $z_4 = 1[\cos\pi + i\sin\pi] = -1 + 0i = -1$

When $k = 4$: $z_5 = 1\left[\cos\frac{4\pi}{3} + i\sin\frac{4\pi}{3}\right] = -\frac{1}{2} - \frac{\sqrt{3}}{2}i$

When $k = 5$: $z_6 = 1\left[\cos\frac{5\pi}{3} + i\sin\frac{5\pi}{3}\right] = \frac{1}{2} - \frac{\sqrt{3}}{2}i$

So the sixth roots of 1 are $1, \frac{1}{2} + \frac{\sqrt{3}}{2}i, -\frac{1}{2} + \frac{\sqrt{3}}{2}i, -1, -\frac{1}{2} - \frac{\sqrt{3}}{2}i$, and $\frac{1}{2} - \frac{\sqrt{3}}{2}$.

77. Let $z = r(\cos\theta + i\sin\theta)$ and:

$$\sqrt{2} - \sqrt{2}\,i = 2\left(\frac{\sqrt{2}}{2} - \frac{\sqrt{2}}{2}i\right) = 2\left[\cos\frac{7\pi}{4} + i\sin\frac{7\pi}{4}\right]$$

Then $z^2 = r^2(\cos 2\theta + i\sin 2\theta) = 2\left[\cos\frac{7\pi}{4} + i\sin\frac{7\pi}{4}\right]$.

So $r^2 = 2$, and $r = \sqrt{2}$, and also $2\theta = \frac{7\pi}{4} + 2\pi k$, so $\theta = \frac{7\pi}{8} + \pi k$.

When $k = 0$: $z_1 = \sqrt{2}\left[\cos\dfrac{7\pi}{8} + i\sin\dfrac{7\pi}{8}\right]$

$= \sqrt{2}\left[\dfrac{-\sqrt{2+\sqrt{2}}}{2} + i\,\dfrac{\sqrt{2-\sqrt{2}}}{2}\right]$

(by the half angle identities)

$= \dfrac{-\sqrt{4+2\sqrt{2}}}{2} + \dfrac{\sqrt{4-2\sqrt{2}}}{2}\,i$

When $k = 1$: $z_2 = \sqrt{2}\left[\cos\dfrac{15\pi}{8} + i\sin\dfrac{15\pi}{8}\right]$

$= \sqrt{2}\left[\dfrac{\sqrt{2+\sqrt{2}}}{2} - i\,\dfrac{\sqrt{2-\sqrt{2}}}{2}\right]$

$= \dfrac{\sqrt{4+2\sqrt{2}}}{2} - \dfrac{\sqrt{4-2\sqrt{2}}}{2}\,i$

So the square roots of $\sqrt{2} - \sqrt{2}\,i$ are: $\dfrac{-\sqrt{4+2\sqrt{2}}}{2} + \dfrac{\sqrt{4-2\sqrt{2}}}{2}\,i$

and $\dfrac{\sqrt{4+2\sqrt{2}}}{2} - \dfrac{\sqrt{4-2\sqrt{2}}}{2}\,i$.

79.   Let $z = r(\cos\theta + i\sin\theta)$ and $1 + i = \sqrt{2}\left(\dfrac{\sqrt{2}}{2} + \dfrac{\sqrt{2}}{2}i\right) = \sqrt{2}\left[\cos\dfrac{\pi}{4} + i\sin\dfrac{\pi}{4}\right]$

Then $z^5 = r^5[\cos 5\theta + i\sin 5\theta] = \sqrt{2}\,[\cos 45° + i\sin 45°]$

So $r^5 = \sqrt{2}$ and $r = 2^{1/10}$, and $5\theta = 45° + 360°k$, so $\theta = 9° + 72°k$.

When $k = 0$: $z_1 = 2^{1/10}[\cos 9° + i\sin 9°]$

$= (1.0718)[\cos 9° + i\sin 9°]$

$\approx 1.06 + 0.17\,i$

When $k = 1$: $z_2 = 1.0718[\cos 81° + i\sin 81°] \approx 0.17 + 1.06\,i$

When $k = 2$: $z_3 = 1.0718[\cos 153° + i\sin 153°] \approx -0.95 + 0.49\,i$

When $k = 3$: $z_4 = 1.0718[\cos 225° + i\sin 225°] \approx -0.76 - 0.76\,i$

When $k = 4$: $z_5 = 1.0718[\cos 297° + i\sin 297°] \approx 0.49 - 0.95\,i$

So the fifth roots of $1 + i$ are: $1.06 + 0.17\,i$, $0.17 + 1.06\,i$, $-0.95 + 0.49i$, $-0.76 - 0.76i$, and $0.49 - 0.95\,i$.

81. $(\cos \theta + i \sin \theta)^3 = (\cos \theta)^3 + 3(\cos \theta)^2(i \sin \theta) + 3(\cos \theta)(i \sin \theta)^2 + (i \sin \theta)^3$

$= \cos^3\theta + 3\cos^2\theta \sin \theta\, i - 3 \cos \theta \sin^2\theta - \sin^3\theta\, i$

$= (\cos^3\theta - 3 \cos \theta \sin^2\theta) + (3\cos^2\theta \sin \theta - \sin^3\theta)\, i$

Since this is equal to $\cos 3\theta + i \sin 3\theta$, and the real and imaginary parts must be equal, we have the identities:

$\cos 3\theta = \cos^3\theta - 3 \cos \theta \sin^2\theta$

$\sin 3\theta = 3\cos^2\theta \sin \theta - \sin^3\theta$

CHAPTER 10
SYSTEMS OF EQUATIONS

10.1   Systems of Two Linear Equations in Two Unknowns

1.   (a)   yes
      (b)   no -- the xy term makes it non-linear
      (c)   yes
      (d)   yes

3.   Yes. We simply test (5,1) in the two equations and see if it produces true statements:

$$2(5) - 8(1) = 2$$
$$10 - 8 = 2 \quad \surd$$
$$3(5) + 7(1) = 22$$
$$15 + 7 = 22 \quad \surd$$

5.   No. We test (0,-4) in the two equations and see if it produces true statements:

$$\frac{1}{6}(0) + \frac{1}{2}(-4) = -2$$
$$0 - 2 = -2 \quad \surd$$
$$\frac{2}{3}(0) + \frac{3}{4}(-4) = 2$$
$$0 - 3 = 2 \quad \text{false}$$

So (0,-4) is not a solution to the given system.

7.   Yes. We test (3,-2) in the two equations and see if it produces true statements:

$$\frac{2}{7}(3) - \frac{1}{5}(-2) = \frac{44}{35}$$

$$\frac{6}{7} + \frac{2}{5} = \frac{44}{35}$$

$$\frac{30}{35} + \frac{14}{35} = \frac{44}{35} \quad \sqrt{}$$

$$\frac{1}{3}(3) - \frac{5}{4}(-2) = \frac{7}{2}$$

$$1 + \frac{5}{2} = \frac{7}{2}$$

$$\frac{2}{2} + \frac{5}{2} = \frac{7}{2} \quad \sqrt{}$$

So (3,-2) is a solution to the given system.

9.   We solve the second equation for x:

$$x + 4y = -4$$
$$x = -4 - 4y$$

Now substitute x = - 4 - 4y for x in the first equation, and solve for y:

$$3x - 2y = -19$$
$$3(-4 - 4y) - 2y = -19$$
$$-12 - 12y - 2y = -19$$
$$-14y - 12 = -19$$
$$-14y = -7$$
$$y = \frac{1}{2}$$

We substitute this back into the second equation:

$$x = -4 - 4y = -4 - (4)\frac{1}{2} = -4 - 2 = -6$$

So the solution is $\left(-6, \frac{1}{2}\right)$.

11.   We solve the first equation for y:

$$4x + 2y = 3$$
$$2y = 3 - 4x$$
$$y = \frac{3 - 4x}{2}$$

Now substitute $y = \frac{3 - 4x}{2}$ for y in the second equation, and solve for x:

$$10x + 4y = 1$$
$$10x + 4\left(\frac{3 - 4x}{2}\right) = 1$$
$$10x + 2(3 - 4x) = 1$$
$$10x + 6 - 8x = 1$$

$$2x + 6 = 1$$

$$2x = -5, \text{ so } x = -\frac{5}{2}$$

We substitute this back into the first equation:

$$y = \frac{3 - 4x}{2} = \frac{3 - 4\left(-\frac{5}{2}\right)}{2} = \frac{3 + 10}{2} = \frac{13}{2}$$

The solution is $\left(-\frac{5}{2}, \frac{13}{2}\right)$.

13. We solve the second equation for y:

$$-7x + 2y = 0$$
$$2y = 7x$$
$$y = \frac{7x}{2}$$

Now substitute $y = \frac{7x}{2}$ for y in the first equation, and solve for x:

$$13x - 8y = -3$$
$$13x - (8)\frac{7x}{2} = -3$$
$$13x - 28x = -3$$
$$-15x = -3$$
$$x = \frac{1}{5}$$

We substitute this back into the second equation:

$$y = \frac{7x}{2} = \frac{(7)\frac{1}{5}}{2} = \frac{7}{10}$$

The solution is $\left(\frac{1}{5}, \frac{7}{10}\right)$.

15. First we multiply each equation by 20 to clear fractions:

$$20\left(-\frac{2}{5}x + \frac{1}{4}y\right) = 20(3)$$

$$20\left(\frac{1}{4}x - \frac{2}{5}y\right) = 20(-3)$$

So:

$$-8x + 5y = 60$$
$$5x - 8y = -60$$

We solve the first equation for y:

$$-8x + 5y = 60$$
$$5y = 8x + 60$$
$$y = \frac{8x + 60}{5}$$

Now substitute $y = \dfrac{8x + 60}{5}$ for y in the second equation and solve for x:

$$5x - 8y = -60$$

$$5x - 8\left(\dfrac{8x + 60}{5}\right) = -60$$

Multiply by 5 to clear fractions:

$$25x - 8(8x + 60) = -300$$
$$25x - 64x - 480 = -300$$
$$-39x = 180$$
$$x = -\dfrac{180}{39} = -\dfrac{60}{13}$$

We substitute this back into the first equation:

$$y = \dfrac{8x + 60}{5} = \dfrac{8\left(-\dfrac{60}{13}\right) + 60}{5} = \dfrac{-480 + 780}{65} = \dfrac{300}{65} = \dfrac{60}{13}$$

The solution is $\left(-\dfrac{60}{13}, \dfrac{60}{13}\right)$.

17. We solve the first equation for x:

$$\sqrt{2}\, x - \sqrt{3}\, y = \sqrt{3}$$
$$\sqrt{2}\, x = \sqrt{3}\, y + \sqrt{3}$$
$$x = \dfrac{\sqrt{3}\, y + \sqrt{3}}{\sqrt{2}}$$

Now substitute $x = \dfrac{\sqrt{3}\, y + \sqrt{3}}{\sqrt{2}}$ for x in the second equation and solve for y:

$$\sqrt{3}\, x - \sqrt{8}\, y = \sqrt{2}$$
$$\sqrt{3}\left(\dfrac{\sqrt{3}\, y + \sqrt{3}}{\sqrt{2}}\right) - \sqrt{8}\, y = \sqrt{2}$$
$$\dfrac{3y + 3}{\sqrt{2}} - \sqrt{8}\, y = \sqrt{2}$$

Multiply by $\sqrt{2}$ to clear the fractions:

$$3y + 3 - 4y = 2$$
$$3 - y = 2$$
$$-y = -1$$
$$y = 1$$

We substitute this back into the first equation:

$$x = \dfrac{\sqrt{3}\, y + \sqrt{3}}{\sqrt{2}} = \dfrac{\sqrt{3} + \sqrt{3}}{\sqrt{2}} = \dfrac{2\sqrt{3}}{\sqrt{2}} = \dfrac{2\sqrt{6}}{2} = \sqrt{6}$$

The solution is $(\sqrt{6}, 1)$.

19. We multiply the second equation by 2:

$$5x + 6y = 4$$
$$4x - 6y = -6$$

Adding, we get:

$$9x = -2$$
$$x = -\frac{2}{9}$$

We substitute $x = -\frac{2}{9}$ into the first equation:

$$5x + 6y = 4$$
$$5(-\frac{2}{9}) + 6y = 4$$
$$-\frac{10}{9} + 6y = 4$$
$$6y = \frac{46}{9}$$
$$y = \frac{46}{54} = \frac{23}{27}$$

The solution is $\left(-\frac{2}{9}, \frac{23}{27}\right)$.

21. We multiply the second equation by -2:

$$4x + 13y = -5$$
$$-4x + 108y = 2$$

Adding, we get:

$$121y = -3$$
$$y = -\frac{3}{121}$$

We substitute $y = -\frac{3}{121}$ into the first equation:

$$4x + 13y = -5$$
$$4x + 13\left(-\frac{3}{121}\right) = -5$$
$$4x - \frac{39}{121} = -5$$
$$4x = -\frac{566}{121}$$
$$x = -\frac{283}{242}$$

The solution is $\left(-\frac{283}{242}, -\frac{3}{121}\right)$.

23. We multiply the first equation by 12 and the second equation by 70 to clear fractions:

$$12 \left(\frac{1}{4}x - \frac{1}{3}y \right) = 12\,(4)$$

$$70 \left(\frac{2}{7}x - \frac{1}{7}y \right) = 70 \left(\frac{1}{10} \right)$$

So:

$$3x - 4y = 48$$
$$20x - 10y = 7$$

We multiply the first equation by -5 and the second equation by 2:

$$-15x + 20y = -240$$
$$40x - 20y = 14$$

Adding, we get:

$$25x = -226$$
$$x = -\frac{226}{25}$$

We substitute $x = -\frac{226}{25}$ into the second equation:

$$20x - 10y = 7$$

$$20 \left(-\frac{226}{25} \right) - 10y = 7$$

$$-\frac{904}{5} - 10y = 7$$

$$-10y = \frac{939}{5}$$

$$y = -\frac{939}{50}$$

The solution is $\left(-\frac{226}{25}, -\frac{939}{50} \right)$.

25. We multiply the second equation by -4:

$$8x + 16y = 5$$
$$-8x - 20y = -5$$

Adding, we get:

$$-4y = 0, \text{ so } y = 0$$

We substitute $y = 0$ into the first equation:

$$8x + 16y = 5$$
$$8x = 5$$
$$x = \frac{5}{8}$$

The solution is $\left(\frac{5}{8}, 0 \right)$.

27. We multiply the second equation by $-\sqrt{3}$:

$$\sqrt{6}\,x - \sqrt{3}\,y = 3\sqrt{2} - \sqrt{3}$$
$$-\sqrt{6}\,x + \sqrt{15}\,y = -3\sqrt{2} - \sqrt{15}$$

Adding, we get:

$$(\sqrt{15} - \sqrt{3})\,y = -\sqrt{3} - \sqrt{15}$$
$$y = \frac{\sqrt{3} + \sqrt{15}}{\sqrt{3} - \sqrt{15}} = \frac{1 + \sqrt{5}}{1 - \sqrt{5}}$$

Muliply by $\dfrac{1 + \sqrt{5}}{1 + \sqrt{5}}$:

$$y = \frac{1 + 2\sqrt{5} + 5}{1 - 5} = \frac{6 + 2\sqrt{5}}{-4} = \frac{-3 - \sqrt{5}}{2}$$

Now substitute $y = \dfrac{-3 - \sqrt{5}}{2}$ into the second equation:

$$\sqrt{2}\,x - \sqrt{5}\,y = \sqrt{6} + \sqrt{5}$$
$$\sqrt{2}\,x - \sqrt{5}\left(\frac{-3 - \sqrt{5}}{2}\right) = \sqrt{6} + \sqrt{5}$$

We multiply by 2 to clear the fraction:

$$2\sqrt{2}\,x + 3\sqrt{5} + 5 = 2\sqrt{6} + 2\sqrt{5}$$
$$2\sqrt{2}\,x = 2\sqrt{6} - \sqrt{5} - 5$$
$$x = \frac{2\sqrt{6} - \sqrt{5} - 5}{2\sqrt{2}} = \frac{4\sqrt{3} - \sqrt{10} - 5\sqrt{2}}{4}$$

The solution is $\left(\dfrac{4\sqrt{3} - \sqrt{10} - 5\sqrt{2}}{4}, \dfrac{-3 - \sqrt{5}}{2}\right)$.

29. The given points must satisfy the equation, so we get:

$$4 = 0^2 + b \bullet 0 + c$$
$$4 - c$$

and

$$14 = 2^2 + b \bullet 2 + c$$
$$10 = 2b + c$$

This system, $c = 4$ and $2b + c = 10$, is easily solved by substitution:

$$2b + c = 10$$
$$2b + 4 = 10$$
$$2b = 6$$
$$b = 3$$
$$y = x^2 + 3x + 4$$

So the equation of the parabola is $y = x^2 + 3x + 4$, as required.

31.   Again, the points satisfy the equation.

$$Ax + By = 2$$
$$A(-4) + B(5) = 2$$
$$A(7) + B(-9) = 2$$

So, we have:

$$-4A + 5B = 2$$
$$7A - 9B = 2$$

Multiply the first equation by 7 and the second equation by 4:

$$-28A + 35B = 14$$
$$28A - 36B = 8$$
$$-B = 22$$
$$B = -22$$

Substituting for B:

$$7A - 9(-22) = 2$$
$$7A + 198 = 2$$
$$7A = -196$$
$$A = -28 \text{ as required.}$$

33.   First we graph the region:

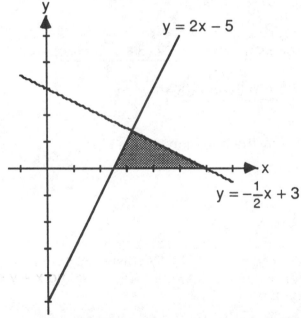

The base of the triangle is the difference between the x-intercepts, so:

$$\text{base} = 6 - \frac{5}{2} = \frac{7}{2}$$

The height is the y-coordinate of the intersection of the two lines $y = -\frac{1}{2}x + 3$ and $y = 2x - 5$, so:

$$-\frac{1}{2}x + 3 = 2x - 5$$

$$8 = \frac{5}{2}x$$

$$\frac{16}{5} = x$$

So $y = 2\left(\frac{16}{5}\right) - 5 = \frac{32}{5} - 5 = \frac{7}{5}$. So the area is:

$$\frac{1}{2}(\text{base})(\text{height}) = \frac{1}{2}\left(\frac{7}{2}\right)\left(\frac{7}{5}\right) = \frac{49}{20} \text{ square units.}$$

35. If we follow example 7 in this section, we let x = the amount of 10% solution and y = the amount of the 35% solution. Then x + y = 200 cc. Also, we know that the amount of acid in each separate solution, 10% of x and 35% of y must sum to equal the acid in the mixture, 25% of x + y. This second equation is usually in need of simplifying:

$$.10x + .35y = .25 (x + y)$$
$$10x + 35y = 25 (x + y)$$
$$2x + 7y = 5x + 5y$$
$$-3x + 2y = 0$$

This system is now solved by either method:

$$x + y = 200$$
$$-3x + 2y = 0$$

Multiply the first equation by 3:

$$3x + 3y = 600$$
$$-3x + 2y = 0$$

Adding, we get:

$$5y = 600$$
$$y = 120$$

So x = 80, and we need 80 cc of the 10% solution and 120 cc of the 35% solution.

Take a minute to consider what is a simpler solution. Using x + y = 200, substitute in the other equation:

$$10x + 35y = 25(x + y)$$
$$10x + 35(200 - x) = 25(200)$$
$$10x + 70000 - 35x = 5000$$
$$-25x = -2000$$
$$x = 80, \text{ so } y = 120$$

We get the same results with less work.

37. Let x = amount of $5.20 coffee and y = amount of $5.80 coffee. Then
x + y = 16 pounds. The total value of each bean is 5.20x and 5.80y,
respectively, and that of the mixture is 5.50(x + y), so we have:

$$
\begin{aligned}
5.20x + 5.80y &= 5.50(x + y) \\
52x + 58y &= 55(x + y) \\
52x + 58y &= 55x + 55y \\
-3x + 3y &= 0 \\
-x + y &= 0
\end{aligned}
$$

We solve the system:

$$
\begin{aligned}
x + y &= 16 \\
-x + y &= 0
\end{aligned}
$$

Adding, we get:

$$
\begin{aligned}
2y &= 16 \\
y &= 8
\end{aligned}
$$

Since x = 16 - y, then x = 16 - 8 = 8.
So we mix 8 pounds of $5.20 coffee and 8 pounds of $5.80 coffee.

39. Eliminating fractions, we get:

$$
\begin{aligned}
bx + ay &= ab \quad \text{and} \\
ax + by &= ab
\end{aligned}
$$

So:

$$
\begin{aligned}
abx + a^2y &= a^2b \\
-abx - b^2y &= -ab^2 \quad \text{adding gives} \\
(a^2 - b^2)y &= a^2b - ab^2 \\
y &= \frac{ab(a - b)}{a^2 - b^2}
\end{aligned}
$$

If we factor and reduce, we have $y = \dfrac{ab}{a + b}$. Now substitute to get x:

$$
\frac{x}{a} + \frac{\dfrac{ab}{a + b}}{b} = 1
$$

$$
\frac{x}{a} + \frac{a}{a + b} = 1
$$

$$
(a + b)x + a^2 = a(a + b)
$$

$$
(a + b)x = a^2 + ab - a^2
$$

$$
x = \frac{ab}{a + b}
$$

The solution is $\left(\dfrac{ab}{a + b}, \dfrac{ab}{a + b} \right)$. Note that we cannot have a = ± b for this
solution.

41. We multiply the first equation by b and the second equation by -a:

$$abx + a^2by = b$$
$$-abx - ab^2y = -a$$

Adding, we get:

$$(a^2b - ab^2)y = b - a$$
$$y = \frac{b - a}{a^2b - ab^2}$$
$$= \frac{-1}{ab}$$

We substitute $y = \frac{-1}{ab}$ into the first equation:

$$ax + a^2y = 1$$
$$ax - \frac{a}{b} = 1$$
$$ax = \frac{a + b}{b}$$
$$x = \frac{a + b}{ab}$$

So the solution is $\left(\frac{a + b}{ab}, \frac{-1}{ab}\right)$. Note that we cannot have ab = 0, so $a \neq 0$ and $b \neq 0$.

43. Let $x = \frac{1}{s}$ and $y = \frac{1}{t}$. Then we get:

$$\frac{1}{2}x - \frac{1}{2}y = -10$$
$$2x + 3y = 5$$

Multiply the first equation by -4:

$$-2x + 2y = 40$$
$$2x + 3y = 5$$

Adding, we get:

$$5y = 45$$
$$y = 9$$

We substitute y = 9 into the second equation, and solve for x:

$$2x + 3y = 5$$
$$2x + 3(9) = 5$$
$$2x + 27 = 5$$
$$2x = -22$$
$$x = -11$$

Since $s = \frac{1}{x}$ and $t = \frac{1}{y}$, then $s = -\frac{1}{11}$ and $t = \frac{1}{9}$.

So the solution is $\left(-\frac{1}{11}, \frac{1}{9}\right)$.

45. First let's clear of fractions and put into a standard form:

$$\frac{2w - 1}{3} + \frac{z + 2}{4} = 4 \text{ multiplying by 12 we get}$$

$$4(2w - 1) + 3(z + 2) = 12 \cdot 4$$
$$8w - 4 + 3z + 6 = 48$$
$$8w + 3z = 46$$

The second equation will be $w + 2z = 9$.

$$8w + 3z = 46$$
$$w + 2z = 9$$

or

$$8w + 3z = 46$$
$$-8w - 16z = -72$$
$$-13z = -26$$
$$z = 2$$

and $w = 9 - 2(2) = 5$
So the solution is $(w,z) = (5,2)$.

47. Using substitution, we'll solve the first equation for x:

$$1.03x - 2.54y = 5.47$$
$$1.03x = 2.54y + 5.47$$
$$x = 2.4660y + 5.3107$$

Now substitute into the second equation:

$$3.85x + 4.29y = -1.84$$
$$3.85(2.466y + 5.3107) + 4.29y = -1.84$$
$$13.7841y = -22.2862$$
$$y \approx -1.62$$

Substituting back for x:

$$x = 2.4660(-1.62) + 5.3107$$
$$x \approx 1.32$$

So the solution is $(1.32, -1.62)$.

49. We'll use the addition-subtraction method. We eliminate y by multiplying the first equation by 3 and the second equation by 4:

$$3\sqrt{5}\, x - 12\sqrt{3}\, y = 18$$
$$4\sqrt{2}\, x + 12\sqrt{3}\, y = 32$$

Adding, we get:

$$(3\sqrt{5} + 4\sqrt{2})\, x = 50$$
$$x = \frac{50}{3\sqrt{5} + 4\sqrt{2}}$$
$$x \approx 4.04$$

We substitute into the first equation:

$$3\sqrt{5}\, (4.0437) - 12\sqrt{3}\, y = 18$$

$$y = \frac{18 - 3\sqrt{5}(4.0437)}{-12\sqrt{3}}$$

$$y \approx 0.44$$

So the solution is (4.04,0.44)

51. If we take tu as our number, then it is important to distinguish between its value, $10t + u$, and the sum of its digits $t + u$. Here we are told that $t + u = 14$ and that $2t = u + 1$. We solve this system:

$$t + u = 14$$
$$2t - u = 1$$

Adding, we get:

$$3t = 15, \text{ so } t = 5$$

Thus $u = 9$ and our original two-digit number was 59.

53. Let l and w be the length and width, respectively, of the rectangle. Since the perimeter is 34 in., then $2l + 2w = 34$, or $l + w = 17$. We are also given that $l = 2 + 2w$, so we substitute:

$$l + w = 17$$
$$(2 + 2w) + w = 17$$
$$2 + 3w = 17$$
$$3w = 15, \text{ so } w = 5$$

Thus $l = 17 - w = 17 - 5 = 12$. Thus the length is 12 in. and the width is 5 in.

55. (a) We solve the first equation for y:

$$x + y = 100$$
$$y = 100 - x$$

Now substituting into the second equation:

$$-2x + 3y = 0$$
$$-2x + 3(100 - x) = 0$$
$$-2x + 300 - 3x = 0$$
$$300 - 5x = 0$$
$$300 = 5x, \text{ so } x = 60$$

So $y = 100 - 60 = 40$. Thus the solution is (60,40).

(b) We multiply the first equation by 2:

$$2x + 2y = 200$$
$$-2x + 3y = 0$$

Adding, we get:

$$5y = 200, \text{ so } y = 40$$

Substituting back into the first equation:

$$x + y = 100$$
$$x + 40 = 100$$
$$x = 60$$

Again, the solution is (60,40)

57. We solve each equation for x:
$$x = by - ab$$
$$x = cy - ac$$
Setting these equal:
$$by - ab = cy - ac$$
$$by - cy = ab - ac$$
$$y(b - c) = a(b - c)$$
$$y = a, \text{ as long as } b \neq c$$
Plugging into the second equation, we get:
$$x = cy - ac = ac - ac = 0$$
So the solution is $(0, a)$.

59. Let $u = \dfrac{1}{x}$ and $v = \dfrac{1}{y}$. Then we have:
$$\frac{a}{b}u + \frac{b}{a}v = a + b$$
$$bu + av = a^2 + b^2$$
Multiply the first equation by ab to clear the fractions:
$$a^2 u + b^2 v = a^2 b + ab^2$$
$$bu + av = a^2 + b^2$$
We multiply the first equation by $-b$ and the second equation by a^2:
$$-a^2 bu - b^3 v = -a^2 b^2 - ab^3$$
$$a^2 bu + a^3 v = a^4 + a^2 b^2$$
Adding, we get:
$$(a^3 - b^3)v = a^4 - ab^3$$
$$(a^3 - b^3)v = a(a^3 - b^3)$$
$$v = a$$
Substituting $v = a$ into the second equation, we get:
$$bu + av = a^2 + b^2$$
$$bu + a^2 = a^2 + b^2$$
$$bu = b^2$$
$$u = b$$
Since $x = \dfrac{1}{u}$ and $y = \dfrac{1}{v}$, then $x = \dfrac{1}{b}$ and $y = \dfrac{1}{a}$.

So the solution is $\left(\dfrac{1}{b}, \dfrac{1}{a}\right)$.

61. Since the lines are concurrent, the following two systems must possess the same solution:

I. $\quad\begin{aligned} 7x + 5y &= 4 \\ x + ky &= 3 \end{aligned}$ II. $\quad\begin{aligned} x + ky &= 3 \\ 5x + y &= -k \end{aligned}$

Using either method of this section, we find that the solution of system I is
$\left(\dfrac{4k - 15}{7k - 5}, \dfrac{17}{7k - 5}\right)$. Also the solution of system II is found to be
$\left(\dfrac{-3 - k^2}{5k - 1}, \dfrac{k + 15}{5k - 1}\right)$. Since the two solutions are the same, the corresponding
x and y coordinates must be equal. Equating the y-coordinates gives us:
$$\dfrac{17}{7k - 5} = \dfrac{k + 15}{5k - 1}$$
After clearing the fractions and simplifying, this equation becomes
$7k^2 + 15k - 58 = 0$. We factor to get $(7k + 29)(k - 2) = 0$ and therefore
$k = -\dfrac{29}{7}$ or $k = 2$. These are the required values of k. If we equate the
x-coordinates rather than the y-coordinates we obtain the equation
$7k^3 + 15k^2 - 58k = 0$. We factor to get $k(7k + 29)(k - 2) = 0$, which has
solutions $k = 0, -\dfrac{29}{7}$, and 2. The root $k = 0$ is extraneous, for in that case
the two y-coordinates are not equal.

63. (a)   We first draw the triangle:

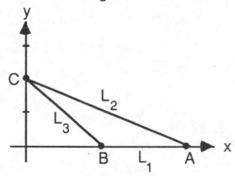

We find the equations for each side:

L_1: $y = 0$

L_2: $m = \dfrac{0 - 2}{2a - 0} = -\dfrac{1}{a}$

So $y = -\dfrac{1}{a}x + 2$

$ay = -x + 2a$

$x + ay = 2a$

L_3: $m = \dfrac{0 - 2}{2b - 0} = -\dfrac{1}{b}$

So $y = -\dfrac{1}{b}x + 2$

$by = -x + 2b$

$x + by = 2b$

(b)   We first find the midpoints of each side:

$$L_1: \quad \text{mid} = \left(\frac{2b + 2a}{2}, \frac{0}{2}\right) \quad = (a + b, 0)$$

$$L_2: \quad \text{mid} = \left(\frac{0 + 2a}{2}, \frac{2 + 0}{2}\right) \quad = (a, 1)$$

$$L_3: \quad \text{mid} = \left(\frac{0 + 2b}{2}, \frac{2 + 0}{2}\right) \quad = (b, 1)$$

Now we find the slopes from each vertex to the adjacent midpoint:

$$CL_1: \quad m = \frac{0 - 2}{a + b - 0} = \frac{-2}{a + b}$$

$$BL_2: \quad m = \frac{1 - 0}{a - 2b} = \frac{1}{a - 2b}$$

$$AL_3: \quad m = \frac{1 - 0}{b - 2a} = \frac{1}{b - 2a}$$

Finally, we use these slopes and vertices in the point-slope formula:

$$CL_1: \qquad y - 2 = \frac{-2}{a + b}(x - 0)$$

$$y = \frac{-2}{a + b}x + 2$$

$$(a + b)y = -2x + 2(a + b)$$

$$2x + (a + b)y = 2(a + b)$$

$$BL_2: \qquad y - 0 = \frac{1}{a - 2b}(x - 2b)$$

$$y = \frac{1}{a - 2b}x - \frac{2b}{a - 2b}$$

$$(a - 2b)y = x - 2b$$

$$-x + (a - 2b)y = -2b$$

$$x + (2b - a)y = 2b$$

$$AL_3: \qquad y - 0 = \frac{1}{b - 2a}(x - 2a)$$

$$y = \frac{1}{b - 2a}x - \frac{2a}{b - 2a}$$

$$(b - 2a)y = x - 2a$$

$$-x + (b - 2a)y = -2a$$

$$x + (2a - b)y = 2a$$

(c)   We find the intersection of the three lines:

$$2x + (a + b)y = 2(a + b)$$
$$x + (2b - a)y = 2b$$
$$x + (2a - b)y = 2a$$

We will solve the second and third equations for x:

$$x = 2b - (2b - a)y$$
$$x = 2a - (2a - b)y$$

Setting these equal:
$$2b - (2b - a)y = 2a - (2a - b)y$$
$$(2a - b)y - (2b - a)y = 2a - 2b$$
$$(2a - b - 2b + a)y = 2a - 2b$$
$$(3a - 3b)y = 2a - 2b$$
$$y = \frac{2a - 2b}{3a - 3b} = \frac{2(a - b)}{3(a - b)} = \frac{2}{3}$$

We substitute $y = \frac{2}{3}$ into the second equation:

$$x = 2b - (2b - a)\frac{2}{3}$$
$$= \frac{6b - 4b + 2a}{3}$$
$$= \frac{2b + 2a}{3}$$
$$= \frac{2(a + b)}{3}$$

We must still show that this point $\left(\frac{2(a + b)}{3}, \frac{2}{3}\right)$ lies on the first line:
$$2x + (a + b)y = 2(a + b)$$
$$4\left(\frac{a + b}{3}\right) + (a + b)\frac{2}{3} = 2(a + b)$$
$$6\frac{(a + b)}{3} = 2(a + b) \quad \surd$$

Thus the point $\left(\frac{2(a + b)}{3}, \frac{2}{3}\right)$ is the intersection of all three medians:

(d) The altitudes will be perpendicular to the slopes of each side, which we found in (a). So:

BL_2: $m = a$
$$y - 0 = a(x - 2b)$$
$$y = ax - 2ab$$
$$-ax + y = -2ab$$
$$ax - y = 2ab$$

CL_1: $m = $ undefined
$$x = 0$$

AL_3: $m = b$
$$y - 0 = b(x - 2a)$$
$$y = bx - 2ab$$
$$-bx + y = -2ab$$
$$bx - y = 2ab$$

(e)   We find the intersection of the three lines:
$$ax - y = 2ab$$
$$bx - y = 2ab$$
$$x = 0$$
Since $x = 0$, substituting into the first equation yields:
$$-y = 2ab$$
$$y = -2ab$$
We must still show that this point $(0,-2ab)$ lies on the second line:
$$bx - y = 2ab$$
$$b(0) - (-2ab) = 2ab$$
$$2ab = 2ab \ \sqrt{}$$
Thus, the point $(0,-2ab)$ is the intersection of all three altitudes.

(f) Recall that the perpendicular bisectors must be perpendicular and pass through the midpoints (which we found in (b)):
L_1:   mid $= (a + b, 0)$
  $m = $ undefined
  $x = a + b$

L_2:   mid $= (a, 1)$
  $m = a$
  $y - 1 = a(x - a)$
  $y - 1 = ax - a^2$
  $-ax + y = 1 - a^2$
  $ax - y = a^2 - 1$

L_3:   mid $= (b, 1)$
  $m = b$
  $y - 1 = b(x - b)$
  $y - 1 = bx - b^2$
  $-bx + y = 1 - b^2$
  $bx - y = b^2 - 1$

(g)   We find the intersection of the three lines:
$$ax - y = a^2 - 1$$
$$bx - y = b^2 - 1$$
$$x = a + b$$
Substituting into the first equation yields:
$$a(a + b) - y = a^2 - 1$$
$$a^2 + ab - y = a^2 - 1$$
$$-y = -ab - 1$$
$$y = ab + 1$$
We must still show that the point $(a + b, ab + 1)$ lies on the second line:

$$bx - y = b^2 - 1$$
$$b(a + b) - (ab + 1) = b^2 - 1$$
$$ab + b^2 - ab - 1 = b^2 - 1$$
$$b^2 - 1 = b^2 - 1 \quad \checkmark$$

Thus the point $(a + b, ab + 1)$ is the intersection of all three perpendicular bisectors.

(h) We find the line that passes through $\left(\dfrac{2(a + b)}{3}, \dfrac{2}{3}\right)$, $(0, -2ab)$, and $(a + b, ab + 1)$. We work with the last two points:

$$m = \frac{ab + 1 - (-2ab)}{a + b - 0} = \frac{3ab + 1}{a + b}$$

Since $(0, -2ab)$ is the y-intercept, then the line should be:

$$y = \frac{3ab + 1}{a + b}x - 2ab$$

We must still show that the point $\left(\dfrac{2(a + b)}{3}, \dfrac{2}{3}\right)$ lies on this line:

$$\frac{2}{3} = \left(\frac{3ab + 1}{a + b}\right)\left(\frac{2(a + b)}{3}\right) - 2ab$$

$$\frac{2}{3} = \frac{2(3ab + 1)}{3} - 2ab$$

$$\frac{2}{3} = \frac{6ab + 2 - 6ab}{3}$$

$$\frac{2}{3} = \frac{2}{3} \quad \checkmark$$

Thus, $y = \dfrac{3ab + 1}{a + b}x - 2ab$ is the Euler line.

10.2   Gaussian Elimination

1. Given:
$$2x + y + z = -9$$
$$3y - 2z = -4$$
$$8z = -8$$

We solve for z in the third equation:
$$8z = -8$$
$$z = -1$$

Substitute into the second equation:
$$3y - 2z = -4$$
$$3y - 2(-1) = -4$$
$$3y + 2 = -4$$
$$3y = -6$$

$$y = -2$$

Substitute into the first equation:

$$2x + y + z = -9$$
$$2x + (-2) + (-1) = -9$$
$$2x - 3 = 9$$
$$2x = -6$$
$$x = -3$$

So the solution is $(-3, -2, -1)$

3.   Given:

$$8x + 5y + 3z = 1$$
$$3y + 4z = 2$$
$$5z = 3$$

We solve for z in the third equation:

$$5z = 3$$
$$z = \frac{3}{5}$$

Substitute into the second equation:

$$3y + 4z = 2$$
$$3y + (4)\frac{3}{5} = 2$$
$$3y + \frac{12}{5} = 2$$
$$3y = -\frac{2}{5}$$
$$y = -\frac{2}{15}$$

Substitute into the first equation:

$$8x + 5y + 3z = 1$$
$$8x + 5\left(-\frac{2}{15}\right) + (3)\frac{3}{5} = 1$$
$$8x - \frac{2}{3} + \frac{9}{5} = 1$$
$$8x - \frac{10}{15} + \frac{27}{15} = 1$$
$$8x = -\frac{2}{15}$$
$$x = -\frac{1}{60}$$

So the solution is $\left(-\frac{1}{60}, -\frac{2}{15}, \frac{3}{5}\right)$

5.   Given:

$$-4x + 5y = 0$$
$$3y + 2z = 1$$

$$3z = -1$$

We solve for z in the third equation:

$$3z = -1$$

$$z = -\frac{1}{3}$$

Substitute into the second equation:

$$3y + 2z = 1$$

$$3y + 2\left(-\frac{1}{3}\right) = 1$$

$$3y - \frac{2}{3} = 1$$

$$3y = \frac{5}{3}$$

$$y = \frac{5}{9}$$

Substitute into the first equation:

$$-4x + 5y = 0$$

$$-4x + (5)\frac{5}{9} = 0$$

$$-4x + \frac{25}{9} = 0$$

$$-4x = -\frac{25}{9}$$

$$x = \frac{25}{36}$$

So the solution is $\left(\dfrac{25}{36}, \dfrac{5}{9}, -\dfrac{1}{3}\right)$.

7. Given:

$$-x + 8y + 3z = 0$$

$$2z = 0$$

We solve for z in the second equation:

$$2z = 0$$

$$z = 0$$

Substitute into the first equation:

$$-x + 8y + 3z = 0$$

$$-x + 8y + 3(0) = 0$$

$$-x + 8y = 0$$

$$8y = x$$

$$y = \frac{x}{8}$$

So the solution is $(x, \frac{x}{8}, 0)$, where x is any real number.

9.   Given:
$$2x + 3y + z + w = -6$$
$$y + 3z - 4w = 23$$
$$6z - 5w = 31$$
$$-2w = 10$$

We solve for w in the fourth equation:
$$-2w = 10$$
$$w = -5$$

Substitute into the third equation:
$$6z - 5w = 31$$
$$6z - 5(-5) = 31$$
$$6z + 25 = 31$$
$$6z = 6$$
$$z = 1$$

Substitute into the second equation:
$$y + 3z - 4w = 23$$
$$y + 3(1) - 4(-5) = 23$$
$$y + 23 = 23$$
$$y = 0$$

Substitute into the first equation:
$$2x + 3y + z + w = -6$$
$$2x + 3(0) + 1 + (-5) = -6$$
$$2x - 4 = -6$$
$$2x = -2$$
$$x = -1$$

So the solution is (-1,0,1,-5)

11.   We must arrange this according to echelon form. First add negative two times the first equation to the second one, and -3 times it to the third:
$$x + y + z = 12$$
$$-3y - 3z = -25$$
$$-y - 2z = -14$$

We want to eliminate the y term from the third equation so let's interchange the 2nd and 3rd equations:
$$x + y + z = 12$$
$$-y - 2z = -14$$
$$-3y - 3z = -25$$

Add -3 times the 2nd to the third:
$$x + y + z = 12$$
$$-y - 2z = -14$$
$$3z = 17$$

Solve for z in the third equation:
$$3z = 17$$
$$z = \frac{17}{3}$$

Sustitute into the second equation:

$$-y - 2z = -14$$

$$-y - (2)\frac{17}{3} = -14$$

$$-y - \frac{34}{3} = -14$$

$$-y = -\frac{8}{3}$$

$$y = \frac{8}{3}$$

Substitute into the first equation:

$$x + y + z = 12$$

$$x + \frac{8}{3} + \frac{17}{3} = 12$$

$$x + \frac{25}{3} = 12$$

$$x = \frac{11}{3}$$

So the solution is $\left(\frac{11}{3}, \frac{8}{3}, \frac{17}{3}\right)$

13. We must arrange the system in echelon form. Multiply the first equation by -2 and add it to the second equation:

$$-4x + 6y - 4z = -8$$
$$\underline{4x + 2y + 3z = 7}$$
$$8y - z = -1$$

Multiply the first equation by $-\frac{5}{2}$ and add it to the third equation:

$$-5x + \frac{15}{2}y - 5z = -10$$
$$\underline{5x + 4y + 2z = 7}$$
$$\frac{23}{2}y - 3z = -3$$
$$23y - 6z = -6$$

So we have the system:

$$2x - 3y + 2z = 4$$
$$8y - z = -1$$
$$23y - 6z = -6$$

Multiply the second equation by $-\frac{23}{8}$ and add it to the third equation:

$$-23y + \frac{23}{8}z = \frac{23}{8}$$
$$\underline{23y - 6z = -6}$$
$$-\frac{25}{8}z = -\frac{25}{8}$$

So we have the system in echelon form:
$$2x - 3y + 2z = 4$$
$$8y - z = -1$$
$$-\frac{25}{8}z = -\frac{25}{8}$$

Solve for z in the third equation:
$$-\frac{25}{8}z = -\frac{25}{8}$$
$$z = 1$$

Substitute into the second equation:
$$8y - z = -1$$
$$8y - 1 = -1$$
$$8y = 0$$
$$y = 0$$

Substitute into the first equation:
$$2x - 3y + 2z = 4$$
$$2x - 3(0) + 2(1) = 4$$
$$2x + 2 = 4$$
$$2x = 2$$
$$x = 1$$

So the solution is (1,0,1)

15. We must arrange the system in echelon form. Multiply the first equation by -2 and add it to the second equation:
$$-6x - 6y + 4z = -26$$
$$\underline{6x + 2y - 5z = 13}$$
$$-4y - z = -13$$

Multiply the first equation by $-\frac{7}{3}$ and add it to the third equation:

$$-7x - 7y + \frac{14}{3}z = -\frac{91}{3}$$
$$\underline{7x + 5y - 3z = 26}$$
$$-2y + \frac{5}{3}z = -\frac{13}{3}$$
$$-6y + 5z = -13$$

So we have the system:
$$3x + 3y - 2z = 13$$
$$-4y - z = -13$$
$$-6y + 5z = -13$$

Multiply the second equation by $-\frac{3}{2}$ and add it to the third equation:

$$6y + \frac{3}{2}z = \frac{39}{2}$$
$$\underline{-6y + 5z = -13}$$
$$\frac{13}{2}z = \frac{13}{2}$$

So we have the system in echelon form:
$$3x + 3y - 2z = 13$$
$$-4y - z = -13$$
$$\frac{13}{2}z = \frac{13}{2}$$

Solve for z in the third equation:
$$\frac{13}{2}z = \frac{13}{2}$$
$$z = 1$$

Substitute into the second equation:
$$-4y - z = -13$$
$$-4y - 1 = -13$$
$$-4y = -12$$
$$y = 3$$

Substitute into the first equation:
$$3x + 3y - 2z = 13$$
$$3x + 3(3) - 2(1) = 13$$
$$3x + 7 = 13$$
$$3x = 6$$
$$x = 2$$

So the solution is (2,3,1)

17. We must arrange the system in echelon form. Multiply the first equation by 2 and add it to the second equation:
$$2x + 2y + 2z = 2$$
$$\underline{-2x + y + z = -2}$$
$$3y + 3z = 0$$
$$y + z = 0$$

Multiply the first equation by -3 and add it to the third equation:
$$-3x - 3y - 3z = -3$$
$$\underline{3x + 6y + 6z = 5}$$
$$3y + 3z = 2$$

So we have the system:
$$x + y + z = 1$$
$$y + z = 0$$
$$3y + 3z = 2$$

Multiply the second equation by -3 and add it to the third equation:
$$-3y - 3z = 0$$
$$\underline{3y + 3z = 2}$$
$$0 = 2$$

Since this equation is false, there is no solution. This system is inconsistent.

19. We first re-arrange the system as:
$$x + 3y - 2z = 2$$
$$2x - y + z = -1$$
$$-5x + 6y - 5z = 5$$
Multiply the first equation by -2 and add it to the second equation:
$$-2x - 6y + 4z = -4$$
$$\underline{2x - y + z = -1}$$
$$-7y + 5z = -5$$
Multiply the first equation by 5 and add it to the third equation:
$$5x + 15y - 10z = 10$$
$$\underline{-5x + 6y - 5z = 5}$$
$$21y - 15z = 15$$
$$7y - 5z = 5$$
So we have the system:
$$x + 3y - 2z = 2$$
$$-7y + 5z = -5$$
$$7y - 5z = 5$$
Adding the second and third equations yields 0 = 0, so the system is dependent. Solving for x and y in terms of z yields the solution $\left(\dfrac{z+1}{-7}, \dfrac{5(z+1)}{7}, z \right)$, where z is any real number.

21. We first re-arrange the system as:
$$x + 3y + 2z = -1$$
$$2x - y + z = 4$$
$$7x + 5z = 11$$
Multiply the first equation by -2 and add it to the second equation:
$$-2x - 6y - 4z = 2$$
$$\underline{2x - y + z = 4}$$
$$-7y - 3z = 6$$
Multiply the first equation by -7 and add it to the third equation:
$$-7x - 21y - 14z = 7$$
$$\underline{7x + 5z = 11}$$
$$-21y - 9z = 18$$
$$-7y - 3z = 6$$
So we have the system:
$$x + 3y + 2z = -1$$
$$-7y - 3z = 6$$
$$-7y - 3z = 6$$
Multiply the second equation by -1 and add it to the third equation:
$$7y + 3z = -6$$
$$\underline{-7y - 3z = 6}$$
$$0 = 0$$

So we have the system:
$$x + 3y + 2z = -1$$
$$-7y - 3z = 6$$
We solve the second equation for y:
$$-7y - 3z = 6$$
$$-7y = 3z + 6$$
$$y = \frac{-3z - 6}{7}$$
Substitute into the first equation:
$$x + 3y + 2z = -1$$
$$x + 3\left(\frac{-3z - 6}{7}\right) + 2z = -1$$
$$x + \frac{-9z - 18 + 14z}{7} = -1$$
$$x + \frac{5z - 18}{7} = -1$$
$$x = \frac{-7 - 5z + 18}{7}$$
$$x = \frac{-5z + 11}{7}$$
So the solution is $\left(\frac{11 - 5z}{7}, \frac{-3z - 6}{7}, z\right)$ where z is any real number.

23. Multiply the first equation by -1 and add it to the second equation:
$$-x - y - z - w = -4$$
$$\underline{x - 2y - z - w = 3}$$
$$-3y - 2z - 2w = -1$$
$$3y + 2z + 2w = 1$$
Multiply the first equation by -2 and add it to the third equation:
$$-2x - 2y - 2z - 2w = -8$$
$$\underline{2x - y + z - w = 2}$$
$$-3y - z - 3w = -6$$
$$3y + z + 3w = 6$$
Multiply the first equation by -1 and add it to the fourth equation:
$$-x - y - z - w = -4$$
$$\underline{x - y + 2z - 2w = -7}$$
$$-2y + z - 3w = -11$$
$$2y - z + 3w = 11$$
So we have the system:
$$x + y + z + w = 4$$
$$3y + 2z + 2w = 1$$
$$3y + z + 3w = 6$$
$$2y - z + 3w = 11$$

Multiply the second equation by -1 and add it to the third equation:

$$-3y - 2z - 2w = -1$$
$$\underline{3y + z + 3w = 6}$$
$$-z + w = 5$$
$$z - w = -5$$

Multiply the second equation by $-\frac{2}{3}$ and add it to the fourth equation:

$$-2y - \frac{4}{3}z - \frac{4}{3}w = -\frac{2}{3}$$
$$\underline{2y - z + 3w = 11}$$
$$-\frac{7}{3}z + \frac{5}{3}w = \frac{31}{3}$$
$$-7z + 5w = 31$$

So we have the system:

$$x + y + z + w = 4$$
$$3y + 2z + 2w = 1$$
$$z - w = -5$$
$$-7z + 5w = 31$$

Multiply the third equation by 7 and add it to the fourth equation:

$$7z - 7w = -35$$
$$\underline{-7z + 5w = 31}$$
$$-2w = -4$$

So we have the system:

$$x + y + z + w = 4$$
$$3y + 2z + 2w = 1$$
$$z - w = -5$$
$$-2w = -4$$

We solve the fourth equation for w:

$$-2w = -4$$
$$w = 2$$

Substitute into the third equation:

$$z - w = -5$$
$$z - 2 = -5$$
$$z = -3$$

Substitute into the second equation:

$$3y + 2z + 2w = 1$$
$$3y + 2(-3) + 2(2) = 1$$
$$3y - 2 = 1$$
$$3y = 3$$
$$y = 1$$

Substitute into the first equation:

$$x + y + z + w = 4$$
$$x + 1 - 3 + 2 = 4$$
$$x = 4$$

So the solution is (4,1,-3,2)

25. We first re-arrange the system as:
$$x + 4y - 3z = 1$$
$$2x + 3y + 2z = 5$$
Multiply the first equation by -2 and add it to the second equation:
$$-2x - 8y + 6z = -2$$
$$\underline{2x + 3y + 2z = 5}$$
$$-5y + 8z = 3$$
So we have the system:
$$x + 4y - 3z = 1$$
$$-5y + 8z = 3$$
We solve the second equation for y:
$$-5y + 8z = 3$$
$$-5y = 3 - 8z$$
$$y = \frac{8z - 3}{5}$$
Substitute into the first equation:
$$x + 4y - 3z = 1$$
$$x + 4\left(\frac{8z - 3}{5}\right) - 3z = 1$$
$$x + \frac{17z - 12}{5} = 1$$
$$x = \frac{17 - 17z}{5}$$
So the solution is $\left(\dfrac{17 - 17z}{5}, \dfrac{8z - 3}{5}, z\right)$, where z is any real number.

27. Multiply the first equation by -3 and add it to the second equation:
$$-3x + 6y + 6z - 6w = 30$$
$$\underline{3x + 4y - z - 3w = 11}$$
$$10y + 5z - 9w = 41$$
Multiply the first equation by 4 and add it to the third equation:
$$4x - 8y - 8z + 8w = -40$$
$$\underline{-4x - 3y - 3z + 8w = -21}$$
$$-11y - 11z + 16w = -61$$
So we have the system:
$$x - 2y - 2z + 2w = -10$$
$$10y + 5z - 9w = 41$$
$$-11y - 11z + 16w = -61$$
We add the second and third equations:
$$10y + 5z - 9w = 41$$
$$\underline{-11y - 11z + 16w = -61}$$
$$-y - 6z + 7w = -20$$
$$y + 6z - 7w = 20$$

So we have the system:
$$x - 2y - 2z + 2w = -10$$
$$y + 6z - 7w = 20$$
$$-11y - 11z + 16w = -61$$
Multiply the second equation by 11 and add it to the third equation:
$$11y + 66z - 77w = 220$$
$$\underline{-11y - 11z + 16w = -61}$$
$$55z - 61w = 159$$
So we have the system:
$$x - 2y - 2z + 2w = -10$$
$$y + 6z - 7w = 20$$
$$55z - 61w = 159$$
We solve the third equation for z:
$$55z - 61w = 159$$
$$55z = 61w + 159$$
$$z = \frac{61w + 159}{55}$$
Substitute into the second equation:
$$y + 6z - 7w = 20$$
$$y + 6\left(\frac{61w + 159}{55}\right) - 7w = 20$$
$$y + \frac{954 - 19w}{55} = 20$$
$$y = \frac{146 + 19w}{55}$$
Substitute into the first equation:
$$x - 2y - 2z + 2w = -10$$
$$x - 2\left(\frac{146 + 19w}{55}\right) - 2\left(\frac{61w + 159}{55}\right) + 2w = -10$$
$$x + \frac{-122 - 10w}{11} = -10$$
$$x = \frac{12 + 10w}{11}$$
So the solution is $\left(\dfrac{12 + 10w}{11}, \dfrac{146 + 19w}{55}, \dfrac{61w + 159}{55}, w\right)$, where w is any real number.

29. Solving the second equation for y yields $y = \dfrac{2z + 3}{3}$. We substitute this into the first equation to get $x = -\dfrac{5z}{12}$. So the solution is $\left(-\dfrac{5z}{12}, \dfrac{2z + 3}{3}, z\right)$, where z is any real number.

31. (a)   Multiply by $(x - 2)(x + 2)$, so:

$$1 = A(x + 2) + B(x - 2)$$
$$1 = Ax + 2A + Bx - 2B$$
$$1 = (A + B)x + (2A - 2B)$$

Since A and B are constants (cannot contain x), then we must have:

$$A + B = 0$$
$$2A - 2B = 1$$

Multiply the first equation by -2 and add it to the second equation:

$$-2A - 2B = 0$$
$$\underline{2A - 2B = 1}$$
$$-4B = 1$$
$$B = -\frac{1}{4}$$

Substituting into the first equation:

$$A + B = 0$$
$$A - \frac{1}{4} = 0$$
$$A = \frac{1}{4}$$

So $A = \frac{1}{4}$ and $B = -\frac{1}{4}$

(b)   Multiply by $(x - 2)(x + 2)$, so:

$$x = A(x + 2) + B(x - 2)$$
$$x = Ax + 2A + Bx - 2B$$
$$x = (A + B)x + (2A - 2B)$$

Since A and B are constants then we have the system:

$$A + B = 1$$
$$2A - 2B = 0$$

Multiply the first equation by -2 and add it to the second equation:

$$-2A - 2B = -2$$
$$\underline{2A - 2B = 0}$$
$$-4B = -2$$
$$B = \frac{1}{2}$$

Substituting into the first equation:

$$A + B = 1$$
$$A + \frac{1}{2} = 1$$
$$A = \frac{1}{2}$$

So $A = \frac{1}{2}$ and $B = \frac{1}{2}$

33.   Multiply by $(x + 4)(x - 5)$, so:
$$3x = A(x - 5) + B(x + 4)$$
$$3x = Ax - 5A + Bx + 4B$$
$$3x = (A + B)x + (-5A + 4B)$$
Since A and B are constants, then we have the system:
$$A + B = 3$$
$$-5A + 4B = 0$$
Multiply the first equation by 5 and add it to the second equation:
$$5A + 5B = 15$$
$$\underline{-5A + 4B = 0}$$
$$9B = 15$$
$$B = \frac{5}{3}$$
Substituting into the first equation:
$$A + B = 3$$
$$A + \frac{5}{3} = 3$$
$$A = \frac{4}{3}$$
So $A = \frac{4}{3}$ and $B = \frac{5}{3}$

35.   (a)   Multiply by $(x - 4)(x + 4)$, so:
$$3 = A(x + 4) + B(x - 4)$$
$$3 = Ax + 4A + Bx - 4B$$
$$3 = (A + B)x + (4A - 4B)$$
Since A and B are constants, we have:
$$A + B = 0$$
$$4A - 4B = 3$$
Multiply the first equation by -4 and add it to the second equation:
$$-4A - 4B = 0$$
$$\underline{4A - 4B = 3}$$
$$-8B = 3$$
$$B = -\frac{3}{8}$$
Substituting into the first equation:
$$A + B = 0$$
$$A - \frac{3}{8} = 0$$
$$A = \frac{3}{8}$$
So $A = \frac{3}{8}$ and $B = -\frac{3}{8}$

(b) Multiply by $(x - 4)(x + 4)^2$, so:

$$3 = A(x + 4)^2 + B(x - 4)(x + 4) + C(x - 4)$$
$$3 = Ax^2 + 8Ax + 16A + Bx^2 - 16B + Cx - 4C$$
$$3 = (A + B)x^2 + (8A + C)x + (16A - 16B - 4C)$$

Since A, B, and C are constants, we have:

$$A + B = 0$$
$$8A + C = 0$$
$$16A - 16B - 4C = 3$$

Multiply the first equation by -8 and add it to the second equation:

$$-8A - 8B = 0$$
$$\underline{8A + \quad C = 0}$$
$$-8B + C = 0$$

Multiply the first equation by -16 and add it to the third equation:

$$-16A - 16B = 0$$
$$\underline{16A - 16B - 4C = 3}$$
$$-32B - 4C = 3$$

So we have the system:

$$A + B = 0$$
$$-8B + C = 0$$
$$-32B - 4C = 3$$

Multiply the second equation by -4 and add it to the third equation:

$$32B - 4C = 0$$
$$\underline{-32B - 4C = 3}$$
$$-8C = 3$$
$$C = -\frac{3}{8}$$

Substitute into the second equation:

$$-8B + C = 0$$
$$-8B - \frac{3}{8} = 0$$
$$-8B = \frac{3}{8}$$
$$B = -\frac{3}{64}$$

Substitute into the first equation:

$$A + B = 0$$
$$A - \frac{3}{64} = 0$$
$$A = \frac{3}{64}$$

So $A = \frac{3}{64}$, $B = -\frac{3}{64}$, and $C = -\frac{3}{8}$

37. Multiply by $(x + 1)(x^2 - x + 1)$, so:

$$1 = A(x^2 - x + 1) + (Bx + C)(x + 1)$$
$$1 = Ax^2 - Ax + A + Bx^2 + Cx + Bx + C$$
$$1 = (A + B)x^2 + (-A + B + C)x + (A + C)$$

Since A, B, and C are constants, we have:

$$A + B = 0$$
$$-A + B + C = 0$$
$$A + C = 1$$

Add the first two equations:

$$A + B = 0$$
$$\underline{-A + B + C = 0}$$
$$2B + C = 0$$

Multiply the first equation by -1 and add it to the third equation:

$$-A - B = 0$$
$$\underline{A + C = 1}$$
$$-B + C = 1$$

So we have the system:

$$A + B = 0$$
$$-B + C = 1$$
$$2B + C = 0$$

Multiply the second equation by 2 and add it to the third equation:

$$-2B + 2C = 2$$
$$\underline{2B + C = 0}$$
$$3C = 2$$
$$C = \frac{2}{3}$$

Substitute into the second equation:

$$-B + C = 1$$
$$-B + \frac{2}{3} = 1$$
$$-B = \frac{1}{3}$$
$$B = -\frac{1}{3}$$

Substitute into the first equation:

$$A + B = 0$$
$$A - \frac{1}{3} = 0$$
$$A = \frac{1}{3}$$

So $A = \frac{1}{3}$, $B = -\frac{1}{3}$, and $C = \frac{2}{3}$

39. Multiply by x(1 - x), so:

$$4 = A(1 - x) + B(x)$$
$$4 = (-A + B)x + A$$

Since A and B are constants, wehave:

$$-A + B = 0$$
$$A = 4$$

Substituting yields -4 + B = 0, so B = 4.
So A = 4 and B = 4.

41. Multiply by $(x^2 + x + 1)(x^2 - x + 1)$, so:

$$1 = (Ax + B)(x^2 - x + 1) + (Cx + D)(x^2 + x + 1)$$
$$1 = (A + C)x^3 + (-A + B + C + D)x^2 + (A - B + C + D)x + (B + D)$$

Since A, B, C, and D are constants, we have:

$$A \quad + C \quad = 0$$
$$-A + B + C + D = 0$$
$$A - B + C + D = 0$$
$$B \quad + D = 1$$

Add the first and second equations:

$$A \quad + C \quad = 0$$
$$\underline{-A + B \ + \ C + D = 0}$$
$$B + 2C + D = 0$$

Multiply the first equation by -1 and add it to the third equation:

$$-A \quad - C \quad = 0$$
$$\underline{A - B + C + D \ = 0}$$
$$-B \quad + D = 0$$

So we have the system:

$$A \quad + C \quad = 0$$
$$-B \quad + D = 0$$
$$B + 2C + D = 0$$
$$B \quad + D = 1$$

Add the second and third equations:

$$- B \quad + D = 0$$
$$\underline{B + 2C \ + D = 0}$$
$$2C + 2D = 0$$
$$C + D = 0$$

Add the second and the fourth equations:

$$-B + D = 0$$
$$B + D = 1$$
$$2D = 1$$
$$D = \frac{1}{2}$$

So we have the system:

$$A \quad + C \qquad = 0$$
$$\quad -B \qquad + D = 0$$
$$\qquad C + D = 0$$
$$\qquad\qquad D = \frac{1}{2}$$

Substituting into the third equation yields $C = -\frac{1}{2}$

Substitution into the second equation yields $B = \frac{1}{2}$

Substituting into the first equation yields $A = \frac{1}{2}$

So $A = \frac{1}{2}$, $B = \frac{1}{2}$, $C = -\frac{1}{2}$, and $D = \frac{1}{2}$

43. We know its form is $(x - h)^2 + (y - k)^2 = r^2$, so:

$$(-1 - h)^2 + (-5 - k)^2 = r^2$$
$$(1 - h)^2 + (2 - k)^2 = r^2$$
$$(-2 - h)^2 + k^2 = r^2$$

Or:

$$1 + 2h + h^2 + 25 + 10k + k^2 = r^2$$
$$1 - 2h + h^2 + 4 - 4k + k^2 = r^2$$
$$4 + 4h + h^2 + k^2 = r^2$$

Setting the first two equations equal yields $4h + 14k = -21$ and setting the last two equations equal yields $6h + 4k = 1$.
So we solve the system:

$$4h + 14k = -21$$
$$6h + 4k = 1$$

Multiplying the first equation by -3 and the second equation by 2, then adding, yields $k = -\frac{65}{34}$, and substituting into the second equation yields $h = \frac{49}{34}$.
We find r by the original third equation:

$$r^2 = 4 + 4h + h^2 + k^2$$
$$= 4 + \frac{98}{17} + \left(\frac{49}{34}\right)^2 + \left(-\frac{65}{34}\right)^2$$
$$= \frac{17914}{34^2}$$
$$= \frac{8957}{578}$$

So we have $\left(x - \frac{49}{34}\right)^2 + \left(y + \frac{65}{34}\right)^2 = \frac{8957}{578}$, which simplifies to:

$$17x^2 + 17y^2 - 49x + 65y - 166 = 0$$

45. Using the hint, we let $A = e^x$, $B = e^y$, and $C = e^z$. Then we have the system:

$$A + B - 2C = 2a$$
$$A + 2B - 4C = 3a$$
$$\frac{1}{2}A - 3B + C = -5a$$

Multiply the first equation by -1 and add it to the second equation:

$$-A - B + 2C = -2a$$
$$\underline{A + 2B - 4C = 3a}$$
$$B - 2C = a$$

Multiply the first equation by -1 and the third equation by 2, then add the resulting equations:

$$-A - B + 2C = -2a$$
$$\underline{A - 6B + 2C = -10a}$$
$$-7B + 4C = -12a$$

So we have the system:

$$A + B - 2C = 2a$$
$$B - 2C = a$$
$$-7B + 4C = -12a$$

Multiply the second equation by 7 and add it to the third equation:

$$7B - 14C = 7a$$
$$\underline{-7B + 4C = -12a}$$
$$-10C = -5a$$

$$C = \frac{a}{2}$$

Substituting into the second equation:

$$B - 2C = a$$
$$B - 2\left(\frac{a}{2}\right) = a$$
$$B - a = a$$
$$B = 2a$$

Substituting into the first equation:

$$A + B - 2C = 2a$$
$$A + 2a - a = 2a$$
$$A + a = 2a$$
$$A = a$$

So $A = a$, $B = 2a$, $C = \frac{a}{2}$. Since $A = e^x$, $B = e^y$, $C = e^z$, then $x = \ln a$, $y = \ln 2a$, and $z = \ln \frac{a}{2}$

47. From the figure in the text, we obtain the system of three equations:

$$r_1 + r_2 = a$$
$$r_2 + r_3 = b$$
$$r_1 + r_3 = c$$

This system can be solved by repeated substitution, or by using the following technique. Add the three equations and then divide by 2 to obtain

$r_1 + r_2 + r_3 = \dfrac{a+b+c}{2}$. Now replace $r_2 + r_3$ in this last equation by b. The

result is $r_1 = \dfrac{a+b+c}{2} - b$. Thus $r_1 = \dfrac{a-b+c}{2}$. Similarly, we find that

$r_2 = \dfrac{a+b-c}{2}$, and $r_3 = \dfrac{b+c-a}{2}$.

49. (a) Multiply by (x - a)(x - b), so:

$$1 = A(x - b) + B(x - a)$$
$$1 = (A + B)x + (-bA - aB)$$

Since A and B are constants, we have:

$$A + B = 0$$
$$-bA - aB = 1$$

Multiplying the first equation by b and adding it to the second equation,

yields $B = \dfrac{1}{b-a}$. We re-solve for A. Multiplying the first equation by a

and adding it to the second equation, yields $A = \dfrac{1}{a-b}$.

So $A = \dfrac{1}{a-b}$ and $B = \dfrac{1}{b-a}$.

(b) Multiply by (x - a)(x - b), so:

$$px + q = A(x - b) + B(x - a)$$
$$px + q = (A + B)x + (-bA - aB)$$

Since A and B are constants, we have:

$$A + B = p$$
$$-bA - aB = q$$

Multiplying the first equation by b and adding it to the second equation

yields $B = \dfrac{bp+q}{b-a}$. We re-solve for A. Multiplying the first equation by

a and adding it to the second equation yields $A = \dfrac{ap+q}{a-b}$.

So $A = \dfrac{ap+q}{a-b}$ and $B = \dfrac{bp+q}{b-a}$.

51. We multiply by $(x - a)(x - b)(x - c)$ to get:
$$x^2 + px + q = A(x - b)(x - c) + B(x - a)(x - c) + C(x - a)(x - b)$$
For this problem, I'll show you a different method. Since this equation is an identity for all x, then it must be an identity for $x = a$, $x = b$, and $x = c$.

$x = a$: $\qquad a^2 + pa + q = A(a - b)(a - c) + 0 + 0$

$$A = \frac{a^2 + pa + q}{(a - b)(a - c)}$$

$x = b$: $\qquad b^2 + pb + q = 0 + B(b - a)(b - c) + 0$

$$B = \frac{b^2 + pb + q}{(b - a)(b - c)}$$

$x = c$: $\qquad c^2 + pc + q = 0 + 0 + C(c - a)(c - b)$

$$C = \frac{c^2 + pc + q}{(c - a)(c - b)}$$

So $A = \dfrac{a^2 + pa + q}{(a - b)(a - c)}$, $B = \dfrac{b^2 + pb + q}{(b - a)(b - c)}$, and $C = \dfrac{c^2 + pc + q}{(c - a)(c - b)}$

53. Let α, β, and γ be the distances opposite towns A, B, and C. The walking, riding, and driving rates are, respectively, $\dfrac{1}{a}$ mi/min, $\dfrac{1}{b}$ mi/min, and $\dfrac{1}{c}$ mi/min.
From the statement of the problem we can obtain the following system of three equations:

$$\alpha a + \beta b + \gamma c = 60(a + c - b)$$
$$\beta a + \gamma b + \alpha c = 60(b + a - c)$$
$$\gamma a + \alpha b + \beta c = 60(c + b - a)$$

By adding all three equations, we obtain:
$$\alpha(a + b + c) + \beta(a + b + c) + \gamma(a + b + c) = 60(a + b + c)$$

Now divide through by the quantity $a + b + c$. This yields $\alpha + \beta + \gamma = 60$ miles, as required.

10.3 Matrices

1. (a) two by three (2 x 3)
   (b) three by two (3 x 2)

3. five by four (5 x 4)

5.   coefficient matrix: $\begin{pmatrix} 2 & 3 & 4 \\ 5 & 6 & 7 \\ 8 & 9 & 10 \end{pmatrix}$

augmented matix: $\begin{pmatrix} 2 & 3 & 4 & 10 \\ 5 & 6 & 7 & 9 \\ 8 & 9 & 10 & 8 \end{pmatrix}$

7.   coefficient matix: $\begin{pmatrix} 1 & 0 & 1 & 1 \\ 1 & 1 & 0 & 2 \\ 0 & 1 & 1 & 1 \\ 2 & -1 & -1 & 0 \end{pmatrix}$

augmented matix: $\begin{pmatrix} 1 & 0 & 1 & 1 & -1 \\ 1 & 1 & 0 & 2 & 0 \\ 0 & 1 & 1 & 1 & 1 \\ 2 & -1 & -1 & 0 & 2 \end{pmatrix}$

9.   Form the augmented matrix: $\begin{pmatrix} 1 & -1 & 2 & 7 \\ 3 & 2 & -1 & -10 \\ -1 & 3 & 1 & -2 \end{pmatrix}$

Adding -3 times row 1 to row 2 and adding row 1 to row 3 yields:

$\begin{pmatrix} 1 & -1 & 2 & 7 \\ 0 & 5 & -7 & -31 \\ 0 & 2 & 3 & 5 \end{pmatrix}$

Multiplying row 3 by -3 and adding to row 2 yields:

$\begin{pmatrix} 1 & -1 & 2 & 7 \\ 0 & -1 & -16 & -46 \\ 0 & 2 & 3 & 5 \end{pmatrix}$

Multiplying row 2 by 2 and adding to row 3 yields:

$\begin{pmatrix} 1 & -1 & 2 & 7 \\ 0 & -1 & -16 & -46 \\ 0 & 0 & -29 & -87 \end{pmatrix}$

So we have the system of equations:

$$x - y + 2z = 7$$
$$-y - 16z = -46$$
$$-29z = -87$$

Solve equation 3 for z:

$$-29z = -87$$
$$z = 3$$

Substitute into equation 2:

$$-y - 48 = -46$$
$$-y = 2$$
$$y = -2$$

Substitute into equation 1:
$$x + 2 + 6 = 7$$
$$x = -1$$
So the solution is (-1,-2,3)

11. Form the augmented matrix:
$$\begin{pmatrix} 1 & 0 & 1 & -2 \\ -3 & 2 & 0 & 17 \\ 1 & -1 & -1 & -9 \end{pmatrix}$$

Adding 3 times row 1 to row 2, and -1 times row 1 to row 3 yields:
$$\begin{pmatrix} 1 & 0 & 1 & -2 \\ 0 & 2 & 3 & 11 \\ 0 & -1 & -2 & -7 \end{pmatrix}$$

Switching row 2 and row 3:
$$\begin{pmatrix} 1 & 0 & 1 & -2 \\ 0 & -1 & -2 & -7 \\ 0 & 2 & 3 & 11 \end{pmatrix}$$

Multiplying row 2 by 2 and adding it to row 3 yields:
$$\begin{pmatrix} 1 & 0 & 1 & -2 \\ 0 & -1 & -2 & -7 \\ 0 & 0 & -1 & -3 \end{pmatrix}$$

So we have the system:
$$x \quad + z = -2$$
$$-y - 2z = -7$$
$$-z = -3$$

Solve equation 3 for z:
$$-z = -3$$
$$z = 3$$

Substitute into equation 2:
$$-y - 6 = -7$$
$$-y = -1$$
$$y = 1$$

Substitute into equation 1:
$$x + 3 = -2$$
$$x = -5$$
So the solution is (-5,1,3)

13. Form the augmented matrix:
$$\begin{pmatrix} 1 & 1 & 1 & -4 \\ 2 & -3 & 1 & -1 \\ 4 & 2 & -3 & 33 \end{pmatrix}$$

Adding -2 times row 1 to row 2, and -4 times row 1 to row 4 yields:
$$\begin{pmatrix} 1 & 1 & 1 & -4 \\ 0 & -5 & -1 & 7 \\ 0 & -2 & -7 & 49 \end{pmatrix}$$

Adding -3 times row 3 to row 2 (to get a 1 entry) yields:

$$\begin{pmatrix} 1 & 1 & 1 & -4 \\ 0 & 1 & 20 & -140 \\ 0 & -2 & -7 & 49 \end{pmatrix}$$

Adding 2 times row 2 to row 3 yields:

$$\begin{pmatrix} 1 & 1 & 1 & -4 \\ 0 & 1 & 20 & -140 \\ 0 & 0 & 33 & -231 \end{pmatrix}$$

So we have the system of equations:

$$\begin{aligned} x + y + \quad z &= -4 \\ y + 20z &= -140 \\ 33z &= -231 \end{aligned}$$

Solving the last equation for z:

$$\begin{aligned} 33z &= -231 \\ z &= -7 \end{aligned}$$

Substituting into the second equation:

$$\begin{aligned} y + 20z &= -140 \\ y - 140 &= -140 \\ y &= 0 \end{aligned}$$

Substituting into the first equation:

$$\begin{aligned} x + y + z &= -4 \\ x + 0 - 7 &= -4 \\ x &= 3 \end{aligned}$$

So the solution is (3,0,-7)

15. Form the augmented matrix:

$$\begin{pmatrix} 3 & -2 & 6 & 0 \\ 1 & 3 & 20 & 15 \\ 10 & -11 & -10 & -9 \end{pmatrix}$$

Switching row 1 and row 2 yields:

$$\begin{pmatrix} 1 & 3 & 20 & 15 \\ 3 & -2 & 6 & 0 \\ 10 & -11 & -10 & -9 \end{pmatrix}$$

Adding -3 times row 1 to row 2, and -10 times row 1 to row 3 yields:

$$\begin{pmatrix} 1 & 3 & 20 & 15 \\ 0 & -11 & -54 & -45 \\ 0 & -41 & -210 & -159 \end{pmatrix}$$

Multiplying row 2 by -4 and adding it to row 3 yields:

$$\begin{pmatrix} 1 & 3 & 20 & 15 \\ 0 & -11 & -54 & -45 \\ 0 & 3 & 6 & 21 \end{pmatrix}$$

Dividing row 3 by 3 and then switching it with row 2 yields:

$$\begin{pmatrix} 1 & 3 & 20 & 15 \\ 0 & 1 & 2 & 7 \\ 0 & -11 & -54 & -45 \end{pmatrix}$$

Multiplying row 2 by 11 and adding it to row 3 yields:

$$\begin{pmatrix} 1 & 3 & 20 & 15 \\ 0 & 1 & 2 & 7 \\ 0 & 0 & -32 & 32 \end{pmatrix}$$

So we have the system of equations:

$$x + 3y + 20z = 15$$
$$y + 2z = 7$$
$$-32z = 32$$

Solve equation 3 for z:

$$-32z = 32$$
$$z = -1$$

Substitute into equation 2:

$$y - 2 = 7$$
$$y = 9$$

Substitute into equation 1:

$$x + 27 - 20 = 15$$
$$x + 7 = 15$$
$$x = 8$$

So the solution is (8,9,-1)

17. Form the augmented matrix:

$$\begin{pmatrix} 4 & -3 & 3 & 2 \\ 5 & 1 & -4 & 1 \\ 9 & -2 & -1 & 3 \end{pmatrix}$$

Subtracting row 1 from row 2 yields:

$$\begin{pmatrix} 4 & -3 & 3 & 2 \\ 1 & 4 & -7 & -1 \\ 9 & -2 & -1 & 3 \end{pmatrix}$$

Switching row 1 and row 2 yields:

$$\begin{pmatrix} 1 & 4 & -7 & -1 \\ 4 & -3 & 3 & 2 \\ 9 & -2 & -1 & 3 \end{pmatrix}$$

Adding -4 times row 1 to row 2, and -9 times row 1 to row 3 yields:

$$\begin{pmatrix} 1 & 4 & -7 & -1 \\ 0 & -19 & 31 & 6 \\ 0 & -38 & 62 & 12 \end{pmatrix}$$

Multiplying row 2 by -2 and adding it to row 3 yields:

$$\begin{pmatrix} 1 & 4 & -7 & -1 \\ 0 & -19 & 31 & 6 \\ 0 & 0 & 0 & 0 \end{pmatrix}$$

So we have the system of equations:

$$x + 4y - 7z = -1$$
$$-19y + 31z = 6$$

We solve equation 2 for y:
$$-19y = 6 - 31z$$
$$y = \frac{31z - 6}{19}$$

Substitute into equation 1:
$$x + 4\left(\frac{31z - 6}{19}\right) - 7z = -1$$
$$x + \frac{-9z - 24}{19} = -1$$
$$x = \frac{9z + 5}{19}$$

So the solution is $\left(\dfrac{9z + 5}{19}, \dfrac{31z - 6}{19}, z\right)$ for any real number z.

19. Form the augmented matrix:

$$\begin{pmatrix} 1 & -1 & 1 & 1 & 6 \\ 1 & 1 & -1 & 1 & 4 \\ 1 & 1 & 1 & -1 & -2 \\ -1 & 1 & 1 & 1 & 0 \end{pmatrix}$$

Adding -1 times row 1 to both row 2 and row 3, and adding row 1 to row 4 yields:

$$\begin{pmatrix} 1 & -1 & 1 & 1 & 6 \\ 0 & 2 & -2 & 0 & -2 \\ 0 & 2 & 0 & -2 & -8 \\ 0 & 0 & 2 & 2 & 6 \end{pmatrix}$$

Dividing rows 2, 3, and 4 by 2 and subtracting row 2 from row 3 yields:

$$\begin{pmatrix} 1 & -1 & 1 & 1 & 6 \\ 0 & 1 & -1 & 0 & -1 \\ 0 & 0 & 1 & -1 & -3 \\ 0 & 0 & 1 & 1 & 3 \end{pmatrix}$$

Multiplying row 3 by -1 and adding it to row 4 yields:

$$\begin{pmatrix} 1 & -1 & 1 & 1 & 6 \\ 0 & 1 & -1 & 0 & -1 \\ 0 & 0 & 1 & -1 & -3 \\ 0 & 0 & 0 & 2 & 6 \end{pmatrix}$$

So we have the system of equations:
$$x - y + z + w = 6$$
$$y - z = -1$$
$$z - w = -3$$
$$2w = 6$$

Solve equation 4 for w:
$$2w = 6$$
$$w = 3$$

Substitute into equation 3:
$$z - 3 = -3$$
$$z = 0$$
Substitute into equation 2:
$$y - 0 = -1$$
$$y = -1$$
Substitute into equation 1:
$$x + 1 + 0 + 3 = 6$$
$$x + 4 = 6$$
$$x = 2$$
So the solution is $(2, -1, 0, 3)$

21. Form the augmented matrix:
$$\begin{pmatrix} 15 & 14 & 26 & 1 \\ 18 & 17 & 32 & -1 \\ 21 & 20 & 38 & 0 \end{pmatrix}$$
We reduce coefficients by subtracting row 2 from row 3, and row 1 from row 2:
$$\begin{pmatrix} 15 & 15 & 26 & 1 \\ 3 & 3 & 6 & -2 \\ 3 & 3 & 6 & 1 \end{pmatrix}$$
Subtracting row 2 from row 3 yields:
$$\begin{pmatrix} 15 & 15 & 26 & 1 \\ 3 & 3 & 6 & -2 \\ 0 & 0 & 0 & 3 \end{pmatrix}$$
But this last row corresponds to the equation $0 = 3$, which is false. So the system has no solution.

23. $A + B$ will be:
$$\begin{pmatrix} 2 & 3 \\ -1 & 4 \end{pmatrix} + \begin{pmatrix} 1 & -1 \\ 3 & 0 \end{pmatrix} = \begin{pmatrix} 3 & 2 \\ 2 & 4 \end{pmatrix}$$
We simply add the corresponding terms.

25. We have:
$$2A = \begin{pmatrix} 4 & 6 \\ -2 & 8 \end{pmatrix} \text{ and } 2B = \begin{pmatrix} 2 & -2 \\ 6 & 0 \end{pmatrix}$$
So:
$$2A + 2B = \begin{pmatrix} 6 & 4 \\ 4 & 8 \end{pmatrix}$$

27. The multiplication is defined, since # col in A = # rows in B:
     row 1, col 1: 2(1) + 3(3) = 2 + 9 = 11
     row 1, col 2: 2(-1) + 3(0) = -2 + 0 = -2
     row 2, col 1: -1(1) + 4(3) = -1 + 12 = 11
     row 2, col 2: -1(-1) + 4(0) = 1 + 0 = 1

So $AB = \begin{pmatrix} 11 & -2 \\ 11 & 1 \end{pmatrix}$

29. The multiplication is defined, since # col in A = # rows in C:
     row 1, col 1: 2(1) + 3(0) = 2 + 0 = 2
     row 1, col 2: 2(0) + 3(1) = 0 + 3 = 3
     row 2, col 1: -1(1) + 4(0) = -1 + 0 = -1
     row 2, col 2: -1(0) + 4(1) = 0 + 4 = 4

So $AC = \begin{pmatrix} 2 & 3 \\ -1 & 4 \end{pmatrix}$

31. This operation is not defined, since D and E do not have the same size.

33. We have:

$$2F - 3G = \begin{pmatrix} 10 & -2 \\ -8 & 0 \\ 4 & 6 \end{pmatrix} - \begin{pmatrix} 0 & 0 \\ 0 & 0 \\ 0 & 0 \end{pmatrix} = \begin{pmatrix} 10 & -2 \\ -8 & 0 \\ 4 & 6 \end{pmatrix}$$

35. The multiplication is defined, since # col of E = # rows of D.
     row 1, col 1: 2(-1) + 1(4) = -2 + 4 = 2
     row 1, col 2: 2(2) + 1(0) = 4 + 0 = 4
     row 1, col 3: 2(3) + 1(5) = 6 + 5 = 11
     row 2, col 1: 8(-1) - 1(4) = -8 - 4 = -12
     row 2, col 2: 8(2) - 1(0) = 16 - 0 = 16
     row 2, col 3: 8(3) - 1(5) = 24 - 5 = 19
     row 3, col 1: 6(-1) + 5(4) = -6 + 20 = 14
     row 3, col 2: 6(2) + 5(0) = 12 + 0 = 12
     row 3, col 3: 6(3) + 5(5) = 18 + 25 = 43

So ED = $\begin{pmatrix} 2 & 4 & 11 \\ -12 & 16 & 19 \\ 14 & 12 & 43 \end{pmatrix}$

37. The multiplication is defined, since # col of F = # rows of D.
     row 1, col 1: 5(-1) - 1(4) = -5 - 4 = -9
     row 1, col 2: 5(2) - 1(0) = 10 - 0 = 10
     row 1, col 3: 5(3) - 1(5) = 15 - 5 = 10
     row 2, col 1: -4(-1) + 0(4) = 4 + 0 = 4
     row 2, col 2: -4(2) + 0(0) = -8 + 0 = -8
     row 2, col 3: -4(3) + 0(5) = -12 + 0 = -12
     row 3, col 1: 2(-1) + 3(4) = -2 + 12 = 10

row 3, col 2: $2(2) + 3(0) = 4 + 0 = 4$
row 3, col 3: $2(3) + 3(5) = 6 + 15 = 21$

So $FD = \begin{pmatrix} -9 & 10 & 10 \\ 4 & -8 & -12 \\ 10 & 4 & 21 \end{pmatrix}$

39. The operation is not defined, since G and A are not the same size.

41. The multiplication is defined, since # col G = # rows of D.

$$GD = \begin{pmatrix} 0 & 0 & 0 \\ 0 & 0 & 0 \\ 0 & 0 & 0 \end{pmatrix}$$

43. $A + (B + C) = \begin{pmatrix} 2 & 3 \\ -1 & 4 \end{pmatrix} + \begin{pmatrix} 2 & -1 \\ 3 & 1 \end{pmatrix} = \begin{pmatrix} 4 & 2 \\ 2 & 5 \end{pmatrix}$

45. The multiplication is not defined, since # col of D $\neq$ # rows of C.

47. The multiplication is defined, since # col of A = # rows A.
row 1, col 1: $2(2) + 3(-1) = 4 - 3 = 1$
row 1, col 2: $2(3) + 3(4) = 6 + 12 = 18$
row 2, col 1: $-1(2) + 4(-1) = -2 - 4 = -6$
row 2, col 2: $-1(3) + 4(4) = -3 + 16 = 13$

So $A^2 = \begin{pmatrix} 1 & 18 \\ -6 & 13 \end{pmatrix}$

49. $AA^2 = \begin{pmatrix} 2 & 3 \\ -1 & 4 \end{pmatrix}\begin{pmatrix} 1 & 18 \\ -6 & 13 \end{pmatrix} = \begin{pmatrix} -16 & 75 \\ -25 & 34 \end{pmatrix}$

51. (a) $A(B + C) = \begin{pmatrix} -1 & 3 & 4 \\ 3 & 2 & -3 \\ 9 & 1 & 6 \end{pmatrix}\begin{pmatrix} 11 & 6 & 2 \\ 2 & 1 & 6 \\ -2 & 1 & 6 \end{pmatrix} = \begin{pmatrix} -13 & 1 & 40 \\ 43 & 17 & 0 \\ 89 & 61 & 60 \end{pmatrix}$

(b) $AB + AC = \begin{pmatrix} -1 & 3 & 4 \\ 3 & 2 & -3 \\ 9 & 1 & 6 \end{pmatrix}\begin{pmatrix} 7 & 0 & 1 \\ 0 & 0 & 3 \\ -1 & 2 & 4 \end{pmatrix} + \begin{pmatrix} -1 & 3 & 4 \\ 3 & 2 & -3 \\ 9 & 1 & 6 \end{pmatrix}\begin{pmatrix} 4 & 6 & 1 \\ 2 & 1 & 3 \\ -1 & -1 & 2 \end{pmatrix}$

$= \begin{pmatrix} -11 & 8 & 24 \\ 24 & -6 & -3 \\ 57 & 12 & 36 \end{pmatrix} + \begin{pmatrix} -2 & -7 & 16 \\ 19 & 23 & 3 \\ 32 & 49 & 24 \end{pmatrix}$

$= \begin{pmatrix} -13 & 1 & 40 \\ 43 & 17 & 0 \\ 89 & 61 & 60 \end{pmatrix}$

(c) $(AB)C = \left[\begin{pmatrix} -1 & 3 & 4 \\ 3 & 2 & -3 \\ 9 & 1 & 6 \end{pmatrix}\begin{pmatrix} 7 & 0 & 1 \\ 0 & 0 & 3 \\ -1 & 2 & 4 \end{pmatrix}\right]\begin{pmatrix} 4 & 6 & 1 \\ 2 & 1 & 3 \\ -1 & -1 & 2 \end{pmatrix}$

$= \begin{pmatrix} -11 & 8 & 24 \\ 24 & -6 & -3 \\ 57 & 12 & 36 \end{pmatrix}\begin{pmatrix} 4 & 6 & 1 \\ 2 & 1 & 3 \\ -1 & -1 & 2 \end{pmatrix}$

$= \begin{pmatrix} -52 & -82 & 61 \\ 87 & 141 & 0 \\ 216 & 318 & 165 \end{pmatrix}$

(d) $A(BC) = \begin{pmatrix} -1 & 3 & 4 \\ 3 & 2 & -3 \\ 9 & 1 & 6 \end{pmatrix}\begin{pmatrix} 27 & 41 & 9 \\ -3 & -3 & 6 \\ -4 & -8 & 13 \end{pmatrix} = \begin{pmatrix} -52 & -82 & 61 \\ 87 & 141 & 0 \\ 216 & 318 & 165 \end{pmatrix}$

53.   (a) $A^2 = \begin{pmatrix} 3 & 5 \\ 7 & 9 \end{pmatrix}\begin{pmatrix} 3 & 5 \\ 7 & 9 \end{pmatrix} = \begin{pmatrix} 44 & 60 \\ 84 & 116 \end{pmatrix}$

$B^2 = \begin{pmatrix} 2 & 4 \\ 6 & 8 \end{pmatrix}\begin{pmatrix} 2 & 4 \\ 6 & 8 \end{pmatrix} = \begin{pmatrix} 28 & 40 \\ 60 & 88 \end{pmatrix}$

So $A^2 - B^2 = \begin{pmatrix} 16 & 20 \\ 24 & 28 \end{pmatrix}$

(b) $A - B = \begin{pmatrix} 1 & 1 \\ 1 & 1 \end{pmatrix}$ $A + B = \begin{pmatrix} 5 & 9 \\ 13 & 17 \end{pmatrix}$ and thus

$(A - B)(A + B) = \begin{pmatrix} 1 & 1 \\ 1 & 1 \end{pmatrix}\begin{pmatrix} 5 & 9 \\ 13 & 17 \end{pmatrix} = \begin{pmatrix} 18 & 26 \\ 18 & 26 \end{pmatrix}$

(c)   Here we want $(A + B)(A - B) = \begin{pmatrix} 5 & 9 \\ 13 & 17 \end{pmatrix}\begin{pmatrix} 1 & 1 \\ 1 & 1 \end{pmatrix} = \begin{pmatrix} 14 & 14 \\ 30 & 30 \end{pmatrix}$

(d)   We compute $AB = \begin{pmatrix} 3 & 5 \\ 7 & 9 \end{pmatrix}\begin{pmatrix} 2 & 4 \\ 6 & 8 \end{pmatrix} = \begin{pmatrix} 36 & 52 \\ 68 & 100 \end{pmatrix}$

$BA = \begin{pmatrix} 2 & 4 \\ 6 & 8 \end{pmatrix}\begin{pmatrix} 3 & 5 \\ 7 & 9 \end{pmatrix} = \begin{pmatrix} 34 & 46 \\ 74 & 102 \end{pmatrix}$

So $A^2 + AB - BA - B^2 =$

$\begin{pmatrix} 44 & 60 \\ 84 & 116 \end{pmatrix} + \begin{pmatrix} 36 & 52 \\ 68 & 100 \end{pmatrix} - \begin{pmatrix} 34 & 46 \\ 74 & 102 \end{pmatrix} - \begin{pmatrix} 28 & 40 \\ 60 & 88 \end{pmatrix}$

which is equal to $\begin{pmatrix} 18 & 26 \\ 18 & 26 \end{pmatrix}$

55. (a) $AZ = \begin{pmatrix} 1 & 0 \\ 0 & -1 \end{pmatrix}\begin{pmatrix} x \\ y \end{pmatrix} = \begin{pmatrix} x \\ -y \end{pmatrix}$

    (b) $BZ = \begin{pmatrix} -1 & 0 \\ 0 & 1 \end{pmatrix}\begin{pmatrix} x \\ y \end{pmatrix} = \begin{pmatrix} -x \\ y \end{pmatrix}$

    (c) $AB = \begin{pmatrix} 1 & 0 \\ 0 & -1 \end{pmatrix}\begin{pmatrix} -1 & 0 \\ 0 & 1 \end{pmatrix} = \begin{pmatrix} -1 & 0 \\ 0 & -1 \end{pmatrix}$

    So $(AB)Z = \begin{pmatrix} -1 & 0 \\ 0 & -1 \end{pmatrix}\begin{pmatrix} x \\ y \end{pmatrix} = \begin{pmatrix} -x \\ -y \end{pmatrix}$

    This would represent a reflection about the origin. Or, if you prefer, a reflection about the x-axis followed by a reflection about the y-axis.

57. (a) $f(A) = 1(4) - 2(3) = 4 - 6 = -2$
    $f(B) = 3(8) - (-1)5 = 24 + 5 = 29$

    $AB = \begin{pmatrix} 1 & 2 \\ 3 & 4 \end{pmatrix}\begin{pmatrix} 3 & -1 \\ 5 & 8 \end{pmatrix} = \begin{pmatrix} 13 & 15 \\ 29 & 29 \end{pmatrix}$, so

    $f(AB) = 13(29) - 15(29) = 377 - 435 = -58$
    So $f(A) \bullet f(B) = -2(29) = -58 = f(AB)$

    (b) $f(A) = ad - bc$ and $f(B) = eh - fg$, so
    $f(A) \bullet f(B) = (ad - bc)(eh - fg) = adeh - bceh - adfg + bcfg$

    Now $AB = \begin{pmatrix} a & b \\ c & d \end{pmatrix}\begin{pmatrix} e & f \\ g & h \end{pmatrix} = \begin{pmatrix} ae + bg & af + bh \\ ce + dg & cf + dh \end{pmatrix}$

    Thus $f(AB) = (ae + bg)(cf + dh) - (af + bh)(ce + dg)$
    $= (acef + bcfg + adeh + bdgh) - (acef + bceh + adfg + bdgh)$
    $= bcfg + adeh - bceh - adfg$
    $= f(A) \bullet f(B)$

59. (a) Let $A = \begin{pmatrix} a & b \\ c & d \end{pmatrix}$ and $B = \begin{pmatrix} e & f \\ g & h \end{pmatrix}$

    Then $A + B = \begin{pmatrix} a + e & b + f \\ c + g & d + h \end{pmatrix}$, so $(A + B)^T = \begin{pmatrix} a + e & c + g \\ b + f & d + h \end{pmatrix}$

    Now $A^T = \begin{pmatrix} a & c \\ b & d \end{pmatrix}$ and $B^T = \begin{pmatrix} e & g \\ f & h \end{pmatrix}$, so we have

    $A^T + B^T = \begin{pmatrix} a + e & c + g \\ b + f & d + h \end{pmatrix}$ Thus $(A + B)^T = A^T + B^T$

    (b) $A^T = \begin{pmatrix} a & c \\ b & d \end{pmatrix}$, so $(A^T)^T = \begin{pmatrix} a & b \\ c & d \end{pmatrix}$. Thus $(A^T)^T = A$.

(c) $AB = \begin{pmatrix} ae + bg & af + bh \\ ce + dg & cf + dh \end{pmatrix}$, so $(AB)^T = \begin{pmatrix} ae + bg & ce + dg \\ af + bh & cf + dh \end{pmatrix}$

$B^T A^T = \begin{pmatrix} e & g \\ f & h \end{pmatrix} \begin{pmatrix} a & c \\ b & d \end{pmatrix} = \begin{pmatrix} ae + bg & ce + dg \\ af + bh & cf + dh \end{pmatrix}$

So we see that $(AB)^T = B^T A^T$.

10.4   The Inverse of a Square Matrix

1. $AI_2 = \begin{pmatrix} 4 & -1 \\ -5 & 2 \end{pmatrix} \begin{pmatrix} 1 & 0 \\ 0 & 1 \end{pmatrix} = \begin{pmatrix} 4 & -1 \\ -5 & 2 \end{pmatrix} = A$

$I_2 A = \begin{pmatrix} 1 & 0 \\ 0 & 1 \end{pmatrix} \begin{pmatrix} 4 & -1 \\ -5 & 2 \end{pmatrix} = \begin{pmatrix} 4 & -1 \\ -5 & 2 \end{pmatrix} = A$

3. $CI_3 = \begin{pmatrix} 3 & 0 & -2 \\ 0 & 5 & 6 \\ 1 & 4 & -7 \end{pmatrix} \begin{pmatrix} 1 & 0 & 0 \\ 0 & 1 & 0 \\ 0 & 0 & 1 \end{pmatrix} = \begin{pmatrix} 3 & 0 & -2 \\ 0 & 5 & 6 \\ 1 & 4 & -7 \end{pmatrix} = C$

$I_3 C = \begin{pmatrix} 1 & 0 & 0 \\ 0 & 1 & 0 \\ 0 & 0 & 1 \end{pmatrix} \begin{pmatrix} 3 & 0 & -2 \\ 0 & 5 & 6 \\ 1 & 4 & -7 \end{pmatrix} = \begin{pmatrix} 3 & 0 & -2 \\ 0 & 5 & 6 \\ 1 & 4 & -7 \end{pmatrix} = C$

5.   We need to find numbers a, b, c, and d such that:

$\begin{pmatrix} 7 & 9 \\ 4 & 5 \end{pmatrix} \begin{pmatrix} a & b \\ c & d \end{pmatrix} = \begin{pmatrix} 1 & 0 \\ 0 & 1 \end{pmatrix}$ and $\begin{pmatrix} a & b \\ c & d \end{pmatrix} \begin{pmatrix} 7 & 9 \\ 4 & 5 \end{pmatrix} = \begin{pmatrix} 1 & 0 \\ 0 & 1 \end{pmatrix}$

We compute the left-hand product:

$\begin{pmatrix} 7 & 9 \\ 4 & 5 \end{pmatrix} \begin{pmatrix} a & b \\ c & d \end{pmatrix} = \begin{pmatrix} 7a + 9c & 7b + 9d \\ 4a + 5c & 4b + 5d \end{pmatrix} = \begin{pmatrix} 1 & 0 \\ 0 & 1 \end{pmatrix}$

So we have the following systems of equations:

$$7a + 9c = 1 \quad \text{and} \quad 7b + 9d = 0$$
$$4a + 5c = 0 \qquad\qquad 4b + 5d = 1$$

Multiplying the first equation by 5 and the second equation by -9, then adding the results, yields:

$$35a + 45c = 5 \quad \text{and} \quad 35b + 45d = 0$$
$$\underline{-36a - 45c = 0} \qquad\quad \underline{-36b - 45d = -9}$$
$$-a = 5 \qquad\qquad\qquad -b = -9$$
$$a = -5 \qquad\qquad\qquad b = 9$$

Substituting for c and d, respectively:

$$4a + 5c = 0 \qquad\qquad 4b + 5d = 1$$
$$-20 + 5c = 0 \qquad\qquad 36 + 5d = 1$$
$$5c = 20 \qquad\qquad 5d = -35$$
$$c = 4 \qquad\qquad d = -7$$

So the inverse matrix is A $^{-1}$ = $\begin{pmatrix} -5 & 9 \\ 4 & -7 \end{pmatrix}$

7.   We need to find numbers a, b, c, and d such that:

$$\begin{pmatrix} -3 & 1 \\ 5 & 6 \end{pmatrix}\begin{pmatrix} a & b \\ c & d \end{pmatrix} = \begin{pmatrix} 1 & 0 \\ 0 & 1 \end{pmatrix}$$

We compute the left-hand product:

$$\begin{pmatrix} -3a + c & -3b + d \\ 5a + 6c & 5b + 6d \end{pmatrix} = \begin{pmatrix} 1 & 0 \\ 0 & 1 \end{pmatrix}$$

So we have the following systems of equations:

$$-3a + c = 1 \quad \text{and} \quad -3b + d = 0$$
$$5a + 6c = 0 \qquad\qquad 5b + 6d = 1$$

Solving for c and d, respectively, then substituting:

$$-3a + c = 1 \qquad\qquad -3b + d = 0$$
$$c = 3a + 1 \qquad\qquad d = 3b$$

Substituting:

$$5a + 6(3a + 1) = 0 \qquad 5b + 6(3b) = 1$$
$$23a + 6 = 0 \qquad\qquad 23b = 1$$
$$23a = -6 \qquad\qquad b = \frac{1}{23}$$
$$a = \frac{-6}{23}$$

Now substituting to find c and d:

$$c = 3a + 1 \qquad\qquad d = 3b$$
$$c = \frac{-18}{23} + 1 \qquad\qquad d = \frac{3}{23}$$
$$c = \frac{5}{23}$$

So the inverse matrix is A $^{-1}$ = $\begin{pmatrix} -6/23 & 1/23 \\ 5/23 & 3/23 \end{pmatrix}$

9.   We need to find numbers a, b, c, and d such that:

$$\begin{pmatrix} -2 & 3 \\ -4 & 6 \end{pmatrix}\begin{pmatrix} a & b \\ c & d \end{pmatrix} = \begin{pmatrix} 1 & 0 \\ 0 & 1 \end{pmatrix}$$

We compute the left hand product:

$$\begin{pmatrix} -2a + 3c & -2b + 3d \\ -4a + 6c & -4b + 6d \end{pmatrix} = \begin{pmatrix} 1 & 0 \\ 0 & 1 \end{pmatrix}$$

So we have the following systems of equations:

$$-2a + 3c = 1 \quad \text{and} \quad -2b + 3d = 0$$
$$-4a + 6c = 0 \qquad\qquad -4b + 6d = 1$$

Multiplying the top equation by -2 and adding yields:

$$4a - 6c = -2 \qquad\qquad 4b - 6d = 0$$
$$\underline{-4a + 6c = 0} \qquad\qquad \underline{-4b + 6d = 1}$$
$$0 = -2 \qquad\qquad\quad 0 = 1$$

Since both of these equations are false, no A^{-1} exists.

11. We need to find numbers a, b, c, and d such that:

$$\begin{pmatrix} 1/3 & 1/3 \\ -1/9 & 2/9 \end{pmatrix} \begin{pmatrix} a & b \\ c & d \end{pmatrix} = \begin{pmatrix} 1 & 0 \\ 0 & 1 \end{pmatrix}$$

We compute the left-hand product:

$$\begin{pmatrix} \frac{1}{3}a + \frac{1}{3}c & \frac{1}{3}b + \frac{1}{3}d \\ -\frac{1}{9}a + \frac{2}{9}c & -\frac{1}{9}b + \frac{2}{9}d \end{pmatrix} = \begin{pmatrix} 1 & 0 \\ 0 & 1 \end{pmatrix}$$

So we have the following systems of equations:

$$\frac{1}{3}a + \frac{1}{3}c = 1 \quad \text{and} \quad \frac{1}{3}b + \frac{1}{3}d = 0$$
$$-\frac{1}{9}a + \frac{2}{9}c = 0 \qquad\qquad -\frac{1}{9}b + \frac{2}{9}d = 1$$

Multiplying the first equation by 3 and the second by 9, then adding yields:

$$a + c = 3 \qquad\qquad b + d = 0$$
$$\underline{-a + 2c = 0} \qquad\qquad \underline{-b + 2d = 9}$$
$$3c = 3 \qquad\qquad 3d = 9$$
$$c = 1 \qquad\qquad d = 3$$

Now substituting to find a and b:

$$a + c = 3 \qquad\qquad b + d = 0$$
$$a + 1 = 3 \qquad\qquad b + 3 = 0$$
$$a = 2 \qquad\qquad b = -3$$

So the inverse is $A^{-1} = \begin{pmatrix} 2 & -3 \\ 1 & 3 \end{pmatrix}$

13. Form the augmented matrix: $\begin{pmatrix} 2 & 1 & 1 & 0 \\ 3 & 2 & 0 & 1 \end{pmatrix}$

Multiply row 1 by -1 and add to row 2:

$$\begin{pmatrix} 2 & 1 & 1 & 0 \\ 1 & 1 & -1 & 1 \end{pmatrix}$$

Switch rows 1 and 2:

$$\begin{pmatrix} 1 & 1 & -1 & 1 \\ 2 & 1 & 1 & 0 \end{pmatrix}$$

Multiply row 1 by -2 and add to row 2:

$$\begin{pmatrix} 1 & 1 & -1 & 1 \\ 0 & -1 & 3 & -2 \end{pmatrix}$$

Add row 2 to row 1:

$$\begin{pmatrix} 1 & 0 & 2 & -1 \\ 0 & -1 & 3 & -2 \end{pmatrix}$$

Multiply row 2 by -1:

$$\begin{pmatrix} 1 & 0 & 2 & -1 \\ 0 & 1 & -3 & 2 \end{pmatrix}$$

So the inverse is $\begin{pmatrix} 2 & -1 \\ -3 & 2 \end{pmatrix}$

15. Form the augmented matrix: $\begin{pmatrix} 0 & -11 & 1 & 0 \\ 1 & 6 & 0 & 1 \end{pmatrix}$

Switch rows 1 and 2:

$$\begin{pmatrix} 1 & 6 & 0 & 1 \\ 0 & -11 & 1 & 0 \end{pmatrix}$$

Multiply row 2 by $-\frac{1}{11}$:

$$\begin{pmatrix} 1 & 6 & 0 & 1 \\ 0 & 1 & -1/11 & 0 \end{pmatrix}$$

Multiply row 2 by -6 and add to row 1:

$$\begin{pmatrix} 1 & 0 & 6/11 & 1 \\ 0 & 1 & -1/11 & 0 \end{pmatrix}$$

So the inverse is $\begin{pmatrix} 6/11 & 1 \\ -1/11 & 0 \end{pmatrix}$

17. Form the augmented matrix: $\begin{pmatrix} 2/3 & -1/4 & 1 & 0 \\ -8 & 3 & 0 & 1 \end{pmatrix}$

Multiply row 1 by 12:

$$\begin{pmatrix} 8 & -3 & 12 & 0 \\ -8 & 3 & 0 & 1 \end{pmatrix}$$

Add row 1 to row 2:

$$\begin{pmatrix} 8 & -3 & 12 & 0 \\ 0 & 0 & 12 & 1 \end{pmatrix}$$

So the inverse does not exist.

19. Form the augmented matrix:
$$\begin{pmatrix} -5 & 4 & -3 & 1 & 0 & 0 \\ 10 & -7 & 6 & 0 & 1 & 0 \\ 8 & -6 & 5 & 0 & 0 & 1 \end{pmatrix}$$

Multiply row 1 by 2 and add to row 2:
$$\begin{pmatrix} -5 & 4 & -3 & 1 & 0 & 0 \\ 0 & 1 & 0 & 2 & 1 & 0 \\ 8 & -6 & 5 & 0 & 0 & 1 \end{pmatrix}$$

Add row 3 to row 1 (to reduce the numbers):
$$\begin{pmatrix} 3 & -2 & 2 & 1 & 0 & 1 \\ 0 & 1 & 0 & 2 & 1 & 0 \\ 8 & -6 & 5 & 0 & 0 & 1 \end{pmatrix}$$

Multiply row 2 by 2 and add to row 1, and also multiply row 2 by 6 and add to row 3:
$$\begin{pmatrix} 3 & 0 & 2 & 5 & 2 & 1 \\ 0 & 1 & 0 & 2 & 1 & 0 \\ 8 & 0 & 5 & 12 & 6 & 1 \end{pmatrix}$$

Multiply row 1 by $-\dfrac{8}{3}$ and add to row 3:
$$\begin{pmatrix} 3 & 0 & 2 & 5 & 2 & 1 \\ 0 & 1 & 0 & 2 & 1 & 0 \\ 0 & 0 & -1/3 & -4/3 & 2/3 & -5/3 \end{pmatrix}$$

Multiply row 3 by -3:
$$\begin{pmatrix} 3 & 0 & 2 & 5 & 2 & 1 \\ 0 & 1 & 0 & 2 & 1 & 0 \\ 0 & 0 & 1 & 4 & -2 & 5 \end{pmatrix}$$

Multiply row 3 by -2 and add to row 1:
$$\begin{pmatrix} 3 & 0 & 0 & -3 & 6 & -9 \\ 0 & 1 & 0 & 2 & 1 & 0 \\ 0 & 0 & 1 & 4 & -2 & 5 \end{pmatrix}$$

Multiply row 1 by $\dfrac{1}{3}$:
$$\begin{pmatrix} 1 & 0 & 0 & -1 & 2 & -3 \\ 0 & 1 & 0 & 2 & 1 & 0 \\ 0 & 0 & 1 & 4 & -2 & 5 \end{pmatrix}$$

So the inverse is
$$\begin{pmatrix} -1 & 2 & -3 \\ 2 & 1 & 0 \\ 4 & -2 & 5 \end{pmatrix}$$

21. Form the augmented matrix:
$$\begin{pmatrix} 1 & 2 & -1 & 1 & 0 & 0 \\ 0 & 3 & 0 & 0 & 1 & 0 \\ -4 & 0 & 5 & 0 & 0 & 1 \end{pmatrix}$$

Multiply row 1 by 4 and add to row 3:
$$\begin{pmatrix} 1 & 2 & -1 & 1 & 0 & 0 \\ 0 & 3 & 0 & 0 & 1 & 0 \\ 0 & 8 & 1 & 4 & 0 & 1 \end{pmatrix}$$

Multiply row 2 by $\frac{1}{3}$:
$$\begin{pmatrix} 1 & 2 & -1 & 1 & 0 & 0 \\ 0 & 1 & 0 & 0 & 1/3 & 0 \\ 0 & 8 & 1 & 4 & 0 & 1 \end{pmatrix}$$

Multiply row 2 by -2 and add to row 1, and multiply row 2 by -8 and add to row 3:
$$\begin{pmatrix} 1 & 0 & -1 & 1 & -2/3 & 0 \\ 0 & 1 & 0 & 0 & 1/3 & 0 \\ 0 & 0 & 1 & 4 & -8/3 & 1 \end{pmatrix}$$

Add row 3 to row 1:
$$\begin{pmatrix} 1 & 0 & 0 & 5 & -10/3 & 1 \\ 0 & 1 & 0 & 0 & 1/3 & 0 \\ 0 & 0 & 1 & 4 & -8/3 & 1 \end{pmatrix}$$

So the inverse is
$$\begin{pmatrix} 5 & -10/3 & 1 \\ 0 & 1/3 & 0 \\ 4 & -8/3 & 1 \end{pmatrix}$$

23. Form the augmented matrix:
$$\begin{pmatrix} -7 & 5 & 3 & 1 & 0 & 0 \\ 3 & -2 & -2 & 0 & 1 & 0 \\ 3 & -2 & -1 & 0 & 0 & 1 \end{pmatrix}$$

Multiply row 2 by -1 and add to row 3:
$$\begin{pmatrix} -7 & 5 & 3 & 1 & 0 & 0 \\ 3 & -2 & -2 & 0 & 1 & 0 \\ 0 & 0 & 1 & 0 & -1 & 1 \end{pmatrix}$$

Multiply row 2 by 2 and add to row 1:
$$\begin{pmatrix} -1 & 1 & -1 & 1 & 2 & 0 \\ 3 & -2 & -2 & 0 & 1 & 0 \\ 0 & 0 & 1 & 0 & -1 & 1 \end{pmatrix}$$

Multiply row 1 by 3 and add to row 2:
$$\begin{pmatrix} -1 & 1 & -1 & 1 & 2 & 0 \\ 0 & 1 & -5 & 3 & 7 & 0 \\ 0 & 0 & 1 & 0 & -1 & 1 \end{pmatrix}$$

Multiply row 3 by 5 and add to row 2, and add row 3 to row 1:

$$\begin{pmatrix} -1 & 1 & 0 & 1 & 1 & 1 \\ 0 & 1 & 0 & 3 & 2 & 5 \\ 0 & 0 & 1 & 0 & -1 & 1 \end{pmatrix}$$

Mutiply row 1 by -1:

$$\begin{pmatrix} 1 & -1 & 0 & -1 & -1 & -1 \\ 0 & 1 & 0 & 3 & 2 & 5 \\ 0 & 0 & 1 & 0 & -1 & 1 \end{pmatrix}$$

Add row 2 to row 1:

$$\begin{pmatrix} 1 & 0 & 0 & 2 & 1 & 4 \\ 0 & 1 & 0 & 3 & 2 & 5 \\ 0 & 0 & 1 & 0 & -1 & 1 \end{pmatrix}$$

So the inverse is $\begin{pmatrix} 2 & 1 & 4 \\ 3 & 2 & 5 \\ 0 & -1 & 1 \end{pmatrix}$

25. Form the augmented matrix: $\begin{pmatrix} 1 & 2 & 3 & 1 & 0 & 0 \\ 4 & 5 & 6 & 0 & 1 & 0 \\ 7 & 8 & 9 & 0 & 0 & 1 \end{pmatrix}$

Multiply row 1 by -4 and add to row 2, and multiply row 1 by -7 and add to row 3:

$$\begin{pmatrix} 1 & 2 & 3 & 1 & 0 & 0 \\ 0 & -3 & -6 & -4 & 1 & 0 \\ 0 & -6 & -12 & -7 & 0 & 1 \end{pmatrix}$$

Multiply row 2 by -2 and add to row 3:

$$\begin{pmatrix} 1 & 2 & 3 & 1 & 0 & 0 \\ 0 & -3 & -6 & -4 & 1 & 0 \\ 0 & 0 & 0 & 1 & -2 & 1 \end{pmatrix}$$

So the inverse does not exist.

27. (a) Since the system can be written as $A \bullet X = B$, where

$X = \begin{pmatrix} x \\ y \end{pmatrix}$ and $B = \begin{pmatrix} 5 \\ 7 \end{pmatrix}$, then $X = A^{-1} \bullet B$.

So $X = \begin{pmatrix} 11 & -8 \\ -4 & 3 \end{pmatrix} \begin{pmatrix} 5 \\ 7 \end{pmatrix} = \begin{pmatrix} -1 \\ 1 \end{pmatrix}$, thus $x = -1$ and $y = 1$.

(b) Again this system can be written as $A \bullet X = B$, where

$X = \begin{pmatrix} x \\ y \end{pmatrix}$ and $B = \begin{pmatrix} -12 \\ 0 \end{pmatrix}$, so $X = A^{-1} \bullet B$.

So $X = \begin{pmatrix} 11 & -8 \\ -4 & 3 \end{pmatrix} \begin{pmatrix} -12 \\ 0 \end{pmatrix} = \begin{pmatrix} -132 \\ 48 \end{pmatrix}$, thus $x = -132$ and $y = 48$.

29. (a) Since the system can be written as A • X = B, where

$$X = \begin{pmatrix} x \\ y \\ z \end{pmatrix} \text{ and } B = \begin{pmatrix} 28 \\ 9 \\ 22 \end{pmatrix}, \text{ then } X = A^{-1} \bullet B.$$

So $X = \begin{pmatrix} 1 & 2 & -2 \\ -1 & 3 & 0 \\ 0 & -2 & 1 \end{pmatrix}\begin{pmatrix} 28 \\ 9 \\ 22 \end{pmatrix} = \begin{pmatrix} 2 \\ -1 \\ 4 \end{pmatrix}$, thus x = 2, y = -1, z = 4.

(b) Again this system can be written as A • X = B, where

$$X = \begin{pmatrix} x \\ y \\ z \end{pmatrix} \text{ and } B = \begin{pmatrix} -7 \\ -2 \\ -6 \end{pmatrix}, \text{ so } X = A^{-1} \bullet B.$$

So $X = \begin{pmatrix} 1 & 2 & -2 \\ -1 & 3 & 0 \\ 0 & -2 & 1 \end{pmatrix}\begin{pmatrix} -7 \\ -2 \\ -6 \end{pmatrix} = \begin{pmatrix} 1 \\ 1 \\ -2 \end{pmatrix}$, thus x = 1, y = 1, and z = -2.

31. (a) $AA = \begin{pmatrix} 1 & -6 & 3 \\ 2 & -7 & 3 \\ 4 & -12 & 5 \end{pmatrix}\begin{pmatrix} 1 & -6 & 3 \\ 2 & -7 & 3 \\ 4 & -12 & 5 \end{pmatrix} = \begin{pmatrix} 1 & 0 & 0 \\ 0 & 1 & 0 \\ 0 & 0 & 1 \end{pmatrix}$

The product is the identity matrix I_3, and thus $A^{-1} = A$.

(b) Since this can be written as A • X = B, where $X = \begin{pmatrix} x \\ y \\ z \end{pmatrix}$ and $B = \begin{pmatrix} 19/2 \\ 11 \\ 19 \end{pmatrix}$

then $X = A^{-1} \bullet B$. Recall from part (a) that $A^{-1} = A$, so:

$X = \begin{pmatrix} 1 & -6 & 3 \\ 2 & -7 & 3 \\ 4 & 12 & 5 \end{pmatrix}\begin{pmatrix} 19/2 \\ 11 \\ 19 \end{pmatrix} = \begin{pmatrix} 1/2 \\ -1 \\ 1 \end{pmatrix}$, thus $x = \frac{1}{2}$, y = -1, and z = 1.

33. We find $\begin{pmatrix} a & b \\ c & d \end{pmatrix}$ where $\begin{pmatrix} 2 & 5 \\ 6 & 15 \end{pmatrix}\begin{pmatrix} a & b \\ c & d \end{pmatrix} = \begin{pmatrix} 1 & 0 \\ 0 & 1 \end{pmatrix}$. Carrying out the multiplication, we have:

$\begin{pmatrix} 2a + 5c & 2b + 5d \\ 6a + 15c & 6b + 15d \end{pmatrix} = \begin{pmatrix} 1 & 0 \\ 0 & 1 \end{pmatrix}$

So we have the following systems of equations:

2a + 5c = 1   and   2b + 5d = 0
6a + 15c = 0   6b + 15d = 1

Multiplying the first equation by -3 and adding to the second equation:

-6a - 15c = -3   -6b - 15d = 0
6a + 15c = 0   6b + 15d = 1
0 = -3   0 = 1

Neither of these systems has a solution, thus the matrix has no inverse.

35. (a) Form the augmented matrix: $\begin{pmatrix} 2 & 3 & 1 & 0 \\ 4 & 5 & 0 & 1 \end{pmatrix}$

Multiply row 1 by -2 and add to row 2:

$$\begin{pmatrix} 2 & 3 & 1 & 0 \\ 0 & -1 & -2 & 1 \end{pmatrix}$$

Multiply row 2 by 3 and add to row 1:

$$\begin{pmatrix} 2 & 0 & -5 & 3 \\ 0 & -1 & -2 & 1 \end{pmatrix}$$

Multiply row 1 by $\frac{1}{2}$ and row 2 by -1:

$$\begin{pmatrix} 1 & 0 & -5/2 & 3/2 \\ 0 & 1 & 2 & -1 \end{pmatrix}$$

So $A^{-1} = \begin{pmatrix} -5/2 & 3/2 \\ 2 & -1 \end{pmatrix}$

Now form the augmented matrix: $\begin{pmatrix} 7 & 8 & 1 & 0 \\ 6 & 7 & 0 & 1 \end{pmatrix}$

Subtract row 2 from row 1:

$$\begin{pmatrix} 1 & 1 & 1 & -1 \\ 6 & 7 & 0 & 1 \end{pmatrix}$$

Multiply row 1 by -6 and add to row 2:

$$\begin{pmatrix} 1 & 1 & 1 & -1 \\ 0 & 1 & -6 & 7 \end{pmatrix}$$

Subtract row 2 from row 1:

$$\begin{pmatrix} 1 & 0 & 7 & -8 \\ 0 & 1 & -6 & 7 \end{pmatrix}$$

So $B^{-1} = \begin{pmatrix} 7 & -8 \\ -6 & 7 \end{pmatrix}$

Then $B^{-1} A^{-1} = \begin{pmatrix} 7 & -8 \\ -6 & 7 \end{pmatrix} \begin{pmatrix} -5/2 & 3/2 \\ 2 & -1 \end{pmatrix} = \begin{pmatrix} -67/2 & 37/2 \\ 29 & -16 \end{pmatrix}$

(b) We first find AB:

$$AB = \begin{pmatrix} 2 & 3 \\ 4 & 5 \end{pmatrix} \begin{pmatrix} 7 & 8 \\ 6 & 7 \end{pmatrix} = \begin{pmatrix} 32 & 37 \\ 58 & 67 \end{pmatrix}$$

Now form the augmented matrix: $\begin{pmatrix} 32 & 37 & 1 & 0 \\ 58 & 67 & 0 & 1 \end{pmatrix}$

Subtract row 1 from row 2 (to reduce numbers):

$$\begin{pmatrix} 32 & 37 & 1 & 0 \\ 26 & 30 & -1 & 1 \end{pmatrix}$$

Subtract row 2 from row 1 (to reduce numbers):

$$\begin{pmatrix} 6 & 7 & 2 & -1 \\ 26 & 30 & -1 & 1 \end{pmatrix}$$

Multiply row 1 by -4 and add to row 2:

$$\begin{pmatrix} 6 & 7 & 2 & -1 \\ 2 & 2 & -9 & 5 \end{pmatrix}$$

Multiply row 2 by -3 and add to row 1:

$$\begin{pmatrix} 0 & 1 & 29 & -16 \\ 2 & 2 & -9 & 5 \end{pmatrix}$$

Multiply row 1 by -2 and add to row 2:

$$\begin{pmatrix} 0 & 1 & 29 & -16 \\ 2 & 0 & -67 & 37 \end{pmatrix}$$

Multiply row 2 by $\frac{1}{2}$, then swith rows 1 and 2:

$$\begin{pmatrix} 1 & 0 & -67/2 & 37/2 \\ 0 & 1 & 29 & -16 \end{pmatrix}$$

So $(AB)^{-1} = \begin{pmatrix} -67/2 & 37/2 \\ 29 & -16 \end{pmatrix}$, which is the same as $B^{-1} A^{-1}$ from part (a).

10.5 Determinants and Cramer's Rule

1. (a) $\begin{vmatrix} 2 & -17 \\ 1 & 6 \end{vmatrix} = 2(6) - (-17)(1) = 12 + 17 = 29$

    (b) $\begin{vmatrix} 1 & 6 \\ 2 & -17 \end{vmatrix} = 1(-17) - 6(2) = -17 - 12 = -29$

3. (a) $\begin{vmatrix} 7 & 7 \\ 500 & 700 \end{vmatrix} = 100 \begin{vmatrix} 5 & 7 \\ 5 & 7 \end{vmatrix} = 100 [5(7) - 7(5)] = 100(35 - 35) = 0$

    (b) $\begin{vmatrix} 5 & 500 \\ 7 & 700 \end{vmatrix} = 100 \begin{vmatrix} 5 & 5 \\ 7 & 7 \end{vmatrix} = 100 [5(7) - 5(7)] = 100(35 - 35) = 0$

5. $\begin{vmatrix} \sqrt{2} - 1 & \sqrt{2} \\ \sqrt{2} & \sqrt{2} + 1 \end{vmatrix} = (\sqrt{2} - 1)(\sqrt{2} + 1) - \sqrt{2}(\sqrt{2}) = (2 - 1) - 2 = -1$

7. $\begin{vmatrix} 5 & 1 \\ 10 & -10 \end{vmatrix} = 10 \begin{vmatrix} 5 & 1 \\ 1 & -1 \end{vmatrix} = 10 [5(-1) - 1(1)] = 10(-6) = -60$

9. $\begin{vmatrix} -6 & 3 \\ 5 & -4 \end{vmatrix} = 3 \begin{vmatrix} -2 & 1 \\ 5 & -4 \end{vmatrix} = 3 [-2(-4) - 1(5)] = 3(3) = 9$

11. (a) $-6\begin{vmatrix} -4 & 1 \\ 9 & -10 \end{vmatrix} + 3\begin{vmatrix} 5 & 1 \\ 10 & -10 \end{vmatrix} + 8\begin{vmatrix} 5 & -4 \\ 10 & 9 \end{vmatrix} = -6(31) + 3(-60) + 8(85) = 314$

(b) $-6\begin{vmatrix} -4 & 1 \\ 9 & -10 \end{vmatrix} - 3\begin{vmatrix} 5 & 1 \\ 10 & -10 \end{vmatrix} + 8\begin{vmatrix} 5 & -4 \\ 10 & 9 \end{vmatrix} = -6(31) - 3(-60) + 8(85) = 674$

(c) The answer in part (b) would be the determinant.

13. (a) $-4\begin{vmatrix} 2 & 3 \\ 8 & 9 \end{vmatrix} + 5\begin{vmatrix} 1 & 3 \\ 7 & 9 \end{vmatrix} - 6\begin{vmatrix} 1 & 2 \\ 7 & 8 \end{vmatrix} = -4(-6) + 5(-12) - 6(-6) = 0$

(b) $7\begin{vmatrix} 2 & 3 \\ 5 & 6 \end{vmatrix} - 8\begin{vmatrix} 1 & 3 \\ 4 & 6 \end{vmatrix} + 9\begin{vmatrix} 1 & 2 \\ 4 & 5 \end{vmatrix} = 7(-3) - 8(-6) + 9(-3) = 0$

(c) $1\begin{vmatrix} 5 & 6 \\ 8 & 9 \end{vmatrix} - 4\begin{vmatrix} 2 & 3 \\ 8 & 9 \end{vmatrix} + 7\begin{vmatrix} 2 & 3 \\ 5 & 6 \end{vmatrix} = 1(-3) - 4(-6) + 7(-3) = 0$

(d) $3\begin{vmatrix} 4 & 5 \\ 7 & 8 \end{vmatrix} - 6\begin{vmatrix} 1 & 2 \\ 7 & 8 \end{vmatrix} + 9\begin{vmatrix} 1 & 2 \\ 4 & 5 \end{vmatrix} = 3(-3) - 6(-6) + 9(-3) = 0$

15. $\begin{vmatrix} 5 & 10 & 15 \\ 1 & 2 & 3 \\ -9 & 11 & 7 \end{vmatrix} = 5\begin{vmatrix} 1 & 2 & 3 \\ 1 & 2 & 3 \\ -9 & 11 & 7 \end{vmatrix} = 5\begin{vmatrix} 0 & 0 & 0 \\ 1 & 2 & 3 \\ -9 & 11 & 7 \end{vmatrix} = 0$

17. $\begin{vmatrix} 1 & 2 & -3 \\ 4 & 5 & -9 \\ 0 & 0 & 1 \end{vmatrix} = 0\begin{vmatrix} 2 & -3 \\ 5 & -9 \end{vmatrix} - 0\begin{vmatrix} 1 & -3 \\ 4 & -9 \end{vmatrix} + 1\begin{vmatrix} 1 & 2 \\ 4 & 5 \end{vmatrix} = 1(-3) = -3$

19. $\begin{vmatrix} -6 & -8 & 18 \\ 25 & 12 & 15 \\ -9 & 4 & 13 \end{vmatrix} = 2\begin{vmatrix} -3 & -4 & 9 \\ 25 & 12 & 15 \\ -9 & 4 & 13 \end{vmatrix} = 8\begin{vmatrix} -3 & -1 & 9 \\ 25 & 3 & 15 \\ -9 & 1 & 13 \end{vmatrix}$

Now $\begin{vmatrix} -3 & -1 & 9 \\ 25 & 3 & 15 \\ -9 & 1 & 13 \end{vmatrix} = -3\begin{vmatrix} 3 & 15 \\ 1 & 13 \end{vmatrix} + 1\begin{vmatrix} 25 & 15 \\ -9 & 13 \end{vmatrix} + 9\begin{vmatrix} 25 & 3 \\ -9 & 1 \end{vmatrix}$

$= -3(24) + 1(460) + 9(52)$

$= 856$

So $8\begin{vmatrix} -3 & -1 & 9 \\ 25 & 3 & 15 \\ -9 & 1 & 13 \end{vmatrix} = 8(856) = 6848$

21.
$$\begin{vmatrix} 16 & 0 & -64 \\ -8 & 15 & -12 \\ 30 & -20 & 10 \end{vmatrix} = 16\begin{vmatrix} 1 & 0 & -4 \\ -8 & 15 & -12 \\ 30 & -20 & 10 \end{vmatrix} = 160\begin{vmatrix} 1 & 0 & -4 \\ -8 & 15 & -12 \\ 3 & -2 & 1 \end{vmatrix}$$

$$\text{Now } \begin{vmatrix} 1 & 0 & -4 \\ -8 & 15 & -12 \\ 3 & -2 & 1 \end{vmatrix} = 1\begin{vmatrix} 15 & -12 \\ -2 & 1 \end{vmatrix} - 0\begin{vmatrix} -8 & -12 \\ 3 & 1 \end{vmatrix} - 4\begin{vmatrix} -8 & 15 \\ 3 & 2 \end{vmatrix}$$

$$= 1(-9) - 4(-29)$$
$$= 107$$

$$\text{So } 160\begin{vmatrix} 1 & 0 & -4 \\ -8 & 15 & -12 \\ 3 & -2 & 1 \end{vmatrix} = 160(107) = 17120$$

23.
$$\begin{vmatrix} 1 & x & x^2 \\ 1 & y & y^2 \\ 1 & z & z^2 \end{vmatrix} = \begin{vmatrix} 1 & x & x^2 \\ 0 & y-x & y^2-x^2 \\ 0 & z-x & z^2-x^2 \end{vmatrix}$$

$$= \begin{vmatrix} y-x & y^2-x^2 \\ z-x & z^2-x^2 \end{vmatrix}$$

$$= \begin{vmatrix} y-x & (y+x)(y-x) \\ z-x & (z+x)(z-x) \end{vmatrix}$$

$$= (y-x)(z-x)\begin{vmatrix} 1 & y+x \\ 1 & z+x \end{vmatrix}$$

$$= (y-x)(z-x)[z+x-y-x]$$
$$= (y-x)(z-x)(z-y)$$

25.
$$\begin{vmatrix} 1 & 1 & 1 \\ 1 & 1+x & 1 \\ 1 & 1 & 1+y \end{vmatrix}$$

Subtract row 1 from row 2 and row 1 from row 3:

$$= \begin{vmatrix} 1 & 1 & 1 \\ 0 & x & 0 \\ 0 & 0 & y \end{vmatrix}$$

$$= 1\begin{vmatrix} x & 0 \\ 0 & y \end{vmatrix}$$

$$= xy$$

27.
$$\begin{vmatrix} 1 & -1 & 0 & 2 \\ 0 & 1 & -1 & 0 \\ 2 & 1 & 0 & -1 \\ -2 & 2 & 1 & 1 \end{vmatrix}$$

Add column 2 to column 3:

$$= \begin{vmatrix} 1 & -1 & -1 & 2 \\ 0 & 1 & 0 & 0 \\ 2 & 1 & 1 & -1 \\ -2 & 2 & 3 & 1 \end{vmatrix}$$

$$= 1 \begin{vmatrix} 1 & -1 & 2 \\ 2 & 1 & -1 \\ -2 & 3 & 1 \end{vmatrix}$$

Add twice column 3 to column 1:

$$= \begin{vmatrix} 5 & -1 & 2 \\ 0 & 1 & -1 \\ 0 & 3 & 1 \end{vmatrix}$$

$$= 5 \begin{vmatrix} 1 & -1 \\ 3 & 1 \end{vmatrix}$$

$$= 5(4)$$

$$= 20$$

29.
$$\begin{vmatrix} 2 & 0 & 0 & 0 \\ 0 & 3 & 0 & 0 \\ 0 & 0 & 4 & 0 \\ 0 & 0 & 0 & 5 \end{vmatrix} = 2 \begin{vmatrix} 3 & 0 & 0 \\ 0 & 4 & 0 \\ 0 & 0 & 5 \end{vmatrix} = 2(3) \begin{vmatrix} 4 & 0 \\ 0 & 5 \end{vmatrix} = 6(20) = 120$$

31. (a)   Subtract the first column from the second; add twice the first column to the third. The result is:

$$\begin{vmatrix} -20 & 22 & -43 \\ 6 & -10 & 13 \\ -1 & 0 & 0 \end{vmatrix} = -1 [22(13) - (-43)(-10)] = 144$$

(b)   Multiply the second row by 2 and subtract it from the first row; multiply the second row by 4 and subtract it from the third row. This yields:

$$\begin{vmatrix} 0 & -32 & -5 \\ 1 & 6 & 1 \\ 0 & -25 & -2 \end{vmatrix} = -1 [(-32)(-2) - (-5)(-25)] = 61$$

(c)   Subtract the first column from the second; add 10 times the first column to the third. This yields:

$$\begin{vmatrix} 2 & 0 & 0 \\ 1 & -5 & 16 \\ 4 & -5 & 39 \end{vmatrix} = 2 [(-5)(39) - 16(-5)] = -230$$

33. Compute $D = \begin{vmatrix} 3 & 4 & -1 \\ 1 & -3 & 2 \\ 5 & 0 & -6 \end{vmatrix} = 5 \begin{vmatrix} 4 & -1 \\ -3 & 2 \end{vmatrix} - 6 \begin{vmatrix} 3 & 4 \\ 1 & -3 \end{vmatrix} = 5(5) - 6(-13) = 103$

$D_x = \begin{vmatrix} 5 & 4 & -1 \\ 2 & -3 & 2 \\ -7 & 0 & -6 \end{vmatrix} = -7 \begin{vmatrix} 4 & -1 \\ -3 & 2 \end{vmatrix} - 6 \begin{vmatrix} 5 & 4 \\ 2 & -3 \end{vmatrix} = -7(5) - 6(-23) = 103$

$D_y = \begin{vmatrix} 3 & 5 & -1 \\ 1 & 2 & 2 \\ 5 & -7 & -6 \end{vmatrix}$

Adding -2 times column 1 to both column 2 and column 3 yields:

$-\begin{vmatrix} 3 & -1 & -7 \\ 1 & 0 & 0 \\ 5 & -17 & -16 \end{vmatrix} = -1 \begin{vmatrix} -1 & -7 \\ -17 & -16 \end{vmatrix} = -(-103) = 103$

$D_z = \begin{vmatrix} 3 & 4 & 5 \\ 1 & -3 & 2 \\ 5 & 0 & -7 \end{vmatrix}$

Adding 3 times column 1 to column 2, and -2 times column 1 to column 3 yields:

$= \begin{vmatrix} 3 & 13 & -1 \\ 1 & 0 & 0 \\ 5 & 15 & -17 \end{vmatrix} = -1 \begin{vmatrix} 13 & 1 \\ 15 & -17 \end{vmatrix} = -(-206) = 206$

So $x = \dfrac{D_x}{D} = 1$, $y = \dfrac{D_y}{D} = 1$, and $z = \dfrac{D_z}{D} = 2$.
So the solution is (1,1,2).

35. $D = \begin{vmatrix} 3 & 2 & -1 \\ 2 & -3 & -4 \\ 1 & 1 & 1 \end{vmatrix}$

Subtracting column 1 from both column 2 and column 3 yields:

$= \begin{vmatrix} 3 & -1 & -4 \\ 2 & -5 & -6 \\ 1 & 0 & 0 \end{vmatrix} = 1 \begin{vmatrix} -1 & -4 \\ -5 & -6 \end{vmatrix} = -14$

$D_x = \begin{vmatrix} -6 & 2 & -1 \\ -11 & -3 & -4 \\ 5 & 1 & 1 \end{vmatrix}$

Adding -5 times column 3 to column 1, and subtracting column 3 from column 2 yields:

$= \begin{vmatrix} -1 & 3 & -1 \\ 9 & 1 & -4 \\ 0 & 0 & 1 \end{vmatrix} = 1 \begin{vmatrix} -1 & 3 \\ 9 & 1 \end{vmatrix} = -28$

$$D_y = \begin{vmatrix} 3 & -6 & -1 \\ 2 & -11 & -4 \\ 1 & 5 & 1 \end{vmatrix}$$

Adding row 3 to row 1, and 4 times row 3 to row 2 yields:

$$= \begin{vmatrix} 4 & -1 & 0 \\ 6 & 9 & 0 \\ 1 & 5 & 1 \end{vmatrix} = 1 \begin{vmatrix} 4 & -1 \\ 6 & 9 \end{vmatrix} = 42$$

$$D_z = \begin{vmatrix} 3 & 2 & -6 \\ 2 & -3 & -11 \\ 1 & 1 & 5 \end{vmatrix}$$

Adding -2 times row 3 to row 1, and 3 times row 3 to row 2 yields:

$$= \begin{vmatrix} 1 & 0 & -16 \\ 5 & 0 & 4 \\ 1 & 1 & 5 \end{vmatrix} = -1 \begin{vmatrix} 1 & -16 \\ 5 & 4 \end{vmatrix} = -(84) = -84$$

So $x = \dfrac{D_x}{D} = 2$, $y = \dfrac{D_y}{D} = -3$, and $z = \dfrac{D_z}{D} = 6$

So the solution is (2,-3,6).

37. $D = \begin{vmatrix} 2 & 5 & 2 \\ 3 & -1 & -4 \\ 1 & 2 & -3 \end{vmatrix}$

Adding -2 times row 3 to row 1, and -3 times row 3 to row 2 yields:

$$= \begin{vmatrix} 0 & 1 & 8 \\ 0 & -7 & 5 \\ 1 & 2 & -3 \end{vmatrix} = 1 \begin{vmatrix} 1 & 8 \\ -7 & 5 \end{vmatrix} = 61$$

$$D_x = \begin{vmatrix} 0 & 5 & 2 \\ 0 & -1 & -4 \\ 0 & 2 & 3 \end{vmatrix} = 0$$

$$D_y = \begin{vmatrix} 2 & 0 & 2 \\ 3 & 0 & -4 \\ 1 & 0 & -3 \end{vmatrix} = 0$$

$$D_z = \begin{vmatrix} 2 & 5 & 0 \\ 3 & -1 & 0 \\ 1 & 2 & 0 \end{vmatrix} = 0$$

So $x = \dfrac{D_x}{D} = 0$, $y = \dfrac{D_y}{D} = 0$, and $z = \dfrac{D_z}{D} = 0$

So the solution is (0,0,0).

39. $D = \begin{vmatrix} 12 & 0 & -11 \\ 6 & 6 & -4 \\ 6 & 2 & -5 \end{vmatrix} = 6 \begin{vmatrix} 2 & 0 & -11 \\ 1 & 6 & -4 \\ 1 & 2 & -5 \end{vmatrix} = 12 \begin{vmatrix} 2 & 0 & -11 \\ 1 & 3 & -4 \\ 1 & 1 & -5 \end{vmatrix}$

Adding -3 times row 3 to row 2 yields:

$= 12 \begin{vmatrix} 2 & 0 & -11 \\ -2 & 0 & 11 \\ 1 & 1 & -5 \end{vmatrix} = 12(-1) \begin{vmatrix} 2 & -11 \\ -2 & 11 \end{vmatrix} = -12(0) = 0$

So Cramer's Rule will not work. We form the augmented matrix (using equation 2 as row 1):

$\begin{pmatrix} 6 & 6 & -4 & 26 \\ 12 & 0 & -11 & 13 \\ 6 & 2 & -5 & 13 \end{pmatrix}$

Adding -2 times row 1 to row 2 and -1 times row 1 to row 3 yields:

$\begin{pmatrix} 6 & 6 & -4 & 26 \\ 0 & -12 & -3 & -39 \\ 0 & -4 & -1 & -13 \end{pmatrix}$

Multiply row 1 by $\frac{1}{2}$ and row 2 by $\frac{1}{3}$:

$\begin{pmatrix} 3 & 3 & -2 & 13 \\ 0 & 4 & 1 & 13 \\ 0 & -4 & -1 & -13 \end{pmatrix}$

Adding row 2 to row 3 yields:

$\begin{pmatrix} 3 & 3 & -2 & 13 \\ 0 & 4 & 1 & 13 \\ 0 & 0 & 0 & 0 \end{pmatrix}$

So:

$3x + 3y - 2z = 13$

$4y + z = 13$

Solve equation 2 for z:

$4y + z = 13$

$z = 13 - 4y$

Substitute into equation 1:

$3x + 3y - 26 + 8y = 13$

$3x = 39 - 11y$

$x = 13 - \frac{11}{3}y$

So the solution is $(13 - \frac{11}{3}y, y, 13 - 4y)$, for any real number y.

41. $D = \begin{vmatrix} 1 & 1 & 1 & 1 \\ 1 & -1 & 1 & -1 \\ 2 & -2 & -3 & -3 \\ 3 & 2 & 1 & -1 \end{vmatrix}$

Adding row 1 to row 2, 3 times row 1 to row 3, and row 1 to row 4 yields:

$$= \begin{vmatrix} 1 & 1 & 1 & 1 \\ 2 & 0 & 2 & 0 \\ 5 & 1 & 0 & 0 \\ 4 & 3 & 2 & 0 \end{vmatrix} = -1 \begin{vmatrix} 2 & 0 & 2 \\ 5 & 1 & 0 \\ 4 & 3 & 2 \end{vmatrix}$$

Subtracting column 3 from col 1 yields:

$$= -1 \begin{vmatrix} 0 & 0 & 2 \\ 5 & 1 & 0 \\ 2 & 3 & 2 \end{vmatrix} = -2 \begin{vmatrix} 5 & 1 \\ 2 & 3 \end{vmatrix} = -2(13) = -26$$

$$D_x = \begin{vmatrix} -7 & 1 & 1 & 1 \\ -11 & -1 & 1 & -1 \\ 26 & -2 & -3 & -3 \\ -9 & 2 & 1 & -1 \end{vmatrix}$$

Adding row 1 ro row 2, 3 times row 1 to row 3, and row 1 to row 4 yields:

$$= \begin{vmatrix} -7 & 1 & 1 & 1 \\ -18 & 0 & 2 & 0 \\ 5 & 1 & 0 & 0 \\ -16 & 3 & 2 & 0 \end{vmatrix} = -1 \begin{vmatrix} -18 & 0 & 2 \\ 5 & 1 & 0 \\ -16 & 3 & 2 \end{vmatrix}$$

Subtracting row 3 from row 1 yields:

$$= -1 \begin{vmatrix} -2 & -3 & 0 \\ 5 & 1 & 0 \\ -16 & 3 & 2 \end{vmatrix} = -2 \begin{vmatrix} -2 & -3 \\ 5 & 1 \end{vmatrix} = -2(13) = -26$$

$$D_y = \begin{vmatrix} 1 & -7 & 1 & 1 \\ 1 & -11 & 1 & -1 \\ 2 & 26 & -3 & -3 \\ 3 & -9 & 1 & -1 \end{vmatrix}$$

Adding row 1 to row 2, 3 times row 1 to row 3, and row 1 to row 4 yields:

$$= \begin{vmatrix} 1 & -7 & 1 & 1 \\ 2 & -18 & 2 & 0 \\ 5 & 5 & 0 & 0 \\ 4 & -16 & 2 & 0 \end{vmatrix} = -1 \begin{vmatrix} 2 & -18 & 2 \\ 5 & 5 & 0 \\ 4 & -16 & 2 \end{vmatrix}$$

Subtracting row 3 from row 1 yields:

$$= -1 \begin{vmatrix} -2 & -2 & 0 \\ 5 & 5 & 0 \\ 4 & -16 & 2 \end{vmatrix} = -2 \begin{vmatrix} -2 & -2 \\ 5 & 5 \end{vmatrix} = -2(0) = 0$$

$$D_z = \begin{vmatrix} 1 & 1 & -7 & 1 \\ 1 & -1 & -11 & -1 \\ 2 & -2 & 26 & -3 \\ 3 & 2 & -9 & -1 \end{vmatrix}$$

Adding row 1 to row 2, 3 times row 1 to row 3, and row 1 to row 4 yields:

$$= \begin{vmatrix} 1 & 1 & -7 & 1 \\ 2 & 0 & -18 & 0 \\ 5 & 1 & 5 & 0 \\ 4 & 3 & -16 & 0 \end{vmatrix} = -1 \begin{vmatrix} 2 & 0 & -18 \\ 5 & 1 & 5 \\ 4 & 3 & -16 \end{vmatrix}$$

Adding -3 times row 2 to row 3 yields:

$$= -1 \begin{vmatrix} 2 & 0 & -18 \\ 5 & 1 & 5 \\ 11 & 0 & -31 \end{vmatrix} = -1 \begin{vmatrix} 2 & -18 \\ -11 & -31 \end{vmatrix} = -1(-260) = 260$$

$$D_w = \begin{vmatrix} 1 & 1 & 1 & -7 \\ 1 & -1 & 1 & -11 \\ 2 & -2 & -3 & 26 \\ 3 & 2 & 1 & -9 \end{vmatrix}$$

Adding row 1 to row 2, 2 times row 1 to row 3, and -2 times row 1 to row 4 yields:

$$= \begin{vmatrix} 1 & 1 & 1 & -7 \\ 2 & 0 & 2 & -18 \\ 4 & 0 & -1 & 12 \\ 1 & 0 & -1 & 5 \end{vmatrix} = -1 \begin{vmatrix} 2 & 2 & -18 \\ 4 & -1 & 12 \\ 1 & -1 & 5 \end{vmatrix} = -2 \begin{vmatrix} 1 & 1 & -9 \\ 4 & -1 & 12 \\ 1 & -1 & 5 \end{vmatrix}$$

Adding row 1 to both row 2 and row 3 yields:

$$= -2 \begin{vmatrix} 1 & 1 & -9 \\ 5 & 0 & 3 \\ 2 & 0 & -4 \end{vmatrix} = 2 \begin{vmatrix} 5 & 3 \\ 2 & -4 \end{vmatrix} = 2(-26) = -52$$

So $x = \dfrac{D_x}{D} = 1$, $y = \dfrac{D_y}{D} = 0$, $z = \dfrac{D_z}{D} = -10$, and $w = \dfrac{D_w}{D} = 2$.

So the solution is $(1,0,-10,2)$

43.

$$\begin{vmatrix} x-4 & 0 & 0 \\ 0 & x+4 & 0 \\ 0 & 0 & x+1 \end{vmatrix} = (x-4) \begin{vmatrix} x+4 & 0 \\ 0 & x+1 \end{vmatrix}$$

$$= (x-4)(x+4)(x+1)$$

This will equal 0 when $x = 4$, $x = -4$, or $x = -1$.

45.

$$\begin{vmatrix} a & b & c \\ a & b & c \\ d & e & f \end{vmatrix} = a \begin{vmatrix} b & c \\ e & f \end{vmatrix} - a \begin{vmatrix} b & c \\ e & f \end{vmatrix} + d \begin{vmatrix} b & c \\ b & c \end{vmatrix}$$

$$= a(bf - ec) - a(bf - ec) + d(bc - bc)$$
$$= abf - aec - abf + aec + 0$$
$$= 0$$

47. $\begin{vmatrix} a_1 + A_1 & b_1 & c_1 \\ a_2 + A_2 & b_2 & c_2 \\ a_3 + A_3 & b_3 & c_3 \end{vmatrix}$

$$= (a_1 + A_1)\begin{vmatrix} b_2 & c_2 \\ b_3 & c_3 \end{vmatrix} - (a_2 + A_2)\begin{vmatrix} b_1 & c_1 \\ b_3 & c_3 \end{vmatrix} + (a_3 + A_3)\begin{vmatrix} b_1 & c_1 \\ b_2 & c_2 \end{vmatrix}$$

$$= \left\{ a_1\begin{vmatrix} b_2 & c_2 \\ b_3 & c_3 \end{vmatrix} - a_2\begin{vmatrix} b_1 & c_1 \\ b_3 & c_3 \end{vmatrix} + a_3\begin{vmatrix} b_1 & c_1 \\ b_2 & c_2 \end{vmatrix} \right\}$$

$$+ \left\{ A_1\begin{vmatrix} b_2 & c_2 \\ b_3 & c_3 \end{vmatrix} - A_2\begin{vmatrix} b_1 & c_1 \\ b_3 & c_3 \end{vmatrix} + A_3\begin{vmatrix} b_1 & c_1 \\ b_2 & c_2 \end{vmatrix} \right\}$$

Now observe that the expression in the first set of braces is

$$\begin{vmatrix} a_1 & b_1 & c_1 \\ a_2 & b_2 & c_2 \\ a_3 & b_3 & c_3 \end{vmatrix}$$

the expression in the second set of braces is

$$\begin{vmatrix} A_1 & b_1 & c_1 \\ A_2 & b_2 & c_2 \\ A_3 & b_3 & c_3 \end{vmatrix}$$

49. Expanding the determinant on the left-hand side of the given equation along its first row, we obtain:

$$\begin{vmatrix} a_1 & b_1 & c_1 \\ a_2 & b_2 & c_2 \\ a_3 & b_3 & c_3 \end{vmatrix} = a_1\begin{vmatrix} b_2 & c_2 \\ b_3 & c_3 \end{vmatrix} - b_1\begin{vmatrix} a_2 & c_2 \\ a_3 & c_3 \end{vmatrix} + c_1\begin{vmatrix} a_2 & b_2 \\ a_3 & b_3 \end{vmatrix}$$

Next, expanding the determinant on the right-hand side of the given equation along its second row, we obtain:

$$\begin{vmatrix} a_2 & b_2 & c_2 \\ a_1 & b_1 & c_1 \\ a_3 & b_3 & c_3 \end{vmatrix} = -a_1\begin{vmatrix} b_2 & c_2 \\ b_3 & c_3 \end{vmatrix} + b_1\begin{vmatrix} a_2 & c_2 \\ a_3 & c_3 \end{vmatrix} - c_1\begin{vmatrix} a_2 & b_2 \\ a_3 & b_3 \end{vmatrix}$$

By inspection now, we observe that the two expressions for the determinants are negatives of one another.

51. Subtract the fourth row from each of the other three rows. After that, we have:

$$\begin{vmatrix} a & 0 & 0 & -d \\ 0 & b & 0 & -d \\ 0 & 0 & c & -d \\ 1 & 1 & 1 & 1+d \end{vmatrix} = abcd \begin{vmatrix} 1 & 0 & 0 & -1 \\ 0 & 1 & 0 & -1 \\ 0 & 0 & 1 & -1 \\ 1/a & 1/b & 1/c & 1+1/d \end{vmatrix}$$

$$= abcd \begin{vmatrix} 1 & 0 & 0 & 0 \\ 0 & 1 & 0 & -1 \\ 0 & 0 & 1 & -1 \\ 1/a & 1/b & 1/c & 1 + 1/a + 1/d \end{vmatrix}$$

$$= abcd \begin{vmatrix} 1 & 0 & -1 \\ 0 & 1 & -1 \\ 1/b & 1/c & 1 + 1/a + 1/d \end{vmatrix}$$

$$= abcd \begin{vmatrix} 1 & 0 & 0 \\ 0 & 1 & -1 \\ 1/b & 1/c & 1 + 1/a + 1/b + 1/d \end{vmatrix}$$

$$= abcd \begin{vmatrix} 1 & -1 \\ 1/c & 1 + 1/a + 1/b + 1/d \end{vmatrix}$$

$$= abcd \left(1 + \frac{1}{a} + \frac{1}{b} + \frac{1}{c} + \frac{1}{d} \right)$$

53. By expanding D along its first column, we obtain the equation:

$$a_1 D = a_1 [a_1(b_2 c_3 - b_3 c_2) - a_2(b_1 c_3 - b_3 c_1) + a_3(b_1 c_2 - b_2 c_1)] \quad \text{**}$$

On the other hand $\begin{vmatrix} B_2 & C_2 \\ B_3 & C_3 \end{vmatrix}$ is equal to

$$B_2 C_3 - B_3 C_2 = (a_1 c_3 - a_3 c_1)(a_1 b_2 - a_2 b_1) - (a_1 c_2 - a_2 c_1)(a_1 b_3 - a_3 b_1)$$

$$= a_1{}^2 b_2 c_3 - a_1 a_3 b_2 c_1 - a_1 a_2 b_1 c_3 + a_2 a_3 b_1 c_1$$

$$- a_1{}^2 b_3 c_2 + a_1 a_3 b_1 c_2 + a_1 a_2 b_3 c_1 - a_2 a_3 b_1 c_1$$

$$= a_1 [a_1 b_2 c_3 - a_3 b_2 c_1 - a_2 b_1 c_3 - a_1 b_3 c_2 + a_3 b_1 c_2 + a_2 b_3 c_1]$$

$$= a_1 [a_1(b_2 c_3 - b_3 c_2) - a_2(b_1 c_3 - b_3 c_1) + a_3(b_1 c_2 - b_2 c_1)]$$

By inspection now, we see that this last expression agrees with the right-hand side of equation **. This proves that:

$$\begin{vmatrix} B_2 & C_2 \\ B_3 & C_3 \end{vmatrix} = a_1 D, \text{ as required.}$$

55. (a) $\begin{vmatrix} 1 & 0 & 0 \\ x & 1 & 0 \\ x & y & 1 \end{vmatrix} = 1 \begin{vmatrix} 1 & 0 \\ y & 1 \end{vmatrix} = 1(1) = 1$

(b) $\begin{vmatrix} 1 & 0 & 0 & 0 \\ x & 1 & 0 & 0 \\ x & y & 1 & 0 \\ x & y & z & 1 \end{vmatrix} = 1 \begin{vmatrix} 1 & 0 & 0 \\ y & 1 & 0 \\ y & z & 1 \end{vmatrix} = 1 \begin{vmatrix} 1 & 0 \\ z & 1 \end{vmatrix} = 1(1) = 1$

57.
$$\begin{vmatrix} 1 & a & a & a \\ 1 & b & a & a \\ 1 & a & b & a \\ 1 & a & a & b \end{vmatrix}$$

Subracting row 1 from each of row 2, row 3, and row 4 yields:

$$= \begin{vmatrix} 1 & a & a & a \\ 0 & b-a & 0 & 0 \\ 0 & 0 & b-a & 0 \\ 0 & 0 & 0 & b-a \end{vmatrix}$$

$$= 1 \begin{vmatrix} b-a & 0 & 0 \\ 0 & b-a & 0 \\ 0 & 0 & b-a \end{vmatrix}$$

$$= (b-a) \begin{vmatrix} b-a & 0 \\ 0 & b-a \end{vmatrix}$$

$$= (b-a)(b-a)^2$$

$$= (b-a)^3$$

59. Just for some variety, let's use augmented matrices.

Form the augmented matrix: $\begin{pmatrix} a & b & c & k \\ a^2 & b^2 & c^2 & k^2 \\ a^3 & b^3 & c^3 & k^3 \end{pmatrix}$

Adding $-a$ times row 1 to row 2 and $-a^2$ times row 1 to row 3:

$$\begin{pmatrix} a & b & c & k \\ 0 & b^2-ab & c^2-ac & k^2-ak \\ 0 & b^3-a^2b & c^3-a^2c & k^3-a^2k \end{pmatrix}$$

Factoring:

$$\begin{pmatrix} a & b & c & k \\ 0 & b(b-a) & c(c-a) & k(k-a) \\ 0 & b(b+a)(b-a) & c(c+a)(c-a) & k(k+a)(k-a) \end{pmatrix}$$

Adding $-(b+a)$ times row 2 to row 3:

$$\begin{pmatrix} a & b & c & k \\ 0 & b(b-a) & c(c-a) & k(k-a) \\ 0 & 0 & c(c-a)(c-b) & k(k-a)(k-b) \end{pmatrix}$$

So:

$$\begin{aligned} ax + by + cz &= k \\ b(b-a)y + c(c-a)z &= k(k-a) \\ c(c-a)(c-b)z &= k(k-a)(k-b) \end{aligned}$$

Solving the third equation for z:

$$c(c-a)(c-b)z = k(k-a)(k-b)$$

$$z = \frac{k(k-a)(k-b)}{c(c-a)(c-b)}$$

Substitute into the second equation:

$$b(b - a)y + \frac{k(k - a)(k - b)}{c - b} = k(k - a)$$

$$b(b - a)(c - b)y = k(k - a)(c - b - k + b)$$

$$y = \frac{k(k - a)(k - c)}{b(b - a)(b - c)}$$

Substitute into the first equation:

$$ax + \frac{k(k - a)(k - c)}{(b - a)(b - c)} + \frac{k(k - a)(k - b)}{(c - a)(c - b)} = k$$

$$ax = \frac{k(k - b)(k - c)}{(b - a)(c - a)}$$

$$x = \frac{k(k - b)(k - c)}{a(a - b)(a - c)}$$

So the solution is $\left(\dfrac{k(k - b)(k - c)}{a(a - b)(a - c)}, \dfrac{k(k - a)(k - c)}{b(b - a)(b - c)}, \dfrac{k(k - a)(k - b)}{c(c - a)(c - b)}\right)$

61. We re-draw the figure:

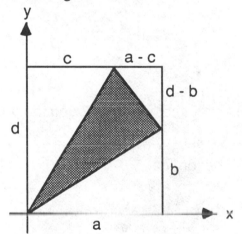

The area of the rectangle is ad, and the three triangles have areas of $\frac{1}{2}(ab)$, $\frac{1}{2}(a - c)(d - b)$, and $\frac{1}{2}(cd)$, so the area of the shaded triangle is:

$$ad - [\tfrac{1}{2}ab + \tfrac{1}{2}ad - \tfrac{1}{2}cd - \tfrac{1}{2}ab + \tfrac{1}{2}bc + \tfrac{1}{2}cd]$$

$$= \tfrac{1}{2}ad - \tfrac{1}{2}bc$$

$$= \tfrac{1}{2}(ad - bc)$$

$$= \tfrac{1}{2}\begin{vmatrix} a & b \\ c & d \end{vmatrix}$$

63.   (a)   From exercise 36, we found $A^{-1} = \begin{pmatrix} \dfrac{d}{ad-bc} & \dfrac{-b}{ad-bc} \\ \dfrac{-c}{ad-bc} & \dfrac{a}{ad-bc} \end{pmatrix}$

Since $D = ad - bc$, then $A^{-1} = \dfrac{1}{D}\begin{pmatrix} d & -b \\ -c & a \end{pmatrix}$

(b) $D = -6(9) - 7(1) = -54 - 7 = -61$, so the inverse is:

$$-\frac{1}{61}\begin{pmatrix} 9 & -7 \\ -1 & -6 \end{pmatrix} \quad \text{or} \quad \begin{pmatrix} -9/61 & 7/61 \\ 1/61 & 6/61 \end{pmatrix}$$

10.6   Nonlinear Systems of Equations

1. $y = 3x$
$y = x^2$
Substituting, we get:
$$x^2 = 3x$$
$$x^2 - 3x = 0$$
$$x(x - 3) = 0$$
From which we get $x = 0$ or $x = 3$. If $x = 0$, $y = 3 \bullet 0 = 0$ and if $x = 3$, $y = 9$. Our solutions are $(0,0)$ and $(3,9)$. Note that we have found the points of intersection of a line and a parabola.

3.   Since $x^2 = 24y$, $x^2 + y^2 = 25$ becomes:
$$24y + y^2 = 25$$
$$y^2 + 24y - 25 = 0$$
$$(y + 25)(y - 1) = 0$$
$$y = -25 \text{ and } y = 1$$
When $y = 1$ we get $x^2 = 24$ or $x = \pm 2\sqrt{6}$ but $y = -25$ means $x^2 = -600$ which is impossible. Our two solutions are $(2\sqrt{6}, 1)$ and $(-2\sqrt{6}, 1)$.

5.   Substitute into the first equation:
$$x(-x^2) = 1$$
$$-x^3 = 1$$
$$x = -1$$
Since $y = \dfrac{1}{x}$, then $y = -1$.
So the only solution is $(-1,-1)$.

7. Multiply the first equation by -2:
$$-4x^2 - 2y^2 = -34$$
$$x^2 + 2y^2 = 22$$
Adding, we get:
$$-3x^2 = -12$$
$$x^2 = 4$$
$$x = \pm 2$$
When x = 2, we have:
$$2(4) + y^2 = 17$$
$$y^2 = 9$$
$$y = \pm 3$$
When x = -2, we have:
$$2(4) + y^2 = 17$$
$$y^2 = 9$$
$$y = \pm 3$$
So the solutions are (2,3), (2,-3), (-2,3), and (-2,-3)

9. Substitute into the first equation:
$$x^2 - 1 = 1 - x^2$$
$$2x^2 = 2$$
$$x^2 = 1$$
$$x = \pm 1$$
So y = 1 - 1 = 0 for each value of x.
So the solutions are (1,0) and (-1,0)

11. Substitute into the first equation:
$$x(4x + 1) = 4$$
$$4x^2 + x - 4 = 0$$
$$x = \frac{-1 \pm \sqrt{1 + 64}}{8} = \frac{-1 \pm \sqrt{65}}{8}$$
When $x = \frac{-1 + \sqrt{65}}{8}$, we have $y = \frac{-1 + \sqrt{65}}{2} + 1 = \frac{1 + \sqrt{65}}{2}$

When $x = \frac{-1 - \sqrt{65}}{8}$, we have $y = \frac{-1 - \sqrt{65}}{2} + 1 = \frac{1 - \sqrt{65}}{2}$

So the solutions are $\left(\frac{-1 + \sqrt{65}}{8}, \frac{1 + \sqrt{65}}{2} \right)$ and $\left(\frac{-1 - \sqrt{65}}{8}, \frac{1 - \sqrt{65}}{2} \right)$.

13.   Let $a = \dfrac{1}{x^2}$ and $b = \dfrac{1}{y^2}$, so
$$a - 3b = 14$$
$$2a + b = 35$$
Multiply the first equation by -2:
$$-2a + 6b = -28$$
$$2a + b = 35$$
Adding, we get:
$$7b = 7$$
$$b = 1$$
So $a - 3 = 14$, and $a = 17$.

Since $a = \dfrac{1}{x^2}$ and $b = \dfrac{1}{y^2}$, we have $x^2 = \dfrac{1}{17}$ and $y^2 = 1$

So $x = \dfrac{\pm\sqrt{17}}{17}$ and $y = \pm 1$

So the solutions are $\left(\dfrac{\sqrt{17}}{17}, 1\right)$, $\left(\dfrac{\sqrt{17}}{17}, -1\right)$, $\left(\dfrac{-\sqrt{17}}{17}, 1\right)$, and $\left(\dfrac{-\sqrt{17}}{17}, -1\right)$.

15.   Substitute into the second equation:
$$(x - 3)^2 + (-\sqrt{x - 1})^2 = 4$$
$$x^2 - 6x + 9 + x - 1 = 4$$
$$x^2 - 5x + 4 = 0$$
$$(x - 1)(x - 4) = 0$$
$$x = 1 \text{ or } x = 4$$
When $x = 1$, $y = -\sqrt{1 - 1} = 0$ and when $x = 4$, $y = -\sqrt{4 - 1} = -\sqrt{3}$.
So the solutions are $(1,0)$ and $(4, -\sqrt{3})$.

17.   Since $y = 2^{2x} - 12 = (2^x)^2 - 12$, we substitute into the second equation:
$$y = y^2 - 12$$
$$0 = y^2 - y - 12$$
$$0 = (y - 4)(y + 3)$$
$$y = 4 \text{ or } y = -3$$
When $y = 4$, we have $2^x = 4$, so $x = 2$. $y = -3$ will not have a solution.
So the only solution is $(2,4)$.

19.   Let $u = \log_{10} x$ and $v = \log_{10} y$, so:
$$2u^2 - v^2 = -1$$
$$4u^2 - 3v^2 = -11$$
Multiply the first equation by -2:
$$-4u^2 + 2v^2 = 2$$
$$4u^2 - 3v^2 = -11$$

Adding, we get:

$$-v^2 = -9$$
$$v^2 = 9$$
$$v = \pm 3$$

Substitute into the first equation:

$$2u^2 - 9 = -1$$
$$2u^2 = 8$$
$$u^2 = 4$$
$$u^2 = \pm 2$$

Since $u = \log_{10} x$, then $x = 10^{\pm 2}$. Similarly, $y = 10^{\pm 3}$

So the solutions are $(100, 1000)$, $\left(100, \dfrac{1}{1000}\right)$, $\left(\dfrac{1}{100}, 1000\right)$,

and $\left(\dfrac{1}{100}, \dfrac{1}{1000}\right)$.

21. First take the logarithm (ln) of each side of the first equation:

$$\ln(2^x 3^y) = \ln 4$$
$$\ln(2^x) + \ln(3^y) = \ln 2^2$$
$$(\ln 2)x + (\ln 3)y = 2\ln 2$$

Multiply the second equation by - ln 2

$$(\ln 2)x + (\ln 3)y = 2\ln 2$$
$$(-\ln 2)x - (\ln 2)y = -5\ln 2$$

Adding, we get:

$$(\ln 3 - \ln 2)y = -3\ln 2$$
$$y = \frac{3\ln 2}{\ln 2 - \ln 3}$$

Substitute into the second equation:

$$x = 5 - \frac{3\ln 2}{\ln 2 - \ln 3}$$
$$= \frac{2\ln 2 - 5\ln 3}{\ln 2 - \ln 3}$$

So the solution is $\left(\dfrac{2\ln 2 - 5\ln 3}{\ln 2 - \ln 3}, \dfrac{3\ln 2}{\ln 2 - \ln 3}\right)$

23. $y = 3x + 1 = \dfrac{-3 + 3\sqrt{13}}{6} + 1 = \dfrac{3 + 3\sqrt{13}}{6} = \dfrac{1 + \sqrt{13}}{2}$

$y = \dfrac{1}{x} = \dfrac{6}{-1 + \sqrt{13}} \cdot \dfrac{-1 - \sqrt{13}}{-1 - \sqrt{13}} = \dfrac{-6(1 + \sqrt{13})}{1 - 13} = \dfrac{-6(1 + \sqrt{13})}{-12} = \dfrac{1 + \sqrt{13}}{2}$

So they both yield the same y-value.

25.   Since $ax + by = 2$, then $by = 2 - ax$. Substitute into the second equation:
$$ax(by) = 1$$
$$ax(2 - ax) = 1$$
$$2ax - a^2x^2 = 1$$
$$a^2x^2 - 2ax + 1 = 0$$
$$(ax - 1)^2 = 0$$
$$ax = 1$$
$$x = \frac{1}{a}$$

When $ax = 1$, $by = 2 - 1 = 1$, so $y = \frac{1}{b}$.

So the solution is $\left(\frac{1}{a}, \frac{1}{b}\right)$.

27.   Solve the second equation for y to get $y = 23 - x$. Substitute into the first equation:
$$x^3 + (23 - x)^3 = 3473$$
$$x^3 + 12167 - 1587x + 69x^2 - x^3 = 3473$$
$$69x^2 - 1587x + 8694 = 0$$
$$x^2 - 23x + 126 = 0$$
$$(x - 9)(x - 14) = 0$$
$$x = 9 \text{ or } x = 14$$

When $x = 9$, $y = 14$ and when $x = 14$, $y = 9$.
So the solutions are $(9,14)$ and $(14,9)$

29.   First draw the rectangle:

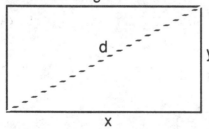

Now $x^2 + y^2 = d^2$ and $2x + 2y = 2p$. Solve the second equation for y:
$$2x + 2y = 2p$$
$$2y = 2p - 2x$$
$$y = p - x$$
Substitute into the first equation:
$$x^2 + (p - x)^2 = d2$$
$$x^2 + p^2 - 2px + x^2 = d^2$$
$$2x^2 - 2px + p^2 - d^2 = 0$$

$$x = \frac{2p \pm \sqrt{4p^2 - 8(p^2 - d^2)}}{4}$$

$$= \frac{2p \pm 2\sqrt{2d^2 - p^2}}{4}$$

$$= \frac{p \pm \sqrt{2d^2 - p^2}}{2}$$

When $x = \dfrac{p + \sqrt{2d^2 - p^2}}{2}$, $y = p - \dfrac{p + \sqrt{2d^2 - p^2}}{2} = \dfrac{p - \sqrt{2d^2 - p^2}}{2}$

When $x = \dfrac{p - \sqrt{2d^2 - p^2}}{2}$, $y = p - \dfrac{p - \sqrt{2d^2 - p^2}}{2} = \dfrac{p + \sqrt{2d^2 - p^2}}{2}$

So the rectangle has dimensions $\dfrac{p - \sqrt{2d^2 - p^2}}{2}$ by $\dfrac{p + \sqrt{2d^2 - p^2}}{2}$

31. If we follow the lead offered we have:

$$(\sqrt{u + v} + \sqrt{u - v})^2 = 4^2$$

$$u + v + 2\sqrt{u^2 - v^2} + u - v = 16$$

But since $u^2 - v^2 = 9$ from the first equation:

$$2u + 2\sqrt{9} = 16$$
$$2u + 6 = 16$$
$$2u = 10, \text{ so } u = 5$$

When $u = 5$, we have:

$$5^2 - v^2 = 9$$
$$v^2 = 16$$
$$v = \pm 4$$

So the solutions are (5,4) and (5,-4). Note that $u \neq -5$.

33. Let $w = x + y + z$, so:

$$xw = p^2$$
$$yw = q^2$$
$$zw = r^2$$

Adding the three equations, we get:

$$(x + y + z)w = p^2 + q^2 + r^2$$
$$w^2 = p^2 + q^2 + r^2$$
$$w = \pm\sqrt{p^2 + q^2 + r^2}$$

Substitute into the first equation:

$$x = \frac{p^2}{\pm\sqrt{p^2 + q^2 + r^2}}$$

Similarly $y = \dfrac{q^2}{\pm A}$ and $z = \dfrac{r^2}{\pm A}$ where $A = \sqrt{p^2 + q^2 + r^2}$.

So the solutions are $\left(\dfrac{p^2}{A}, \dfrac{q^2}{A}, \dfrac{r^2}{A}\right)$ and $\left(\dfrac{-p^2}{A}, \dfrac{-q^2}{A}, \dfrac{-r^2}{A}\right)$

where $A = \sqrt{p^2 + q^2 + r^2}$.

35. $A = \dfrac{1}{2}bh$, where b and h are the missing legs. We have:

$$180 = \dfrac{1}{2}bh, \text{ so } bh = 360, \text{ so } b = \dfrac{360}{h}$$

Also from the Pythagorean Theorem $b^2 + h^2 = 41^2$. so:

$$\left(\dfrac{360}{h}\right)^2 + h^2 = 41^2$$

$$\dfrac{129600}{h^2} + h^2 = 1681$$

$$129600 + h^4 = 1681h^2$$

$$h^4 - 1681h^2 + 129600 = 0$$

$$(h^2 - 1600)(h^2 - 81) = 0$$

$$h^2 = 1600 \quad \text{or} \quad h^2 = 81$$

$$h = \pm 40 \quad \text{or} \quad h = \pm 9$$

Since these must be the length of sides, we can neglect the negative values.
So the legs are 9 cm and 40 cm.

37.   We have $LW = 60$ and $2L + 2W = 46$, so $L + W = 23$ and $L = 23 - W$. We
substitute this into the first equation:

$$(23 - W)(W) = 60$$

$$23W - W^2 = 60$$

$$W^2 - 23w + 60 = 0$$

$$(W - 20)(W - 3) = 0$$

$$W = 20 \text{ or } W = 3$$

When $W = 20$ we have $L = 3$, and when $W = 3$ we have $L = 20$. So the
rectangle must be 3 cm by 20 cm.

39.   Solve $xy = 2$ to get $y = \dfrac{2}{x}$. Now substitute into the first equation:

$$x^2 + \dfrac{4}{x^2} = 5$$

$$x^4 + 4 = 5x^2$$

$$x^4 - 5x^2 + 4 = 0$$

$$(x^2 - 1)(x^2 - 4) = 0$$

$$x^2 = 1 \quad \text{or} \quad x^2 = 4$$

$$x = \pm 1 \qquad x = \pm 2$$

When $x = 1$, $y = 2$; when $x = -1$, $y = -2$; when $x = 2$, $y = 1$; when $x = -2$, $y = -1$.
So the solutions are $(1,2)$, $(-1,-2)$, $(2,1)$, and $(-2,-1)$.

41. Multiply the second equation by 2:

$$2xy = 6$$

Adding to the first we get:

$$x^2 + 2xy + y^2 = 13$$
$$(x + y)^2 = 13$$
$$x + y = \pm \sqrt{13}$$

Subtracting from the first equation, we get:

$$x^2 - 2xy + y^2 = 1$$
$$(x - y)^2 = 1$$
$$x - y = \pm 1$$

We solve the four systems of equations:

$$\begin{array}{llll}
\underline{\begin{array}{l} x + y = \sqrt{13} \\ x - y = 1 \end{array}} & \underline{\begin{array}{l} x + y = \sqrt{13} \\ x - y = -1 \end{array}} & \underline{\begin{array}{l} x + y = \sqrt{13} \\ x - y = 1 \end{array}} & \underline{\begin{array}{l} x + y = -\sqrt{3} \\ x - y = -1 \end{array}} \\
2x = 1 + \sqrt{13} & 2x = -1 + \sqrt{13} & 2x = 1 - \sqrt{13} & 2x = -1 - \sqrt{13} \\
x = \dfrac{1 + \sqrt{13}}{2} & x = \dfrac{-1 + \sqrt{13}}{2} & x = \dfrac{1 - \sqrt{13}}{2} & x = \dfrac{-1 - \sqrt{13}}{2} \\
y = \dfrac{-1 + \sqrt{13}}{2} & y = \dfrac{1 + \sqrt{13}}{2} & y = \dfrac{-1 - \sqrt{13}}{2} & y = \dfrac{1 - \sqrt{13}}{2}
\end{array}$$

So the solutions are $\left(\dfrac{1 + \sqrt{13}}{2}, \dfrac{-1 + \sqrt{13}}{2} \right)$, $\left(\dfrac{-1 + \sqrt{13}}{2}, \dfrac{1 + \sqrt{13}}{2} \right)$,

$\left(\dfrac{1 - \sqrt{13}}{2}, \dfrac{-1 - \sqrt{13}}{2} \right)$, and $\left(\dfrac{-1 - \sqrt{13}}{2}, \dfrac{1 - \sqrt{13}}{2} \right)$.

43. $2m^2 - 7m + 6 = 0$

$(2m - 3)(m - 2) = 0$

$$m = \frac{3}{2} \quad \text{or} \quad m = 2$$

So $x^2(\frac{9}{2} - 4) = 2 \quad$ or $\quad x^2(6 - 4) = 2$

$$\begin{array}{ll}
x^2 = 4 & x^2 = 1 \\
x = \pm 2 & x = \pm 1 \\
y = \pm 3 & y = \pm 2
\end{array}$$

So the solutions are $(2,3)$, $(-2,-3)$, $(1,2)$, and $(-1,-2)$.

45. Taking logs in the first equation:

$$\ln (x^4) = \ln (y^6)$$
$$4 \ln x = 6 \ln y$$
$$2 \ln x = 3 \ln y$$

The second equation is: $\quad \ln x - \ln y = \dfrac{\ln x}{\ln y}$

$$\ln x \ln y - (\ln y)^2 = \ln x$$

Let $u = \ln x$ and $v = \ln y$, so we have the equations $2u = 3v$ and $uv - v^2 = u$. Solving the first equation for u yields $u = \dfrac{3v}{2}$, and substituting into the second equation yields:

$$\left(\frac{3v}{2}\right) v - v^2 = \frac{3v}{2}$$
$$3v^2 - 2v^2 = 3v$$
$$v^2 - 3v = 0$$
$$v(v - 3) = 0$$
$$v = 0 \quad \text{or} \quad v = 3$$

When $v = 0$, $u = 0$ and when $v = 3$, $u = \dfrac{9}{2}$. Since $v = \ln y$, $v = 0$ cannot be a solution to the original second equation ($\ln y$ is in the denominator). Thus $u = \ln x$ and $v = \ln y$ yields:

$$\ln x = \frac{9}{2} \text{ so } x = e^{9/2}$$

$$\ln y = 3, \text{ so } y = e^3$$

So the only solution is $(e^{9/2}, e^3)$.

10.7   Systems of Inequalities; Linear Programming

1.   (a)   Since substituting the pair $(1,2)$ into $4x - 6y + 3 \geq 0$ gives $4(1) - 6(2) + 3 \geq 0$, which says $-5 \geq 0$, our answer is no.

(b)   Substitute $\left(0, \dfrac{1}{2}\right)$: $4(0) - 6\left(\dfrac{1}{2}\right) + 3 \geq 0$
$$0 \geq 0$$

Our answer is yes.

3. $2x - 3y > 6$

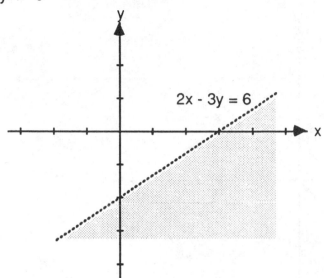

5. $2x - 3y \geq 6$

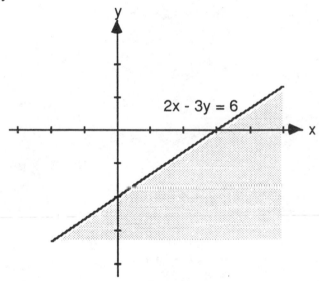

7.   x - y < 0

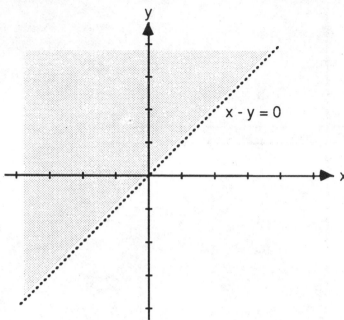

9.   x ≥ 1

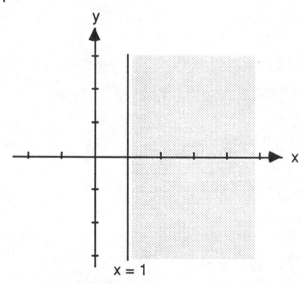

11. $x > 0$

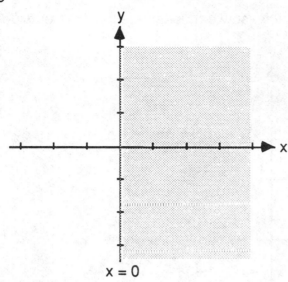

$x = 0$

13. $y > x^3 + 1$

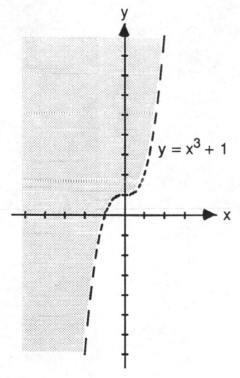

$y = x^3 + 1$

15. $x^2 + y^2 \geq 25$

We know $x^2 + y^2 = 25$ is a circle, so we must shade the area outside the circle:

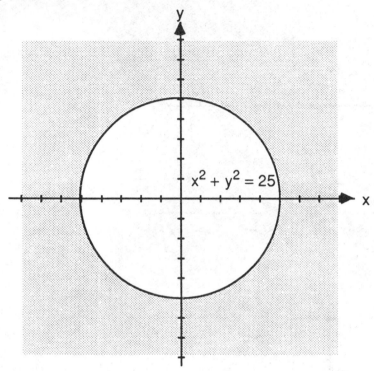

17. $y \leq x^2$
     $x^2 + y^2 \leq 1$

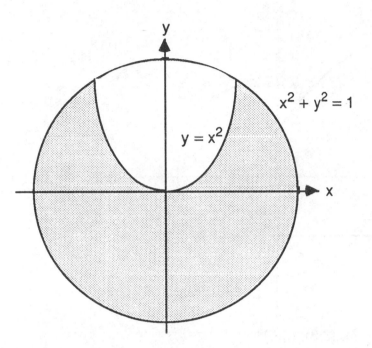

19. $y \geq 1$
     $y \leq |x|$

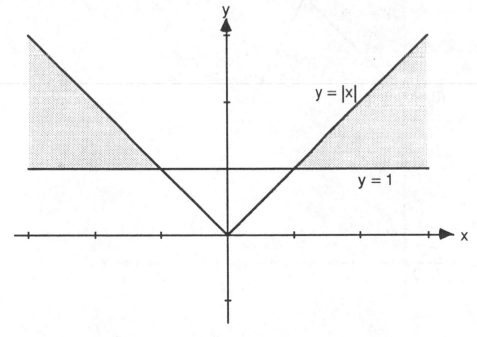

21. $x \geq 0$
    $y \geq 0$
    $y \leq 1 - x^2$

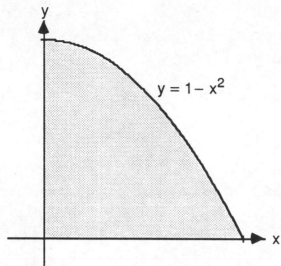

$y = 1 - x^2$

23. convex: yes
    bounded: yes
    vertices: (0,0), (7,0), (3,8), (0,5)

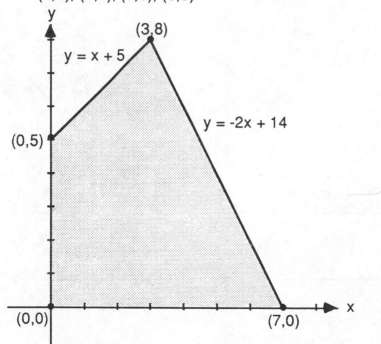

(3,8)

$y = x + 5$

$y = -2x + 14$

(0,5)

(0,0)

(7,0)

25. We simply graph each inequality, and where necessary solve to find vertices. In this case:

$$-x + 3y = 12$$
$$x + y = 8$$

So $4y = 20$, thus $y = 5$ and $x = 3$

convex: yes
bounded: yes
vertices: (0,0), (0,4), (3,5), (8,0)

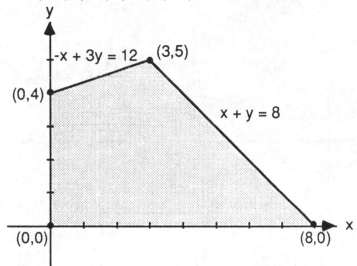

27. convex: yes
     bounded: no
     vertices: (2,7), (8,5)

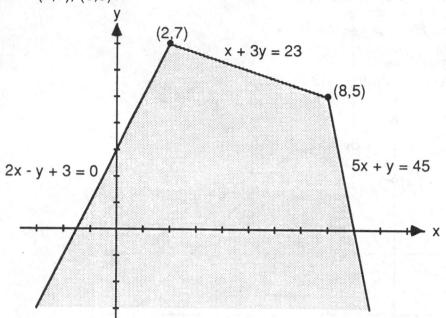

29. convex: yes
     bounded: no
     vertex: (6,0)

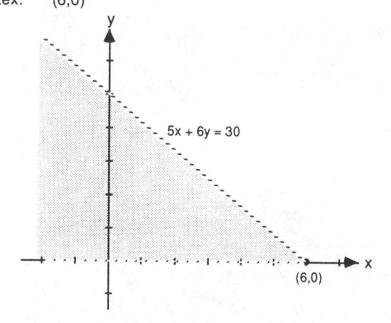

31. convex: yes
    bounded: no
    vertices: (0,0), (0,5), (6,0)

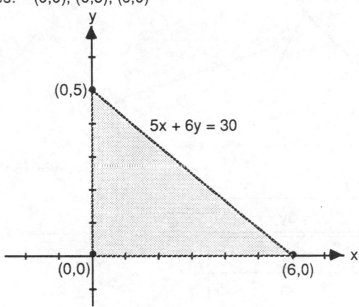

33. convex: yes
    bounded: yes
    vertices: (5,30), (10,30), (20,15), (20,20)

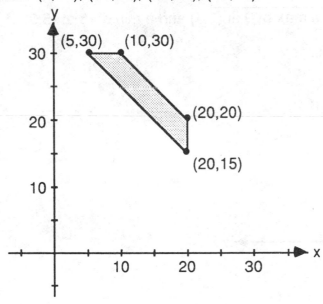

35.   We first graph the conditions:

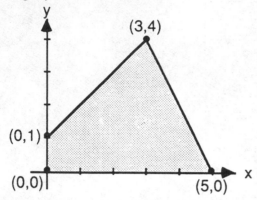

Now set up the table:

Vertices	C = 3y - x
(0,0)	0
(5,0)	-5
(3,4)	9
(0,1)	3

Thus we see that C has a max of 9 at (3,4) and a min of -5 at (5,0).

37.   We first graph the conditions:

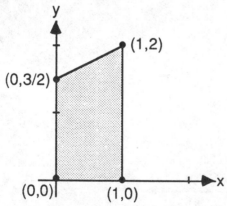

Now set up the table:

Vertices	C = 2x + y
(0,0)	0
(0,3/2)	3/2
(1,0)	2
(1,2)	4

The max value is 4 at (1,2), and the min value is 0 at (0,0).

39. We first graph the conditions:

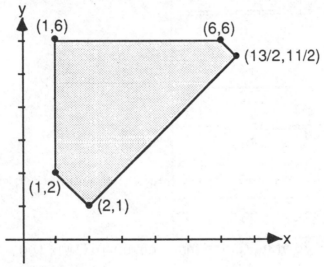

Now set up the table:

Vertices	C = 10y + 9x - 1
(1,2)	28
(2,1)	27
(13/2,11/2)	112.5
(6,6)	113
(1,6)	68

The max value is 113 at (6,6), and the min value is 27 at (2,1).

41. We first graph the conditions:

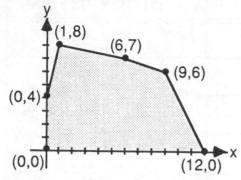

Now set up the table:

Vertices	C = 10y + 3x + 100
(0,0)	100
(0,4)	140
(1,8)	183
(6,7)	188
(9,6)	187
(12,0)	136

The maximum value is 188 at (6,7), and the minimum value is 100 at (0,0).

43. We first graph the conditions:

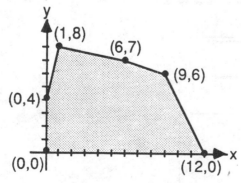

Now set up a table with both objective functions:

Vertices	(a) C = 19x + 100y	(b) C = 21x + 100y
(0,0)	0	0
(0,4)	400	400
(1,8)	819	821
(6,7)	814	826
(9,6)	771	789
(12,0)	228	252

(a)   We see max = 819 at (1,8) and min = 0 at (0,0)
(b)   We see max = 826 at (6,7) and min = 0 at (0,0)

45.   We first organize the data in tables:

Shipping: Cost   Supply: Demand
W_1 to D_1 180 W_1 has 30 W_2 has 50
W_1 to D_2 150 D_1 wants 40 D_2 wants 25
W_2 to D_1 160
W_2 to D_2 170

Let $x = W_1$ to D_1, so $40 - x = W_2$ to D_1
Let $y = W_1$ to D_2, so $25 - y = W_2$ to D_2
The cost function is C $= 180(x) + 150(y) + 160(40 - x) + 170(25 - y)$
$= 180x + 150y + 6400 - 160x + 4250 - 170y$
$= 10650 + 20x - 20y$

The constrants are: (1) $x \geq 0$
(2) $y \geq 0$
(3) $x \leq 40$
(4) $y \leq 25$
(5) $x + y \leq 30$
(6) $(40 - x) + (25 - y) \leq 50$, or $x + y \geq 15$

We graph these constraints:

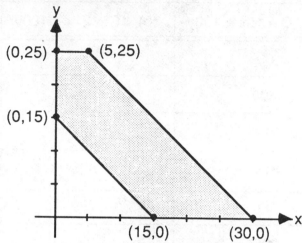

We set up a table of values:

Vertices	$C = 10650 + 20x - 20y$
(0,15)	10350
(0,25)	10150
(5,25)	10250
(30,0)	11250

So the minimum cost is $10,150 when $x = 0$ and $y = 25$.
Shipping instructions:
  W_1 to D_1: 0 cars
  W_2 to D_1: 40 cars
  W_1 to D_2: 25 cars
  W_2 to D_2: 0 cars

47. Let x = number of A units produced and y = number of B units produced. We
    have $P = 0.60x + 0.80y$
    Constraints: (1) $x \geq 0$
                 (2) $y \geq 0$
                 (3) $4x + 5y \leq 5000$
                 (4) $x + 2y \leq 1500$

We graph these constraints:

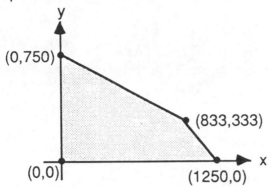

Now set up a table:

Vertices	P = 0.60x + 0.80y
(0,0)	0
(0,750)	600
(1250,0)	750
(833,333)	766.20

So the maximum profit is $766.20 when 833 units of A and 333 units of B are produced.

49. Let x = acres of cherry tomatoes and y = acres of regular tomatoes. Then
P = 50x + 36y
Constraints: (1) x ≥ 0
             (2) y ≥ 0
             (3) x + y ≤ 600
             (4) 3x + 2y ≤ 1350

We graph the constraints:

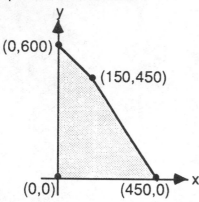

We set up a table:

Vertices	P = 50x + 36y
(0,0)	0
(0,600)	21600
(450,0)	22500
(150,450)	23700

So the maximum profit is $23,700 when 150 acres of cherry tomatoes and 450 acres of regular tomatoes are planted.

51. Let x = amount to invest in A and y = amount to invest in B. Then
     R = 0.06x + 0.08y.
     Constraints: (1) $x \geq 0$
                   (2) $y \geq 2000$
                   (3) $x + y \leq 12000$
                   (4) $x \leq 6000$
                   (5) $y \leq 2x$

We graph the constraints:

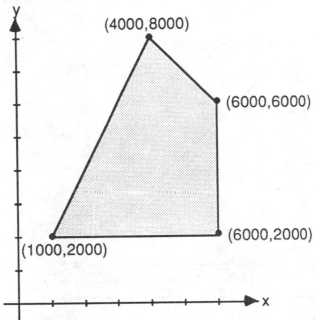

We set up a table:

Vertices	P = 0.06x + 0.08y
(1000,2000)	220
(4000,8000)	880
(6000,6000)	840
(6000,2000)	520

Your maximum return will be $880 when you invest $4000 in stock A and $8000 in stock B.

53. We have the same constraints as from exercise #52:

$$(1) \quad x \geq 1000$$
$$(2) \quad y \geq 1000$$
$$(3) \quad 1000 - x - y \geq 1000, \ x + y \leq 9000$$
$$(4) \quad x + y \leq 5000$$
$$(5) \quad y \leq 5x$$
$$P = 0.05x + 0.04y + 0.06(10000 - x - y) = 600 - 0.01x - 0.02y$$

We graph the constraints:

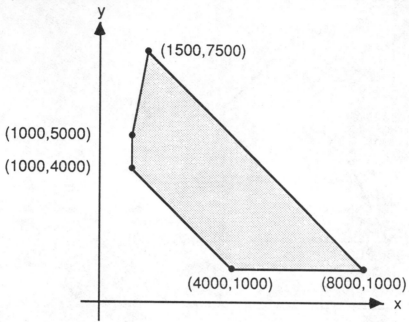

We set up a table:

Vertices	P = 600 - 0.01x - 0.02y
(4000,1000)	540
(8000,1000)	500
(1500,7500)	435
(1000,5000)	490
(1000,4000)	510

We invest $400 in A, $1000 in B and $5000 in C for a maximum return of $540.

55.   Let x = pounds of A and y = pounds of B. Then C = 0.44x + 0.80y
      Constraints: (1) $x \geq 0$
                   (2) $y \geq 0$
                   (3) $3x + 5y \geq 50$
                   (4) $2x + 4y \geq 36$
                   (5) $2x + 8y \geq 40$

We graph the constraints:

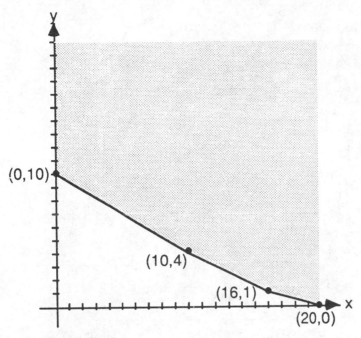

We set up a table:

Vertices	C = 0.44x + 0.80y
(0,10)	8
(10,4)	7.6
(16,1)	7.84
(20,0)	8.8

So 10 pounds of A and 4 pounds of B should be mixed, to produce a mixture with minimum cost of $7.60.

Chapter 10 Review Exercises

1. Adding the two equations yields:
$$2x = 6$$
$$x = 3$$
Substitute into equation 1:
$$3xy = -2$$
$$y = -5$$
So the solution is (3,-5).

3.   Multiply the first equation by -2:
$$-4x - 2y = -4$$
$$x + 2y = 7$$
Adding , we get:
$$-3x = 3$$
$$x = -1$$
Substitute into equation 1:
$$-2 + y = 2$$
$$y = 4$$
So the solution is (-1,4).

5.   Multiply equation 1 by -5 and equation 2 by 2:
$$-35x - 10y = -45$$
$$8x + 10y = 126$$
Adding, we get:
$$-27x = 81$$
$$x = -3$$
Substitute into equation 1:
$$-21 + 2y = 9$$
$$2y = 30$$
$$y = 15$$
So the solution is (-3,15).

7.   Multiply the first equation by 2 and the second equation by 24 to clear fractions:
$$4x - y = -16$$
$$8x + 3y = -24$$
Multiply equation 1 by -2:
$$-8x + 2y = 32$$
$$8x + 3y = -24$$
Adding, we get:
$$5y = 8$$
$$y = \frac{8}{5}$$
Substitute into equation 1:
$$4x - \frac{8}{5} = -16$$
$$4x = -\frac{72}{5}$$
$$x = -\frac{18}{5}$$
So the solution is $\left(-\frac{18}{5}, \frac{8}{5}\right)$.

9. Multiply the first equation by 2:
$$6x + 10y = 2$$
$$9x - 10y = 8$$
Adding, we get:
$$15x = 10$$
$$x = \frac{2}{3}$$
Substitute into equation 1:
$$2 + 5y = 1$$
$$5y = -1$$
$$y = -\frac{1}{5}$$
So the solution is $\left(\frac{2}{3}, -\frac{1}{5}\right)$.

11. Multiply the first equation by 6 and the second equation by 2 to clear fractions:
$$4x + 3y = -72$$
$$x - 2y = 4$$
Multiply the second by -4:
$$4x + 3y = -72$$
$$-4x + 8y = -16$$
Adding, we get:
$$11y = -88$$
$$y = -8$$
Substitute into equation 2:
$$x + 16 = 4$$
$$x = -12$$
So the solution is (-12,-8).

13. Let $a = \frac{1}{x}$ and $b = \frac{1}{y}$. So we have:
$$a + b = -1$$
$$2a + 5b = -14$$
Multiply the first equation by -2:
$$-2a - 2b = 2$$
$$2a + 5b = -14$$
Adding, we get:
$$3b = -12$$
$$b = -4$$
Substitute into equation 1:
$$a - 4 = -1$$
$$a = 3$$

Since $x = \dfrac{1}{a}$ and $y = \dfrac{1}{b}$, then $x = \dfrac{1}{3}$ and $y = -\dfrac{1}{4}$.

So the solution is $\left(\dfrac{1}{3}, -\dfrac{1}{4}\right)$.

15. Multiply the second equation by $a - 1$:

$$ax + (1 - a)y = 1$$
$$(-a^2 + 2a - 1)x + (a - 1)y = 0$$

Adding, we get:

$$(-a^2 + 3a - 1)x = 1$$
$$x = \frac{-1}{a^2 - 3a + 1}$$

Substitute into equation 2:

$$\frac{a - 1}{a^2 - 3a + 1} + y = 0$$
$$y = \frac{1 - a}{a^2 - 3a + 1}$$

So the solution is $\left(\dfrac{-1}{a^2 - 3a + 1}, \dfrac{1 - a}{a^2 - 3a + 1}\right)$. We must assume that

$a^2 - 3a + 1 \neq 0$, or $a \neq \dfrac{3 \pm \sqrt{5}}{2}$.

17. Multiply the first equation by 2:

$$4x - 2y = 6a^2 - 2$$
$$x + 2y = -a^2 + 2$$

Adding, we get:

$$5x = 5a^2$$
$$x = a^2$$

Substitute into equation 2:

$$2y + a^2 = 2 - a^2$$
$$2y = 2 - 2a^2$$
$$y = 1 - a^2$$

So the solution is $(a^2, 1 - a^2)$.

19. Multiply the first equation by 3:

$$15x - 3y = 12a^2 - 18b^2$$
$$2x + 3y = 5a^2 + b^2$$

Adding, we get:

$$17x = 17a^2 - 17b^2$$
$$x = a^2 - b^2$$

Substitute into equation 1:
$$5a^2 - 5b^2 - y = 4a^2 - 6b^2$$
$$-y = -a^2 - b^2$$
$$y = a^2 + b^2$$
So the solution is $(a^2 - b^2, a^2 + b^2)$.

21. Multiply the first equation by p and the second equation by q:
$$p^2x - pqy = pq^2$$
$$q^2x + pqy = p^2q$$
Adding, we get:
$$(p^2 + q^2)x = pq(p + q)$$
$$x = \frac{pq(p + q)}{p^2 + q^2}$$
We re-solve the system to find y. Multiply the first equation by $-q$ and the second equation by p:
$$-pqx + q^2y = -q^3$$
$$pqx + p^2y = p^3$$
Adding, we get:
$$(p^2 + q^2)y = p^3 - q^3$$
$$y = \frac{p^3 - q^3}{p^2 + q^2}$$
So the solution is $\left(\dfrac{pq(p + q)}{p^2 + q^2}, \dfrac{p^3 - q^3}{p^2 + q^2}\right)$. We must assume that

$(p,q) \neq (0,0)$.

23. Let $u = \dfrac{1}{x}$ and $v = \dfrac{1}{y}$, so we have:
$$4au - 3bv = a - 7b$$
$$2a^2u - 2b^2v = 3a^2 - 5ab - 2b^2$$
Multiply the first equation by $-2b$ and the second equation by 3:
$$-8abu + 6b^2v = 14b^2 - 2ab$$
$$9a^2u - 6b^2v = 9a^2 - 15ab - 6b^2$$
Adding, we get:
$$(9a^2 - 8ab)u = 9a^2 - 17ab + 8b^2$$
$$u = \frac{9a^2 - 17ab + 8b^2}{9a^2 - 8ab}$$
$$= \frac{(9a - 8b)(a - b)}{a(9a - 8b)}$$
$$= \frac{a - b}{a}$$

Substitute into equation 1:

$$4a\left(\frac{a-b}{a}\right) - 3bv = a - 7b$$
$$4a - 4b - 3bv = a - 7b$$
$$-3bv = -3a - 3b$$
$$v = \frac{a+b}{b}$$

Since $x = \frac{1}{u}$ and $y = \frac{1}{v}$, then $x = \frac{a}{a-b}$ and $y = \frac{b}{a+b}$.

So the solution is $\left(\frac{a}{a-b}, \frac{b}{a+b}\right)$. We must assume that $ab \neq 0$, $9a - 8b \neq 0$.

25. Form the augmented matrix:

$$\begin{pmatrix} 1 & 1 & 1 & 9 \\ 1 & -1 & -1 & -5 \\ 2 & 1 & -2 & -1 \end{pmatrix}$$

Add -1 times row 1 to row 2 and -2 times row 1 to row 3:

$$\begin{pmatrix} 1 & 1 & 1 & 9 \\ 0 & -2 & -2 & -14 \\ 0 & -1 & -4 & -19 \end{pmatrix}$$

Switch row 2 and row 3, multiply each by -1:

$$\begin{pmatrix} 1 & 1 & 1 & 9 \\ 0 & 1 & 4 & 19 \\ 0 & 2 & 2 & 14 \end{pmatrix}$$

Add -2 times row 2 to row 3:

$$\begin{pmatrix} 1 & 1 & 1 & 9 \\ 0 & 1 & 4 & 19 \\ 0 & 0 & -6 & -24 \end{pmatrix}$$

So: $x + y + z = 9$
$$y + 4z = 19$$
$$-6z = -24$$

Solve equation 3 for z:
$$-6z = -24$$
$$z = 4$$

Substitute into equation 2:
$$y + 16 = 19$$
$$y = 3$$

Substitute into equation 1:
$$x + 3 + 4 = 9$$
$$x = 2$$

So the solution is (2,3,4).

27. Switching equations 1 and 3, form the augmented matrix:

$$\begin{pmatrix} 1 & 1 & 1 & -3 \\ 2 & 3 & 3 & -8 \\ 4 & -4 & 1 & 4 \end{pmatrix}$$

Add -2 times row 1 to row 2 and -4 times row 1 to row 3:

$$\begin{pmatrix} 1 & 1 & 1 & -3 \\ 0 & 1 & 1 & -2 \\ 0 & -8 & -3 & 16 \end{pmatrix}$$

Add 8 times row 2 to row 3:

$$\begin{pmatrix} 1 & 1 & 1 & -3 \\ 0 & 1 & 1 & -2 \\ 0 & 0 & 5 & 0 \end{pmatrix}$$

So:
$$\begin{aligned} x + y + z &= -3 \\ y + z &= -2 \\ 5z &= 0 \end{aligned}$$

Solve equation 3 for z:
$$\begin{aligned} 5z &= 0 \\ z &= 0 \end{aligned}$$

Substitute into equation 2:
$$\begin{aligned} y + 0 &= -2 \\ y &= -2 \end{aligned}$$

Substitute into equation 1:
$$\begin{aligned} x - 2 + 0 &= -3 \\ x &= -1 \end{aligned}$$

So the solution is $(-1, -2, 0)$.

29. Using equation 3 as row 1, form the augmented matrix:

$$\begin{pmatrix} 1 & 1 & -2 & 4 \\ 1 & -2 & 1 & -2 \\ -2 & 1 & 1 & 1 \end{pmatrix}$$

Add -1 times row 1 to row 2 and 2 times row 1 to row 3:

$$\begin{pmatrix} 1 & 1 & -2 & 4 \\ 0 & -3 & 3 & -6 \\ 0 & 3 & -3 & 9 \end{pmatrix}$$

Multiply row 2 by $\frac{1}{3}$ and row 3 by $\frac{1}{3}$:

$$\begin{pmatrix} 1 & 1 & -2 & 4 \\ 0 & -1 & 1 & -2 \\ 0 & 1 & -1 & 3 \end{pmatrix}$$

Add row 2 to row 3:

$$\begin{pmatrix} 1 & 1 & -2 & 4 \\ 0 & -1 & 1 & -2 \\ 0 & 0 & 0 & 1 \end{pmatrix}$$

Since $0 = 1$ is false, there is no solution to the system.

31. Multiply the second equation by -2:
$$4x + 2y - 3z = 15$$
$$-4x - 2y - 6z = -6$$
Adding, we get:
$$-9z = 9$$
$$z = -1$$
Substitute into the original equation:
$$2x + y - 3 = 3$$
$$2x + y = 6$$
$$y = 6 - 2x$$
So the solution is $(x, 6 - 2x, -1)$, for any real number x.

33. Form the augmented matrix:
$$\begin{pmatrix} 1 & 2 & -3 & -2 \\ 2 & -1 & 1 & 1 \\ 3 & -4 & 5 & 1 \end{pmatrix}$$
Add -2 times row 1 to row 2 and -3 times row 1 to row 3:
$$\begin{pmatrix} 1 & 2 & -3 & -2 \\ 0 & -5 & 7 & 5 \\ 0 & -10 & 14 & 7 \end{pmatrix}$$
Add -2 times row 2 to row 3:
$$\begin{pmatrix} 1 & 2 & -3 & -2 \\ 0 & -5 & 7 & 5 \\ 0 & 0 & 0 & -3 \end{pmatrix}$$
Since $0 = -3$ is false, there is no solution to the system.

35. Form the augmented matrix:
$$\begin{pmatrix} 1 & 1 & 1 & a+b \\ 2 & -1 & 2 & -a+5b \\ 1 & -2 & 1 & -2a+4b \end{pmatrix}$$
Add -2 times row 1 to row 2 and -1 times row 1 to row 3:
$$\begin{pmatrix} 1 & 1 & 1 & a+b \\ 0 & -3 & 0 & -3a+3b \\ 0 & -3 & 0 & -3a+3b \end{pmatrix}$$
Add -1 times row 2 to row 3:
$$\begin{pmatrix} 1 & 1 & 1 & a+b \\ 0 & -3 & 0 & -3a+3b \\ 0 & 0 & 0 & 0 \end{pmatrix}$$
So:
$$x + y + z = a + b$$
$$-3y = -3a + 3b$$
Solve equation 2 for y:
$$-3y = -3a + 3b$$
$$y = a - b$$

Substitute into equation 1:

$$x + a - b + z = a + b$$
$$x = 2b - z$$

So the solution is $(2b - z, a - b, z)$, for any real number z.

37.   Form the augmented matrix:

$$\begin{pmatrix} 1 & 1 & 1 & 1 & 8 \\ 3 & 3 & -1 & -1 & 20 \\ 4 & -1 & -1 & 2 & 18 \\ 2 & 5 & 5 & -5 & 8 \end{pmatrix}$$

Add -3 times row 1 to row 2, -4 times row 1 ro row 3, and -2 times row 1 to row 4:

$$\begin{pmatrix} 1 & 1 & 1 & 1 & 8 \\ 0 & 0 & -4 & -4 & -4 \\ 0 & -5 & -5 & -2 & -14 \\ 0 & 3 & 3 & -7 & -8 \end{pmatrix}$$

Switch row 2 and row 3, and multiply row 3 by $-\frac{1}{4}$:

$$\begin{pmatrix} 1 & 1 & 1 & 1 & 8 \\ 0 & -5 & -5 & -2 & -14 \\ 0 & 0 & 1 & 1 & 1 \\ 0 & 3 & 3 & -7 & -8 \end{pmatrix}$$

Add 2 times row 4 to row 2:

$$\begin{pmatrix} 1 & 1 & 1 & 1 & 8 \\ 0 & 1 & 1 & -16 & -30 \\ 0 & 0 & 1 & 1 & 1 \\ 0 & 3 & 3 & -7 & -8 \end{pmatrix}$$

Add -3 times row 2 to row 4:

$$\begin{pmatrix} 1 & 1 & 1 & 1 & 8 \\ 0 & 1 & 1 & -16 & -30 \\ 0 & 0 & 1 & 1 & 1 \\ 0 & 0 & 0 & 41 & 82 \end{pmatrix}$$

So:
$$x + y + z + w = 8$$
$$y + z - 16w = -30$$
$$z + w = 1$$
$$41w = 82$$

Solve equation 4 for w:
$$41w = 82$$
$$w = 2$$

Substitute into equation 3:
$$z + 2 = 1$$
$$z = -1$$

Substitute into equation 2:
$$y - 1 - 32 = -30$$
$$y = 3$$
Substitute into equation 1:
$$x + 3 - 1 + 2 = 8$$
$$x = 4$$
So the solution is (4,3,-1,2).

39. Multiply by $(x - 10)(x + 10)$, so:
$$1 = A(x + 10) + B(x - 10)$$
$$1 = (A + B)x + (10A - 10B)$$
Since A and B are constants:
$$A + B = 0$$
$$10A - 10B = 1$$
Multiply equation 1 by 10:
$$10A + 10B = 0$$
$$10A - 10B = 1$$
Adding, we get:
$$20A = 1$$
$$A = \frac{1}{20}$$
Substitute into equation 1:
$$\frac{1}{20} + B = 0$$
$$B = -\frac{1}{20}$$
So $A = \frac{1}{20}$ and $B = -\frac{1}{20}$.

41. Multiply by $(x + 1)^2$, so:
$$2x = A(x + 1) + B$$
$$2x = Ax + (A + B)$$
Since A and B are constants:
$$A = 2$$
$$A + B = 0$$
Substitute into equation 2:
$$2 + B = 0$$
$$B = -2$$
So $A = 2$ and $B = -2$.

43. Multiply by $x(x - 4)$, so:
$$5 = A(x - 4) + Bx$$
$$5 = (A + B)x - 4A$$
Since A and B are constants:
$$A + B = 0$$
$$-4A = 5$$

Solve equation 2 for A:
$$-4A = 5$$
$$A = -\frac{5}{4}$$

Substitute into equation 1:
$$-\frac{5}{4} + B = 0$$
$$B = \frac{5}{4}$$

So $A = -\frac{5}{4}$ and $B = \frac{5}{4}$.

45.   Multiply by $(x - 1)(x + 3)^2$, so:
$$1 = A(x + 3)^2 + B(x - 1)(x + 3) + C(x - 1)$$
$$1 = A(x^2 + 6x + 9) + B(x^2 + 2x - 3) + C(x - 1)$$
$$1 = (A + B)x^2 + (6A + 2B + C)x + (9A - 3B - C)$$

Since A, B, and C are constants:
$$A + B = 0$$
$$6A + 2B + C = 0$$
$$9A - 3B - C = 1$$

Add -6 times equation 1 to equation 2 and -9 times equation 1 to equation 3:
$$A + B = 0$$
$$-4B + C = 0$$
$$-12B - C = 1$$

Add equation 2 and 3:
$$-16B = 1$$
$$B = -\frac{1}{16}$$

Substitute into equation 2:
$$\frac{1}{4} + C = 0$$
$$C = -\frac{1}{4}$$

Substitute into equation 1:
$$A - \frac{1}{16} = 0$$
$$A = \frac{1}{16}$$

So $A = \frac{1}{16}$, $B = -\frac{1}{16}$, $C = -\frac{1}{4}$.

47. Multiply by $(x - 1)(x^2 + x + 5)$, so:
$$4x^2 + 2x + 15 = A(x^2 + x + 5) + (Bx + C)(x - 1)$$
$$4x^2 + 2x + 15 = (A + B)x^2 + (A - B + C)x + (5A - C)$$
Since A, B, and C are constants:
$$A + B = 4$$
$$A - B + C = 2$$
$$5A \quad - C = 15$$
Add -1 times equation 1 to equation 2 and -5 times equation 1 to equation 3:
$$A + B = 4$$
$$-2B + C = -2$$
$$-5B - C = -5$$
Add equation 2 and equation 3:
$$-7B = -7$$
$$B = 1$$
Substitute into equation 2:
$$-2 + C = -2$$
$$C = 0$$
Substitute into equation 1:
$$A + 1 = 4$$
$$A = 3$$
So A = 3, B = 1, and C = 0.

49. Multiply by $(x + 4)(x^2 - 4x + 16)$, so:
$$1 = A(x^2 - 4x + 16) + (Bx + C)(x + 4)$$
$$1 = (A + B)x^2 + (-4A + 4B + C)x + (16A + 4C)$$
Since A, B, and C are constants:
$$A + B = 0$$
$$-4A + 4B + C = 0$$
$$16A \quad + 4C = 1$$
Add 4 times equation 1 to equation 2, and -16 times equation 1 to equation 3:
$$A + B = 0$$
$$8B + C = 0$$
$$-16B + 4C = 1$$
Add 2 times equation 2 to equation 3:
$$A + B = 0$$
$$8B + C = 0$$
$$6C = 1$$
Solve equation 3 for C:
$$6C = 1$$
$$C = \frac{1}{6}$$

Substitute into equation 2:

$$8B + \frac{1}{6} = 0$$

$$8B = -\frac{1}{6}$$

$$B = -\frac{1}{48}$$

Substitute into equation 1:

$$A - \frac{1}{48} = 0$$

$$A = \frac{1}{48}$$

So $A = \frac{1}{48}$, $B = -\frac{1}{48}$, and $C = \frac{1}{6}$.

51. Multiply by $(x - a)^3$, so:

$$x = A(x - a)^2 + B(x - a) + C$$
$$x = Ax^2 + (-2aA + B)x + (a^2A - aB + C)$$

Since A, B, and C are constants:

$$A = 0$$
$$-2aA + B = 1$$
$$a^2A - aB + C = 0$$

Substitute into equation 2:

$$0 + B = 1$$
$$B = 1$$

Substitute into equation 3:

$$0 - a + C = 0$$
$$C = a$$

So $A = 0$, $B = 1$, and $C = a$.

53. Multiply by $(x - a)(x - b)$, so:

$$(a - b)(a + b - x) = A(x - b) + B(x - a)$$
$$(a - b)(a + b) - (a - b)x = (A + B)x + (-bA - aB)$$

Since A and B are constants:

$$A + B = b - a$$
$$-bA - aB = a^2 - b^2$$

Multiply equation 1 by b:

$$bA + bB = b^2 - ab$$
$$-bA - aB = a^2 - b^2$$

Adding, we get:

$$(b - a)B = a^2 - ab$$
$$B = \frac{a(a - b)}{b - a}$$
$$B = -a$$

Substitute into equation 1:
$$A - a = b - a$$
$$A = b$$
So $A = b$ and $B = -a$.

55. $\begin{vmatrix} 1 & 5 \\ -6 & 4 \end{vmatrix} = 1(4) - 5(-6) = 4 + 30 = 34$

57. $\begin{vmatrix} 4 & 0 & 3 \\ -2 & 1 & 5 \\ 0 & 2 & -1 \end{vmatrix}$

Adding -2 times row 2 to row 3 yields:

$= \begin{vmatrix} 4 & 0 & 3 \\ -2 & 1 & 5 \\ 4 & 0 & -11 \end{vmatrix} = 1 \bullet \begin{vmatrix} 4 & 3 \\ 4 & -11 \end{vmatrix} = -56$

59. $\begin{vmatrix} 1 & 5 & 7 \\ 1 & 5 & 7 \\ 17 & 19 & 21 \end{vmatrix}$

Subtracting row 2 from row 1 yields:

$= \begin{vmatrix} 0 & 0 & 0 \\ 1 & 5 & 7 \\ 17 & 19 & 21 \end{vmatrix} = 0$

61. $\begin{vmatrix} 1 & 0 & 0 & 0 \\ 0 & 2 & 0 & 0 \\ 0 & 0 & 3 & 0 \\ 0 & 0 & 0 & 4 \end{vmatrix} = 1 \begin{vmatrix} 2 & 0 & 0 \\ 0 & 3 & 0 \\ 0 & 0 & 4 \end{vmatrix} = 2 \begin{vmatrix} 3 & 0 \\ 0 & 4 \end{vmatrix} = 2(12) = 24$

63. By expanding along column 1:

$\begin{vmatrix} a & b & c \\ b & c & a \\ c & a & b \end{vmatrix} = a \begin{vmatrix} c & a \\ a & b \end{vmatrix} - b \begin{vmatrix} b & c \\ a & b \end{vmatrix} + c \begin{vmatrix} b & c \\ c & a \end{vmatrix}$

$= a(bc - a^2) - b(b^2 - ac) + c(ab - c^2)$
$= abc - a^3 - b^3 + abc + abc - c^3$
$= 3abc - a^3 - b^3 - c^3$

65. $\begin{vmatrix} a^2+x & b & c & d \\ -b & 1 & 0 & 0 \\ -c & 0 & 1 & 0 \\ -d & 0 & 0 & 1 \end{vmatrix}$

Adding b times column 2 to column 1 yields:

$$= \begin{vmatrix} a^2 + b^2 + x & b & c & d \\ 0 & 1 & 0 & 0 \\ -c & 0 & 1 & 0 \\ -d & 0 & 0 & 1 \end{vmatrix} = 1 \begin{vmatrix} a^2 + b^2 + x & c & d \\ -c & 1 & 0 \\ -d & 0 & 1 \end{vmatrix}$$

Adding c times column 2 to column 1 yields:

$$= \begin{vmatrix} a^2 + b^2 + c^2 + x & c & d \\ 0 & 1 & 0 \\ -d & 0 & 1 \end{vmatrix}$$

$$= 1 \begin{vmatrix} a^2 + b^2 + c^2 + x & d \\ -d & 1 \end{vmatrix}$$

$$= a^2 + b^2 + c^2 + x - (-d^2)$$

$$= a^2 + b^2 + c^2 + d^2 + x$$

67. Substituting $(x,y) = (-2,5)$ and $(x,y) = (2,9)$, we get:

$$5 = 4a - 2b - 1$$
$$9 = 4a + 2b - 1$$

Adding, we get:

$$14 = 8a - 2$$
$$16 = 8a$$
$$2 = a$$

Substitute into the first equation:

$$5 = 8 - 2b - 1$$
$$-2 = -2b$$
$$1 = b$$

So $a = 2$ and $b = 1$.

69. (a)   Let's first graph the triangle:

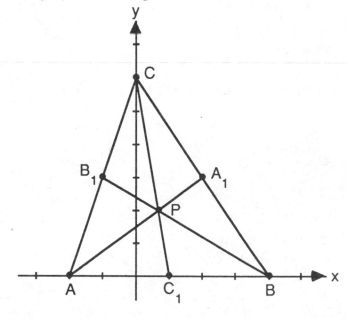

By the midpoint formula:

$$A_1 = \left(\frac{4+0}{2}, \frac{0+6}{2}\right) = (2,3)$$

$$B_1 = \left(\frac{-2+0}{2}, \frac{0+6}{2}\right) = (-1,3)$$

$$C_1 = \left(\frac{-2+4}{2}, \frac{0+0}{2}\right) = (1,0)$$

AA_1:

$$\text{slope} = \frac{3-0}{2-(-2)} = \frac{3}{4}$$

$$\text{point} = (-2,0)$$

$$y - 0 = \frac{3}{4}(x+2)$$

$$y = \frac{3}{4}x + \frac{3}{2}$$

BB_1:

$$\text{slope} = \frac{3-0}{-1-4} = -\frac{3}{5}$$

$$\text{point} = (4,0)$$

$$y - 0 = -\frac{3}{5}(x-4)$$

$$y = -\frac{3}{5}x + \frac{12}{5}$$

We solve $\frac{3}{4}x + \frac{3}{2} = -\frac{3}{5}x + \frac{12}{5}$:

Multiply by 20 to clear fractions:

$$15x + 30 = -12x + 48$$

$$27x = 18$$

$$x = \frac{2}{3}$$

So $y = \frac{3}{4} \cdot \frac{2}{3} + \frac{3}{2} = 2$. Thus the point of intersection is $\left(\frac{2}{3}, 2\right)$.

(b) CC_1:

$$\text{slope} = \frac{6-0}{0-1} = -6$$

$$y = -6x + 6$$

We solve $-6x + 6 = -\frac{3}{5}x + \frac{12}{5}$

Multiply by 5 to clear fractions:

$$-30x + 30 = -3x + 12$$

$$18 = 27x$$

$$\frac{2}{3} = x$$

So $y = -6\left(\dfrac{2}{3}\right) + 6 = 2$. Thus the point of intersection is $\left(\dfrac{2}{3}, 2\right)$.

(c) We solve $-6x + 6 = \dfrac{3}{4}x + \dfrac{3}{2}$

Multiply by 4 to clear fractions:

$$-24x + 24 = 3x + 6$$
$$18 = 27x$$
$$\frac{2}{3} = x$$

So $y = -6\left(\dfrac{2}{3}\right) + 6 = 2$. Thus the point of intersection is $\left(\dfrac{2}{3}, 2\right)$.

(d) We use the distance formula:

$$AP = \sqrt{\left(-2 - \frac{2}{3}\right)^2 + (0 - 2)^2} = \sqrt{\frac{64}{9} + \frac{36}{9}} = \frac{10}{3}$$

$$PA_1 = \sqrt{\left(\frac{2}{3} - 2\right)^2 + (2 - 3)^2} = \sqrt{\frac{16}{9} + \frac{9}{9}} = \frac{5}{3}$$

So $\dfrac{AP}{PA_1} = \dfrac{\frac{10}{3}}{\frac{5}{3}} = 2$

$$BP = \sqrt{\left(4 - \frac{2}{3}\right)^2 + (0 - 2)^2} = \sqrt{\frac{100}{9} + \frac{36}{9}} = \frac{2\sqrt{34}}{3}$$

$$PB_1 = \sqrt{\left(\frac{2}{3} + 1\right)^2 + (2 - 3)^2} = \sqrt{\frac{25}{9} + \frac{9}{9}} = \frac{\sqrt{34}}{3}$$

So $\dfrac{BP}{PB_1} = \dfrac{\frac{2\sqrt{34}}{3}}{\frac{\sqrt{34}}{3}} = 2$

$$CP = \sqrt{\left(0 - \frac{2}{3}\right)^2 + (6 - 2)^2} = \sqrt{\frac{4}{9} + \frac{144}{9}} = \frac{2\sqrt{37}}{3}$$

$$PC_1 = \sqrt{\left(\frac{2}{3} - 1\right)^2 + (2 - 0)^2} = \sqrt{\frac{1}{9} + \frac{36}{9}} = \frac{\sqrt{37}}{3}$$

So $\dfrac{CP}{PC_1} = \dfrac{\frac{2\sqrt{37}}{3}}{\frac{\sqrt{37}}{3}} = 2$

These ratios are all equal.

71.   See the figure:

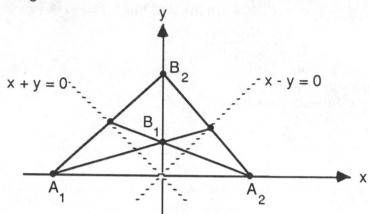

We start with A_2B_2:
$$m = -\frac{b_2}{a_2}$$
    point: (a,a)
By the point slope formula:
$$a_2y + b_2x = aa_2 + ab_2$$
Since $(a_2,0)$ lies on this curve, we have $a_2b_2 = aa_2 + ab_2$ (*)
Now for A_1B_1:
$$m = -\frac{b_1}{a_1}$$
    point: (a,a)
By the point-slope formula:
$$a_1y + b_1x = aa_1 + ab_1$$
Since $(a_1,0)$ lies on this curve, we have $a_1b_1 = aa_1 + ab_1$ (*)
Now we look at A_1B_2:
$$m = -\frac{b_2}{a_1}$$
$$b_2x + a_1y = a_1b_2$$
Also look at A_2B_1:
$$m = -\frac{b_1}{a_2}, \text{ so:}$$
$$b_1x + a_2y = a_2b_1$$
We solve the system:
$$b_2x + a_1y = a_1b_2$$
$$b_1x + a_2y = a_2b_1$$
Multiply equation 1 by $-b_1$ and equation 2 by b_2:
$$-b_1b_2x - a_1b_1y = -a_1b_1b_2$$
$$b_1b_2x + a_2b_2y = a_2b_1b_2$$

Adding:
$$(a_2b_2 - a_1b_1)y = a_2b_1b_2 - a_1b_1b_2 ,$$

So:
$$y = \frac{b_1b_2(a_2 - a_1)}{a_2b_2 - a_1b_1}$$

Substituting into equation 1, we have:
$$b_2x + \frac{a_1b_1b_2(a_2 - a_1)}{a_2b_2 - a_1b_1} = a_1b_2$$

So:
$$x = \frac{a_1a_2(b_2 - b_1)}{a_2b_2 - a_1b_1}$$

Now, we are asked to show that $x + y = 0$, so:
$$x + y = \frac{a_1a_2(b_2 - b_1) + b_1b_2(a_2 - a_1)}{a_2b_2 - a_1b_1}$$
$$= \frac{a_1a_2b_2 - a_1a_2b_1 + a_2b_1b_2 - a_1b_1b_2}{a_2b_2 - a_1b_1}$$

Replacing a_1b_1 and a_2b_2 by equations (*):
$$= \frac{a_1(aa_2+ab_2) - a_2(aa_1+ab_1) + b_1(aa_2+ab_2) - b_2(aa_1+ab_1)}{a_2b_2 - a_1b_1}$$
$$= \frac{a(a_1a_2 + a_1b_2 - a_1a_2 - a_2b_1 + a_2b_1 + b_1b_2 - a_1b_2 - b_1b_2)}{a_2b_2 - a_1b_1}$$

= 0 ! All terms cancel.

If you followed this one through, then perhaps you should take a break. . .

73. We find each intersection point:

$y = x - 1$	$y = x - 1$	$y = -x - 2$
$y = -x - 2$	$y = 2x + 3$	$y = 2x + 3$
$2y = -3$	$x - 1 = 2x + 3$	$-x - 2 = 2x + 3$
$y = -\dfrac{3}{2}$	$-4 = x$	$-5 = 3x$
		$x = -\dfrac{5}{3}$
$x = -\dfrac{1}{2}$	$y = -5$	$y = -\dfrac{1}{3}$
$\left(-\dfrac{1}{2}, -\dfrac{3}{2}\right)$	$(-4, -5)$	$\left(-\dfrac{5}{3}, -\dfrac{1}{3}\right)$

We now substitute into the equation $(x - h)^2 + (y - k)^2 = r^2$:

$$\left(-\frac{1}{2} - h\right)^2 + \left(-\frac{3}{2} - k\right)^2 = r^2$$
$$(-4 - h)^2 + (-5 - k)^2 = r^2$$
$$\left(-\frac{5}{3} - h\right)^2 + \left(-\frac{1}{3} - k\right)^2 = r^2$$

These equations, when multiplied out, become:

$$\frac{5}{2} + h + h^2 + 3k + k^2 = r^2$$

$$41 + 8h + h^2 + 10k + k^2 = r^2$$

$$\frac{26}{9} + \frac{10}{3}h + h^2 + \frac{2}{3}k + k^2 = r^2$$

Subtracting the first equation from the other two yields:

$$\frac{77}{2} + 7h + 7k = 0$$

$$\frac{7}{18} + \frac{7}{3}h - \frac{7}{3}k = 0$$

Which simplify to:

$$6h + 6k = -33$$
$$6h - 6k = -1$$

Adding, we get:

$$12h = -34$$
$$h = -\frac{17}{6}$$

To find k, we subtract the two equations:

$$12k = -32$$
$$k = -\frac{8}{3}$$

Finally, we find r:

$$r^2 = (-4 - h)^2 + (-5 - k)^2 = \left(-\frac{7}{6}\right)^2 + \left(-\frac{7}{3}\right)^2 = \frac{245}{36}$$

The equation of the circle is:

$$\left(x + \frac{17}{6}\right)^2 + \left(y + \frac{8}{3}\right)^2 = \frac{245}{36}$$

75. $2A + 2B = \begin{pmatrix} 6 & -4 \\ 2 & 10 \end{pmatrix} + \begin{pmatrix} 4 & 2 \\ 2 & 16 \end{pmatrix} = \begin{pmatrix} 10 & -2 \\ 4 & 26 \end{pmatrix}$

77. $4B = \begin{pmatrix} 8 & 4 \\ 4 & 32 \end{pmatrix}$

79. $AB = \begin{pmatrix} 4 & -13 \\ 7 & 41 \end{pmatrix}$

81. $AB - BA = \begin{pmatrix} 7 & -13 \\ 7 & 41 \end{pmatrix} - \begin{pmatrix} 7 & 1 \\ 11 & 38 \end{pmatrix} = \begin{pmatrix} -3 & -14 \\ -4 & 3 \end{pmatrix}$

83. $B + C = \begin{pmatrix} 1 & 1 \\ 1 & 7 \end{pmatrix}$

85. $AB + AC = \begin{pmatrix} 4 & -13 \\ 7 & 41 \end{pmatrix} + \begin{pmatrix} -3 & 2 \\ -1 & -5 \end{pmatrix} = \begin{pmatrix} 1 & -11 \\ 6 & 36 \end{pmatrix}$

87. $BA + CA = \begin{pmatrix} 7 & 1 \\ 11 & 38 \end{pmatrix} + \begin{pmatrix} -3 & 2 \\ -1 & -5 \end{pmatrix} = \begin{pmatrix} 4 & 3 \\ 10 & 33 \end{pmatrix}$

89. $DE = \begin{pmatrix} -42 & 58 \\ 5 & 20 \end{pmatrix}$

91. undefined

93. undefined

95. $(A + B) + C = \begin{pmatrix} 5 & -1 \\ 2 & 13 \end{pmatrix} + \begin{pmatrix} -1 & 0 \\ 0 & -1 \end{pmatrix} = \begin{pmatrix} 4 & -1 \\ 2 & 12 \end{pmatrix}$

97. $(AB)C = \begin{pmatrix} 4 & -13 \\ 7 & 41 \end{pmatrix}\begin{pmatrix} -1 & 0 \\ 0 & -1 \end{pmatrix} = \begin{pmatrix} -4 & 13 \\ -7 & -41 \end{pmatrix}$

99. $A^2 = \begin{pmatrix} 1 & 1 \\ 0 & 1 \end{pmatrix}\begin{pmatrix} 1 & 1 \\ 0 & 1 \end{pmatrix} = \begin{pmatrix} 1 & 2 \\ 0 & 1 \end{pmatrix}$

$A^3 = A \bullet A^2 = \begin{pmatrix} 1 & 1 \\ 0 & 1 \end{pmatrix}\begin{pmatrix} 1 & 2 \\ 0 & 1 \end{pmatrix} = \begin{pmatrix} 1 & 3 \\ 0 & 1 \end{pmatrix}$

101. (a) Form the augmented matrix: $\begin{pmatrix} 1 & 5 & 1 & 0 \\ 2 & 9 & 0 & 1 \end{pmatrix}$

Multiply row 1 by -2 and add to row 2:
$\begin{pmatrix} 1 & 5 & 1 & 0 \\ 0 & -1 & -2 & 1 \end{pmatrix}$

Multiply row 2 by 5 and add to row 1:
$\begin{pmatrix} 1 & 0 & -9 & 5 \\ 0 & -1 & -2 & 1 \end{pmatrix}$

Multiply row 2 by -1:
$\begin{pmatrix} 1 & 0 & -9 & 5 \\ 0 & 1 & 2 & -1 \end{pmatrix}$

So the inverse is $\begin{pmatrix} -9 & 5 \\ 2 & -1 \end{pmatrix}$

(b) Since the system is equivalent to $A \bullet X = B$, where $A = \begin{pmatrix} 1 & 5 \\ 2 & 9 \end{pmatrix}$,

$X = \begin{pmatrix} x \\ y \end{pmatrix}$, and $B = \begin{pmatrix} 3 \\ -4 \end{pmatrix}$ then $X = A^{-1} \bullet B$

$$= \begin{pmatrix} -9 & 5 \\ 2 & -1 \end{pmatrix} \begin{pmatrix} 3 \\ -4 \end{pmatrix}$$

$$= \begin{pmatrix} -47 \\ 10 \end{pmatrix}$$

So $x = -47$, $y = 10$.

103.   (a) Form the augmented matrix: $\begin{pmatrix} 1 & -2 & 3 & 1 & 0 & 0 \\ 2 & -5 & 10 & 0 & 1 & 0 \\ -1 & 2 & -2 & 0 & 0 & 1 \end{pmatrix}$

Multiply row 1 by -2 and add to row 2, then add row 1 to row 3:

$$\begin{pmatrix} 1 & -2 & 3 & 1 & 0 & 0 \\ 0 & -1 & 4 & -2 & 1 & 0 \\ 0 & 0 & 1 & 1 & 0 & 1 \end{pmatrix}$$

Multiply row 2 by -1:

$$\begin{pmatrix} 1 & -2 & 3 & 1 & 0 & 0 \\ 0 & 1 & -4 & 2 & -1 & 0 \\ 0 & 0 & 1 & 1 & 0 & 1 \end{pmatrix}$$

Multiply row 2 by 2 and add to row 1:

$$\begin{pmatrix} 1 & 0 & -5 & 5 & -2 & 0 \\ 0 & 1 & -4 & 2 & -1 & 0 \\ 0 & 0 & 1 & 1 & 0 & 1 \end{pmatrix}$$

Multiply row 3 by 4 and add to row 2, then multiply row 3 by 5 and add to row 1:

$$\begin{pmatrix} 1 & 0 & 0 & 10 & -2 & 5 \\ 0 & 1 & 0 & 6 & -1 & 4 \\ 0 & 0 & 1 & 1 & 0 & 1 \end{pmatrix}$$

So the inverse is $\begin{pmatrix} 10 & -2 & 5 \\ 6 & -1 & 4 \\ 1 & 0 & 1 \end{pmatrix}$

(b) Since the system is equivalent to $A \bullet X = B$, where $A = \begin{pmatrix} 1 & -2 & 3 \\ 2 & -5 & 10 \\ -1 & 2 & -2 \end{pmatrix}$,

$X = \begin{pmatrix} x \\ y \\ z \end{pmatrix}$, and $B = \begin{pmatrix} -2 \\ -3 \\ 6 \end{pmatrix}$, then $X = A^{-1} \bullet B$

$$= \begin{pmatrix} 10 & -2 & 5 \\ 6 & -1 & 4 \\ 1 & 0 & 1 \end{pmatrix} \begin{pmatrix} -2 \\ -3 \\ 6 \end{pmatrix}$$

$$= \begin{pmatrix} 16 \\ 15 \\ 4 \end{pmatrix}$$

So $x = 16$, $y = 15$, and $z = 4$.

105. Form the augmented matrix: $\begin{pmatrix} 5 & 3 & 6 & -7 & 1 & 0 & 0 & 0 \\ 3 & -4 & 0 & -9 & 0 & 1 & 0 & 0 \\ 0 & 1 & -1 & -1 & 0 & 0 & 1 & 0 \\ 2 & 2 & 3 & -2 & 0 & 0 & 0 & 1 \end{pmatrix}$

Multiply row 4 by -2 and add to row 1 (to get a 1 value):

$$\begin{pmatrix} 1 & -1 & 0 & -3 & 1 & 0 & 0 & -2 \\ 3 & -4 & 0 & -9 & 0 & 1 & 0 & 0 \\ 0 & 1 & -1 & -1 & 0 & 0 & 1 & 0 \\ 2 & 2 & 3 & -2 & 0 & 0 & 0 & 1 \end{pmatrix}$$

Multiply row 1 by -3 and add to row 2, and multiply row 1 by -2 and add to row 4:

$$\begin{pmatrix} 1 & -1 & 0 & -3 & 1 & 0 & 0 & -2 \\ 0 & -1 & 0 & 0 & -3 & 1 & 0 & 6 \\ 0 & 1 & -1 & -1 & 0 & 0 & 1 & 0 \\ 0 & 4 & 3 & 4 & -2 & 0 & 0 & 5 \end{pmatrix}$$

Add row 2 to row 3, then multiply row 2 by 4 and add to row 4:

$$\begin{pmatrix} 1 & -1 & 0 & -3 & 1 & 0 & 0 & -2 \\ 0 & -1 & 0 & 0 & -3 & 1 & 0 & 6 \\ 0 & 0 & -1 & -1 & -3 & 1 & 1 & 6 \\ 0 & 0 & 3 & 4 & -14 & 4 & 0 & 29 \end{pmatrix}$$

Multiply row 3 by 3 and add to row 4:

$$\begin{pmatrix} 1 & -1 & 0 & -3 & 1 & 0 & 0 & -2 \\ 0 & -1 & 0 & 0 & -3 & 1 & 0 & 6 \\ 0 & 0 & -1 & -1 & -3 & 1 & 1 & 6 \\ 0 & 0 & 0 & 1 & -23 & 7 & 3 & 47 \end{pmatrix}$$

Add row 4 to row 3, then multiply row 4 by 3 and add to row 1:

$$\begin{pmatrix} 1 & -1 & 0 & 0 & -68 & 21 & 9 & 139 \\ 0 & -1 & 0 & 0 & -3 & 1 & 0 & 6 \\ 0 & 0 & -1 & 0 & -26 & 8 & 4 & 53 \\ 0 & 0 & 0 & 1 & -23 & 7 & 3 & 47 \end{pmatrix}$$

Multiply row 2 by -1 and row 3 by -1:

$$\begin{pmatrix} 1 & -1 & 0 & 0 & -68 & 21 & 9 & 139 \\ 0 & 1 & 0 & 0 & 3 & -1 & 0 & -6 \\ 0 & 0 & 1 & 0 & 26 & -8 & -4 & -53 \\ 0 & 0 & 0 & 1 & -23 & 7 & 3 & 47 \end{pmatrix}$$

Add row 2 to row 1:

$$\begin{pmatrix} 1 & 0 & 0 & 0 & -65 & 20 & 9 & 133 \\ 0 & 1 & 0 & 0 & 3 & -1 & 0 & -6 \\ 0 & 0 & 1 & 0 & 26 & -8 & -4 & -53 \\ 0 & 0 & 0 & 1 & -23 & 7 & 3 & 47 \end{pmatrix}$$

So the inverse is:

$$\begin{pmatrix} -65 & 20 & 9 & 133 \\ 3 & -1 & 0 & -6 \\ 26 & -8 & -4 & -53 \\ -23 & 7 & 3 & 47 \end{pmatrix}$$

107. $D = \begin{vmatrix} 2 & -1 & 1 \\ 3 & 2 & 2 \\ 1 & -5 & -3 \end{vmatrix}$

Adding 2 times column 2 to column 1 and column 2 to column 3 yields:

$$= \begin{vmatrix} 0 & -1 & 0 \\ 7 & 2 & 4 \\ -9 & -5 & -8 \end{vmatrix} = -(-1) \begin{vmatrix} 7 & 4 \\ -9 & -8 \end{vmatrix} = 1(-20) = -20$$

$D_x = \begin{vmatrix} 1 & -1 & 1 \\ 0 & 2 & 2 \\ -2 & -5 & -3 \end{vmatrix}$

Adding 2 times row 1 to row 3 yields:

$$= \begin{vmatrix} 1 & -1 & 1 \\ 0 & 2 & 2 \\ 0 & -7 & -1 \end{vmatrix} = 1 \begin{vmatrix} 2 & 2 \\ -7 & -1 \end{vmatrix} = 12$$

$D_y = \begin{vmatrix} 2 & 1 & 1 \\ 3 & 0 & 2 \\ 1 & -2 & -3 \end{vmatrix}$

Adding 2 times row 1 to row 3 yields:

$$= \begin{vmatrix} 2 & 1 & 1 \\ 3 & 0 & 2 \\ 5 & 0 & -1 \end{vmatrix} = -1 \begin{vmatrix} 3 & 2 \\ 5 & -1 \end{vmatrix} = -(-13) = 13$$

$D_z = \begin{vmatrix} 2 & -1 & 1 \\ 3 & 2 & 0 \\ 1 & -5 & -2 \end{vmatrix}$

Adding 2 times row 1 to row 3 yields:

$$= \begin{vmatrix} 2 & -1 & 1 \\ 3 & 2 & 0 \\ 5 & -7 & 0 \end{vmatrix} = 1 \begin{vmatrix} 3 & 2 \\ 5 & -7 \end{vmatrix} = -31$$

So $x = \dfrac{D_x}{D} = -\dfrac{12}{20} = -\dfrac{3}{5}$, $y = \dfrac{D_y}{D} = -\dfrac{13}{20}$, and $z = \dfrac{D_z}{D} = \dfrac{31}{20}$.

So the solution is $\left(-\dfrac{3}{5}, -\dfrac{13}{20}, \dfrac{31}{20} \right)$.

109. $D = \begin{vmatrix} 1 & 2 & 3 \\ 4 & 5 & 6 \\ 7 & 8 & 9 \end{vmatrix}$

Subtracting column 2 from column 3 and column 1 from column 2 yields:

$= \begin{vmatrix} 1 & 1 & 1 \\ 4 & 1 & 1 \\ 7 & 1 & 1 \end{vmatrix}$

Subtracting column 3 from column 2 yields:

$= \begin{vmatrix} 1 & 0 & 1 \\ 4 & 0 & 1 \\ 7 & 0 & 1 \end{vmatrix} = 0$

So Cramer's Rule will not work. Form the augmented matrix:

$\begin{pmatrix} 1 & 2 & 3 & -1 \\ 4 & 5 & 6 & 2 \\ 7 & 8 & 9 & -3 \end{pmatrix}$

Add -4 times row 1 to row 2 and -7 times row 1 to row 3:

$\begin{pmatrix} 1 & 2 & 3 & -1 \\ 0 & -3 & -6 & 6 \\ 0 & -6 & -12 & 4 \end{pmatrix}$

Add -2 times row 2 to row 3:

$\begin{pmatrix} 1 & 2 & 3 & -1 \\ 0 & -3 & -6 & 6 \\ 0 & 0 & 0 & -8 \end{pmatrix}$

So 0 = -8, which is false. The system has no solution.

111. $D = 0$ (See problem 110), so form the augmented matrix:

$\begin{pmatrix} 3 & 2 & -2 & 1 \\ 2 & 3 & -1 & -2 \\ 8 & 7 & -5 & 0 \end{pmatrix}$

Subtract row 2 from row 1:

$\begin{pmatrix} 1 & -1 & -1 & 3 \\ 2 & 3 & -1 & -2 \\ 8 & 7 & -5 & 0 \end{pmatrix}$

Add -2 times row 1 to row 2 and -8 times row 1 to row 3:

$\begin{pmatrix} 1 & -1 & -1 & 3 \\ 0 & 5 & 1 & -8 \\ 0 & 15 & 3 & -24 \end{pmatrix}$

Add -3 times row 2 to row 3:

$\begin{pmatrix} 1 & -1 & -1 & 3 \\ 0 & 5 & 1 & -8 \\ 0 & 0 & 0 & 0 \end{pmatrix}$

So: $x - y - z = 3$
         $5y + z = -8$

Solve equation 2 for z:
$$z = -8 - 5y$$
Substitute into equation 1:
$$x - y + 8 + 5y = 3$$
$$x = -5 - 4y$$
So the solution is $(-5 - 4y, y, -8 - 5y)$, for any real number y.

113. $D = \begin{vmatrix} 2 & -1 & 1 & 3 \\ 1 & 2 & 0 & 2 \\ 0 & 3 & 3 & 4 \\ -4 & 1 & -4 & 0 \end{vmatrix}$

Adding 4 times column 2 to both column 1 and column 3 yields:

$$= \begin{vmatrix} -2 & -1 & -3 & 3 \\ 9 & 2 & 8 & 2 \\ 12 & 3 & 15 & 4 \\ 0 & 1 & 0 & 0 \end{vmatrix}$$

$$= 1 \begin{vmatrix} -2 & -3 & 3 \\ 9 & 8 & 2 \\ 12 & 15 & 4 \end{vmatrix}$$

Subtracting row 2 from row 3 yields:

$$= \begin{vmatrix} -2 & -3 & 3 \\ 9 & 8 & 2 \\ 3 & 7 & 2 \end{vmatrix}$$

Adding $\frac{2}{3}$ times column 3 to column 1, and column 3 to column 2 yields:

$$= \begin{vmatrix} 0 & 0 & 3 \\ 31/3 & 10 & 2 \\ 13/3 & 9 & 2 \end{vmatrix} = 3 \begin{vmatrix} 31/3 & 10 \\ 13/3 & 9 \end{vmatrix} = \begin{vmatrix} 31 & 10 \\ 13 & 9 \end{vmatrix} = 149$$

$$D_x = \begin{vmatrix} 15 & -1 & 1 & 3 \\ 12 & 2 & 0 & 2 \\ 12 & 3 & 3 & 4 \\ -11 & 1 & -4 & 0 \end{vmatrix}$$

Adding 11 times column 2 to column 1 and 4 times column 2 to column 3 yields:

$$= \begin{vmatrix} 4 & -1 & -3 & 3 \\ 34 & 2 & 8 & 2 \\ 45 & 3 & 15 & 4 \\ 0 & 1 & 0 & 0 \end{vmatrix}$$

$$= 1 \begin{vmatrix} 4 & -3 & 3 \\ 34 & 8 & 2 \\ 45 & 15 & 4 \end{vmatrix}$$

Subtracting row 2 from row 3 yields:

$$= \begin{vmatrix} 4 & -3 & 3 \\ 34 & 8 & 2 \\ 11 & 7 & 2 \end{vmatrix}$$

Subtracting row 3 from row 2 yields:

$$= \begin{vmatrix} 4 & -3 & 3 \\ 23 & 1 & 0 \\ 11 & 7 & 2 \end{vmatrix}$$

Adding -23 times column 2 to column 1:

$$= \begin{vmatrix} 73 & -3 & 3 \\ 0 & 1 & 0 \\ -150 & 7 & 2 \end{vmatrix} = \begin{vmatrix} 73 & 3 \\ -150 & 2 \end{vmatrix} = 596$$

$$D_y = \begin{vmatrix} 2 & 15 & 1 & 3 \\ 1 & 12 & 0 & 2 \\ 0 & 12 & 3 & 4 \\ -4 & -11 & -4 & 0 \end{vmatrix}$$

Adding -2 times row 2 to row 1 and 4 times row 2 to row 4 yields:

$$= \begin{vmatrix} 0 & -9 & 1 & -1 \\ 1 & 12 & 0 & 2 \\ 0 & 12 & 3 & 4 \\ 0 & 37 & -4 & 8 \end{vmatrix}$$

$$= -1 \begin{vmatrix} -9 & 1 & -1 \\ 12 & 3 & 4 \\ 37 & -4 & 8 \end{vmatrix}$$

Adding 9 times column 2 to column 1 and column 2 to column 3 yields:

$$= -1 \begin{vmatrix} 0 & 1 & 0 \\ 39 & 3 & 7 \\ 1 & -4 & 4 \end{vmatrix} = 1 \begin{vmatrix} 39 & 7 \\ 1 & 4 \end{vmatrix} = 149$$

$$D_z = \begin{vmatrix} 2 & -1 & 15 & 3 \\ 1 & 2 & 12 & 2 \\ 0 & 3 & 12 & 4 \\ -4 & 1 & -11 & 0 \end{vmatrix}$$

Adding -2 times row 2 to row 1 and 4 times row 2 to row 4 yields:

$$= \begin{vmatrix} 0 & -5 & -9 & -1 \\ 1 & 2 & 12 & 2 \\ 0 & 3 & 12 & 4 \\ 0 & 9 & 37 & 8 \end{vmatrix}$$

$$= -1 \begin{vmatrix} -5 & -9 & -1 \\ 3 & 12 & 4 \\ 9 & 37 & 8 \end{vmatrix}$$

Adding 4 times row 1 to row 2 and 8 times row 1 to row 3:

$$= -1 \begin{vmatrix} -5 & -9 & -1 \\ -17 & -24 & 0 \\ -31 & -25 & 0 \end{vmatrix} = 1 \begin{vmatrix} -17 & -24 \\ -31 & -35 \end{vmatrix} = -149$$

$$D_w = \begin{vmatrix} 2 & -1 & 1 & 15 \\ 1 & 2 & 0 & 12 \\ 0 & 3 & 3 & 12 \\ -4 & 1 & -4 & -11 \end{vmatrix}$$

Adding -2 times row 2 to row 1 and 4 times row 2 to row 4:

$$= \begin{vmatrix} 0 & -5 & 1 & -9 \\ 1 & 2 & 0 & 12 \\ 0 & 3 & 3 & 12 \\ 0 & 9 & -4 & 37 \end{vmatrix}$$

$$= -1 \begin{vmatrix} -5 & 1 & -9 \\ 3 & 3 & 12 \\ 9 & -4 & 37 \end{vmatrix}$$

Factoring 3 out of row 2 yields:

$$= -3 \begin{vmatrix} -5 & 1 & -9 \\ 1 & 1 & 4 \\ 9 & -4 & 37 \end{vmatrix}$$

Adding -1 times row 2 to row 1 and 4 times row 2 to row 3:

$$= -3 \begin{vmatrix} -6 & 0 & -13 \\ 1 & 1 & 4 \\ 13 & 0 & 53 \end{vmatrix} = -3 \begin{vmatrix} -6 & -13 \\ 13 & 53 \end{vmatrix} = -3(-149) = 447$$

So $x = \dfrac{D_x}{D} = \dfrac{596}{149} = 4$, $y = \dfrac{D_y}{D} = \dfrac{149}{149} = 1$, $z = \dfrac{D_z}{D} = -\dfrac{149}{149} = -1$,

and $w = \dfrac{D_w}{D} = \dfrac{447}{149} = 3$.

So the solution is $(4,1,-1,3)$.

115.   Substitute to get
$$x^2 = 6x$$
$$x^2 - 6x = 0$$
$$x(x - 6) = 0$$
$$x = 0 \quad \text{or} \quad x = 6$$

When $x = 0$, $y = 0$ and when $x = 6$, $y = 36$.
So the solutions are $(0,0)$ and $(6,36)$.

117.   Substitute to get
$$x^2 - 9 = 9 - x^2$$
$$2x^2 = 18$$
$$x^2 = 9$$
$$x = \pm 3$$

When $x = \pm 3$, $y = 0$.
So the solutions are $(3,0)$ and $(-3,0)$

119. Adding the two equations yields
$$2x^2 = 25$$
$$x^2 = \frac{25}{2}$$
$$x = \frac{\pm 5\sqrt{2}}{2}$$

So:
$$\frac{25}{2} + y^2 = 16$$
$$y^2 = \frac{7}{2}$$
$$y = \frac{\pm\sqrt{14}}{2}$$

So the solutions are $\left(\frac{5\sqrt{2}}{2}, \frac{\sqrt{14}}{2}\right)$, $\left(-\frac{5\sqrt{2}}{2}, \frac{\sqrt{14}}{2}\right)$, $\left(\frac{5\sqrt{2}}{2}, -\frac{\sqrt{14}}{2}\right)$, and $\left(-\frac{5\sqrt{2}}{2}, -\frac{\sqrt{14}}{2}\right)$.

121. Substitute to get:
$$x^2 + x = 1$$
$$x^2 + x - 1 = 0$$
$$x = \frac{-1 \pm \sqrt{1 + 4}}{2} = \frac{-1 \pm \sqrt{5}}{2}$$

Now $x = \frac{-1 - \sqrt{5}}{2}$ doesn't make sense ($y = \sqrt{x}$).

So the only solution is $\left(\frac{-1 + \sqrt{5}}{2}, \sqrt{\frac{-1 + \sqrt{5}}{2}}\right)$ or $\left(\frac{-1 + \sqrt{5}}{2}, \frac{\sqrt{-2 + 2\sqrt{5}}}{2}\right)$.

123. Substitute to get
$$x^2 + (2x^2)^2 = 1$$
$$x^2 + 4x^4 = 1$$
$$4x^4 + x^2 - 1 = 0$$
$$x^2 = \frac{-1 \pm \sqrt{1 + 16}}{8} = \frac{-1 \pm \sqrt{17}}{8}$$

Since $x^2 \neq \frac{-1 - \sqrt{17}}{8}$, we have $x^2 = \frac{-1 + \sqrt{17}}{8}$, so $x = \frac{\pm\sqrt{-2 + 2\sqrt{17}}}{4}$

Since $y = 2x^2$, we have $y = \frac{-1 + \sqrt{17}}{4}$

So the solutions are:
$\left(\frac{\sqrt{-2 + 2\sqrt{17}}}{4}, \frac{-1 + \sqrt{17}}{4}\right)$ and $\left(\frac{-\sqrt{-2 + 2\sqrt{17}}}{4}, \frac{-1 + \sqrt{17}}{4}\right)$.

125.   Multiply the second equation by -3:

$$-9x^2 + 3xy - 3y^2 = -54$$
$$x^2 + 2xy + 3y^2 = 68$$

Adding, we get:

$$-8x^2 + 5xy = 14$$
$$-5xy = 8x^2 + 14$$
$$y = \frac{8x^2 + 14}{5x}$$

Now substitute into the second equation:

$$3x^2 - \frac{8x^2 + 14}{5} + \frac{(8x^2 + 14)^2}{25x^2} = 18$$

Multiply by $25x^2$:

$$75x^4 - 5x^2(8x^2 + 14) + (8x^2 + 14)^2 = 450x^2$$
$$75x^4 - 40x^4 - 70x^2 + 64x^4 + 224x^2 + 196 = 450x^2$$
$$99x^4 - 296x^2 + 196 = 0$$
$$(99x^2 - 98)(x^2 - 2) = 0$$

So: $x^2 = \dfrac{98}{99}$ or $x^2 = 2$

$x = \dfrac{\pm 7\sqrt{22}}{33}$ or $x = \pm\sqrt{2}$

Now $y = \dfrac{8x^2 + 14}{5x}$, so:

When $x = \sqrt{2}$, $y = \dfrac{16 + 14}{5\sqrt{2}} = 3\sqrt{2}$

When $x = -\sqrt{2}$, $y = \dfrac{16 + 14}{-5\sqrt{2}} = -3\sqrt{2}$

When $x = \dfrac{7\sqrt{22}}{33}$, $y = \dfrac{31\sqrt{22}}{33}$

When $x = \dfrac{-7\sqrt{22}}{33}$, $y = \dfrac{-31\sqrt{22}}{33}$

So the solutions are $(\sqrt{2}, 3\sqrt{2})$, $(-\sqrt{2}, -3\sqrt{2})$, $\left(\dfrac{7\sqrt{22}}{33}, \dfrac{31\sqrt{22}}{33}\right)$, and $\left(\dfrac{-7\sqrt{22}}{33}, \dfrac{-31\sqrt{22}}{33}\right)$.

127.   Let $u = x - 3$ and $v = y + 1$, so:

$$2u^2 - v^2 = -1$$
$$-3u^2 + 2v^2 = 6$$

Multiply the first equation by 2 and add:

$$u^2 = 4$$
$$u = \pm 2$$

Substituting, we get:

$$8 - v^2 = -1$$
$$-v^2 = -9$$
$$v = \pm 3$$

So the solutions (u,v) are (2,3), (2,-3), (-2,3), and (-2,-3).
Since $u = x - 3$ and $v = y + 1$, then $x = u + 3$ and $y = v - 1$.
So the solutions are (5,2), (5,-4), (1,2), (1,-4).

129.   Call the numbers x and y. So $x + y = s$ and $\dfrac{x}{y} = \dfrac{a}{b}$.

So $y = s - x$, and substituting:

$$\frac{x}{s - x} = \frac{a}{b}$$
$$bx = as - ax$$
$$(a + b)x = as$$
$$x = \frac{as}{a + b}$$

So $y = s - \dfrac{as}{a + b} = \dfrac{bs}{a + b}$

So the two numbers are $\dfrac{as}{a + b}$ and $\dfrac{bs}{a + b}$.

131.   We have:

$$\frac{1}{2}x + \frac{1}{3}y + \frac{1}{4}z = 62$$
$$\frac{1}{3}x + \frac{1}{4}y + \frac{1}{5}z = 47$$
$$\frac{1}{4}x + \frac{1}{5}y + \frac{1}{6}z = 38$$

Multiply the first equation by 12, the second equation by 60, and the third by 60 to clear the fractions:

$$6x + 4y + 3z = 744$$
$$20x + 15y + 12z = 2820$$
$$15x + 12y + 10z = 2280$$

We use Cramer's Rule:

$$D = \begin{vmatrix} 6 & 4 & 3 \\ 20 & 15 & 12 \\ 15 & 12 & 10 \end{vmatrix}$$

Subtracting row 3 from row 2 yields:

$$= \begin{vmatrix} 6 & 4 & 3 \\ 5 & 3 & 2 \\ 15 & 12 & 10 \end{vmatrix}$$

Subtracting row 2 from row 1 and adding -3 times row 2 to row 3 yields:

$$= \begin{vmatrix} 1 & 1 & 1 \\ 5 & 3 & 2 \\ 0 & 3 & 4 \end{vmatrix}$$

Subtracting column 1 from column 2 and column 3 yields:

$$= \begin{vmatrix} 1 & 0 & 0 \\ 5 & -2 & -3 \\ 0 & 3 & 4 \end{vmatrix} = 1 \begin{vmatrix} -2 & -3 \\ 3 & 4 \end{vmatrix} = 1(1) = 1$$

$$D_x = \begin{vmatrix} 744 & 4 & 3 \\ 2820 & 15 & 12 \\ 2280 & 12 & 10 \end{vmatrix}$$

Subtracting row 3 from row 2 yields:

$$= \begin{vmatrix} 744 & 4 & 3 \\ 540 & 3 & 2 \\ 2280 & 12 & 10 \end{vmatrix}$$

Subtracting row 2 from row 1, and adding -4 times row 2 to row 3 yields:

$$= \begin{vmatrix} 204 & 1 & 1 \\ 540 & 3 & 2 \\ 120 & 0 & 2 \end{vmatrix}$$

Adding -3 times row 1 to row 2 yields:

$$= \begin{vmatrix} 204 & 1 & 1 \\ -72 & 0 & -1 \\ 120 & 0 & 2 \end{vmatrix} = -1 \begin{vmatrix} -72 & -1 \\ 120 & 2 \end{vmatrix} = -(-24) = 24$$

$$D_y = \begin{vmatrix} 6 & 744 & 3 \\ 20 & 2820 & 12 \\ 15 & 2280 & 10 \end{vmatrix}$$

Subtracting row 3 from row 2 yields:

$$= \begin{vmatrix} 6 & 744 & 3 \\ 5 & 540 & 2 \\ 15 & 2280 & 10 \end{vmatrix}$$

Subtracting row 2 from row 1 and adding -3 times row 2 to row 3 yields:

$$= \begin{vmatrix} 1 & 204 & 1 \\ 5 & 540 & 2 \\ 0 & 660 & 4 \end{vmatrix}$$

Adding -5 times row 1 to row 2 yields:

$$= \begin{vmatrix} 1 & 204 & 1 \\ 0 & -480 & -3 \\ 0 & 660 & 4 \end{vmatrix} = 1 \begin{vmatrix} -480 & -3 \\ 660 & 4 \end{vmatrix} = 1(60) = 60$$

$$D_z = \begin{vmatrix} 6 & 4 & 744 \\ 20 & 15 & 2820 \\ 15 & 12 & 2280 \end{vmatrix}$$

Subtracting row 3 from row 2 yields:

$$= \begin{vmatrix} 6 & 4 & 744 \\ 5 & 3 & 540 \\ 15 & 12 & 2280 \end{vmatrix}$$

Subtracting row 2 from row 1 and adding -3 times row 2 to row 3 yields:

$$= \begin{vmatrix} 1 & 1 & 204 \\ 5 & 3 & 540 \\ 0 & 3 & 660 \end{vmatrix}$$

Adding -5 times row 1 to row 2 yields:

$$= \begin{vmatrix} 1 & 1 & 204 \\ 0 & -2 & -480 \\ 0 & 3 & 660 \end{vmatrix} = 1 \begin{vmatrix} -2 & -480 \\ 3 & 660 \end{vmatrix} = 1(120) = 120$$

So $x = \dfrac{D_x}{D} = 24$, $y = \dfrac{D_y}{D} = 60$, and $z = \dfrac{D_z}{D} = 120$

So the numbers are 24,60,120.

133.   We have:

$$xy = m$$
$$x^2 + y^2 = n$$

Add twice the first equation to the second and get:

$$x^2 + 2xy + y^2 = n + 2m$$
$$(x + y)^2 = n + 2m$$
$$x + y = \pm\sqrt{n + 2m}$$

Subtract twice the first equation from the second to get:

$$x^2 - 2xy + y^2 = n - 2m$$
$$(x - y)^2 = n - 2m$$
$$x - y = \pm\sqrt{n - 2m}$$

We solve the systems:

$$x + y = \sqrt{n + 2m}$$
$$\underline{x - y = \sqrt{n - 2m}}$$

$$2x = \sqrt{n + 2m} + \sqrt{n - 2m}$$
$$x = \frac{\sqrt{n + 2m} + \sqrt{n - 2m}}{2}$$
$$y = \frac{\sqrt{n + 2m} - \sqrt{n - 2m}}{2}$$

$$x + y = \sqrt{n + 2m}$$
$$\underline{x - y = -\sqrt{n - 2m}}$$

$$2x = \sqrt{n + 2m} - \sqrt{n - 2m}$$
$$x = \frac{\sqrt{n + 2m} - \sqrt{n - 2m}}{2}$$
$$y = \frac{\sqrt{n + 2m} + \sqrt{n - 2m}}{2}$$

$$x + y = -\sqrt{n + 2m}$$
$$\underline{x - y = \sqrt{n - 2m}}$$

$$x + y = -\sqrt{n + 2m}$$
$$\underline{x - y = -\sqrt{n - 2m}}$$

$$2x = \sqrt{n - 2m} - \sqrt{n + 2m}$$
$$x = \frac{\sqrt{n - 2m} - \sqrt{n + 2m}}{2}$$
$$y = \frac{-\sqrt{n - 2m} - \sqrt{n + 2m}}{2}$$

$$2x = -\sqrt{n + 2m} - \sqrt{n - 2m}$$
$$x = \frac{-\sqrt{n + 2m} - \sqrt{n - 2m}}{2}$$
$$y = \frac{\sqrt{n - 2m} - \sqrt{n + 2m}}{2}$$

So the possible pairs of numbers are:

$$\frac{\sqrt{n + 2m} + \sqrt{n - 2m}}{2} \text{ and } \frac{\sqrt{n + 2m} - \sqrt{n - 2m}}{2},$$

$$\frac{\sqrt{n - 2m} - \sqrt{n + 2m}}{2} \text{ and } \frac{-\sqrt{n - 2m} - \sqrt{n + 2m}}{2}$$

135.   convex: no
        bounded: no

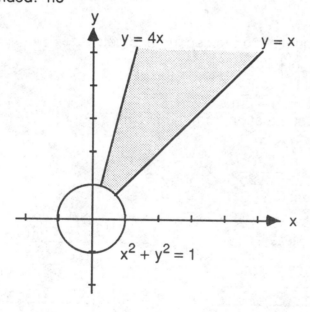

137.   convex: yes
       bounded: yes

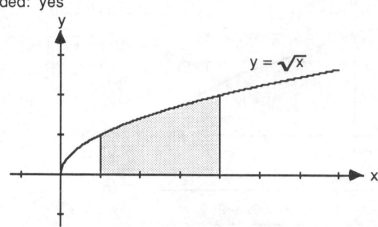

139.   convex: no
       bounded: no

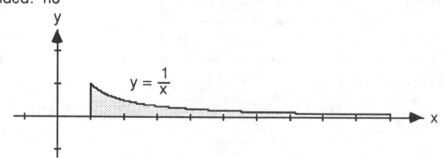

141.   Let x = number of small motors produced and y = number of large motors produced
       Then: Revenue = 40x + 104y
                  Cost   = 15x + 30y + 8(2x + 6y) = 31x + 78y
                Profit   = (40x + 104y) - (31x + 78y) = 9x + 26y
       Constraints:
            (1)   x ≥ 0
            (2)   y ≥ 0
            (3)   15x + 30y ≤ 1500, or x + 2y ≤ 100
            (4)   16x + 48y ≤ 2000, or x + 3y ≤ 125

We graph the constraints:

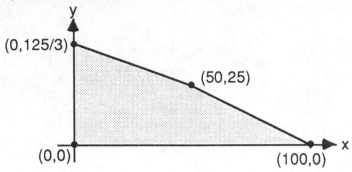

We set up the table:

Vertices	$P = 9x + 26y$
(0,0)	0
(100,0)	900
(50,25)	1100
(0,125/3)	1083.33

The maximum profit is $1100 with 50 small motors and 25 large motors being produced.

CHAPTER 11
ROOTS OF POLYNOMIAL EQUATIONS

11.1   More on Division of Polynomials

1.   We use synthetic division:

$$
\begin{array}{r|rrr}
 & 1 & -6 & -2 \\
5 & & 5 & -5 \\
\hline
 & 1 & -1 & -7
\end{array}
$$

The quotient is x - 1 and the remainder is -7.
So x^2 - 6x - 2 = (x - 5)(x - 1) - 7

3.   We use synthetic division:

$$
\begin{array}{r|rrr}
 & 4 & -1 & -5 \\
-1 & & -4 & 5 \\
\hline
 & 4 & -5 & 0
\end{array}
$$

The quotient is 4x - 5 and the remainder is 0.
So $4x^2$ - x - 5 = (x + 1)(4x - 5) + 0

5.   We use synthetic division:

$$
\begin{array}{r|rrrr}
 & 6 & -5 & 2 & 1 \\
4 & & 24 & 76 & 312 \\
\hline
 & 6 & 19 & 78 & 313
\end{array}
$$

The quotient is $6x^2$ + 19x + 78 and the remainder is 313.
So $6x^3$ - $5x^2$ + 2x + 1 = (x - 4)($6x^2$ + 19x + 78) + 313

7.   We use synthetic division:

$$
\begin{array}{r|rrrr}
 & 1 & 0 & 0 & -1 \\
2 & & 2 & 4 & 8 \\
\hline
 & 1 & 2 & 4 & 7
\end{array}
$$

The quotient is $x^2 + 2x + 4$ and the remainder is 7.
So $x^3 - 1 = (x - 2)(x^2 + 2x + 4) + 7$

9.   We use synthetic division:

$$
\begin{array}{r|rrrrrr}
 & 1 & 0 & 0 & 0 & 0 & -1 \\
-2 & & -2 & 4 & -8 & 16 & -32 \\
\hline
 & 1 & -2 & 4 & -8 & 16 & -33
\end{array}
$$

The quotient is $x^4 - 2x^3 + 4x^2 - 8x + 16$ and the remainder is -33.
So $x^5 - 1 = (x + 2)(x^4 - 2x^3 + 4x^2 - 8x + 16) - 33$

11.   We use synthetic division:

$$
\begin{array}{r|rrrrr}
 & 1 & -6 & 0 & 0 & 2 \\
-4 & & -4 & 40 & -160 & 640 \\
\hline
 & 1 & -10 & 40 & -160 & 642
\end{array}
$$

The quotient is $x^3 - 10x^2 + 40x - 160$ and the remainder is 642.
So $x^4 - 6x^3 + 2 = (x + 4)(x^3 - 10x^2 + 40x - 160) + 642$

13.   We use synthetic division:

$$
\begin{array}{r|rrrr}
 & 1 & -4 & -3 & 6 \\
10 & & 10 & 60 & 570 \\
\hline
 & 1 & 6 & 57 & 576
\end{array}
$$

The quotient is $x^2 + 6x + 57$ and the remainder is 576.
So $x^3 - 4x^2 - 3x + 6 = (x - 10)(x^2 + 6x + 57) + 576$

15.   We use synthetic division:

$$
\begin{array}{r|rrrr}
 & 1 & -1 & 0 & 0 \\
-5 & & -5 & 30 & -150 \\
\hline
 & 1 & -6 & 30 & -150
\end{array}
$$

The quotient is $x^2 - 6x + 30$ and the remainder is -150.
So $x^3 - x^2 = (x + 5)(x^2 - 6x + 30) - 150$

17.   We use synthetic division:

$$
\begin{array}{r|rrrr}
 & 54 & -27 & -27 & 14 \\
2/3 & & 36 & 6 & -14 \\
\hline
 & 54 & 9 & -21 & 0
\end{array}
$$

The quotient is $54x^2 + 9x - 21$ and the remainder is 0.

So $54x^3 - 27x^2 - 27x + 14 = \left(x - \dfrac{2}{3}\right)(54x^2 + 9x - 21) + 0$

19. We use synthetic division:

$$
\begin{array}{r|rrrrr}
 & 1 & 0 & 3 & 0 & 12 \\
3 & & 3 & 9 & 36 & 108 \\
\hline
 & 1 & 3 & 12 & 36 & 120
\end{array}
$$

The quotient is $x^2 + 3x^2 + 12x + 36$ and the remainder is 120.
So $x^4 + 3x^2 + 12 = (x - 3)(x^3 + 3x^2 + 12x + 36) + 120$

21. We use synthetic division:

$$
\begin{array}{r|rrr}
 & a & b & c \\
r & & ra & ar^2 + br \\
\hline
 & a & b + ra & ar^2 + br + c
\end{array}
$$

The quotient is $ax + (ar + b)$ and the remainder is $ar^2 + br + c$.

23. Since the two quotients are the same, we can now perform synthetic division:

$$
\begin{array}{r|rrr}
 & 2 & -\dfrac{8}{3} & \dfrac{1}{3} \\[2mm]
\dfrac{4}{3} & & \dfrac{8}{3} & 0 \\[2mm]
\hline
 & 2 & 0 & \dfrac{1}{3}
\end{array}
$$

The quotient is $2x$ and the remainder is $\dfrac{1}{3}$.

25. Using the hint from exercise #23, we first divide the numerator and

denominator by 2 to form the quotient: $\dfrac{3x^3 + \dfrac{1}{2}}{x + \dfrac{1}{2}}$

We use synthetic division:

$$
\begin{array}{r|rrrr}
 & 3 & 0 & 0 & \dfrac{1}{2} \\[2mm]
-\dfrac{1}{2} & & -\dfrac{3}{2} & \dfrac{3}{4} & -\dfrac{3}{8} \\[2mm]
\hline
 & 3 & -\dfrac{3}{2} & \dfrac{3}{4} & \dfrac{1}{8}
\end{array}
$$

The quotient is $3x^2 - \dfrac{3}{2}x + \dfrac{3}{4}$ and the remainder is $\dfrac{1}{8}$.

27. We use synthetic division:

$$
\begin{array}{r|rrrr}
 & 1 & 0 & k & 1 \\
-1 & & -1 & 1 & -k-1 \\
\hline
 & 1 & -1 & k+1 & -k
\end{array}
$$

So -k = -4, and thus k = 4.

29. We use synthetic division:

$$
\begin{array}{r|rrr}
 & 1 & 2p & -3q^2 \\
p & & p & 3p^2 \\
\hline
 & 1 & 3p & 3p^2-3q^2
\end{array}
$$

Since the remainder is 0, we have:

$$3p^2 - 3q^2 = 0$$
$$3p^2 = 3q^2$$
$$p^2 = q^2, \text{ as desired.}$$

31. We use synthetic division:

$$
\begin{array}{r|rrr}
 & 1 & -4 & 1 \\
i & & i & -1-4i \\
\hline
 & 1 & -4+i & -4i
\end{array}
$$

The quotient is x + (-4 + i) and the remainder is -4i.

33. We use synthetic division:

$$
\begin{array}{r|rrr}
 & 1 & -2 & 2 \\
1+i & & 1+i & -2 \\
\hline
 & 1 & -1+i & 0
\end{array}
$$

The quotient is x + (-1 + i) and the remainder is 0.

11.2   Roots of Polynomial Equations: The Remainder Theorem and the Factor Theorem

1. $12(10) - 8 = 112$
     $120 - 8 = 112$ √
   Yes, it is a root.

3. $(1 - \sqrt{5})^2 - 2(1 - \sqrt{5}) - 4 = 0$
   $1 - 2\sqrt{5} + 5 - 2 + 2\sqrt{5} - 4 = 0$
                $4 - 4 = 0$ √
   Yes, it is a root.

5. $2\left(\frac{1}{2}\right)^2 - 3\left(\frac{1}{2}\right) + 1 = 0$

$$\frac{1}{2} - \frac{3}{2} + 1 = 0$$

$$-1 + 1 = 0 \ \sqrt{}$$

Yes, it is a root.

7. $f\left(\frac{2}{3}\right) = 3\left(\frac{2}{3}\right) - 2 = 2 - 2 = 0$

$x = \frac{2}{3}$ is a zero of f(x).

9. $h(-1) = 5(-1)^3 - (-1)^2 + 2(-1) + 8 = -5 - 1 - 2 + 8 = 0$
    $x = -1$ is a zero of h(x).

11. $f(2) = 1 + 2(2) + (2)^3 - (2)^5 = 1 + 4 + 8 - 32 = -19$
    $t = 2$ is not a zero of f(t).

13. (a) $f\left(\frac{\sqrt{3}-1}{2}\right) = 2\left(\frac{\sqrt{3}-1}{2}\right)^3 - 3\left(\frac{\sqrt{3}-1}{2}\right) + 1$

$$= \frac{3\sqrt{3}-5}{2} - \frac{3\sqrt{3}-3}{2} + 1$$

$$= -1 + 1$$

$$= 0$$

$x = \frac{\sqrt{3}-1}{2}$ is a zero of f(x).

(b) $f\left(\frac{\sqrt{3}+1}{2}\right) = 2\left(\frac{\sqrt{3}+1}{2}\right)^3 - 3\left(\frac{\sqrt{3}+1}{2}\right) + 1$

$$= \frac{5+3\sqrt{3}}{2} - \frac{3\sqrt{3}-3}{2} + 1$$

$$= 4 + 1$$

$$= 5$$

$x = \frac{\sqrt{3}+1}{2}$ is not a zero of f(x).

15. (a) $x = 1$
         $x = 2$ (multiplicity 3)
         $x = 3$

    (b) $x = 1$ (multiplicity 3)

(c) $x = 5$ (multiplicity 6)
       $x = -1$ (multiplicity 4)

(d) $x = 0$ (multiplicity 5)
       $x = 1$

17.   We use synthetic division:

$$-3 \mid \begin{array}{rrrr} 4 & -6 & 1 & -5 \\ & -12 & 54 & -165 \\ \hline 4 & -18 & 55 & -170 \end{array}$$

So $f(-3) = -170$

19.   We use synthetic division:

$$1/2 \mid \begin{array}{rrrrr} 6 & 5 & -8 & -10 & -3 \\ & 3 & 4 & -2 & -6 \\ \hline 6 & 8 & -4 & -12 & -9 \end{array}$$

So $f\left(\dfrac{1}{2}\right) = -9$

21.   We use synthetic division:

$$-\sqrt{2} \mid \begin{array}{rrr} 1 & 3 & -4 \\ & -\sqrt{2} & -3\sqrt{2}+2 \\ \hline 1 & 3-\sqrt{2} & -3\sqrt{2}-2 \end{array}$$

So $f(-\sqrt{2}) = -3\sqrt{2} - 2$

23.   We use synthetic division:

$$12 \mid \begin{array}{rrrr} 1/2 & -5 & -13 & -10 \\ & 6 & 12 & -12 \\ \hline 1/2 & 1 & -1 & -22 \end{array}$$

So $f(12) = -22$

25.   We use synthetic division:

$$-3 \mid \begin{array}{rrrr} 1 & -4 & -9 & 36 \\ & -3 & 21 & -36 \\ \hline 1 & -7 & 12 & 0 \end{array}$$

So $x^3 - 4x^2 - 9x + 36 = (x + 3)(x^2 - 7x + 12) = (x + 3)(x - 4)(x - 3)$
So the roots are -3, 4, and 3.

27. We use synthetic division:

$$
\begin{array}{r|rrrr}
 & 1 & 1 & -7 & 5 \\
1 & & 1 & 2 & -5 \\
\hline
 & 1 & 2 & -5 & 0
\end{array}
$$

So $x^3 + x^2 - 7x + 5 = (x - 1)(x^2 + 2x - 5)$
$x = 1$ is a root. We use the quadratic formula:

$$x = \frac{-2 \pm \sqrt{4 + 20}}{2} = \frac{-2 \pm 2\sqrt{6}}{2} = -1 \pm \sqrt{6}$$

So the roots are 1, $-1 + \sqrt{6}$, and $-1 - \sqrt{6}$.

29. We use synthetic division:

$$
\begin{array}{r|rrrr}
 & 3 & -5 & -16 & 12 \\
-2 & & -6 & 22 & -12 \\
\hline
 & 3 & -11 & 6 & 0
\end{array}
$$

So $3x^3 - 5x^2 - 16x + 12 = (x + 2)(3x^2 - 11x + 6) = (x + 2)(3x - 2)(x - 3)$

So the roots are -2, $\frac{2}{3}$, and 3.

31. We use synthetic division:

$$
\begin{array}{r|rrrr}
 & 2 & 1 & -5 & -3 \\
-3/2 & & -3 & 3 & 3 \\
\hline
 & 2 & -2 & -2 & 0
\end{array}
$$

So $2x^3 + x^2 - 5x - 3 = \left(x + \frac{3}{2}\right)(2x^2 - 2x - 2) = 2\left(x + \frac{3}{2}\right)(x^2 - x - 1)$

$x = -\frac{3}{2}$ is a root. We use the quadratic formula:

$$x = \frac{1 \pm \sqrt{1 + 4}}{2} = \frac{1 \pm \sqrt{5}}{2}$$

So the roots are $-\frac{3}{2}$, $\frac{1 + \sqrt{5}}{2}$, and $\frac{1 - \sqrt{5}}{2}$.

33. We use synthetic division:

$$
\begin{array}{r|rrrrr}
 & 1 & -15 & 75 & -125 & 0 \\
5 & & 5 & -50 & 125 & 0 \\
\hline
 & 1 & -10 & 25 & 0 & 0
\end{array}
$$

So $\quad x^4 - 15x^3 + 75x^2 - 125x = (x - 5)(x^3 - 10x^2 + 25x)$
$$= x(x - 5)(x^2 - 10x + 25)$$
$$= x(x - 5)^3$$

So the roots are 0 and 5.

35. We use synthetic division:

$$
\begin{array}{r|rrrrr}
 & 1 & 2 & -23 & -24 & 144 \\
-4 & & -4 & 8 & 60 & -144 \\
\hline
 & 1 & -2 & -15 & 36 & 0
\end{array}
$$

Use synthetic division again:

$$
\begin{array}{r|rrrr}
 & 1 & -2 & -15 & 36 \\
3 & & 3 & 3 & -36 \\
\hline
 & 1 & 1 & -12 & 0
\end{array}
$$

So $x^4 + 2x^3 - 23x^2 - 24x + 144 = (x + 4)(x - 3)(x^2 + x - 12) = (x + 4)^2(x - 3)^2$
So the roots are -4 and 3.

37. We use synthetic division:

$$
\begin{array}{r|rrrr}
 & 1 & 7 & -19 & -9 \\
-9 & & -9 & 18 & 9 \\
\hline
 & 1 & -2 & -1 & 0
\end{array}
$$

So $x^3 + 7x^2 - 19x - 9 = (x + 9)(x^2 - 2x - 1)$
So $x = -9$ is a root. Use the quadratic formula:

$$x = \frac{2 \pm \sqrt{4 + 4}}{2} = \frac{2 \pm 2\sqrt{2}}{2} = 1 \pm \sqrt{2}$$

So the roots are -9, $1 + \sqrt{2}$, and $1 - \sqrt{2}$.

39. It will be $(x - 3)(x - 5)(x + 4) = 0$. Multiplying out, we get
$x^3 - 4x^2 - 17x + 60 = 0$

41. Its form will be $(x + 1)^2(x + 6) = 0$. Multiplying out, we have
$x^3 + 8x^2 + 13x + 6 = 0$.

43. We use synthetic division:

$$
\begin{array}{r|rrrr}
 & 1 & -4 & c & d \\
1 & & 1 & -3 & c - 3 \\
\hline
 & 1 & -3 & c - 3 & c + d - 3
\end{array}
$$

Use synthetic division again:

$$
\begin{array}{r|rrrr}
 & 1 & -4 & c & d \\
2 & & 2 & -4 & 2c - 8 \\
\hline
 & 1 & -2 & c - 4 & 2c + d - 8
\end{array}
$$

Since 1 and 2 are roots, we must have:

$c + d - 3 = 0$
$2c + d - 8 = 0$

Subtracting the first equation, we have $c - 5 = 0$, so $c = 5$. Substituting, we
have $d = -2$. So $c = 5$ and $d = -2$.

45. We use synthetic division:

$$
\begin{array}{r|rrrr}
 & 1 & -3 & 12 & 9 \\
1.16 & & 1.16 & -2.1344 & 11.44 \\
\hline
 & 1 & -1.84 & 9.8656 & 20.44
\end{array}
$$

So $f(1.16)$ is approximately equal to 20.44

47. (a) We use synthetic division:

$$
\begin{array}{r|rrrr}
 & 1 & 0 & -5 & -2 \\
2.41 & & 2.41 & 5.8081 & 1.9475 \\
\hline
 & 1 & 2.41 & 0.8081 & -0.05
\end{array}
$$

So $f(2.41)$ is approximately equal to -0.05

(b) We use synthetic division:

$$
\begin{array}{r|rrrr}
 & 1 & 0 & -5 & -2 \\
2.42 & & 2.42 & 5.8564 & 2.0725 \\
\hline
 & 1 & 2.42 & 0.8564 & 0.07
\end{array}
$$

So $f(2.42)$ is approximately equal to 0.07

49.
$$
\begin{aligned}
f(-b - \sqrt{b^2 - 2c}) &= \tfrac{1}{2}(-b - \sqrt{b^2 - 2c})^2 + b(-b - \sqrt{b^2 - 2c}) + c \\
&= \tfrac{1}{2}(b^2 + 2b\sqrt{b^2 - 2c} + b^2 - 2c) - b^2 - b\sqrt{b^2 - 2c} + c \\
&= b^2 + b\sqrt{b^2 - 2c} - c - b^2 - b\sqrt{b^2 - 2c} + c \\
&= 0
\end{aligned}
$$

$x = -b - \sqrt{b^2 - 2c}$ is a zero of $f(x)$.

51. $F\left(\dfrac{-\sqrt{2} + \sqrt{2\sqrt{2} - 2}}{2}\right)$

$$
\begin{aligned}
&= 2\left(\frac{-\sqrt{2} + \sqrt{2\sqrt{2} - 2}}{2}\right)^4 + 4\left(\frac{-\sqrt{2} + \sqrt{2\sqrt{2} - 2}}{2}\right) + 1 \\
&= -1 + 2\sqrt{2} - 2\sqrt{2\sqrt{2} - 2} - 2\sqrt{2} + 2\sqrt{2\sqrt{2} - 2} + 1 \\
&= 0
\end{aligned}
$$

Yes, it is a zero.

53. We use synthetic division:

$$
\begin{array}{r|rrrr}
 & 1 & 1 & a & b \\
1 & & 1 & 2 & a+2 \\
\hline
 & 1 & 2 & a+2 & a+b+2
\end{array}
$$

Using synthetic division again:

$$\begin{array}{c|cccc} & 1 & -1 & -a & b \\ 1 & & 1 & 0 & -a \\ \hline & 1 & 0 & -a & -a+b \end{array}$$

If 1 is a root, then:

$$a + b + 2 = 0$$
$$-a + b = 0$$

Adding these, we get $2b + 2 = 0$, so $b = -1$. Substituting we get $a = -1$. So $a = -1$ and $b = -1$.

55. Let r_1 and r_2 be the roots, so $r_2 = 2r_1$.
Then $x^2 + bx + 1 = (x - r_1)(x - 2r_1) = x^2 - 3r_1x + 2r_1^2$

Since r_1 is a constant, then $-3r_1 = b$ and $2r_1^2 = 1$, so $r_1^2 = \frac{1}{2}$ and thus

$r_1 = \frac{\pm\sqrt{2}}{2}$. So $b = \frac{\pm 3\sqrt{2}}{2}$.

11.3   The Fundamental Theorem of Algebra

1. (a)   yes
    (b)   yes
    (c)   yes
    (d)   no -- not a polynomial equation

3. $x^2 - 2x - 3 = (x + 1)(x - 3) = \left(x - (-1)\right)(x - 3)$

5. $4x^2 + 23x - 6 = (4x - 1)(x + 6) = 4\left(x - \frac{1}{4}\right)\left(x - (-6)\right)$

7. $x^2 - 5 = (x + \sqrt{5})(x - \sqrt{5}) = \left(x - (-\sqrt{5})\right)(x - \sqrt{5})$

9. $x^2 - 10x + 26 = 0$

$x = \frac{10 \pm \sqrt{100 - 104}}{2} = \frac{10 \pm 2i}{2} = 5 \pm i$

So $x^2 - 10x + 26 = \left(x - (5 + i)\right)\left(x - (5 - i)\right)$

11. $f(x) = (x - 1)^2(x + 3) = x^3 + x^2 - 5x + 3$

13. $f(x) = (x - 2)(x + 2)(x - 2i)(x + 2i) = x^4 - 16$

15. $f(x) = \left(x - \sqrt{3}\right)^2\left(x - (-\sqrt{3})\right)^2\left(x - 4i\right)\left(x - (-4i)\right) = x^6 - 10x^4 - 87x^2 + 144$

17. $f(x) = a(x + 4)(x - 9)$
Since $f(3) = 5$, then $5 = a(7)(-6)$
$$a = -\frac{5}{42}$$
So $f(x) = -\frac{5}{42}(x^2 - 5x - 36) = -\frac{5}{42}x^2 + \frac{25}{42}x + \frac{30}{7}$

19. $f(x) = a(x + 5)(x - 2)(x - 3)$
Since $f(0) = 1$, then $1 = a(5)(-2)(-3)$
$$a = \frac{1}{30}$$
So $f(x) = \frac{1}{30}(x^3 - 19x + 30) = \frac{1}{30}x^3 - \frac{19}{30}x + 1$

21. $-b = -i - \sqrt{3}$, so $b = i + \sqrt{3}$
$c = -i(-\sqrt{3}) = i\sqrt{3}$
So $x^2 + (i + \sqrt{3})x + i\sqrt{3} = 0$

23. $-b = 3$, so $b = -3$
$c = (9)(-6) = -54$
So $x^2 - 3x - 54 = 0$

25. $-b = 2$, so $b = -2$
$c = (1 + \sqrt{5})(1 - \sqrt{5}) = -4$
So $x^2 - 2x - 4 = 0$

27. $-B = 2a$, so $B = -2a$
$C = (a + \sqrt{b})(a - \sqrt{b}) = a^2 - b$
So $x^2 - 2ax + a^2 - b = 0$

29. $x^4 + 64 = x^4 + 16x^2 + 64 - 16x^2$
$$= (x^2 + 8)^2 - (4x)^2$$
$$= (x^2 + 8 + 4x)(x^2 + 8 - 4x)$$
$$= (x^2 + 4x + 8)(x^2 - 4x + 8)$$
Now $x^2 + 4x + 8 = 0$ when $x = \dfrac{-4 \pm \sqrt{16 - 32}}{2} = \dfrac{-4 \pm 4i}{2} = -2 \pm 2i$

and $x^2 - 4x + 8 = 0$ when $x = \dfrac{4 \pm \sqrt{16 - 32}}{2} = \dfrac{4 \pm 4i}{2} = 2 \pm 2i$

So $x^4 + 64 = (x^2 + 4x + 8)(x^2 - 4x + 8)$
$$= \left(x - (-2 + 2i)\right)\left(x - (-2 - 2i)\right)\left(x - (2 + 2i)\right)\left(x - (2 - 2i)\right)$$
$$= (x + 2 - 2i)(x + 2 + 2i)(x - 2 - 2i)(x - 2 + 2i)$$

31.   We know $x^3 + bx^2 + cx + d = (x - r_1)(x - r_2)(x - r_3)$
$$= x^3 - (r_1 + r_2 + r_3)x^2 + (r_1r_2 + r_1r_3 + r_2r_3)x - r_1r_2r_3$$

So: $r_1 + r_2 + r_3 = -b$
$$r_1r_2 + r_1r_3 + r_2r_3 = c$$
$$r_1r_2r_3 = -d$$

33.   Let r_1, r_2, and r_3 be the roots and assume $r_2 = -r_1$ (their sum is therefore, 0).
The identities from exercise #31 give us:

$r_1 + r_2 + r_3 = 4$ $r_1r_2r_3 = -36$
$r_1 - r_1 + r_3 = 4$ $-r_1^2(4) = -36$
$r_3 = 4$ $r_1^2 = 9$
$r_1 = \pm 3$

So $r_1 = 3$ and $r_2 = -3$ (or switch them, it doesn't matter)
So the roots are 4, 3, and -3.

35.   (a) $\alpha^2 + \beta^2 = (\alpha + \beta)^2 - 2\alpha\beta$
$$= (-b)^2 - 2c$$
$$= b^2 - 2c$$

(b) $\left(\dfrac{1}{\alpha}\right)^2 + \left(\dfrac{1}{\beta}\right)^2 = \dfrac{\alpha^2 + \beta^2}{(\alpha\beta)^2} = \dfrac{b^2 - 2c}{c^2}$

(c) $\alpha^3 + \beta^3 = (\alpha + \beta)(\alpha^2 - \alpha\beta + \beta^2)$
$$= (-b)(\alpha^2 + \beta^2 - \alpha\beta)$$
$$= (-b)(b^2 - 2c - c)$$
$$= -b(b^2 - 3c)$$

37.   (a)   Suppose $A \neq 0$ or $B \neq 0$. Then $f(x) = Ax^2 + Bx + C = 0$ can have at most two distinct roots by the Linear Factor Theorem (re-read it!).
So $A = B = 0$. But this implies $C = 0$, and thus $f(x) = 0$ for all values of x.

(b) Using the hint, let:

$$f(x) = \frac{a^2 - x^2}{(a-b)(a-c)} + \frac{b^2 - x^2}{(b-c)(b-a)} + \frac{c^2 - x^2}{(c-a)(c-b)} - 1$$

$$f(a) = 0 + \frac{b^2 - a^2}{(b-c)(b-a)} + \frac{c^2 - a^2}{(c-a)(c-b)} - 1$$

$$= \frac{b+a}{b-c} + \frac{c+a}{c-b} - 1$$

$$= \frac{-b-a+c+a}{c-b} - 1$$

$$= \frac{c-b}{c-b} - 1$$

$$= 0$$

$$f(b) = \frac{a^2 - b^2}{(a-b)(a-c)} + 0 + \frac{c^2 - b^2}{(c-a)(c-b)} - 1$$

$$= \frac{a+b}{a-c} + \frac{c+b}{c-a} - 1$$

$$= \frac{-a-b+c+b}{c-a} - 1$$

$$= \frac{c-a}{c-a} - 1$$

$$= 0$$

$$f(c) = \frac{a^2 - c^2}{(a-b)(a-c)} + \frac{b^2 - c^2}{(b-c)(b-a)} + 0 - 1$$

$$= \frac{a+c}{a-b} + \frac{b+c}{b-a} - 1$$

$$= \frac{-a-c+b+c}{b-a} - 1$$

$$= \frac{b-a}{b-a} - 1$$

$$= 0$$

Since a, b, and c are distinct (for denominators to be nonzero), and all three are roots, then by part (a) $f(x) = 0$ for all values of x. Thus the equation is an identity.

11.4   Rational and Irrational Roots

1.   p-factors: ±1, ±3
    q-factors: ±1, ±2, ± 4

   possible rational roots $\frac{p}{q}$: $\pm 1, \pm \frac{1}{2}, \pm \frac{1}{4}, \pm 3, \pm \frac{3}{2}, \pm \frac{3}{4}$

3.   p-factors: ±1, ±3, ±9
      q-factors: ±1, ±2, ±4, ±8

      possible rational roots $\frac{p}{q}$: $\pm 1, \pm\frac{1}{2}, \pm\frac{1}{4}, \pm\frac{1}{8}, \pm 3, \pm\frac{3}{2}, \pm\frac{3}{4}, \pm\frac{3}{8},$

      $$\pm 9, \pm\frac{9}{2}, \pm\frac{9}{4}, \pm\frac{9}{8}$$

5.   First multiply by 3 (we need integer coefficients) to get:
      $$2x^3 - 3x^2 - 15x + 6 = 0$$
      p-factors: ±1, ±2, ±3, ±6
      q-factors: ±1, ±2

      possible rational roots $\frac{p}{q}$: $\pm 1, \pm\frac{1}{2}, \pm 2, \pm 3, \pm\frac{3}{2}, \pm 6$

7.   The possible rational roots are ±1
      We use synthetic division:

      $$
      \begin{array}{r|rrrr}
       & 1 & 0 & -3 & 1 \\
      1 & & 1 & 1 & -2 \\
      \hline
       & 1 & 1 & -2 & -1
      \end{array}
      $$

      So x = 1 is not a root.

      $$
      \begin{array}{r|rrrr}
       & 1 & 0 & -3 & 1 \\
      -1 & & -1 & 1 & 2 \\
      \hline
       & 1 & -1 & -2 & 3
      \end{array}
      $$

      So x = -1 is not a root. There are no rational roots.

9.   The possible rational roots are ±1
      We use synthetic division:

      $$
      \begin{array}{r|rrrr}
       & 1 & 1 & -1 & 1 \\
      1 & & 1 & 2 & 1 \\
      \hline
       & 1 & 2 & 1 & 2
      \end{array}
      $$

      So x = 1 is not a root.

      $$
      \begin{array}{r|rrrr}
       & 1 & 1 & -1 & 1 \\
      -1 & & -1 & 0 & 1 \\
      \hline
       & 1 & 0 & -1 & 2
      \end{array}
      $$

      So x = -1 is not a root. There are no rational roots.

11.   The possible rational roots are $\pm 1, \pm\frac{1}{2}, \pm\frac{1}{3}, \pm\frac{1}{4}, \pm\frac{1}{6}, \pm\frac{1}{12}, \pm 2, \pm\frac{2}{3}, \pm 3,$

      $$\pm\frac{3}{2}, \pm\frac{3}{4}, \pm 6$$

We use synthetic division:

$$
\begin{array}{r|rrrrr}
 & 12 & 0 & -1 & 0 & -6 \\
1 & & 12 & 12 & 11 & 11 \\
\hline
 & 12 & 12 & 11 & 11 & 5 \\
\end{array}
$$

So x = 1 is not a root. Since this row is all positive, we can exclude
x = 2, x = 3, x = $\frac{3}{2}$ and x = 6.

$$
\begin{array}{r|rrrrr}
 & 12 & 0 & -1 & 0 & -6 \\
-1 & & -12 & 12 & -11 & 11 \\
\hline
 & 12 & -12 & 11 & -11 & 5 \\
\end{array}
$$

So x = -1 is not a root. Since this row alternates signs, we can exclude
x = -2, x = -3, x = $-\frac{3}{2}$, and x = -6.

$$
\begin{array}{r|rrrrr}
 & 12 & 0 & -1 & 0 & -6 \\
1/4 & & 3 & 3/4 & -1/16 & -1/64 \\
\hline
 & 12 & 3 & -1/4 & -1/16 & -6\,1/64 \\
\end{array}
$$

So x = $\frac{1}{4}$ is not a root.

$$
\begin{array}{r|rrrrr}
 & 12 & 0 & -1 & 0 & -6 \\
1/3 & & 4 & 4/3 & 1/9 & 1/27 \\
\hline
 & 12 & 4 & 1/3 & 1/9 & -5\,26/27 \\
\end{array}
$$

Proceeding in a similar fashion, we find that none of the candidates are rational roots.

13. The possible rational roots are ±1, ±3
    We use synthetic division:

$$
\begin{array}{r|rrrr}
 & 1 & 3 & -1 & -3 \\
1 & & 1 & 4 & 3 \\
\hline
 & 1 & 4 & 3 & 0 \\
\end{array}
$$

So $x^3 + 3x^2 - x - 3 = (x - 1)(x^2 + 4x + 3) = (x - 1)(x + 1)(x + 3)$
So the roots are 1, -1, and -3.

15. The possible rational roots are $\pm 1, \pm\frac{1}{2}, \pm\frac{1}{4}, \pm 5, \pm\frac{5}{2}, \pm\frac{5}{4}$
    We use synthetic division:

$$
\begin{array}{r|rrrr}
 & 4 & 1 & -20 & -5 \\
-1/4 & & -1 & 0 & 5 \\
\hline
 & 4 & 0 & -20 & 0 \\
\end{array}
$$

So $4x^3 + x^2 - 20x - 5 = \left(x + \frac{1}{4}\right)(4x^2 - 20)$

$$= 4\left(x + \frac{1}{4}\right)(x^2 - 5)$$

$$= 4\left(x + \frac{1}{4}\right)(x + \sqrt{5})(x - \sqrt{5})$$

So the roots are $-\frac{1}{4}$, $-\sqrt{5}$, and $\sqrt{5}$

17. The possible rational roots are $\pm 1, \pm\frac{1}{3}, \pm\frac{1}{9}, \pm 2, \pm\frac{2}{3}, \pm\frac{2}{9}$
     We use synthetic division:

$$
\begin{array}{r|rrrr}
 & 9 & 18 & 11 & 2 \\
1 & & 9 & 27 & 38 \\
\hline
 & 9 & 27 & 38 & 40 \\
\end{array}
$$

So $x = 2$ is excluded also (the row is positive).

$$
\begin{array}{r|rrrr}
 & 9 & 18 & 11 & 2 \\
-1 & & -9 & -9 & -2 \\
\hline
 & 9 & 9 & 2 & 0 \\
\end{array}
$$

So $9x^3 + 18x^2 + 11x + 2 = (x + 1)(9x^2 + 9x + 2) = (x + 1)(3x + 2)(3x + 1)$
So the roots are -1, $-\frac{2}{3}$, and $-\frac{1}{3}$

19. The possible rational roots are $\pm 1, \pm 2, \pm 3, \pm 4, \pm 6, \pm 8, \pm 12, \pm 24$
     We use synthetic division:

$$
\begin{array}{r|rrrrr}
 & 1 & 1 & -25 & -1 & 24 \\
1 & & 1 & 2 & -23 & -24 \\
\hline
 & 1 & 2 & -23 & -24 & 0 \\
\end{array}
$$

Using synthetic division again:

$$
\begin{array}{r|rrrr}
 & 1 & 2 & -23 & -24 \\
-1 & & -1 & -1 & 24 \\
\hline
 & 1 & 1 & -24 & 0 \\
\end{array}
$$

So $x^4 + x^3 - 25x^2 - x + 24 = (x - 1)(x + 1)(x^2 + x - 24)$

Use the quadratic formula: $x = \dfrac{-1 \pm \sqrt{1 + 96}}{2} = \dfrac{-1 \pm \sqrt{97}}{2}$

So the roots are $1, -1, \dfrac{-1 + \sqrt{97}}{2}$, and $\dfrac{-1 - \sqrt{97}}{2}$

21. The possible rational roots are ±1
    We use synthetic division:

$$
\begin{array}{r|rrrrr}
 & 1 & -4 & 6 & -4 & 1 \\
1 & & 1 & -3 & 3 & -1 \\
\hline
 & 1 & -3 & 3 & -1 & 0
\end{array}
$$

Using synthetic division again:

$$
\begin{array}{r|rrrr}
 & 1 & -3 & 3 & -1 \\
1 & & 1 & -2 & 1 \\
\hline
 & 1 & -2 & 1 & 0
\end{array}
$$

So $x^4 - 4x^3 + 6x^2 - 4x + 1 = (x - 1)^2(x^2 - 2x + 1) = (x - 1)^4$
So the only root is 1 (with multiplicity 4).

23. First multiply by 2 to get integer coefficients:
    $$2x^3 - 5x^2 - 46x + 24 = 0$$

    So the possible rational roots are ± 1, $\pm\frac{1}{2}$, ± 2, ± 3, $\pm\frac{3}{2}$, ± 4, ± 6, ± 8, ± 12, ± 24

    We use synthetic division:

$$
\begin{array}{r|rrrr}
 & 2 & -5 & -46 & 24 \\
1/2 & & 1 & -2 & -24 \\
\hline
 & 2 & -4 & -48 & 0
\end{array}
$$

So $2x^3 - 5x^2 - 46x + 24 = \left(x - \frac{1}{2}\right)(2x^2 - 4x - 48)$

$$= 2\left(x - \frac{1}{2}\right)(x^2 - 2x - 24)$$

$$= 2\left(x - \frac{1}{2}\right)(x - 6)(x + 4)$$

So the roots are $\frac{1}{2}$, 6, and -4.

25. First multiply by 20 to get integer coefficients:
    $$40x^4 - 18x^3 - 58x^2 + 27x - 3 = 0$$

    The possible rational roots are $\pm 1, \pm\frac{1}{2}, \pm\frac{1}{4}, \pm\frac{1}{5}, \pm\frac{1}{8}, \pm\frac{1}{10}, \pm\frac{1}{20}, \pm\frac{1}{40}, \pm 3,$
    $$\pm\frac{3}{2}, \pm\frac{3}{4}, \pm\frac{3}{5}, \pm\frac{3}{8}, \pm\frac{3}{10}, \pm\frac{3}{20}, \pm\frac{3}{40}$$

    We use synthetic division:

$$
\begin{array}{r|rrrrr}
 & 40 & -18 & -58 & 27 & -3 \\
1/4 & & 10 & -2 & -15 & 3 \\
\hline
 & 40 & -8 & -60 & 12 & 0
\end{array}
$$

Using synthetic division again:

$$
\begin{array}{r|rrrr}
 & 40 & -8 & -60 & 12 \\
1/5 & & 8 & 0 & -12 \\
\hline
 & 40 & 0 & -60 & 0
\end{array}
$$

So $40x^4 - 18x^3 - 58x^2 + 27x - 3 = \left(x - \dfrac{1}{4}\right)\left(x - \dfrac{1}{5}\right)(40x^2 - 60)$

$$= 10\left(x - \frac{1}{4}\right)\left(x - \frac{1}{5}\right)(4x^2 - 6)$$

$$= 10\left(x - \frac{1}{4}\right)\left(x - \frac{1}{5}\right)(2x + \sqrt{6})(2x - \sqrt{6})$$

So the roots are $\dfrac{1}{4}, \dfrac{1}{5}, -\dfrac{\sqrt{6}}{2}$, and $\dfrac{\sqrt{6}}{2}$

27. (a) The possible rational roots are: $\pm 1, \pm\dfrac{1}{5}, \pm 2, \pm\dfrac{2}{5}, \pm 3, \pm\dfrac{3}{5}, \pm 4, \pm\dfrac{4}{5}, \pm 6,$

$$\pm\frac{6}{5}, \pm 12, \pm\frac{12}{5}$$

We use synthetic division:

$$
\begin{array}{r|rrrrr}
 & 5 & 0 & 0 & -10 & -12 \\
2 & & 10 & 20 & 40 & 60 \\
\hline
 & 5 & 10 & 20 & 30 & 48
\end{array}
$$

Since this row is all positive, x = 2 is the upper bound.

$$
\begin{array}{r|rrrrr}
 & 5 & 0 & 0 & -10 & -12 \\
-1 & & -5 & 5 & -5 & 15 \\
\hline
 & 5 & -5 & 5 & -15 & 3
\end{array}
$$

Since this row alternates signs, x = -1 is the lower bound.
Final results: 2 upper, -1 lower.

(b) The possible rational roots are $\pm 1, \pm\dfrac{1}{3}, \pm 2, \pm\dfrac{2}{3}, \pm 4, \pm\dfrac{4}{3}$

We use synthetic division:

$$
\begin{array}{r|rrrrr}
 & 3 & -4 & 5 & -2 & -4 \\
4/3 & & 4 & 0 & 20/3 & 56/9 \\
\hline
 & 3 & 0 & 5 & 14/3 & 20/9
\end{array}
$$

So $x = \dfrac{4}{3}$ is the upper bound.

$$
\begin{array}{r|rrrrr}
 & 3 & -4 & 5 & -2 & -4 \\
-2/3 & & -2 & 4 & -6 & 16/3 \\
\hline
 & 3 & -6 & 9 & -8 & 4/3
\end{array}
$$

So $x = -\frac{2}{3}$ is the lower bound.

Final results: $\frac{4}{3}$ upper, $-\frac{2}{3}$ lower

To have integral bounds, we have: 2 upper, -1 lower

(c)   The possible rational roots are ± 1, $\pm\frac{1}{2}$, ± 2, ± 3, $\pm\frac{3}{2}$, ± 4, ± 6, ± 12

We use synthetic division:

$$
\begin{array}{r|rrrrr}
 & 2 & -7 & -5 & 28 & -12 \\
6 & & 12 & 30 & 150 & 1068 \\
\hline
 & 2 & 5 & 25 & 178 & 1056
\end{array}
$$

So x = 6 is the upper bound

$$
\begin{array}{r|rrrrr}
 & 2 & -7 & -5 & 28 & -12 \\
-2 & & -4 & 22 & -34 & 12 \\
\hline
 & 2 & -11 & 17 & -6 & 0
\end{array}
$$

Actually, -2 is a root, but also a lower bound.
Final results: 6 upper, -2 lower.

29. Let $f(x) = x^3 + x - 1$
    $f(0) = -1$
    $f(1) = 1$
So the root lies between 0 and 1.
    $f(0.5) = -0.375$
    $f(0.7) = 0.043$
    $f(0.6) = -0.373$
So the root lies between 0.6 and 0.7
    $f(0.65) = -0.075$
    $f(0.66) = -0.052$
    $f(0.67) = -0.029$
    $f(0.68) = -0.005$
    $f(0.69) = 0.018$
So the root lies between 0.68 and 0.69

31. Let $f(x) = x^5 - 200$
    $f(2) = -168$
    $f(3) = 43$
So the root lies between 2 and 3
    $f(2.5) = -102$
    $f(2.8) = -27.9$
    $f(2.9) = 5.11$
So the root lies between 2.8 and 2.9

$$f(2.87) = -5.28$$
$$f(2.88) = -1.86$$
$$f(2.89) = 1.60$$
So the root lies between 2.88 and 2.89

33. Let $f(x) = x^3 - 8x^2 + 21x - 22 = 0$
$$f(4) = -2$$
$$f(8) = 8$$
So the root lies between 4 and 5
$$f(4.5) = 1.63$$
$$f(4.4) = 0.704$$
$$f(4.3) = -0.113$$
So the root lies between 4.3 and 4.4
$$f(4.33) = 0.12$$
$$f(4.32) = 0.04$$
$$f(4.31) = -0.03$$
So the root lies between 4.31 and 4.32

35. Let $f(x) = x^3 + x^2 - 2x + 1$
$$f(-2) = 1$$
$$f(-3) = -11$$
So the root lies between -3 and -2
$$f(-2.1) = 0.35$$
$$f(-2.2) = -0.41$$
So the root lies between -2.2 and -2.1
$$f(-2.15) = -0.02$$
$$f(-2.14) = 0.05$$
So the root lies between -2.15 and -2.14

37. Let $f(x) = x^3 + 2x^2 + 2x + 101$
$$f(-5) = 16$$
$$f(-6) = -55$$
So the root lies between -6 and -5
$$f(-5.4) = -8.94$$
$$f(-5.3) = -2.30$$
$$f(-5.2) = 4.07$$
So the root lies between -5.3 and -5.2
$$f(-5.26) = 0.28$$
$$f(-5.27) = -0.36$$
So the root lies between -5.27 and -5.26

39. (a)   Since 2 is a factor of $8 \cdot 5 = 40$, and 2 is not a factor of 5, then 2 must be a factor of 8, which is true.

(b)　The result doesn't say that 20 has to be a factor of 8, just that they have no factors in common. Since 20 and 8 have a 2 factor in common, the result does not apply.

(c)　Since $x = \dfrac{p}{q}$ is a root of the equation, this statement must be true.

(d)　Subtract a_0 and multiply by q^n to get:

$$a_n p^n + a_{n-1} q p^{n-1} + a_{n-2} q^2 p^{n-2} + \ldots + a_1 q^{n-1} p = -a_0 q^n$$

So:

$$p(a_n p^{n-1} + a_{n-1} q p^{n-2} + a_{n-2} q^2 p^{n-3} + \ldots + a_1 q^{n-1}) = -a_0 q^n$$

41.　We sketch the graph:

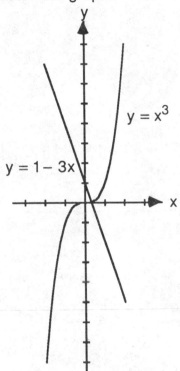

We find where $x^3 = 1 - 3x$

$\qquad x^3 + 3x - 1 = 0$

Let $f(x) = x^3 + 3x - 1$

$\qquad\quad f(0) = -1$

$\qquad\quad f(1) = 3$

So the root lies between 0 and 1.

$\qquad\quad f(0.3) = -0.07$

$\qquad\quad f(0.4) = 0.264$

So the root lies between 0.3 and 0.4

$f(0.32) = -0.007$
$f(0.33) = 0.02$
So the root lies between 0.32 and 0.33
$f(0.325) = 0.009$
So the root lies between 0.32 and 0.325, thus the x-coordinate is x = 0.32, accurate to two decimal places,

43. We find where $\sqrt{x} = x^2 - 1$
$$x = x^4 - 2x^2 + 1$$
$$x^4 - 2x^2 - x + 1 = 0$$
Let $f(x) = x^4 - 2x^2 - x + 1$
$f(1) = -1$
$f(2) = 7$
So the root lies between 1 and 2
$f(1.4) = -0.48$
$f(1.5) = 0.06$
So the root lies between 1.4 and 1.5
$f(1.48) = -0.06$
$f(1.49) = -0.001$
So the root lies between 1.49 and 1.50
$f(1.495) = 0.03$
So the root lies between 1.49 and 1.495, thus the x-coordinate is x = 1.49, accurate to two decimal places.

45. As in exercise #44, the possible rational roots are $\pm 1, \pm p$
Let $f(x) = x^3 + x^2 + x - p$
$f(1) = 1 + 1 + 1 - p = 3 - p$
p = 3 is a root to this.
$f(-1) = -1 + 1 - 1 - p = -1 - p$
p = -1 is the only root to this, and it is not prime.
$f(p) = p^3 + p^2 + p - p = p^3 + p^2 = p^2(p + 1)$
So p = 0 or p = -1, neither of which is prime.
$f(-p) = -p^3 + p^2 - p - p = -p^3 + p^2 - 2p = -p(p^2 - p + 2)$
So p = 0 or $p = \dfrac{1 \pm \sqrt{1 - 8}}{2}$, neither of which is prime.
So p = 3 is the only prime number such that f(x) = 0 will have rational roots.
When p = 3, we have $x^3 + x^2 + x - 3 = 0$
We use synthetic division:

$$
\begin{array}{r|rrrr}
 & 1 & 1 & 1 & -3 \\
1 & & 1 & 2 & 3 \\
\hline
 & 1 & 2 & 3 & 0 \\
\end{array}
$$

So x = 1 is a root.
Now $x^2 + 2x + 3 = 0$ has no real roots, so x = 1 is the only root.

47. (a) If $P(a,b)$ lies on $y = x^2$, then $b = a^2$

The distance is $\sqrt{a^2 + b^2} = \sqrt{a^2 + a^4}$

This is equal to $ab = a^3$, so:

$$\sqrt{a^2 + a^4} = a^3$$
$$a^2 + a^4 = a^6$$
$$a^6 - a^4 - a^2 = 0$$

Since $a \neq 0$, we have $a^4 - a^2 - 1 = 0$ (dividing by a^2)

Let $f(a) = a^4 - a^2 = 1$

$f(1) = -1$

$f(2) = 11$

So the root lies between 1 and 2.

$f(1.1) = -0.75$

$f(1.2) = -0.37$

$f(1.3) = 0.17$

So the root lies between 1.2 and 1.3

$f(1.25) = -0.12$

$f(1.27) = -0.011$

$f(1.28) = 0.045$

So the root lies between 1.27 and 1.28

$f(1.275) = 0.017$

So the root lies between 1.27 and 1.275, thus $a = 1.27$, accurate to two decimal places.

(b) We solve $a^4 - a^2 - 1 = 0$ directly:

$$a^2 = \frac{1 \pm \sqrt{1 + 4}}{2} = \frac{1 \pm \sqrt{5}}{2}$$

$a^2 \neq \frac{1 - \sqrt{5}}{2}$ $(a^2 \geq 0)$, so $a = \sqrt{\dfrac{1 + \sqrt{5}}{2}} = \dfrac{\sqrt{2 + 2\sqrt{5}}}{2}$

This is 1.272. . . Note that our approximation was accurate to two decimal places.

11.5 Conjugate Roots and Descartes's Rule of Signs

1. The other root must be $7 + 2i$

3.   One other root must be 5 - 2i. So $\left(x - (5 - 2i)\right)\left(x - (5 + 2i)\right)$ are factors, or $x^2 - 10x + 29$. We divide:

$$
\begin{array}{r}
x \;-\; 3 \\[2pt]
x^2 - 10x + 29\; \overline{\smash{\big)}\; x^3 - 13x^2 + 59x - 87} \\[2pt]
\underline{x^3 - 10x^2 + 29x} \\[2pt]
-3x^2 + 30x - 87 \\[2pt]
\underline{-3x^2 + 30x - 87} \\[2pt]
0
\end{array}
$$

Since x - 3 is the other factor, then 3 is the other root. So the other two roots are 5 - 2i and 3.

5.   One other root must be -2 - i, so $\left(x - (-2 + i)\right)\left(x - (-2 - i)\right)$ are factors, or $x^2 + 4x + 5$. We divide:

$$
\begin{array}{r}
x^2 + \;6x \;+\; 9 \\[2pt]
x^2 + 4x + 5\; \overline{\smash{\big)}\; x^4 + 10x^3 + 38x^2 + 66x + 45} \\[2pt]
\underline{x^4 + \;4x^3 + \;5x^2} \\[2pt]
6x^3 + 33x^2 + 66x \\[2pt]
\underline{6x^3 + 24x^2 + 30x} \\[2pt]
9x^2 + 36x + 45 \\[2pt]
\underline{9x^2 + 36x + 45} \\[2pt]
0
\end{array}
$$

Since $x^2 + 6x + 9 = (x + 3)^2$, the other root is -3. So the remaining roots are -2 - i and -3 (multiplicity 2).

7.   One other root must be 6 + 5i, so $\left(x - (6 - 5i)\right)\left(x - (6 + 5i)\right)$ are factors, or $x^2 - 12x + 61$. We divide:

$$
\begin{array}{r}
4x \;+\; 1 \\[2pt]
x^2 - 12x + 61\; \overline{\smash{\big)}\; 4x^3 - 47x^2 + 232x + 61} \\[2pt]
\underline{4x^3 - 48x^2 + 244x} \\[2pt]
x^2 - \;12x + 61 \\[2pt]
\underline{x^2 - \;12x + 61} \\[2pt]
0
\end{array}
$$

Since $4x + 1$ is the other factor, then $-\frac{1}{4}$ is the other root. So the remaining

roots are $6 + 5i$ and $-\frac{1}{4}$.

9. One other root must be $4 - \sqrt{2}\,i$, so $\left(x - (4 + \sqrt{2}i)\right)\left(x - (4 - \sqrt{2}i)\right)$ are
    factors, or $x^2 - 8x + 18$. We divide:

$$
\begin{array}{r}
4x^2 + 9 \\
x^2 - 8x + 18 \,\overline{\big)\; 4x^4 - 32x^3 + 81x^2 - 72x + 162} \\
\underline{4x^4 - 32x^3 + 72x^2} \\
9x^2 - 72x + 162 \\
\underline{9x^2 - 72x + 162} \\
0
\end{array}
$$

Since $4x^2 + 9 = (2x + 3i)(2x - 3i)$, the other roots are $-\frac{3i}{2}$ and $\frac{3i}{2}$. So the

remaining roots are $4 - \sqrt{2}\,i$, $-\frac{3i}{2}$, and $\frac{3i}{2}$.

11. One other root must be $10 - 2i$, so $\left(x - (10 + 2i)\right)\left(x - (10 - 2i)\right)$ are factors,
    or $x^2 - 20x + 104$. We divide:

$$
\begin{array}{r}
x^2 - 2x - 4 \\
x^2 - 20x + 104 \,\overline{\big)\; x^4 - 22x^3 + 140x^2 - 128x - 416} \\
\underline{x^4 - 20x^3 + 104x^2} \\
-2x^3 + 36x^2 - 128x \\
\underline{-2x^3 + 40x^2 - 208x} \\
-4x^2 + 80x - 416 \\
\underline{-4x^2 + 80x - 416} \\
0
\end{array}
$$

So the other factor is $x^2 - 2x - 4$. We use the quadratic formula:
$$
x = \frac{2 \pm \sqrt{4 + 16}}{2} = \frac{2 \pm 2\sqrt{5}}{2} = 1 \pm \sqrt{5}
$$
So the remaining roots are $10 - 2i$, $1 + \sqrt{5}$, and $1 - \sqrt{5}$.

13. One other root must be $\dfrac{1 - \sqrt{2}i}{3}$, so $\left(x - \dfrac{1 + \sqrt{2}i}{2}\right)\left(x - \dfrac{1 - \sqrt{2}i}{2}\right)$ are

factors, or $x^2 - \dfrac{2}{3}x + \dfrac{1}{3}$. We divide:

$$
\begin{array}{r}
15x \;-\; 6 \\
x^2 - 2/3x + 1/3 \,\overline{\big)\, 15x^3 - 16x^2 + 9x - 2} \\
\underline{15x^3 - 10x^2 + 5x } \\
-6x^2 + 4x - 2 \\
\underline{-6x^2 + 4x - 2} \\
0
\end{array}
$$

So the other factor is $15x - 6$, so $x = \dfrac{2}{5}$ is a root. The remaining roots are

$\dfrac{1 - \sqrt{2}i}{2}$ and $\dfrac{2}{5}$.

15. We know $3 + 2i$ is a root, so $\left(x - (3 - 2i)\right)\left(x - (3 + 2i)\right)$ are factors, which
is $x^2 - 6x + 13$. We divide:

$$
\begin{array}{r}
x^5 + 3x^4 + x^3 - 3x^2 - 4x + 2 \\
x^2 - 6x + 13 \,\overline{\big)\, x^7 - 3x^6 - 4x^5 + 30x^4 + 27x^3 - 13x^2 - 64x + 26} \\
\underline{x^7 - 6x^6 + 13x^5 } \\
3x^6 - 17x^5 + 30x^4 \\
\underline{3x^6 - 18x^5 + 39x^4 } \\
x^5 - 9x^4 + 27x^3 \\
\underline{x^5 - 6x^4 + 13x^3 } \\
-3x^4 + 14x^3 - 13x^2 \\
\underline{-3x^4 + 18x^3 - 39x^2 } \\
-4x^3 + 26x^2 - 64x \\
\underline{-4x^3 + 24x^2 - 52x } \\
2x^2 - 12x + 26 \\
\underline{2x^2 - 12x + 26} \\
0
\end{array}
$$

We know $x = -1 - i$ will be a root, so $\left(x - (-1 + i)\right)\left(x - (-1 - i)\right)$ are factors, which is $x^2 + 2x + 2$. We divide:

$$
\begin{array}{r}
x^3 + x^2 - 3x + 1 \\
x^2 + 2x + 2 \, \overline{\smash{\big)}\, x^5 + 3x^4 + x^3 - 3x^2 - 4x + 2} \\
\underline{x^5 + 2x^4 + 2x^3} \\
x^4 - x^3 - 3x^2 \\
\underline{x^4 + 2x^3 + 2x^2} \\
-3x^3 - 5x^2 - 4x \\
\underline{-3x^3 - 6x^2 - 6x} \\
x^2 + 2x + 2 \\
\underline{x^2 + 2x + 2} \\
0
\end{array}
$$

Finally, we know $x = 1$ is a root, so we synthetically divide:

$$
\begin{array}{r|rrrr}
 & 1 & 1 & -3 & 1 \\
1 & & 1 & 2 & 1 \\
\hline
 & 1 & 2 & -1 & 0
\end{array}
$$

So we are left with $x^2 + 2x - 1 = 0$. Using the quadratic formula:

$$
x = \frac{-2 \pm \sqrt{4 + 4}}{2} = \frac{-2 \pm 2\sqrt{2}}{2} = -1 \pm \sqrt{2}
$$

So the remaining roots are $3 + 2i$, $-1 - i$, $-1 + \sqrt{2}$, and $-1 - \sqrt{2}$.

17. $r_1 = 1 + \sqrt{6}$ and $r_2 = 1 - \sqrt{6}$, so $\left(x - (1 + \sqrt{6})\right)\left(x - (1 - \sqrt{6})\right) = 0$. Multiplied out, we get $x^2 - 2x - 5 = 0$.

19. $r_1 = \dfrac{2 + \sqrt{10}}{3}$ and $r_2 = \dfrac{2 - \sqrt{10}}{3}$, so $\left(x - \dfrac{2 + \sqrt{10}}{3}\right)\left(x - \dfrac{2 - \sqrt{10}}{3}\right) = 0$.

Multiplied out, we get $x^2 - \dfrac{4}{3}x - \dfrac{2}{3} = 0$.

21. Let $f(x) = x^3 + 5$. Since there are no sign changes, there will be no positive roots. Now $f(-x) = -x^3 + 5$. Since there is one sign change, there is one negative root. So the equation has two complex roots and one negative real root.

23. Let $f(x) = 2x^5 + 3x + 4$. Since there are no sign changes, there will be no positive roots. Now $f(-x) = -2x^5 - 3x + 4$. Since there is one sign change, there is 1 negative root. So the equation has 4 complex roots and 1 negative real root.

25. Let $f(x) = 5x^4 + 2x - 7$. Since there is one sign change, there will be 1 positive root. Now $f(-x) = 5x^4 - 2x - 7$. SInce there is one sign change, there will be 1 negative root. So the equation has 2 complex roots, 1 positive real root, and 1 negative real root.

27. Let $f(x) = x^3 - 4x^2 - x - 1$. Since there is one sign change, there will be 1 positive root. Now $f(-x) = -x^3 - 4x^2 + x - 1$. Since there are two sign changes, there will be 0 or 2 negative roots. So the equation has either 1 positive real root and 2 negative real roots, or 1 positive real root and 2 complex roots.

29. Let $f(x) = 3x^8 + x^6 - 2x^2 - 4$. Since there is one sign change, there is 1 positive root. Now $f(-x) = 3x^8 + x^6 - 2x^2 - 4$. Since there is one sign change, there is one negative root. So the equation has 1 positive real root, 1 negative real root, and 6 complex roots.

31. Let $f(x) = x^9 - 2$. Since there is one sign change, there is 1 positive root. Now $f(-x) = -x^9 - 2$. Since there are no sign changes, there are no negative roots. So the equation has 1 positive real root and 8 complex roots.

33. Let $f(x) = x^8 - 2$. Since there is one sign change, there is one positive root. Now $f(-x) = x^8 - 2$. Since there is one sign change, there is one negative root. So the equation has 1 positive real root, 1 negative real root, and 6 complex roots.

35. Let $f(x) = x^6 + x^2 - x - 1$. Since there is one sign change, there is one positive root. Now $f(-x) = x^6 + x^2 + x - 1$. Since there is one sign change, there is one negative root. So the equation has 1 positive real root, 1 negative real root and 4 complex roots.

37. Let $f(x) = x^4 + cx^2 + dx - e$. Since there is one sign change, there is one positive root. Now $f(-x) = x^4 + cx^2 - dx - e$. Since there is one sign change, there is one negative root. So the equation has 1 positive real root, 1 negative real root, and 2 complex roots.

39. The two roots $\sqrt{3} + 2i$ and $\sqrt{3} - 2i$ must be included, so:
$$f(x) = \left(x - (\sqrt{3} + 2i)\right)\left(x - (\sqrt{3} - 2i)\right) = x^2 - 2\sqrt{3}\,x + 7 = 0$$

Unfortunately, not all coefficients are rational:
$$x^2 + 7 = 2\sqrt{3}\,x$$
Squaring, we get:
$$x^4 + 14x^2 + 49 = 12x^2$$
$$x^4 + 2x^2 + 29 = 0$$
So $f(x) = x^4 + 2x^2 + 49$ is the desired polynomial.

41. (a) If $b = 0$, then $a + b\sqrt{c} = a = a - b\sqrt{c}$, so obviously $a - b\sqrt{c}$ is also a root.

(b) $$d(a + b\sqrt{c}) = \left(a + b\sqrt{c} - (a + b\sqrt{c})\right)\left(a + b\sqrt{c} - (a - b\sqrt{c})\right)$$
$$= 0\left(2b\sqrt{c}\right)$$
$$= 0$$

(c) $$d(x) = x^2 - 2ax + a^2 - b^2c = (x - a)^2 - b^2c$$

(d) If $x = a + b\sqrt{c}$, we have:
$$f(a + b\sqrt{c}) = d(a + b\sqrt{c})\,Q(a + b\sqrt{c}) + C(a + b\sqrt{c}) + D$$
$$0 = 0 \cdot Q(a + b\sqrt{c}) + Ca + D + bC\sqrt{c}$$
$$0 = Ca + D + bC\sqrt{c}$$
But if C and D are rational, then $C = 0$ (otherwise $\sqrt{c}$ will not be "cancelled" out). If $C = D$, then $D = 0$. So $C = D = 0$.

(e) $$f(a - b\sqrt{c}) = \left(a - b\sqrt{c} - (a + b\sqrt{c})\right)\left(a - b\sqrt{c} - (a - b\sqrt{c})\right)Q(x)$$
$$= \left(-2b\sqrt{c}\right)\left(0\right)Q(x)$$
$$= 0$$
So $x = a\ b\sqrt{c}$ is also a root of $f(x) = 0$.

Chapter 11 Review Exercises

1. We use synthetic division:

$$
\begin{array}{r|rrrrr}
 & 1 & 0 & -2 & 0 & 8 \\
3 & & 3 & 9 & 21 & 63 \\
\hline
 & 1 & 3 & 7 & 21 & 71 \\
\end{array}
$$

So the quotient is $x^3 + 3x^2 + 7x + 21$ and the remainder is 71.
So $x^4 - 2x^2 + 8 = (x - 3)(x^3 + 3x^2 + 7x + 21) + 71$

3.   We use synthetic division:

$$\begin{array}{r|rrrr} & 2 & -5 & -6 & -3 \\ -4 & & -8 & 52 & -184 \\ \hline & 2 & -13 & 46 & -187 \end{array}$$

So the quotient is $2x^2 - 13x + 46$ and the remainder is -187.
So $2x^3 - 5x^2 - 6x - 3 = (x + 4)(2x^2 - 13x + 46) - 187$

5.   We use synthetic division:

$$\begin{array}{r|rrr} & 5 & -19 & -4 \\ -0.2 & & -1 & 4 \\ \hline & 5 & -20 & 0 \end{array}$$

So the quotient is $5x - 20$ and the remainder is zero.
So $5x^2 - 19x - 4 = (x + 0.2)(5x - 20) + 0$

7.   Using synthetic division:

$$\begin{array}{r|rrr} & 1 & -6 & 13 \\ 3 + 2i & & 3 + 2i & -13 \\ \hline & 1 & -3 + 2i & 0 \end{array}$$

So the quotient is $x + (-3 + 2i)$ and the remainder is 0.
So $x^2 - 6x + 13 = \left(x - (3 + 2i)\right)\left(x + (-3 + 2i)\right) + 0$

9.   (a)   Let $p(x)$ and $d(x)$ be polynomials where $d(x) \neq 0$. Then there are unique polynomials $q(x)$ and $R(x)$ such that:

$$p(x) = d(x) \bullet q(x) + R(x)$$

where either $R(x) = 0$ or the degree of $R(x)$ is less than the degree of $d(x)$.

(b)   When a polynomial $f(x)$ is divided by $x - r$, the remainder is $f(r)$.

11.   We use synthetic division:

$$\begin{array}{r|rrrrr} & 1 & 2 & 0 & -1 & 0 \\ -2 & & -2 & 0 & 0 & 2 \\ \hline & 1 & 0 & 0 & -1 & 2 \end{array}$$

So $f(-2) = 2$

13.   We use synthetic division:

$$\begin{array}{r|rrrrr} & 1 & 0 & -2a^2 & 3a^3 & -a^4 \\ -a & & -a & a^2 & a^3 & -4a^4 \\ \hline & 1 & -a & -a^2 & 4a^3 & -5a^4 \end{array}$$

So $f(-a) = -5a^4$

15. We use synthetic division:

$$
\begin{array}{c|cccc}
 & 1 & 0 & 0 & -1 \\
1.1 & & 1.1 & 1.21 & 1.331 \\
\hline
 & 1 & 1.1 & 1.21 & 0.331
\end{array}
$$

So $f(1.1) = 0.331$

17. (a) Let $f(x)$ be a polynomial. If $f(r) = 0$, then $x - r$ is a factor of $f(x)$. Conversely, if $x - r$ is a factor of $f(x)$, then $f(r) = 0$.

 (b) Every polynomial equation of the form:
 $$a_n x^n + a_{n-1} x^{n-1} + \ldots + a_1 x + a_0 = 0 \quad (n \geq 1, a_n \neq 0)$$
 has at least one root among the complex numbers (This root may be a real number.)

19. We use synthetic division:

$$
\begin{array}{c|cccc}
 & 1 & 2b^2 & 1 & -48 \\
-1 & & -1 & 1 - 2b^2 & 2b^2 - 2 \\
\hline
 & 1 & 2b^2 - 1 & 2 - 2b^2 & 2b^2 - 50
\end{array}
$$

So, if -1 is a root, then:
$$
\begin{aligned}
2b^2 - 50 &= 0 \\
b^2 &= 25 \\
b &= \pm 5
\end{aligned}
$$
So $b = 5$ or $b = -5$.

21. Such a function would be $y = a(x - 1)(x + 8)$. Now $y = -24$ when $x = 0$, so: $-24 = a(-1)(8)$, so $a = 3$. So the function is $y = 3(x - 1)(x + 8)$, or $f(x) = 3x^2 + 21x - 24$.

23. $f(x) = (x - 2)(x - 3i)^3 \left(x - (1 + \sqrt{2}) \right)^2$
 Note that had a restriction of rational coefficients been added, we would also have $-3i$ (multiplicity 3) and $1 - \sqrt{2}$ (muliplicity 2) as roots.

25. (a) Let $f(x + h) = 0$, and let $x = r - h$. Then $f(r - h + h) = f(r) = 0$, since r is a root of $f(x) = 0$.

 (b) Let $f(-x) = 0$, and let $x = -r$. Then $f\left(-(-r)\right) = f(r) = 0$, since r is a root of $f(x) = 0$.

(c)   Let $f\left(\dfrac{x}{k}\right) = 0$, and let $x = kr$. Then $f\left(\dfrac{kr}{k}\right) = f(r) = 0$, since r is a root of $f(x) = 0$.

27.   (a) $\pm 1, \pm 2, \pm 3, \pm 4, \pm 6, \pm 8, \pm 12, \pm 24$

(b)   We use synthetic division:

$$
\begin{array}{r|rrrrr}
 & 1 & -1 & 0 & 0 & 24 \\
2 & & 2 & 2 & 4 & 8 \\
\hline
 & 1 & 1 & 2 & 4 & 32
\end{array}
$$

Since this last row consists of all positive numbers, we know that 2 is an upper bound for the roots of this equation.

(c)   Only $x = 1$, since $x = 2$ is an upper bound and not a root.

(d)   We use synthetic division:

$$
\begin{array}{r|rrrrr}
 & 1 & -1 & 0 & 0 & 24 \\
1 & & 1 & 0 & 0 & 1 \\
\hline
 & 1 & 0 & 0 & 0 & 25
\end{array}
$$

Since $x = 1$ was the only possibility, there are no positive rational roots.

29.   First multiply by 6 to obtain $x^5 - 12x^3 + x - 18 = 0$
p-factors: $\pm 1, \pm 2, \pm 3, \pm 6, \pm 9, \pm 18$
q-factors: ± 1
possible rational roots: $\pm 1, \pm 2, \pm 3, \pm 6, \pm 9, \pm 18$

31.   p-factors: $\pm p, \pm 1$
q-factors: ± 1
possible rational roots: $\pm p, \pm 1$

33.   possible rational roots: $\pm 1, \pm \dfrac{1}{2}, \pm 2, \pm 3, \pm \dfrac{3}{2}, \pm 6$

We use synthetic division:

$$
\begin{array}{r|rrrr}
 & 2 & 1 & -7 & -6 \\
2 & & 4 & 10 & 6 \\
\hline
 & 2 & 5 & 3 & 0
\end{array}
$$

So $2x^3 + x^2 - 7x - 6 = (x - 2)(2x^2 + 5x + 3) = (x - 2)(2x + 3)(x + 1)$
So the roots are $2, -\dfrac{3}{2}$, and -1

35. possible rational roots: $\pm1, \pm\frac{1}{2}, \pm2, \pm5, \pm\frac{5}{2}, \pm10$

We use synthetic division:

$$
\begin{array}{r|rrrr}
 & 2 & -1 & -14 & 10 \\
5/2 & & 5 & 10 & -10 \\
\hline
 & 2 & 4 & -4 & 0
\end{array}
$$

So $2x^3 - x^2 - 14x + 10 = \left(x - \frac{5}{2}\right)(2x^2 + 4x - 4) = 2\left(x - \frac{5}{2}\right)(x^2 + 2x - 2)$

We use the quadratic formula: $x = \dfrac{-2 \pm \sqrt{4+8}}{2} = \dfrac{-2 \pm 2\sqrt{3}}{2} = -1 \pm \sqrt{3}$

So the roots are $\frac{5}{2}$, $-1 + \sqrt{3}$, and $-1 - \sqrt{3}$.

37. First multiply by 2: $3x^3 + x^2 + x - 2 = 0$

possible rational roots: $\pm1, \pm\frac{1}{3}, \pm2, \pm\frac{2}{3}$

We use synthetic division:

$$
\begin{array}{r|rrrr}
 & 3 & 1 & 1 & -2 \\
2/3 & & 2 & 2 & 2 \\
\hline
 & 3 & 3 & 3 & 0
\end{array}
$$

So $3x^3 + x^2 + x - 2 = \left(x - \frac{2}{3}\right)(3x^2 + 3x + 3) = 3\left(x - \frac{2}{3}\right)(x^2 + x + 1)$

Using the quadratic formula: $x = \dfrac{-1 \pm \sqrt{1-4}}{2} = \dfrac{-1 \pm i\sqrt{3}}{2}$

So the roots are $\frac{2}{3}$, $\dfrac{-1 + i\sqrt{3}}{2}$, and $\dfrac{-1 - i\sqrt{3}}{2}$.

39. Possible rational roots: $\pm1, \pm7, \pm49$

We use synthetic division:

$$
\begin{array}{r|rrrrrr}
 & 1 & 1 & -14 & -14 & 49 & 49 \\
-1 & & -1 & 0 & 14 & 0 & -49 \\
\hline
 & 1 & 0 & -14 & 0 & 49 & 0
\end{array}
$$

So $x^5 + x^4 - 14x^3 - 14x^2 + 49x + 49$
$$= (x + 1)(x^4 - 14x^2 + 49)$$
$$= (x + 1)(x^2 - 7)^2$$
$$= (x + 1)(x + \sqrt{7})^2(x - \sqrt{7})^2$$

So the roots are -1, $-\sqrt{7}$ (multiplicity 2), and $\sqrt{7}$ (multiplicity 2).

41. Since $x^3 - 9x^2 + 24x - 20 = 0$ has a root r with multiplicity 2, we can use synthetic division by r twice, each time the remainder must be 0:

$$
\begin{array}{c|cccc}
 & 1 & -9 & 24 & -20 \\
r & & r & r^2 - 9r & r^3 - 9r^2 + 24r \\
\hline
 & 1 & r - 9 & r^2 - 9r + 24 & r^3 - 9r^2 + 24r - 20
\end{array}
$$

We continue the division:

$$
\begin{array}{c|ccc}
 & 1 & r - 9 & r^2 - 9r + 24 \\
r & & r & 2r^2 - 9r \\
\hline
 & 1 & 2r - 9 & 3r^2 - 18r + 24
\end{array}
$$

So $3r^2 - 18r + 24 = 3(r^2 - 6r + 8) = 3(r - 4)(r - 2) = 0$, thus r = 4 or r = 2. We check these in $r^3 - 9r^2 + 24r - 20 = 0$:
r = 4: $(4)^3 - 9(4)^2 + 24(4) - 20 = 64 - 144 + 96 - 20 = -4 \neq 0$
        So r = 4 cannot be a root.
r = 2: $(2)^3 - 9(2)^2 + 24(2) - 20 = 8 - 36 + 48 - 20 = 0$
So r = 2 is the root with multiplicity two. SInce the synthetic division resulted in x + (2r - 9) = 0, then x + (-5) = 0, thus x = 5. So the roots are 2 (multiplicity 2) and 5.

Note: Actually, an easier (and more direct) approach is to find the roots directly:
possible rational roots: ±1, ±2, ±4, ±5, ±10, ±20
Note that there are 3 sign changes, so there can be 1 or 3 positive real roots. Since f(-x) has no sign changes, all 3 roots must be positive real numbers for one of them to have multiplicity of 2 (note that it cannot have a radical or be complex - why?). We use synthetic division:

$$
\begin{array}{c|cccc}
 & 1 & -9 & 24 & -20 \\
2 & & 2 & -14 & 20 \\
\hline
 & 1 & -7 & 10 & 0
\end{array}
$$

So $x^3 - 9x^2 + 24x - 20 = (x - 2)(x^2 - 7x + 10) = (x - 2)^2(x - 5)$
So the roots are 2 (with multiplicity 2) and 5.

43. Use synthetic division:

$$
\begin{array}{c|cccc}
 & 1 & 1 & -11 & -15 \\
-3 & & -3 & 6 & 15 \\
\hline
 & 1 & -2 & -5 & 0
\end{array}
$$

So $x^3 + x^2 - 11x - 15 = (x + 3)(x^2 - 2x - 5)$
Using the quadratic equation, we get:

$$
x = \frac{2 \pm \sqrt{4 + 20}}{2} = \frac{2 \pm 2\sqrt{6}}{2} = 1 \pm \sqrt{6}
$$

So the roots of the equation are -3, $1 + \sqrt{6}$, and $1 - \sqrt{6}$.

45. $6x^2 + 7x - 20 = (3x - 4)(2x + 5) = 6\left(x - \frac{4}{3}\right)\left(x - \left(-\frac{5}{2}\right)\right)$

47. $x^4 - 4x^3 + 5x - 20 = x^3(x - 4) + 5(x - 4)$
$$= (x - 4)(x^3 + 5)$$
$$= (x - 4)(x + \sqrt[3]{5})(x^2 - \sqrt[3]{5}\,x + \sqrt[3]{25})$$

We solve $x^2 - \sqrt[3]{5}\,x + \sqrt[3]{25} = 0$ in the quadratic formula, which yields:

$$x = \frac{\sqrt[3]{5} \pm i\sqrt{3\sqrt[3]{25}}}{2}$$

So $x^4 - 4x^3 + 3x - 20$

$$= (x - 4)\left(x - (-\sqrt[3]{5})\right)\left(x - \frac{\sqrt[3]{5} + i\sqrt{3\sqrt[3]{25}}}{2}\right)\left(x - \frac{\sqrt[3]{5} - i\sqrt{3\sqrt[3]{25}}}{2}\right)$$

49.   One other root is $2 + 3i$, so $\left(x - (2 - 3i)\right)\left(x - (2 + 3i)\right)$ are factors, which is $x^2 - 4x + 13$. We divide:

$$
\begin{array}{r}
x - 3 \\
x^2 - 4x + 13 \overline{\smash{\big)}\ x^3 - 7x^2 + 25x - 39} \\
\underline{x^3 - 4x^2 + 13x} \\
-3x^2 + 12x - 39 \\
\underline{-3x^2 + 12x - 39} \\
0
\end{array}
$$

So $x - 3$ is the other factor. So the roots are $2 - 3i$, $2 + 3i$, and 3.

51.   One other root is $1 - i\sqrt{2}$, so $\left(x - (1 + i\sqrt{2})\right)\left(x - (1 - i\sqrt{2})\right)$ are factors, which is $x^2 - 2x + 3$. We divide:

$$
\begin{array}{r}
x^2 - 4 \\
x^2 - 2x + 3 \overline{\smash{\big)}\ x^4 - 2x^3 - 4x^2 + 14x - 21} \\
\underline{x^4 - 2x^3 + 3x^2} \\
-7x^2 + 14x - 21 \\
\underline{-7x^2 + 14x - 21} \\
0
\end{array}
$$

So $x^2 - 7 = (x + \sqrt{7})(x - \sqrt{7})$ is the other factor. So the roots are $1 + i\sqrt{2}$, $1 - i\sqrt{2}$, $\sqrt{7}$, and $-\sqrt{7}$.

53. (a) The possible rational roots are ± 1, $\pm\frac{1}{2}$, ± 3, $\pm\frac{3}{2}$

We use synthetic division:

$$
\begin{array}{r|rrrr}
 & 2 & -1 & -1 & -3 \\
3/2 & & 3 & 3 & 3 \\
\hline
 & 2 & 2 & 2 & 0
\end{array}
$$

So $2x^3 - x^2 - x - 3 = \left(x - \frac{3}{2}\right)(2x^2 + 2x + 2) = 2\left(x - \frac{3}{2}\right)(x^2 + x + 1)$

Using the quadratic equation, we have:

$$x = \frac{-1 \pm \sqrt{1 - 4}}{2} = \frac{-1 \pm i\sqrt{3}}{2}$$

So the rational roots are $\frac{3}{2}$.

(b) All solutions are $\frac{3}{2}$, $\frac{-1 + i\sqrt{3}}{2}$, and $\frac{-1 - i\sqrt{3}}{2}$.

55. (a) Let $f(x) = x^3 - 3x + 1$, so $f(-x) = -x^3 + 3x + 1$
Since there is one sign change, there will be 1 negative real root.

(b) Use synthetic division:

$$
\begin{array}{r|rrrr}
 & 1 & 0 & -3 & 1 \\
-2 & & -2 & 4 & -2 \\
\hline
 & 1 & -2 & 1 & -1
\end{array}
$$

Since the signs alternate, there cannot be any roots less than -2.

(c) $f(-1) = 3$ and $f(-2) = -1$, so there is a root between -2 and -1.
$f(-1.8) = 0.56$ and $f(-1.9) = -0.16$, so there is a root between -1.9 and -1.8
$f(-1.88) = -0.004$ and $f(-1.87) = 0.07$, so there is a root between -1.88 and -1.87

57. Let $f(x) = 3x^4 + x^2 - 5x - 1$. Since there is one sign change, there is one positive root. $f(-x) = 3x^4 + x^2 + 5x - 1$. Since there is one sign change, there is 1 negative root. So the equation has 1 positive real root, 1 negative real root, and 2 complex roots.

59. Let $f(x) = x^3 + 8x - 7$. There is one sign change, so there is one positive root. Now $f(-x) = -x^3 - 8x - 7$. Since there are no sign changes, there are no negative roots. So the equation has 1 positive real root and 2 complex roots.

61. Let $f(x) = x^3 + 3x + 1$. There are no sign changes, so there are no positive roots. Now $f(-x) = -x^3 - 3x + 1$. Since there is one sign change, there is one negative root. So the equation has 1 negative real root and 2 complex roots.

63. Let $f(x) = x^4 - 10$. There is one sign change, so there is 1 positive root. Since $f(-x) = f(x)$, there is also 1 negative root. So the equation has 1 positive real root, 1 negative real root, and 2 complex roots.

65. Since $-3i$ is a root, then so is $3i$. Those factors are $(x + 3i)(x - 3i) = x^2 + 9$. We use long division:

$$
\begin{array}{r}
x^3 - 6x - 4 \\
x^2 + 9 \overline{\smash{\big)}\ x^5 + 0x^4 + 3x^3 - 4x^2 - 54x - 36} \\
\underline{x^5 \qquad\quad + 9x^3} \\
-6x^3 - 4x^2 - 54x \\
\underline{-6x^3 \qquad\quad - 54x} \\
-4x^2 \qquad\quad - 36 \\
\underline{-4x^2 \qquad\quad - 36} \\
0
\end{array}
$$

The remaining roots will be roots of $x^3 - 6x - 4$. Since $1 + \sqrt{3}$ is a root, then so is $1 - \sqrt{3}$. Those factors are $(x - 1 - \sqrt{3})(x - 1 + \sqrt{3}) = (x - 1)^2 - 3 = x^2 - 2x - 2$. Again we use long division:

$$
\begin{array}{r}
x + 2 \\
x^2 - 2x - 2 \overline{\smash{\big)}\ x^3 + 0x^2 - 6x - 4} \\
\underline{x^3 - 2x^2 - 2x} \\
2x^2 - 4x - 4 \\
\underline{2x^2 - 4x - 4} \\
0
\end{array}
$$

So the other factor is $x + 2$, and thus -2 is a root. So the roots are $-3i$, $3i$, $1 + \sqrt{3}$, $1 - \sqrt{3}$, -2.

67. $x^2 + (x^3)^2 = 1$, so $x^6 + x^2 - 1 = 0$
Let $f(x) = x^6 + x^2 - 1$
       $f(0) = -1$
       $f(1) = 1$
So there is a root between 0 and 1
       $f(0.8) = -0.09$
       $f(0.9) = 0.34$
So there is a root between 0.8 and 0.9
       $f(0.82) = -0.02$
       $f(0.83) = 0.01$
So there is a root between 0.82 and 0.83
So the x-coordinate lies between 0.82 and 0.83

69.   F   (example $x^2 + 1 = 0$)

71.   T

73.   F   (the sum is + 12)

75.   F

77.   Another root will be $4 + \sqrt{5}$, so:
$$\left(x - (4 - \sqrt{5})\right)\left(x - (4 + \sqrt{5})\right) = 0$$
$$x^2 - 8x + 11 = 0$$

79.   Other roots will be $6 + 2i$ and $-\sqrt{5}$:
$$\left(x - \sqrt{5}\right)\left(x - (-\sqrt{5})\right)\left(x - (6 - 2i)\right)\left(x - (6 + 2i)\right) = 0$$
$$(x^2 - 5)(x^2 - 12x + 40) = 0$$
$$x^4 - 12x^3 + 35x^2 + 60x - 200 = 0$$

81.   The factors are $x + 2$, $x - (1 - 3i)$ and $x - (1 + 3i)$, so:
$$\left(x + 2\right)\left(x - (1 - 3i)\right)\left(x - (1 + 3i)\right) = 0$$
$$(x + 2)(x^2 - 2x + 10) = 0$$
$$x^3 + 6x + 20 = 0$$

83. $y = x^4 + 3x^3 + 3x^2 + x$
$y = x(x^3 + 3x^2 + 3x + 1)$
$y = x(x + 1)^3$
zeros: 0, -1

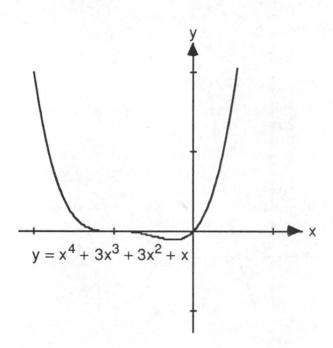

$$y = x^4 + 3x^3 + 3x^2 + x$$

85. $y = x^3 + 6x^2 + 5x - 12$
Using synthetic division to find rational roots:

$$
\begin{array}{r|rrrr}
 & 1 & 6 & 5 & -12 \\
1 & & 1 & 7 & 12 \\
\hline
 & 1 & 7 & 12 & 0
\end{array}
$$

$y = (x - 1)(x^2 + 7x + 12)$
$y = (x - 1)(x + 4)(x + 3)$
zeros: 1, -4, -3

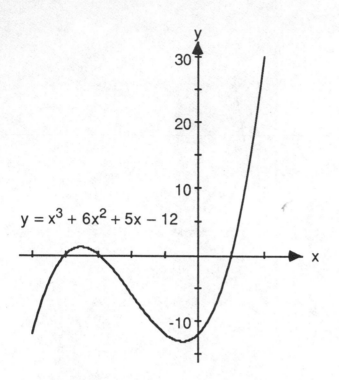

$$y = x^3 + 6x^2 + 5x - 12$$

87. $x - 1 = \sqrt{2} + \sqrt{3}$
      Squaring both sides, we get:
$$x^2 - 2x + 1 = 5 + 2\sqrt{6}$$
$$x^2 - 2x - 4 = 2\sqrt{6}$$
      Squaring both sides again, we get:
$$x^4 - 4x^3 - 4x^2 + 16x + 16 = 24$$
$$x^4 - 4x^3 - 4x^2 + 16x - 8 = 0$$

CHAPTER 12
THE CONIC SECTIONS

12.1   The Parabola

1. $x^2 = 4y$
Focus: $4p = 4$, so $p = 1$
focus: $(0,1)$; directrix: $y = -1$; focal width: 4

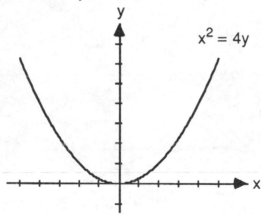

3. $y^2 = -8x$
Focus: $4p = -8$, so $p = -2$
focus: $(-2,0)$; directrix: $x = 2$; focal width: 8

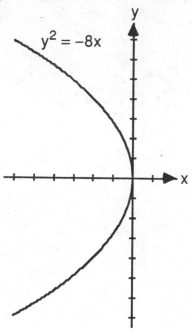

5. $x^2 = -20y$
Focus: $4p = -20$, so $p = -5$
focus: $(0,-5)$; directrix: $y = 5$; focal width: 20

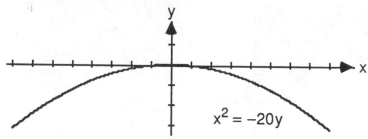

7. $y^2 + 28x = 0$
    $y^2 = -28x$
    Focus: $4p = -28$, so $p = -7$
    focus: $(-7,0)$; directrix: $x = 7$; focal width: 28

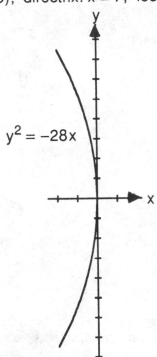

$y^2 = -28x$

9. $x^2 = 6y$

    Focus: $4p = 4$, so $p = \dfrac{3}{2}$

    focus: $\left(0, \dfrac{3}{2}\right)$; directrix: $y = -\dfrac{3}{2}$; focal width: 6

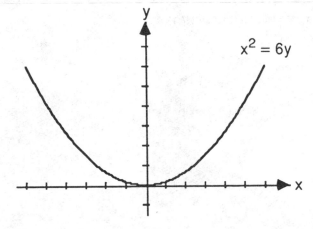

$x^2 = 6y$

11. $4x^2 = 7y$

$x^2 = \dfrac{7}{4}y$

Focus: $4p = \dfrac{7}{4}$, so $p = \dfrac{7}{16}$

focus: $\left(0, \dfrac{7}{16}\right)$; directrix: $y = -\dfrac{7}{16}$; focal width: $\dfrac{7}{4}$

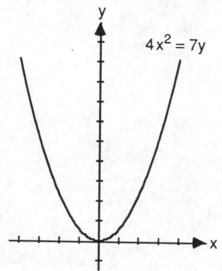

$4x^2 = 7y$

13. $y^2 - 6y - 4x + 17 = 0$

$y^2 - 6y = 4x - 17$

$y^2 - 6y + 9 = 4x - 17 + 9$

$(y - 3)^2 = 4x - 8$

$(y - 3)^2 = 4(x - 2)$

vertex: (2,3)

Focus: $4p = 4$, so $p = 1$

focus: (3,3); directrix: $x = 1$; focal width: 4

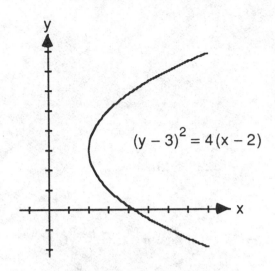

$$(y - 3)^2 = 4(x - 2)$$

15. $x^2 - 8x - y + 18 = 0$

$x^2 - 8x = y - 18$

$x^2 - 8x + 16 = y - 18 + 16$

$(x - 4)^2 = y - 2$

vertex: $(4,2)$

Focus: $4p = 1$, so $p = \dfrac{1}{4}$

focus: $\left(4, \dfrac{9}{4}\right)$; directrix: $y = \dfrac{7}{4}$; focal width: 1

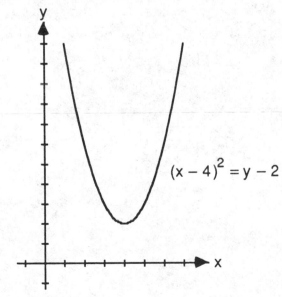

$$(x - 4)^2 = y - 2$$

17. $y^2 + 2y - x + 1 = 0$

$\qquad y^2 + 2y = x - 1$

$\qquad y^2 + 2y + 1 = x - 1 + 1$

$\qquad (y + 1)^2 = x$

vertex: $(0, -1)$

Focus: $4p = 1$, so $p = \dfrac{1}{4}$

focus: $\left(\dfrac{1}{4}, -1\right)$; directrix: $x = -\dfrac{1}{4}$; focal width: 1

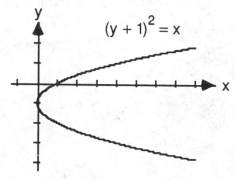

$(y + 1)^2 = x$

19. $2x^2 - 12x - y + 18 = 0$

$\qquad 2x^2 - 12x = y - 18$

$\qquad x^2 - 6x = \dfrac{1}{2}y - 9$

$\qquad x^2 - 6x + 9 = \dfrac{1}{2}y - 9 + 9$

$\qquad (x - 3)^2 = \dfrac{1}{2}y$

vertex: $(3, 0)$

Focus: $4p = \dfrac{1}{2}$, so $p = \dfrac{1}{8}$

focus: $\left(3, \dfrac{1}{8}\right)$; directrix: $y = -\dfrac{1}{8}$; focal width: $\dfrac{1}{2}$

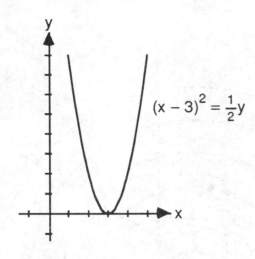

$(x - 3)^2 = \frac{1}{2}y$

21. $2x^2 - 16x - y + 33 = 0$

$$2x^2 - 16x = y - 33$$

$$2(x - 4)^2 = y - 1$$

$$(x - 4)^2 = \frac{1}{2}(y - 1)$$

vertex: (4,1)

Focus: $4p = \frac{1}{2}$, so $p = \frac{1}{8}$

focus: $\left(4, \frac{9}{8}\right)$; directrix: $y = \frac{7}{8}$; focal width: $\frac{1}{2}$

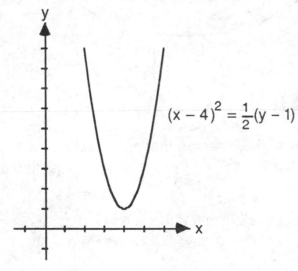

$(x - 4)^2 = \frac{1}{2}(y - 1)$

23.   We re-draw the figure:

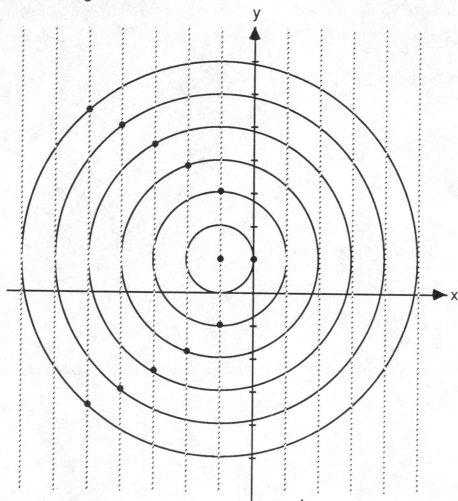

Line of symmetry: $y = 1$

25.   Given that the focus is at (0,3), we see that $p = 3$ and $4p = 12$. Since the parabola opens up, it has the $x^2 = 4py$ form, and its equation must be $x^2 = 12y$

27.   The directrix is $x = -32$, so (32,0) is the focus and the parabola opens to the right. So the parabola is of the form $y^2 = 4px$, where $p = 32$. Thus the equation is $y^2 = 128x$.

29.   Since the parabola is symmetric about the x-axis, then $y^2 = 4px$ is the form (here p can be positive or negative). Since the x-coordinate of the focus is negative, then $y^2 = -4px$ where $p > 0$. Finally we are given $4p = 9$, so the equation is $y^2 = -9x$.

31. (a) Since $4p = 8$, then $p = 2$, and thus the focus is $(0,2)$. So the slope of the line is $\frac{8-2}{8-0} = \frac{3}{4}$, and thus the equation is $y = \frac{3}{4}x + 2$.

(b) We solve the system:
$$y = \frac{3}{4}x + 2$$
$$x^2 = 8y$$
Substituting:
$$x^2 = 8\left(\frac{3}{4}x + 2\right)$$
$$x^2 = 6x + 16$$
$$x^2 - 6x - 16 = 0$$
$$(x - 8)(x + 2) = 0$$
$$x = 8, -2$$
$$y = 8, \frac{1}{2}$$
Since $(8,8)$ repeats our original point, then Q must be $(-2, \frac{1}{2})$

(c) Use the distance formula:
$$PQ = \sqrt{(8 + 2)^2 + \left(8 - \frac{1}{2}\right)^2} = \sqrt{100 + \frac{225}{4}} = \sqrt{\frac{625}{4}} = \frac{25}{2}$$

(d) We know the radius is $\frac{25}{4}$, and the center of the circle will be the midpoint of the line segment PQ:
$$\text{center} = \left(\frac{8-2}{2}, \frac{8 + \frac{1}{2}}{2}\right) = \left(3, \frac{17}{4}\right)$$
So the equation is $(x - 3)^2 + \left(y - \frac{17}{4}\right)^2 = \frac{625}{16}$

(e) The directrix is $y = -2$. The vertical distance from the center of the circle to the directrix is $\left|\frac{17}{4} - (-2)\right| = \frac{25}{4}$. But the radius of the circle is also $\frac{25}{4}$. This implies that the directrix must be tangent to the circle.

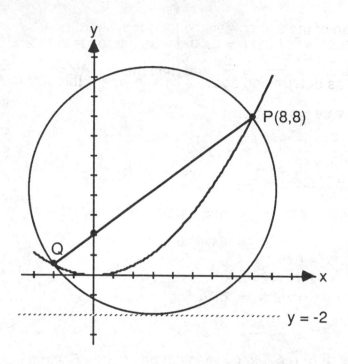

33. Call (0,0) the vertex, thus the ends of the arch are at (20,-15) and (-20,-15). The parabola is of the form $x^2 = -4py$, so we substitute:

$$400 = -4p(-15)$$

$$-\frac{80}{3} = -4p$$

So the equation is $x^2 = -\frac{80}{3}y$. We wish to find the y-coordinate when the base is 20 ft, so we substitute $x = \pm10$ into the equation:

$$100 = -\frac{80}{3}y$$

$$-\frac{15}{4} = y$$

So the height above the base is $15 - \frac{15}{4} = \frac{45}{4} = 11.25$ feet.

35. For ease in writing, let us agree to write a in place of x_0. Then the coordinates of P are $(a, \frac{a^2}{4p})$. Now the focus is $(0, p)$. So the slope of the focal chord is:

$$m = \frac{\frac{a^2}{4p} - p}{a - 0} = \frac{a^2 - 4p^2}{4ap}$$

The equation of the line containing the focal chord is:

$$y - \frac{a^2}{4p} = m(x - a)$$

where m is as determined above. To see where this line meets the parabola, we replace y by $\frac{x^2}{4p}$ to obtain:

$$\frac{x^2}{4p} - \frac{a^2}{4p} = m(x - a)$$

$$\frac{(x - a)(x + a)}{4p} = m(x - a)$$

Now we divide by x - a. (Clearly, for the required point Q, x ≠ a) Thus we have:

$$\frac{x + a}{4p} = m$$

$$x + a = 4pm = 4p\left(\frac{a^2 - 4p^2}{4ap}\right)$$

$$x + a = \frac{a^2 - 4p^2}{a}$$

$$x = \frac{a^2 - 4p^2 - a^2}{a} = -\frac{4p^2}{a}$$

Thus $x = -\frac{4p^2}{a}$, or returning to the original notation, $x = -\frac{4p^2}{x_0}$. This is the required x-coordinate for Q. Since $y = \frac{1}{4p}x^2$, it follows then that the y-coordinate of Q is:

$$\frac{1}{4p}\left[\frac{16p^4}{x_0^2}\right] = \frac{4p^3}{x_0^2} = \frac{4p^3}{4py_0} = \frac{p^2}{y_0}, \text{ as required.}$$

12.2   The Ellipse

1. $4x^2 + 9y^2 = 36$

   $$\frac{x^2}{9} + \frac{y^2}{4} = 1$$

   major axis: 6; minor axis: 4

   $c^2 = 9 - 4 = 5$, so $c = \sqrt{5}$

   foci: $(\sqrt{5},0)$ and $(-\sqrt{5},0)$; eccentricity $= \frac{\sqrt{5}}{3}$

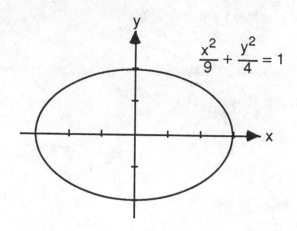

$$\frac{x^2}{9} + \frac{y^2}{4} = 1$$

3. $x^2 + 16y^2 = 16$

$$\frac{x^2}{16} + \frac{y^2}{1} = 1$$

major axis: 8; minor axis: 2

$$c^2 = 16 - 1 = 15, \text{ so } c = \sqrt{15}$$

foci: $(\sqrt{15},0)$ and $(-\sqrt{15},0)$; eccentricity $= \dfrac{\sqrt{15}}{4}$

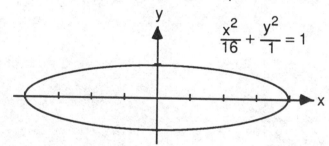

$$\frac{x^2}{16} + \frac{y^2}{1} = 1$$

5. $x^2 + 2y^2 = 2$

$$\frac{x^2}{2} + \frac{y^2}{1} = 1$$

major axis: $2\sqrt{2}$; minor axis: 2

$$c^2 = 2 - 1 = 1, \text{ so } c = 1$$

foci: $(1,0)$ and $(-1,0)$; eccentricity $= \dfrac{\sqrt{2}}{2}$

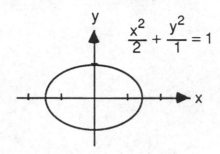

$$\frac{x^2}{2} + \frac{y^2}{1} = 1$$

7. $16x^2 + 9y^2 = 144$

$$\frac{x^2}{9} + \frac{y^2}{16} = 1$$

major axis: 8; minor axis: 6

$$c^2 = 16 - 9 = 7, \text{ so } c = \sqrt{7}$$

foci: $(0,\sqrt{7})$ and $(0,-\sqrt{7})$; eccentricity $= \dfrac{\sqrt{7}}{4}$

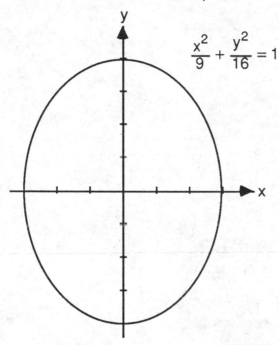

$$\frac{x^2}{9} + \frac{y^2}{16} = 1$$

9. $15x^2 + 3y^2 = 5$

$\dfrac{x^2}{1/3} + \dfrac{y^2}{5/3} = 1$

major axis: $2\sqrt{\dfrac{5}{3}} = \dfrac{2\sqrt{15}}{3}$

minor axis: $2\sqrt{\dfrac{1}{3}} = \dfrac{2\sqrt{3}}{3}$

$c^2 = \dfrac{5}{3} - \dfrac{1}{3} = \dfrac{4}{3}$, so $c = \dfrac{2}{\sqrt{3}} = \dfrac{2\sqrt{3}}{3}$

foci: $\left(0, \dfrac{2\sqrt{3}}{3}\right)$ and $\left(0, -\dfrac{2\sqrt{3}}{3}\right)$

eccentricity $= \dfrac{2\sqrt{3}/3}{\sqrt{15}/3} = \dfrac{2\sqrt{3}}{\sqrt{15}} = \dfrac{2}{\sqrt{5}} = \dfrac{2\sqrt{5}}{5}$

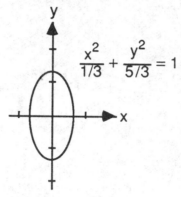

$\dfrac{x^2}{1/3} + \dfrac{y^2}{5/3} = 1$

11. $2x^2 + y^2 = 4$

$\dfrac{x^2}{2} + \dfrac{y^2}{4} = 1$

major axis: 4; minor axis: $2\sqrt{2}$

$c^2 = 4 - 2 = 2$, so $c = \sqrt{2}$

foci: $(0, \sqrt{2})$ and $(0, -\sqrt{2})$; eccentricity $= \dfrac{\sqrt{2}}{2}$

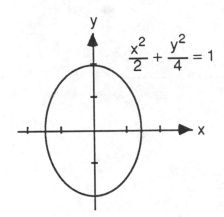

$$\frac{x^2}{2} + \frac{y^2}{4} = 1$$

13. $\dfrac{(x-5)^2}{5^2} + \dfrac{(y+1)^2}{3^2} = 1$

center: (5,-1); major axis: 10; minor axis: 6

   $c^2 = 25 - 9 = 16$, so c = 4

foci: (5 + 4,-1) and (5 - 4,-1), or (9,-1) and (1,-1)

eccentricity $= \dfrac{4}{5}$

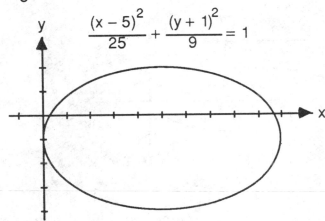

$$\frac{(x-5)^2}{25} + \frac{(y+1)^2}{9} = 1$$

15. $\dfrac{(x-1)^2}{1^2} + \dfrac{(y-2)^2}{2^2} = 1$

center: (1,2); major axis: 4; minor axis: 2

   $c^2 = 4 - 1 = 3$, so c $= \sqrt{3}$

foci: (1,2 + $\sqrt{3}$) and (1,2 - $\sqrt{3}$); eccentricity $= \dfrac{\sqrt{3}}{2}$

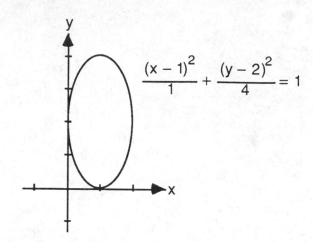

17. $\dfrac{(x + 3)^2}{3^2} + \dfrac{y^2}{1^2} = 1$

center: (-3,0); major axis: 6; minor axis: 2

$c^2 = 9 - 1 = 8$, so $c = \sqrt{8} = 2\sqrt{2}$

foci: $(-3 + 2\sqrt{2}, 0)$ and $(-3 - 2\sqrt{2}, 0)$; eccentricity $= \dfrac{2\sqrt{2}}{3}$

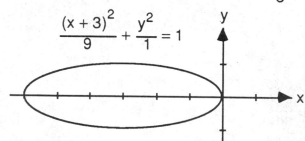

19. $3x^2 + 4y^2 - 6x + 16y + 7 = 0$

$3(x^2 - 2x) + 4(y^2 + 4y) = -7$

$3(x^2 - 2x + 1) + 4(y^2 + 4y + 4) = -7 + 3 + 16$

$3(x - 1)^2 + 4(y + 2)^2 = 12$

$\dfrac{(x - 1)^2}{4} + \dfrac{(y + 2)^2}{3} = 1$

center: (1,-2); major axis: 4; minor axis: $2\sqrt{3}$

$c^2 = 4 - 3 = 1$, so $c = 1$

foci: (1 + 1,-2) and (1 - 1,-2), or (2,-2) and (0,-2)

eccentricity $= \dfrac{1}{2}$

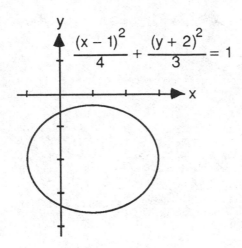

$$\frac{(x-1)^2}{4} + \frac{(y+2)^2}{3} = 1$$

21.

$$5x^2 + 3y^2 - 40x - 36y + 188 = 0$$
$$5(x^2 - 8x) + 3(y^2 - 12y) = -188$$
$$5(x^2 - 8x + 16) + 3(y^2 - 12y + 36) = -188 + 80 + 108$$
$$5(x - 4)^2 + 3(y - 6)^2 = 0$$

Notice that the only solution to this is the center (4,6). This is called a degenerate ellipse.

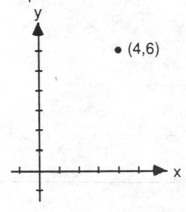

• (4,6)

23.

$$16x^2 + 25y^2 - 64x - 100y + 564 = 0$$
$$16(x^2 - 4x) + 25(y^2 - 4y) = -564$$
$$16(x^2 - 4x + 4) + 25(y^2 - 4y + 4) = -564 + 64 + 100$$
$$16(x - 2)^2 + 25(y - 2)^2 = -400$$

Notice that there is no solution to this equation, since the left-hand side is non-negative. So there is no graph.

25. We are given c = 3 and a = 5, so we have the equation in the form:

$$\frac{x^2}{5^2} + \frac{y^2}{b^2} = 1$$

Since $c^2 = a^2 - b^2$, we find b:

$$9 = 25 - b^2$$
$$16 = b^2$$
$$4 = b$$

So the equation is $\frac{x^2}{5^2} + \frac{y^2}{4^2} = 1$, or $16x^2 + 25y^2 = 400$.

27. We are given a = 4, so the equation has a form of:

$$\frac{x^2}{16} + \frac{y^2}{b^2} = 1$$

Now $\frac{c}{a} = \frac{1}{4}$, so: $\frac{c}{4} = \frac{1}{4}$, thus c = 1

We find b:

$$c^2 = a^2 - b^2$$
$$1 = 16 - b^2$$
$$b^2 = 15$$

So the equation is $\frac{x^2}{16} + \frac{y^2}{15} = 1$, or $15x^2 + 16y^2 = 240$

29. We have c = 2 and a = 5, so the equation has a form of:

$$\frac{x^2}{b^2} + \frac{y^2}{25} = 1$$

We find b:

$$c^2 = a^2 - b^2$$
$$4 = 25 - b^2$$
$$21 = b^2$$

So the equation is $\frac{x^2}{21} + \frac{y^2}{25} = 1$, or $25x^2 + 21y^2 = 525$

31. We know a = 2b and that the equation has a form of:

$$\frac{x^2}{a^2} + \frac{y^2}{b^2} = 1$$

Using the point $(1, \sqrt{2})$ and a = 2b, we have:

$$\frac{1}{(2b)^2} + \frac{2}{b^2} = 1$$
$$\frac{1}{4b^2} + \frac{2}{b^2} = 1$$

Multiply by $4b^2$:

$$1 + 8 = 4b^2$$

$$\frac{9}{4} = b^2$$

$$\frac{3}{2} = b$$

Since $a = 2b$, then $a = 3$.

So the equation is $\dfrac{x^2}{3^2} + \dfrac{y^2}{(3/2)^2} = 1$, or $x^2 + 4y^2 = 9$

33. $5x^2 + 6y^2 = 60$

$$\frac{x^2}{12} + \frac{y^2}{10} = 1$$

So $a = \sqrt{12} = 2\sqrt{3}$ and $b = \sqrt{10}$. Thus the area is given by:

$$A = \pi ab = \pi(2\sqrt{3})(\sqrt{10}) = \pi(2\sqrt{30}) \text{ or } 2\sqrt{30}\,\pi$$

35. $\dfrac{x^2}{9} + \dfrac{y^2}{4} = 1$

$$\frac{y^2}{4} = 1 - \frac{x^2}{9}$$

$$\frac{y^2}{4} = \frac{9 - x^2}{9}$$

$$y^2 = \frac{36 - 4x^2}{9}$$

Taking roots:

$$y = \pm\sqrt{\frac{36 - 4x^2}{9}}$$

$$y = \pm\frac{\sqrt{36 - 4x^2}}{3}$$

We use a calculator to fill in the table:

x	0	0.5	1.0	1.5	2.0	2.5	3.0
y	± 2	± 1.97	± 1.89	± 1.73	± 1.49	± 1.11	0

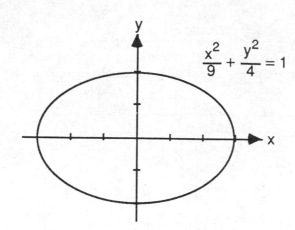

$$\frac{x^2}{9} + \frac{y^2}{4} = 1$$

37. (a)

$$\sqrt{(x-c)^2 + y^2} = 2a - \sqrt{(x+c)^2 + y^2}$$

$$(x-c)^2 + y^2 = 4a^2 - 4a\sqrt{(x+c)^2 + y^2} + (x+c)^2 + y^2$$

$$x^2 - 2xc + c^2 + y^2 = 4a^2 - 4a\sqrt{(x+c)^2 + y^2} + x^2 + 2cx + c^2 + y^2$$

$$-4cx - 4a^2 = -4a\sqrt{(x+c)^2 + y^2}$$

$$a^2 + cx = a\sqrt{(x+c)^2 + y^2}$$

(b) Squaring each side again, we get:

$$(a^2 + cx)^2 = a^2\left((x+c)^2 + y^2\right)$$

$$a^4 + 2a^2cx + c^2x^2 = a^2(x^2 + 2cx + c^2 + y^2)$$

$$a^4 + 2a^2cx + c^2x^2 = a^2x^2 + 2a^2cx + a^2c^2 + a^2y^2$$

$$a^4 - a^2c^2 = a^2x^2 - c^2x^2 + a^2y^2$$

(c) We simply factor each side (a^2 on the left, x^2 on the right) to get:

$$a^2(a^2 - c^2) = (a^2 - c^2)x^2 + a^2y^2$$

(d) Call $b^2 = a^2 - c^2$, so we can rewrite the equation from (c) as:

$$b^2x^2 + a^2y^2 = a^2b^2$$

Dividing by a^2b^2:

$$\frac{x^2}{a^2} + \frac{y^2}{b^2} = 1$$

39. We use $a = 5$ and $b = 3$ in each formula:

	Approximation Obtained	Percentage Error
C_1	25.531776	0.019
C_2	25.526986	0.000049
C_3	25.519489	0.029

Since C_2 has the smallest percentage error, it would be the best approximation of the circumference of the three.

12.3   The Hyperbola

1. $x^2 - 4y^2 = 4$

$$\frac{x^2}{4} - \frac{y^2}{1} = 1$$

vertices: (2,0) and (-2,0)
transverse axis: 4; conjugate axis: 2
asymptotes: $y = \pm\frac{1}{2}x$

foci: $(\sqrt{5},0)$ and $(-\sqrt{5},0)$; eccentricity $= \frac{\sqrt{5}}{2}$

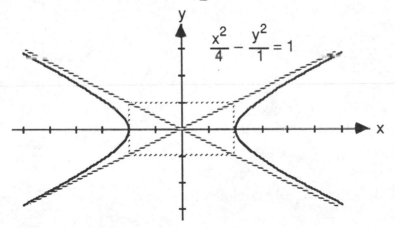

3. $y^2 - 4x^2 = 4$

$\dfrac{y^2}{4} - \dfrac{x^2}{1} = 1$

vertices: (0,2) and (0,-2)
transverse axis: 4; conjugate axis: 2
asymptotes: $y = \pm 2x$

foci: $(0,\sqrt{5})$ and $(0,-\sqrt{5})$; eccentricity $= \dfrac{\sqrt{5}}{2}$

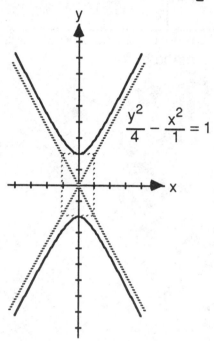

5. $16x^2 - 25y^2 = 400$

$\dfrac{x^2}{25} - \dfrac{y^2}{16} = 1$

vertices: (5,0) and (-5,0)
transverse axis: 10; conjugate axis: 8

asymptotes: $y = \pm \dfrac{4}{5}x$

foci: $(\sqrt{41},0)$ and $(-\sqrt{41},0)$; eccentricity $= \dfrac{\sqrt{41}}{5}$

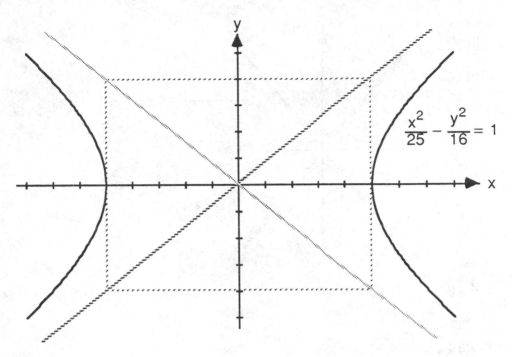

$$\frac{x^2}{25} - \frac{y^2}{16} = 1$$

7. $2y^2 - 3x^2 = 4$

$\dfrac{y^2}{1/2} - \dfrac{x^2}{1/3} = 1$

vertices: $\left(0, \sqrt{\dfrac{1}{2}}\right)$ and $\left(0, -\sqrt{\dfrac{1}{2}}\right)$

transverse axis: $\sqrt{2}$; conjugate axis: $\dfrac{2\sqrt{3}}{3}$

asymptotes: $y = \pm \sqrt{\dfrac{3}{2}} \, x$

foci: $\left(0, \sqrt{\dfrac{5}{6}}\right)$ and $\left(0, -\sqrt{\dfrac{5}{6}}\right)$

eccentricity: $\sqrt{\dfrac{5}{3}} = \dfrac{\sqrt{15}}{3}$

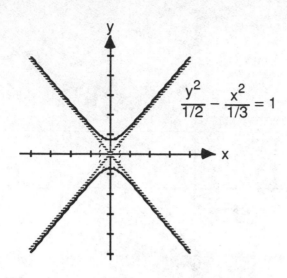

$$\frac{y^2}{1/2} - \frac{x^2}{1/3} = 1$$

9. $4y^2 - 25x^2 = 100$

$$\frac{y^2}{25} - \frac{x^2}{4} = 1$$

vertices: (0,5) and (0,-5)

transverse axis: 10; conjugate axis: 4

asymptotes: $y = \pm \dfrac{5}{2}x$

foci: $(0,\sqrt{29})$ and $(0,-\sqrt{29})$; eccentricity $= \dfrac{\sqrt{29}}{5}$

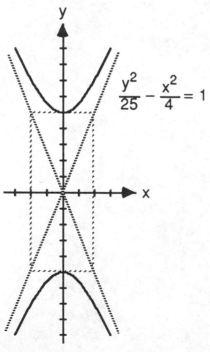

$$\frac{y^2}{25} - \frac{x^2}{4} = 1$$

11. $\dfrac{(x-5)^2}{25} - \dfrac{(y+1)^2}{9} = 1$

center: (5,-1)

vertices: (10,-1) and (0,-1)

transverse axis: 10; conjugate axis: 6

asymptotes: $y = \dfrac{3}{5}x - 4$; $y = -\dfrac{3}{5}x + 2$

foci: $(5 + \sqrt{34}, -1)$ and $(5 - \sqrt{34}, -1)$; eccentricity $= \dfrac{\sqrt{34}}{5}$

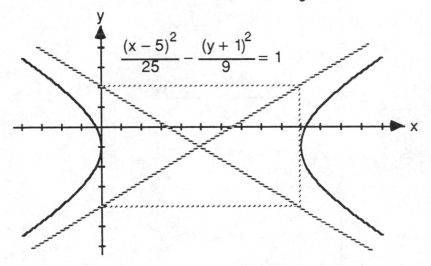

13. $\dfrac{(y-2)^2}{4} - \dfrac{(x-1)^2}{1} = 1$

center: (1,2)
vertices: (1,4) and (1,0)
transverse axis: 4; conjugate axis: 2
asymptotes: y = 2x; y = -2x + 4

foci: (1,2 + √5) and (1,2 - √5); eccentricity $= \dfrac{\sqrt{5}}{2}$

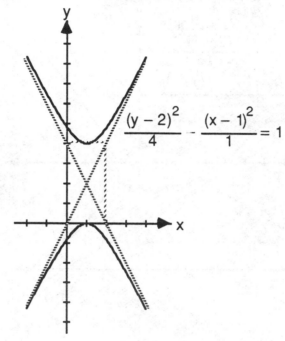

15. $\dfrac{(x+3)^2}{16} - \dfrac{(y-4)^2}{16} = 1$

center: (-3,4)
vertices: (1,4) and (-7,4)
transverse axis: 8; conjugate axis: 8
asymptotes: $y = x + 7$; $y = -x + 1$

foci: $(-3 + 4\sqrt{2}, 4)$ and $(-3 - 4\sqrt{2}, 4)$; eccentricity $= \dfrac{4\sqrt{2}}{4} = \sqrt{2}$

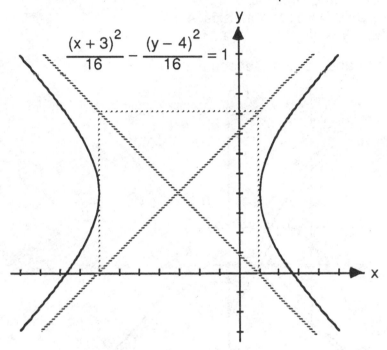

17. $x^2 - y^2 + 2y - 5 = 0$
$x^2 - (y^2 - 2y) = 5$
$x^2 - (y^2 - 2y + 1) = 5 - 1$
$x^2 - (y - 1)^2 = 4$
$\dfrac{x^2}{4} - \dfrac{(y - 1)^2}{4} = 1$

center: (0,1)
vertices: (2,1) and (-2,1)
transverse axis: 4; conjugate axis: 4
asymptotes: $y = x + 1$; $y = -x + 1$

foci: $(2\sqrt{2},1)$ and $(-2\sqrt{2},1)$; eccentricity $= \dfrac{2\sqrt{2}}{2} = \sqrt{2}$

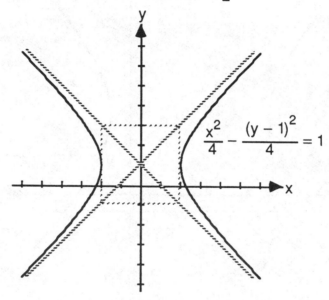

19.
$$x^2 - y^2 - 4x + 2y - 6 = 0$$
$$(x^2 - 4x) - (y^2 - 2y) = 6$$
$$(x^2 - 4x + 4) - (y^2 - 2y + 1) = 6 + 4 - 1$$
$$(x - 2)^2 - (y - 1)^2 = 9$$
$$\frac{(x - 2)^2}{9} - \frac{(y - 1)^2}{9} = 1$$

center: (2,1)
vertices: (-1,1) and (5,1)
transverse axis: 6; conjugate axis: 6
asymptotes: $y = x - 1$; $y = -x + 3$

foci: $(2 + 3\sqrt{2},1)$ and $(2 - 3\sqrt{2},1)$; eccentricity $= \dfrac{3\sqrt{2}}{3} = \sqrt{2}$

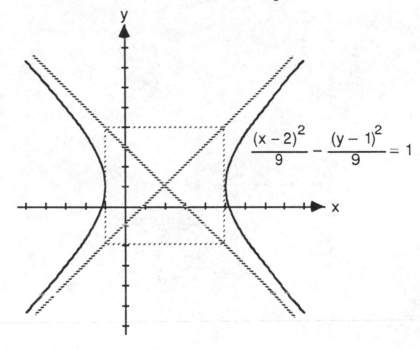

21.

$$y^2 - 25x^2 + 8y - 9 = 0$$
$$(y^2 + 8y) - 25x^2 = 9$$
$$(y^2 + 8y + 16) - 25x^2 = 9 + 16$$
$$(y + 4)^2 - 25x^2 = 25$$
$$\frac{(y + 4)^2}{25} - \frac{x^2}{1} = 1$$

center: (0,-4)
vertices: (0,-9) and (0,1)
transverse axis: 10; conjugate axis: 2
asymptotes: $y = 5x - 4$; $y = -5x - 4$

foci: $(0,-4 + \sqrt{26})$ and $(0,-4 - \sqrt{26})$; eccentricity $= \dfrac{\sqrt{26}}{5}$

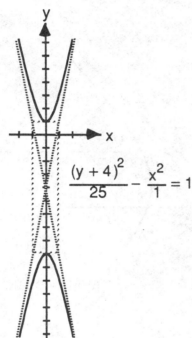

$$\frac{(y + 4)^2}{25} - \frac{x^2}{1} = 1$$

23.

$$x^2 + 7x - y^2 - y + 12 = 0$$
$$(x^2 + 7x) - (y^2 + y) = -12$$
$$\left(x^2 + 7x + \frac{49}{4}\right) - \left(y^2 + y + \frac{1}{4}\right) = -12 + \frac{49}{4} - \frac{1}{4}$$
$$\left(x + \frac{7}{2}\right)^2 - \left(y + \frac{1}{2}\right)^2 = 0$$

Notice that this is a degenerate hyperbola, and the graph consists of the two lines: $y = x + 3$ and $y = -x - 4$

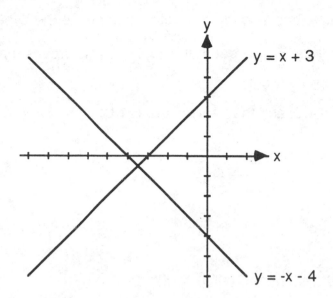

$y = x + 3$

$y = -x - 4$

25. Since P(x,y) lies on $\frac{x^2}{4} - \frac{y^2}{1} = 1$, we can find y in terms of x:

$$y^2 = \frac{x^2}{4} - 1$$

$$y^2 = \frac{x^2 - 4}{4}$$

Taking roots, we have $y = \frac{\sqrt{x^2 - 4}}{2}$, since P(x,y) lies in the first quadrant.

So the coordinates of P are $\left(x, \frac{\sqrt{x^2 - 4}}{2}\right)$.

Since Q(x,y) lies in the first quadrant on the asymptote, we find the equation of the asymptote:

$$y - 0 = \frac{1}{2}(x - 0)$$

$$y = \frac{1}{2}x$$

So the coordinates of Q are $\left(x, \frac{1}{2}x\right)$

We find PQ by using the distance formula:

$$PQ = \sqrt{(x - x)^2 + \left(\frac{\sqrt{x^2 - 4}}{2} - \frac{x}{2}\right)^2}$$

$$= \sqrt{\left[\frac{\sqrt{x^2 - 4} - x}{2}\right]^2}$$

$$= \frac{x - \sqrt{x^2 - 4}}{2}$$

The choice of signs is because the asymptote lies above the hyperbola in the first quadrant, and thus $\frac{x}{2}$ is larger than $\frac{\sqrt{x^2 - 4}}{2}$. This proves the desired result.

27.   Since the foci are $(\pm 4, 0)$ and the vertices are $(\pm 1, 0)$, then $c = 4$, $a = 1$, and the hyperbola has the form:

$$\frac{x^2}{1} - \frac{y^2}{b^2} = 1$$

We find b:

$$c^2 = a^2 + b^2$$
$$16 = 1 + b^2$$
$$15 = b^2$$

So the equation is $\frac{x^2}{1} - \frac{y^2}{15} = 1$, or $15x^2 - y^2 = 15$

29.   The slope of the asymptotes, $\pm \frac{1}{2}$, tells us that the ratio $\frac{b}{a} = \frac{1}{2}$ in this hyperbola. Also, since the vertices are $(\pm 2, 0)$, $a = 2$. The required ratio is therefore:

$$\frac{b}{2} = \frac{1}{2} \text{ and } b = 1$$

The equation is:

$$\frac{x^2}{4} - \frac{y^2}{1} = 1, \text{ or } x^2 - 4y^2 = 4$$

31.   Since the asymptotes are $y = \pm \frac{\sqrt{10}}{5} x$, then $\frac{b}{a} = \frac{\sqrt{10}}{5}$, so $b = \frac{\sqrt{10}}{5} a$.

Now, since the foci are $(\pm \sqrt{7}, 0)$, then $c = \sqrt{7}$ and the hyperbola has the form:

$$\frac{x^2}{a^2} - \frac{y^2}{b^2} = 1$$

Since $b = \frac{\sqrt{10}}{5} a$ and $c = \sqrt{7}$, we have:

$$c^2 = a^2 + b^2$$
$$7 = a^2 + \left(\frac{\sqrt{10}}{5} a\right)^2$$
$$7 = a^2 + \frac{2}{5} a^2$$
$$35 = 7a^2$$
$$5 = a^2$$
$$b^2 = \frac{2}{5} a^2 = \frac{2}{5}(5) = 2$$

So the equation is $\dfrac{x^2}{5} - \dfrac{y^2}{2} = 1$, or $2x^2 - 5y^2 = 10$

33. The vertices are at $(0,\pm 7)$ so we know it is a "vertical" hyperbola. Its equation will be $\dfrac{y^2}{49} - \dfrac{x^2}{b^2} = 1$, but we also know that $(1,9)$ is a point satisfying the equation. We use it to find b:

$$\dfrac{81}{49} - \dfrac{1}{b^2} = 1$$

$$81b^2 - 49 = 49b^2$$

$$-49 = -32b^2$$

$$b^2 = \dfrac{49}{32}$$

$$\dfrac{y^2}{49} - \dfrac{32x^2}{49} = 1, \text{ or } y^2 - 32x^2 = 49$$

35. We have $2a = 6$, so $a = 3$. Also $2b = 2$, so $b = 1$. Since the foci are on the y-axis, the hyperbola will have the form:

$$\dfrac{y^2}{a^2} - \dfrac{x^2}{b^2} = 1$$

So the equation is $\dfrac{y^2}{9} - \dfrac{x^2}{1} = 1$, or $y^2 - 9x^2 = 9$

37. Writing the equation as $\dfrac{x^2}{16} - \dfrac{y^2}{16} = 1$, we have $a = b = 4$. So the slopes of the asymptotes are $\pm\dfrac{b}{a} = \pm\dfrac{4}{4} = \pm 1$. But these are negative reciprocals of each other, so the asymptotes are perpendicular to each other.

39. (a) Let's substitute:

$$5(6)^2 - 4(5)^2 = 5(36) - 4(25) = 180 - 100 = 80 \text{ yes!}$$

(b) $$\dfrac{5y^2}{80} - \dfrac{4x^2}{80} = \dfrac{80}{90}$$

$$\dfrac{y^2}{16} - \dfrac{x^2}{20} = 1$$

So $a = 4$ and $b = 2\sqrt{5}$

$$c^2 = a^2 + b^2 = 16 + 20 = 36$$

So $c = 6$ and the foci will be at $(0,\pm 6)$.

(c) $$F_1P = \sqrt{(5 - 0)^2 + (6 - 6)^2} = 5$$

$$F_2P = \sqrt{(5 - 0)^2 + (6 - (-6))^2} = \sqrt{25 + 144} = 13$$

(d) $|F_1P - F_2P| = |5 - 13| = |-8| = 8 = 2a$

41.   (a)   Since the asymptotes must have slopes of $\pm\dfrac{b}{a}$, then:

$$-\frac{b}{a} = \frac{-1}{b/a}$$
$$\frac{b^2}{a^2} = 1$$
$$b^2 = a^2$$
$$b = a$$

Now, since $c^2 = a^2 + b^2 = 2a^2$, then the eccentricity is:

$$\frac{c}{a} = \frac{\sqrt{2a^2}}{a} = \frac{\sqrt{2}\,a}{a} = \sqrt{2}$$

(b)   The slopes of the asymptotes are $\dfrac{\pm a}{a} = \pm 1$, so the hyperbola will have perpendicular asymptotes.

The eccentricity is: $\dfrac{\sqrt{2}\,a}{a} = \sqrt{2}$

43.   (a)   This equation is just $F_1P - F_2P = 2a$, the defining relation of a hyperbola. (Since P is on the right-hand branch, $F_1P > F_2P$)

(b)
$$\sqrt{(x+c)^2 + y^2} = 2a + \sqrt{(x-c)^2 + y^2}$$
$$(x+c)^2 + y^2 = 4a^2 + 4a\sqrt{(x-c)^2 + y^2} + (x-c)^2 + y^2$$
$$4xc = 4a^2 + 4a\sqrt{(x-c)^2 + y^2}$$
$$xc - a^2 = a\sqrt{(x-c)^2 + y^2}$$
$$xc - a^2 = a(F_2P)$$

(c)
$$\frac{xc}{a} - a = F_2P$$
$$xe - a = F_2P$$

45.   For this hyperbola we find $a^2 = b^2 = k^2$, and $e = \sqrt{2}$. Also $d^2 = x^2 + y^2 = x^2 + (x^2 - k^2) = 2x^2 - k^2$. Thus we want to show that $F_1P \bullet F_2P = 2x^2 - k^2$. Using the formulas for F_1P and F_2P developed in exercises #43-44, we have:

$$\begin{aligned} F_1P \bullet F_2P &= (xe + a)(xe - a) \\ &= x^2e^2 - a^2 \\ &= x^2(2) - k^2 \\ &= 2x^2 - k^2 \\ &= d^2 \end{aligned}$$

47. The coordinates of D are $\left(\dfrac{a}{e}, \dfrac{b}{e}\right)$ and those of F are $(c,0)$. Let O denote the center $(0,0)$. We show that angle ODF is a right angle by showing $OD^2 + DF^2 = OF^2$:

$$OF^2 = c^2$$

$$OD^2 = \left(\frac{a}{e}\right)^2 + \left(\frac{b}{e}\right)^2 = \frac{a^2 + b^2}{e^2} = \frac{c^2}{e^2} = a^2$$

$$\begin{aligned} DF^2 &= \left(\frac{a}{e} - c\right)^2 + \left(\frac{b}{e}\right)^2 \\ &= \frac{(a - ec)^2 + b^2}{e^2} \\ &= \frac{a^2 + b^2 - 2aec + e^2c^2}{e^2} \\ &= \frac{c^2 - 2c^2}{e^2} + c^2 \\ &= -\frac{c^2}{e^2} + c^2 \\ &= -a^2 + c^2 \end{aligned}$$

Thus $OD^2 + DF^2 = OF^2$ as required.

Chapter 12 Review Exercises

1. (a)   We have the form $y^2 = 4px$, where $p = 4$. Thus the equation is $y^2 = 16x$.

   (b)   We have the form $x^2 = 4py$, where $p = 4$. Thus the equation is $x^2 = 16y$.

3. Since the parabola is symmetric about the positive y-axis, its equation must be of the form $x^2 = 4py$, where $p > 0$. Now the focal width is 12, so $4p = 12$. Thus the equation is $x^2 = 12y$.

5.   We have c = 2 and a = 8, and the ellipse must have the form:
$$\frac{x^2}{8^2} + \frac{y^2}{b^2} = 1$$
Since $c^2 = a^2 - b^2$, we can find b:
$$4 = 64 - b^2$$
$$b^2 = 60$$
So the equation is $\frac{x^2}{64} + \frac{y^2}{60} = 1$, or $15x^2 + 16y^2 = 960$.

7.   Since one end of the minor axis is (-6,0), then b = 6 and the ellipse has a form of:
$$\frac{x^2}{36} + \frac{y^2}{a^2} = 1$$
Now $\frac{c}{a} = \frac{4}{5}$, so c = $\frac{4}{5}$a. We find a:
$$c^2 = a^2 - b^2$$
$$\left(\frac{4}{5}a\right)^2 = a^2 - 36$$
$$\frac{16}{25}a^2 = a^2 - 36$$
$$36 = \frac{9}{25}a^2$$
$$100 = a^2$$
So the equation is $\frac{x^2}{36} + \frac{y^2}{100} = 1$, or $25x^2 + 9y^2 = 900$.

9.   Since the foci are (±6,0) and the vertices are (±2,0), then c = 6, a = 2, and the equation has the form:
$$\frac{x^2}{4} - \frac{y^2}{b^2} = 1$$
We find b:
$$c^2 = a^2 + b^2$$
$$36 = 4 + b^2$$
$$32 = b^2$$
So the equation is $\frac{x^2}{4} - \frac{y^2}{36} = 1$, or $8x^2 - y^2 = 32$

11.   Since the foci are (±3,0), then c = 3 and the equation has the form:
$$\frac{x^2}{a^2} - \frac{y^2}{b^2} = 1$$
Now $\frac{c}{a} = 4$, so $\frac{3}{a} = 4$, thus a = $\frac{3}{4}$. We substitute to find b:

$$c^2 = a^2 + b^2$$

$$9 = \frac{9}{16} + b^2$$

$$144 = 9 + 16b^2$$

$$135 = 16b^2$$

$$\frac{135}{16} = b^2$$

So the equation is $\dfrac{x^2}{9/16} - \dfrac{y^2}{135/16} = 1$, or $240x^2 - 16y^2 = 135$

13. $x^2 = 10y$

$4p = 10$, so $p = \dfrac{5}{2}$

vertex: $(0,0)$; focus: $\left(0, \dfrac{5}{2}\right)$

directrix: $y = -\dfrac{5}{2}$; focal width: 10

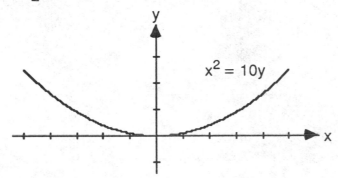

15. $x^2 = -12(y - 3)$
$4p = -12$, so $p = -3$
vertex: $(0,3)$; focus: $(0,0)$
directrix: $y = 6$; focal width: 12

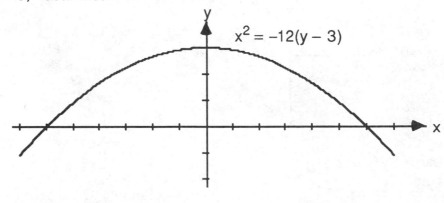

17. $(y - 1)^2 = -4(x - 1)$
     $4p = -4$, so $p = -1$
     vertex: $(1,1)$; focus: $(0,1)$
     directrix: $x = 2$; focal width: 4

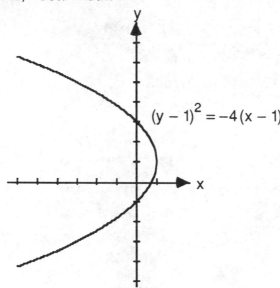

19. $x^2 + 2y^2 = 4$
     $\dfrac{x^2}{4} + \dfrac{y^2}{2} = 1$
     $a = 2$, $b = \sqrt{2}$, $c = \sqrt{2}$
     center: $(0,0)$; foci: $(\pm\sqrt{2},0)$

     major axis: 4; minor axis: $2\sqrt{2}$; eccentricity $= \dfrac{\sqrt{2}}{2}$

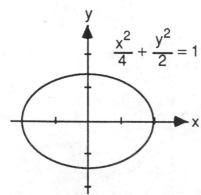

21. $49x^2 + 9y^2 = 441$
     $\dfrac{x^2}{9} + \dfrac{y^2}{49} = 1$

a = 7, b = 3, c = $\sqrt{40}$ = 2$\sqrt{10}$
center: (0,0); foci: (0,±2$\sqrt{10}$)

major axis: 14; minor axis: 6; eccentricity = $\dfrac{2\sqrt{10}}{7}$

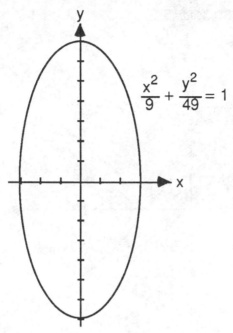

$$\dfrac{x^2}{9} + \dfrac{y^2}{49} = 1$$

23. $\dfrac{(x-1)^2}{25} + \dfrac{(y+2)^2}{9} = 1$
a = 5, b = 3, c = 4
center: (1,-2); foci: (5,-2) and (-3,-2)

major axis: 10; minor axis: 6; eccentricity = $\dfrac{4}{5}$

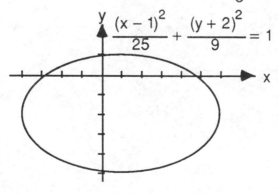

$$\dfrac{(x-1)^2}{25} + \dfrac{(y+2)^2}{9} = 1$$

25. $x^2 - 2y^2 = 4$

$\dfrac{x^2}{4} - \dfrac{y^2}{2} = 1$

$a = 2$, $b = \sqrt{2}$, $c = \sqrt{6}$

center: $(0,0)$; vertices: $(\pm 2, 0)$; foci: $(\pm\sqrt{6}, 0)$

asymptotes: $y = \pm\dfrac{\sqrt{2}}{2}x$; eccentricity $= \dfrac{\sqrt{6}}{2}$

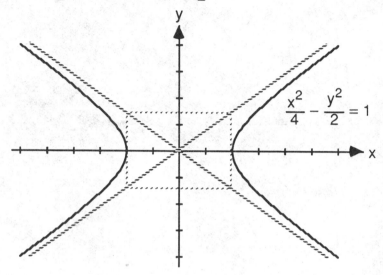

27. $49y^2 - 9x^2 = 441$

$\dfrac{y^2}{9} - \dfrac{x^2}{49} = 1$

$a = 3$, $b = 7$, $c = \sqrt{58}$

center: $(0,0)$; vertices: $(0, \pm 3)$; foci: $(0, \pm\sqrt{58})$

asymptotes: $y = \pm\dfrac{3}{7}x$; eccentricity $= \dfrac{\sqrt{58}}{3}$

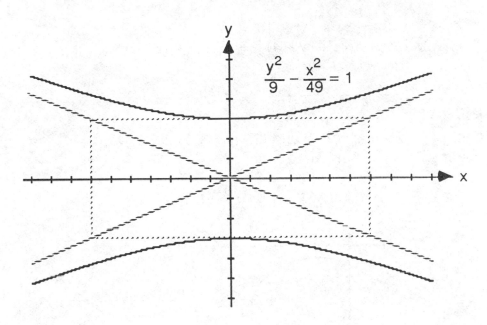

$$\frac{y^2}{9} - \frac{x^2}{49} = 1$$

29. $\dfrac{(x - 1)^2}{25} - \dfrac{(y + 2)^2}{9} = 1$

$a = 5, b = 3, c = \sqrt{34}$

center: $(1,-2)$; vertices: $(6,-2)$ and $(-4,-2)$; foci: $(1 \pm \sqrt{34},-2)$

asymptotes: $y + 2 = \pm \dfrac{3}{5}(x - 1)$; eccentricity: $\dfrac{\sqrt{34}}{5}$

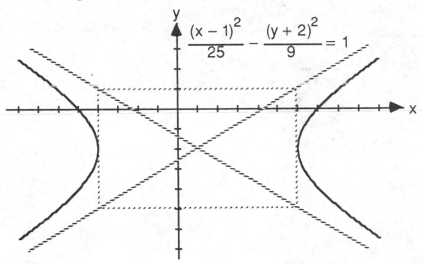

$$\frac{(x - 1)^2}{25} - \frac{(y + 2)^2}{9} = 1$$

31.
$$3x^2 - 6x + 4y^2 + 16 = -7$$
$$3(x^2 - 2x + 1) + 4(y^2 + 4y + 4) = -7 + 3 + 16$$
$$3(x - 1)^2 + 4(y + 2)^2 = 12$$
$$\frac{(x - 1)^2}{4} + \frac{(y + 2)^2}{3} = 1$$

<u>Ellipse:</u>
center: (1,-2); foci: (0,-2) and (2,-2)
major axis: 4; minor axis: $2\sqrt{3}$

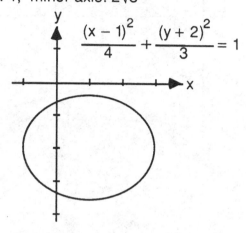

33.
$$y^2 + 2y = -4x + 15$$
$$y^2 + 2y + 1 = -4x + 15 + 1$$
$$(y + 1)^2 = -4(x - 4)$$

<u>Parabola:</u>
vertex: (4,-1); axis: y = -1
focus: (3,-1); directrix: x = 5

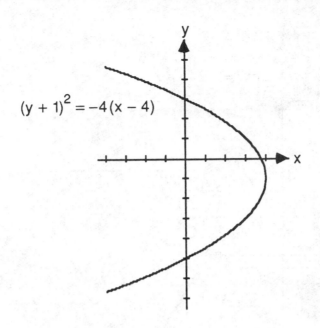

$$(y + 1)^2 = -4(x - 4)$$

35.
$$16(x^2 - 2x) - 9(y^2 - 10y) = 353$$
$$16(x^2 - 2x + 1) - 9(y^2 - 10y + 25) = 353 + 16 - 225$$
$$16(x - 1)^2 - 9(y - 5)^2 = 144$$
$$\frac{(x - 1)^2}{9} - \frac{(y - 5)^2}{16} = 1$$

Hyperbola:
center: (1,5); vertices: (-2,5) and (4,5)

foci: (-4,5) and (6,5); asymptotes: $y = \frac{4}{3}x + \frac{11}{3}$; $y = -\frac{4}{3}x + \frac{19}{3}$

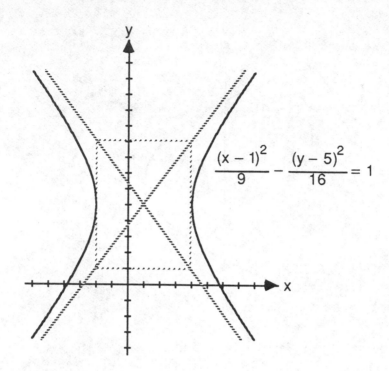

$$\frac{(x-1)^2}{9} - \frac{(y-5)^2}{16} = 1$$

37. $5x^2 + 3y^2 - 40x - 36y + 188 = 0$

$5(x^2 - 8x) + 3(y^2 - 12y) = -188$

$5(x - 4)^2 + 3(y - 6)^2 = -188 + 80 + 108$

$5(x - 4)^2 + 3(y - 6)^2 = 0$

<u>one point</u>: (4,6)

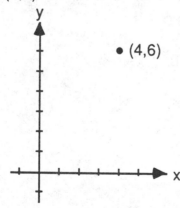

39. $9x^2 - 90x - 16y^2 + 32y = -209$

$9(x^2 - 10x) - 16(y^2 - 2y) = -209$

$9(x - 5)^2 - 16(y - 1)^2 = -209 + 225 - 16$

$9(x - 5)^2 - 16(y - 1)^2 = 0$

$9(x - 5)^2 = 16(y - 1)^2$

$\pm 3(x - 5) = 4(y - 1)$

Two lines:

$3x - 15 = 4y - 4$ or $-3x + 15 = 4y - 4$

$3x - 4y = 11$ $3x + 4y = 19$

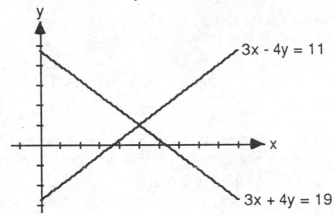

41. $y^2 + 8y - 25x^2 = 9$

$(y + 4)^2 - 25x^2 = 25$

$$\frac{(y + 4)^2}{25} - \frac{x^2}{1} = 1$$

Hyperbola:

center: $(0,-4)$; vertices: $(0,1)$ and $(0,-9)$; foci: $(0,-4 \pm \sqrt{26})$

asymptotes: $y = 5x - 4$; $y = -5x - 4$

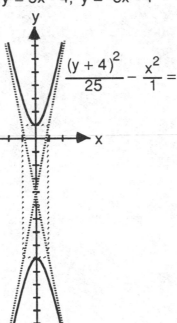

43. $16x^2 - 64x + 25y^2 - 100y\ = -564$

$16(x^2 - 4x) + 25(y^2 - 4y)\ = -564$

$16(x - 2)^2 + 25(y - 2)^2\ = -564 + 64 + 100$

$16(x - 2)^2 + 25(y - 2)^2\ = -400$

No graph (right side is negative).

45. (a)   Using the point (6,5):

$5(36) - 4(25)\ = 80$

$180 - 100\ = 80\ \sqrt{}$

(b)   Since P lies on the hyperbola with foci F_1, F_2, then the quantity $F_1P - F_2P = \pm 2a$ (by the definition of the hyperbola). Thus $(F_1P - F_2P)^2 = 4a^2$. It remains to find a:

$5x^2 - 4y^2\ = 80$

$\dfrac{x^2}{16} - \dfrac{y^2}{20}\ = 1$

So $a^2 = 16$, thus the quantity is $4(16) = 64$.

47. Completing the square, we obtain:

$$A\left(x^2 + \frac{D}{A}x + \frac{D^2}{4A^2}\right) + C\left(y^2 + \frac{E}{C}y + \frac{E^2}{4C^2}\right) = \frac{D^2}{4A} + \frac{E^2}{4C} - F$$

$$A\left(x + \frac{D}{2A}\right)^2 + C\left(y + \frac{E}{2C}\right)^2 = \frac{CD^2 + AE^2 - 4ACF}{4AC}$$

Now if the curve represents an ellipse or a hyperbola, this last equation shows that the center is $\left(-\dfrac{D}{2A}, -\dfrac{E}{2C}\right)$, as required.

CHAPTER 13
ADDITIONAL TOPICS IN ALGEBRA

13.1   Mathematical Induction

1.   Here P_n denotes the statement:
$$1 + 2 + 3 + \ldots + n = \frac{n(n+1)}{2}$$

Since $1 = \frac{1(1+1)}{2} = 1$, then P_1 is true. It remains to show that P_k implies P_{k+1}. Form P_k:
$$1 + 2 + \ldots + k = \frac{k(k+1)}{2}$$

Hence:
$$1 + 2 + \ldots + k + k + 1 = \frac{k(k+1)}{2} + k + 1$$
$$= (k+1)\left(\frac{k}{2} + 1\right)$$
$$= \frac{(k+1)(k+2)}{2}$$
$$= \frac{(k+1)\big((k+1)+1\big)}{2}$$

which is P_{k+1} and the induction is complete.

3.   Here P_n denotes the statement:

$$1 + 4 + 7 + \ldots + (3n - 2) = \frac{n(3n - 1)}{2}$$

Since $1 = \dfrac{1\left(3(1) - 1\right)}{2} = 1$, then P_1 is true.

Form P_k:

$$1 + 4 + \ldots + (3k - 2) = \frac{k(3k - 1)}{2}$$

Therefore:

$$1 + 4 + \ldots + (3k - 2) + \left(3(k + 1) - 2\right)$$

$$= \frac{k(3k - 1)}{2} + 3(k + 1) - 2$$

$$= \frac{1}{2}\left(k(3k - 1) + 6(k + 1) - 4\right)$$

$$= \frac{1}{2}(3k^2 - k + 6k + 2)$$

$$= \frac{1}{2}(3k^2 + 5k + 2)$$

$$= \frac{(k + 1)(3k + 2)}{2}$$

$$= \frac{(k + 1)\left(3(k + 1) - 1\right)}{2}$$

which is P_{k+1} and the induction is complete.

5.   Here P_n denotes:

$$1^2 + 2^2 + 3^2 + \ldots + n^2 = \frac{n(n + 1)(2n + 1)}{6}$$

Since $1^2 = 1 = \dfrac{1(1 + 1)\left(2(1) + 1\right)}{6} = \dfrac{1(2)(3)}{6} = 1$ then P_1 is true.

Form P_k:

$$1^2 + 2^2 + \ldots + k^2 = \frac{k(k + 1)(2k + 1)}{6}$$

Thus:

$$1^2 + 2^2 + \ldots + k^2 + (k + 1)^2$$

$$= \frac{k(k + 1)(2k + 1)}{6} + (k + 1)^2$$

$$= \frac{(k + 1)\left(k(2k + 1)\right) + 6(k + 1)^2}{6}$$

$$= \frac{(k + 1)(2k^2 + k + 6k + 6)}{6}$$

$$= \frac{(k + 1)(2k^2 + 7k + 6)}{6}$$

$$= \frac{(k+1)(k+2)(2k+3)}{6}$$

$$= \frac{(k+1)\big((k+1)+1\big)\big(2(k+1)+1\big)}{6}$$

which is P_{k+1} and the induction is complete.

7. Now we have P_n denoting:

$$1^2 + 3^2 + 5^2 + \ldots + (2n-1)^2 = \frac{n(2n-1)(2n+1)}{3}$$

As $1^2 = 1 = \dfrac{1\big(2(1)-1\big)\big(2(1)+1\big)}{3} = 1$, then P_1 is true.

Form P_k:

$$1^2 + 3^2 + \ldots + (2k-1)^2 = \frac{k(2k-1)(2k+1)}{3}$$

Thus:

$$1^2 + 3^2 + \ldots + (2k-1)^2 + \big(2(k+1)-1\big)^2$$

$$= \frac{k(2k-1)(2k+1)}{3} + \big(2(k+1)-1\big)^2$$

$$= \frac{k(2k-1)(2k+1)}{3} + \frac{3(2k+1)^2}{3}$$

$$= \frac{2k+1}{3}\big(k(2k-1)+3(2k+1)\big)$$

$$= \frac{\big(2(k+1)-1\big)}{3}(2k^2+5k+3)$$

$$= \frac{(k+1)\big(2(k+1)-1\big)(2k+3)}{3}$$

$$= \frac{(k+1)\big(2(k+1)-1\big)\big(2(k+1)+1\big)}{3}$$

which is P_{k+1} and the induction is complete.

9. Here P_n denotes:

$$3 + 3^2 + 3^3 + \ldots + 3^n = \frac{1}{2}(3^{n+1} - 3)$$

Since $3 = \dfrac{1}{2}(3^2 - 3) = \dfrac{1}{2}(6) = 3$ then P_1 is true.

Form P_k:

$$3 + 3^2 + \ldots + 3^k = \frac{1}{2}(3^{k+1} - 3)$$

Hence:

$$3 + 3^2 + \ldots + 3^k + 3^{k+1} = \frac{1}{2}(3^{k+1} - 3) + 3^{k+1}$$

$$= \frac{3}{2}(3^{k+1}) - \frac{3}{2}$$

$$= \frac{1}{2}\left(3(3^{k+1}) - 3\right)$$

$$= \frac{1}{2}(3^{k+2} - 3)$$

$$= \frac{1}{2}\left(3^{(k+1)+1} - 3\right)$$

which is P_{k+1} and the induction is complete.

11. Here P_n denotes:

$$1^3 + 2^3 + 3^3 + \ldots + n^3 = \left(\frac{n(n+1)}{2}\right)^2$$

Since $1^3 = 1 = \left(\frac{1(2)}{2}\right)^2 = 1$, then P_1 is true.

Form P_k:

$$1^3 + 2^3 + \ldots + k^3 = \left(\frac{k(k+1)}{2}\right)^2$$

Therefore:

$$1^3 + 2^3 + \ldots + k^3 + (k+1)^3 = \left(\frac{k(k+1)}{2}\right)^2 + (k+1)^3$$

$$= (k+1)^2\left[\frac{k^2}{4} + (k+1)\right]$$

$$= \frac{(k+1)^2}{4}\left[k^2 + 4k + 4\right]$$

$$= \frac{(k+1)^2(k+2)^2}{4}$$

$$= \frac{(k+1)^2\left((k+1)+1\right)^2}{2^2}$$

$$= \left(\frac{(k+1)\left((k+1)+1\right)}{2}\right)^2$$

which is P_{k+1} and the induction is complete.

13. Here P_n denotes:

$$1^3 + 3^3 + 5^3 + \ldots + (2n-1)^3 = n^2(2n^2 - 1)$$

Since $1^3 = 1(1)^2\left(2(1)^2 - 1\right) = (1)(1) = 1$, then P_1 is true.

Form P_K:

$$1^3 + 3^3 + \ldots + (2k-1)^3 = k^2(2k^2 - 1)$$

Then:

$$1^3 + 3^3 + \ldots + (2k - 1)^3 + \left(2(k + 1) - 1\right)^3$$
$$= k^2(2k^2 - 1) + (2k + 1)^3$$
$$= 2k^4 - k^2 + 8k^3 + 12k^2 + 6k + 1$$
$$= 2k^4 + 8k^3 + 11k^2 + 6k + 1$$
$$= (k + 1)^2(2k^2 + 4k + 1)$$
$$= (k + 1)^2\left(2(k^2 + 2k + 1) - 1\right)$$
$$= (k + 1)^2 \left(2(k + 1)^2 - 1\right)$$

which is P_{k+1} and the induction is complete.

15. Here P_n denotes:

$$1 \times 3 + 3 \times 5 + 5 \times 7 + \ldots + (2n - 1)(2n + 1) = \frac{n(4n^2 + 6n - 1)}{3}$$

Since $1 \times 3 = 3 = \dfrac{(1)\left(4(1)^2 + 6(1) - 1\right)}{3} = \dfrac{9}{3} = 3 = 1 \times 3$, then P_1 is true.

Form P_k:

$$1 \times 3 + 3 \times 5 + \ldots + (2k - 1)(2k + 1) = \frac{k(4k^2 + 6k - 1)}{3}$$

Hence:

$$1 \times 3 + 3 \times 5 + \ldots + (2k - 1)(2k + 1) + \left(2(k + 1) - 1\right)\left(2(k + 1) + 1\right)$$
$$= \frac{k(4k^2 + 6k - 1)}{3} + (2k + 1)(2k + 3)$$
$$= \frac{4k^3 + 6k^2 - k + 12k^2 + 24k + 9}{3}$$
$$= \frac{4k^3 + 18k^2 + 23k + 9}{3}$$

Noting that -1 is a root:

$$= \frac{(k + 1)(4k^2 + 14k + 9)}{3}$$
$$= \frac{(k + 1)\left(4(k + 1)^2 + 6(k + 1) - 1\right)}{3}$$

which is P_{k+1} and the induction is complete.

17. Here P_n denotes:

$$1 + \frac{3}{2} + \frac{5}{2^2} + \ldots + \frac{2n - 1}{2^{n-1}} = 6 - \frac{2n + 3}{2^{n-1}}$$

Since $1 = 6 - \dfrac{\left(2(1) + 3\right)}{2^0} = 6 - 5 = 1$, then P_1 is true.

Form P_k:
$$1 + \frac{3}{2} + \ldots + \frac{2k-1}{2^{k-1}} = 6 - \frac{2k+3}{2^{k-1}}$$

Hence:
$$1 + \frac{3}{2} + \ldots + \frac{2k-1}{2^{k-1}} + \frac{2(k+1)-1}{2^k}$$
$$= 6 - \frac{2k+3}{2^{k-1}} + \frac{2k+1}{2^k}$$
$$= 6 - \frac{4k+6-2k-1}{2^k}$$
$$= 6 - \frac{2k+5}{2^k}$$
$$= 6 - \frac{2(k+1)+3}{2^{(k+1)-1}}$$

which is P_{k+1} and the induction is complete.

19. Let P_n denote the statement:
$$n \le 2^{n-1}$$
Since $2^{1-1} = 2^0 = 1 \ge 1$, then P_1 is true.
Form P_k:
$$k \le 2^{k-1}$$
Hence:
$$k + 1 \le 2^{k-1} + 1$$
Since $1 \le 2^{k-1}$ (use induction to prove this), then:
$$k + 1 \le 2^{k-1} + 1$$
$$\le 2^{k-1} + 2^{k-1}$$
$$= 2(2^{k-1})$$
$$= 2^k$$
$$= 2^{(k+1)-1}$$

which is P_{k+1} and the induction is complete.

21. For $n = 2$:
$$2^2 + 4 = 8 < (2+1)^2$$
Assuming:
$$k^2 + 4 < (k+1)^2$$
Then:
$$k^2 + 2k + 4 < (k+1)^2 + 2k$$
$$(k+1)^2 + 3 < k^2 + 4k + 1$$
$$(k+1)^2 + 4 < k^2 + 4k + 2$$
$$(k+1)^2 + 4 < k^2 + 4k + 4$$
$$(k+1)^2 + 4 < (k+2)^2$$

completing the induction for $n \geq 2$.

23. (a) We fill in the table:

n	1	2	3	4	5
f(n)	1/2	2/3	3/4	4/5	5/6

(b) $\frac{6}{7}$, $f(6) = f(5) + \frac{1}{42} = \frac{5}{6} + \frac{1}{42} = \frac{36}{42} = \frac{6}{7}$

(c) $f(n) = \frac{1}{1 \times 2} + \frac{1}{2 \times 3} + \cdots + \frac{1}{n(n+1)} = \frac{n}{n+1}$

$f(1) = \frac{1}{2} = \frac{1}{1+1} = \frac{1}{2}$

Assuming $f(k) = \frac{k}{k+1}$ then:

$f(k+1) = f(k) + \frac{1}{(k+1)(k+2)}$

$= \frac{k}{k+1} + \frac{1}{(k+1)(k+2)}$

$= \frac{k(k+2) + 1}{(k+1)(k+2)}$

$= \frac{k^2 + 2k + 1}{(k+1)(k+2)}$

$= \frac{(k+1)^2}{(k+1)(k+2)}$

$= \frac{k+1}{k+2}$

completing the induction.

25. (a) We complete the table:

n	1	2	3	4	5
f(n)	1	4	9	16	25

(b) 36, $f(6) = f(5) + 2\sqrt{f(5)} + 1 = 25 + 2\sqrt{25} + 1 = 36$

(c) $f(n) = n^2$
$f(1) = 1 = 1^2$

Assume that for some $k \geq 1$ that $f(k) = k^2$. Then since $k + 1 \geq 2$, we have:

$$
\begin{aligned}
f(k + 1) &= f(k) + 2\sqrt{f(k)} + 1 \\
&= k^2 + 2\sqrt{k^2} + 1 \\
&= k^2 + 2k + 1 \\
&= (k + 1)^2
\end{aligned}
$$

and the induction is complete.

27. For $n = 1$: 13 is prime and P_1 is true.
     For $n = 2$: 17 is prime and P_2 is true.
     For $n = 3$: 23 is prime and P_3 is true.
     For $n = 4$: 31 is prime and P_4 is true.
     For $n = 5$: 41 is prime and P_5 is true.
     For $n = 6$: 53 is prime and P_6 is true.
     For $n = 7$: 67 is prime and P_7 is true.
     For $n = 8$: 83 is prime and P_8 is true.
     For $n = 9$: 101 is prime and P_9 is true.
     However, for $n = 10$, $(10)^2 + 10 + 11 = 121 = (11)(11)$, and so P_{10} is false.

29. Let P_n denote:

$$1 + r + r^2 + \ldots + r^{n-1} = \frac{r^n - 1}{r - 1} \quad \text{when } r \neq 1$$

Then since $1 = \frac{r - 1}{r - 1} = 1$, then P_1 is true.

Assuming P_k is true, then:

$$1 + r + \ldots + r^{k-1} = \frac{r^k - 1}{r - 1}$$

Hence:

$$
\begin{aligned}
1 + r + \ldots + r^{k-1} + r^k &= \frac{r^k - 1}{r - 1} + r^k \\
&= \frac{r^k - 1 + r^k(r - 1)}{r - 1} \\
&= \frac{r^{k+1} - 1}{r - 1}
\end{aligned}
$$

which is P_{k+1} and the induction is complete.

31. Let P_n denote:

$$n^5 - n = 5R \text{ for some natural number R.}$$

Since $2^5 - 2 = 32 - 2 = 30 = 5(6)$, then P_2 is true.

Since:
$$(k + 1)^5 - (k + 1) = k^5 + 5k^4 + 10k^3 + 10k^2 + 4k$$
$$= k^5 - k + 5(k^4 + 2k^3 + 2k^2 + k)$$
then assuming P_k is true results in:
$$(k + 1)^5 - (k + 1) = 5(R + k^4 + 2k^3 + 2k^2 + k)$$
which is P_{k+1} and the induction is complete.

33. Let P_n denote:
$$x^n - y^n = (x - y)\big(Q(x,y)\big) \text{ where } Q(x,y) \text{ is a polynomial in x and y.}$$
Then:
$$x - y = (x - y)(1) \text{ and } P_1 \text{ is true.}$$
While using the suggested identity:
$$x^{k+1} - y^{k+1} = x^k(x - y) + (x^k - y^k)y$$
So assuming P_k:
$$x^{k+1} - y^{k+1} = \big(x^k + yQ(x,y)\big)(x - y)$$
which is P_{k+1} and the induction is complete.

35. For n = 1:
$$(1 + p) \geq (1 + p)$$
When $p > -1$ then $p + 1 > 0$
Assuming $(1 + p)^k \geq 1 + kp$ then:
$$(1 + p)^{k+1} \geq (1 + kp)(1 + p)$$
$$\geq 1 + p + kp + kp^2$$
$$\geq 1 + (k + 1)p$$
and the induction is complete.

13.2 The Binomial Theorem

1. (a) $(a + b)^2 = (a + b)(a + b)$
$$= a^2 + ab + ba + b^2$$
$$= a^2 + 2ab + b^2$$

(b) $(a + b)^3 = (a + b)(a + b)^2$
$$= (a + b)(a^2 + 2ab + b^2)$$
$$= a^3 + 2a^2b + ab^2 + ba^2 + 2ab^2 + b^3$$
$$= a^3 + 3a^2b + 3ab^2 + b^3$$

3. $(a + b)^9$

$$= \binom{9}{0}a^9 + \binom{9}{1}a^8b + \binom{9}{2}a^7b^2 + \binom{9}{3}a^6b^3 + \binom{9}{4}a^5b^4$$

$$+ \binom{9}{5}a^4b^5 + \binom{9}{6}a^3b^6 + \binom{9}{7}a^2b^7 + \binom{9}{8}ab^8 + \binom{9}{9}b^9$$

$$= a^9 + 9a^8b + 36a^7b^2 + 84a^6b^3 + 126a^5b^4 + 126a^4b^5 + 84a^3b^6$$

$$+ 36a^2b^7 + 9ab^8 + b^9$$

5. $(2A + B)^3 = \binom{3}{0}(2A)^3 + \binom{3}{1}(2A)^2B + \binom{3}{2}(2A)B^2 + \binom{3}{3}B^3$

$$= 8A^3 + 12A^2B + 6AB^2 + B^3$$

7. $(1 - 2x)^6 = \binom{6}{0}1^6 - \binom{6}{1}1^5(2x) + \binom{6}{2}1^4(2x)^2 - \binom{6}{3}1^3(2x)^3 + \binom{6}{4}1^2(2x)^4$

$$- \binom{6}{5}1(2x)^5 + \binom{6}{6}(2x)^6$$

$$= 1 - 12x + 60x^2 - 160x^3 + 240x^4 - 192x^5 + 64x^6$$

9. $(\sqrt{x} + \sqrt{y})^4$

$$= \binom{4}{0}(\sqrt{x})^4 + \binom{4}{1}(\sqrt{x})^3(\sqrt{y}) + \binom{4}{2}(\sqrt{x})^2(\sqrt{y})^2 + \binom{4}{3}(\sqrt{x})(\sqrt{y})^3 + \binom{4}{4}(\sqrt{y})^4$$

$$= x^2 + 4x\sqrt{xy} + 6xy + 4y\sqrt{xy} + y^2$$

11. $(x^2 + y^2)^5 = \binom{5}{0}(x^2)^5 + \binom{5}{1}(x^2)^4y^2 + \binom{5}{2}(x^2)^3(y^2)^2 + \binom{5}{3}(x^2)^2(y^2)^3$

$$+ \binom{5}{4}(x^2)(y^2)^4 + \binom{5}{5}(y^2)^5$$

$$= x^{10} + 5x^8y^2 + 10x^6y^4 + 10x^4y^6 + 5x^2y^8 + y^{10}$$

13. $\left(1 - \dfrac{1}{x}\right)^6$

$$= \binom{6}{0} - \binom{6}{1}\dfrac{1}{x} + \binom{6}{2}\left(\dfrac{1}{x}\right)^2 - \binom{6}{3}\left(\dfrac{1}{x}\right)^3 + \binom{6}{4}\left(\dfrac{1}{x}\right)^4 - \binom{6}{5}\left(\dfrac{1}{x}\right)^5 + \binom{6}{6}\left(\dfrac{1}{x}\right)^6$$

$$= 1 - \dfrac{6}{x} + \dfrac{15}{x^2} - \dfrac{20}{x^3} + \dfrac{15}{x^4} - \dfrac{6}{x^5} + \dfrac{1}{x^6}$$

15. $\left(\dfrac{x}{2} - \dfrac{y}{3}\right)^3 = \binom{3}{0}\left(\dfrac{x}{2}\right)^3 - \binom{3}{1}\left(\dfrac{x}{2}\right)^2\left(\dfrac{y}{3}\right) + \binom{3}{2}\left(\dfrac{x}{2}\right)\left(\dfrac{y}{3}\right)^2 - \binom{3}{3}\left(\dfrac{y}{3}\right)^3$

$$= \dfrac{x^3}{8} - \dfrac{x^2y}{4} + \dfrac{xy^2}{6} - \dfrac{y^3}{27}$$

17. $(ab^2 + c)^7$

$$= \binom{7}{0}(ab^2)^7 + \binom{7}{1}(ab^2)^6c + \binom{7}{2}(ab^2)^5c^2 + \binom{7}{3}(ab^2)^4c^3$$

$$+ \binom{7}{4}(ab^2)^3c^4 + \binom{7}{5}(ab^2)^2c^5 + \binom{7}{6}(ab^2)c^6 + \binom{7}{7}c^7$$

$$= a^7b^{14} + 7a^6b^{12}c + 21a^5b^{10}c^2 + 35a^4b^8c^3 + 35a^3b^6c^4 + 21a^2b^4c^5$$
$$+ 7ab^2c^6 + c^7$$

19. $(x + \sqrt{2})^8$

$$= \binom{8}{0}x^8 + \binom{8}{1}x^7\sqrt{2} + \binom{8}{2}x^6(\sqrt{2})^2 + \binom{8}{3}x^5(\sqrt{2})^3 + \binom{8}{4}x^4(\sqrt{2})^4$$

$$+ \binom{8}{5}x^3(\sqrt{2})^5 + \binom{8}{6}x^2(\sqrt{2})^6 + \binom{8}{7}x(\sqrt{2})^7 + \binom{8}{8}(\sqrt{2})^8$$

$$= x^8 + 8\sqrt{2}\,x^7 + 56x^6 + 112\sqrt{2}\,x^5 + 280x^4 + 224\sqrt{2}\,x^3 + 224x^2 + 64\sqrt{2}\,x + 16$$

21. $(\sqrt{2} - 1)^3 = \binom{3}{0}(\sqrt{2})^3 - \binom{3}{1}(\sqrt{2})^2 + \binom{3}{2}(\sqrt{2}) - \binom{3}{3}$

$$= 2\sqrt{2} - 6 + 3\sqrt{2} - 1$$

$$= 5\sqrt{2} - 7$$

23. $(\sqrt{2} + \sqrt{3})^5$

$$= \binom{5}{0}(\sqrt{2})^5 + \binom{5}{1}(\sqrt{2})^4\sqrt{3} + \binom{5}{2}(\sqrt{2})^3(\sqrt{3})^2 + \binom{5}{3}(\sqrt{2})^2(\sqrt{3})^3$$

$$+ \binom{5}{4}(\sqrt{2})(\sqrt{3})^4 + \binom{5}{5}(\sqrt{3})^5$$

$$= 4\sqrt{2} + 20\sqrt{3} + 60\sqrt{2} + 60\sqrt{3} + 45\sqrt{2} + 9\sqrt{3}$$

$$= 89\sqrt{3} + 109\sqrt{2}$$

25. $\left(2\sqrt[3]{2} - \sqrt[3]{4}\right)^3$

$$= \binom{3}{0}(2\sqrt[3]{2})^3 - \binom{3}{1}(2\sqrt[3]{2})^2(\sqrt[3]{4}) + \binom{3}{2}(2\sqrt[3]{2})(\sqrt[3]{4})^2 - \binom{3}{3}(\sqrt[3]{4})^3$$

$$= 16 - 12\sqrt[3]{16} + 6\sqrt[3]{32} - 4$$

$$= 12 - 24\sqrt[3]{2} + 12\sqrt[3]{4}$$

27. $\left(x^2 - (2x + 1)\right)^5$

$= \begin{pmatrix} 5 \\ 0 \end{pmatrix}(x^2)^5 - \begin{pmatrix} 5 \\ 1 \end{pmatrix}(x^2)^4(2x + 1) + \begin{pmatrix} 5 \\ 2 \end{pmatrix}(x^2)^3(2x + 1)^2 - \begin{pmatrix} 5 \\ 3 \end{pmatrix}(x^2)^2(2x + 1)^3$

$\quad + \begin{pmatrix} 5 \\ 4 \end{pmatrix}(x^2)(2x + 1)^4 - \begin{pmatrix} 5 \\ 5 \end{pmatrix}(2x + 1)^5$

$= x^{10} - \left(5x^8(2x + 1)\right) + \left(10x^6(4x^2 + 4x + 1)\right)$

$\quad - \left(10x^4(8x^3 + 12x^2 + 6x + 1)\right)$

$\quad + \left(5x^2(16x^4 + 32x^3 + 24x^2 + 8x + 1)\right)$

$\quad - \left(32x^5 + 80x^4 + 80x^3 + 40x^2 + 10x + 1\right)$

$= x^{10} - (10x^9 + 5x^8) + (40x^8 + 40x^7 + 10x^6) - (80x^7 + 120x^6 + 60x^5 + 10x^4)$

$\quad + (80x^6 + 160x^5 + 120x^4 + 40x^3 + 5x^2)$

$\quad - (32x^5 + 80x^4 + 80x^3 + 40x^2 + 10x + 1)$

$= x^{10} - 10x^9 + 35x^8 - 40x^7 - 30x^6 + 68x^5 + 30x^4 - 40x^3 - 35x^2 - 10x - 1$

29. $5! = (5)(4)(3)(2)(1) = 120$

31. $\begin{pmatrix} 7 \\ 3 \end{pmatrix}\begin{pmatrix} 3 \\ 2 \end{pmatrix} = \dfrac{7!}{3!(4!)} \bullet \dfrac{3!}{2!(1!)} = \dfrac{7 \bullet 6 \bullet 5}{3 \bullet 2} \bullet 3 = 105$

33. (a) $\begin{pmatrix} 5 \\ 3 \end{pmatrix} = \dfrac{5!}{3!(5 - 3)!} = \dfrac{5(4)}{2} = 10$

(b) $\begin{pmatrix} 5 \\ 4 \end{pmatrix} = \dfrac{5!}{4!(5 - 4)!} = 5$

35. $\dfrac{(n + 2)!}{n!} = \dfrac{(n + 2)(n + 1)n!}{n!} = n^2 + 3n + 2$

37. $\begin{pmatrix} 6 \\ 4 \end{pmatrix} + \begin{pmatrix} 6 \\ 3 \end{pmatrix} - \begin{pmatrix} 7 \\ 4 \end{pmatrix} = \dfrac{6!}{4!2!} + \dfrac{6!}{3!3!} - \dfrac{7!}{4!3!}$

$\qquad = \dfrac{6(5)}{2} + \dfrac{6(5)(4)}{6} - \dfrac{7(6)(5)}{6}$

$\qquad = 15 + 20 - 35$

$\qquad = 0$

39. $\begin{pmatrix} 16 \\ 14 \end{pmatrix}a^2b^{14} = 120a^2b^{14}$

41. $\begin{pmatrix} 100 \\ 99 \end{pmatrix}x^{99} = 100x^{99}$

43. Here $n - r + 1 = 8$, so $10 - r + 1 = 8$, so $r = 3$. Hence, the coefficient is:

$$\binom{10}{2} = 45$$

45. Here $r - 1 = 8$, thus $r = 9$. Hence, the coefficient is:

$$\frac{1}{2}(-4)^8 \binom{9}{8} = 9 \cdot \frac{1}{2}(65536) = 294{,}912$$

47. Here $r - 1 = 6$. Hence, $r = 7$, and the coefficient is:

$$\binom{8}{6} = \frac{8(7)}{2} = 28$$

49. Here $(12 - r + 1)(-1) + 2(r - 1) = 0$, so $-12 + r - 1 + 2r - 2 = 0$, then $3r = 15$, so $r = 5$ and the coefficient is:

$$(3)^4 \binom{12}{4} = \frac{(12)(11)(10)(9)}{(4)(3)(2)}(3)^4 = 495(81) = 40095$$

51. Here $r - 1 = n$; so $r = n + 1$, so the coefficient is:

$$\binom{2n}{n} = \frac{(2n)!}{n!n!} = \frac{(2n)!}{(n!)^2}$$

53. (a)   We fill in the table:

k	0	1	2	3	4	5	6	7	8
$\binom{8}{k}$	1	8	28	56	70	56	28	8	1

(b) $1 + 8 + 28 + 56 + 70 + 56 + 28 + 8 + 1 = 256$
While $2^8 = 256$

(c)   Since a^L and b^L equal 1 for any L since $a = b = 1$, then from the binomial theorem:

$$2^n = (1 + 1)^n = \binom{n}{0} + \binom{n}{1} + \ldots + \binom{n}{n}$$

55. (a) $(1 + x)^n \left(1 + \frac{1}{x}\right)^n = (1 + x)^n \left(\frac{x + 1}{x}\right)^n$

$$= (1 + x)^n \cdot \frac{(1 + x)^n}{x^n}$$

$$= \frac{(1 + x)^{2n}}{x^n}$$

(b)   The nth term of expansion on the right is $\dfrac{\dbinom{2n}{n}(1)^n(x)^n}{x^n} = \dbinom{2n}{n}$,

which verifies the result.

(c) $(1 + x)^n = \dbinom{n}{0} + \dbinom{n}{1}x + \dbinom{n}{2}x^2 + \dbinom{n}{3}x^3 + \ldots + \dbinom{n}{n}x^n$, and

$\left(1 + \dfrac{1}{x}\right)^n = \dbinom{n}{0} + \dbinom{n}{1}x^{-1} + \dbinom{n}{2}x^{-2} + \dbinom{n}{3}x^{-3} + \ldots + \dbinom{n}{n}x^{-n}$.

When multiplied, the terms do not contain x come from terms with corresponding positive and negative exponents:

$$\dbinom{n}{1}x \cdot \dbinom{n}{1}x^{-1} + \dbinom{n}{2}x^2 \cdot \dbinom{n}{2}x^{-2} + \ldots + \dbinom{n}{n}x^n \cdot \dbinom{n}{n}x^{-n}$$

$$= \dbinom{n}{1}^2 + \dbinom{n}{2}^2 + \ldots + \dbinom{n}{n}^2$$

This verifies the identity.

13.3   Introduction to Sequences and Series

1.   Since $a_n = \dfrac{n}{n + 1}$, we can write out the first five terms by setting n equal to the natural numbers 1 through 5:

$$a_1 = \frac{1}{1 + 1} = \frac{1}{2}$$

$$a_2 = \frac{2}{2 + 1} = \frac{2}{3}$$

$$a_3 = \frac{3}{3 + 1} = \frac{3}{4}$$

$$a_4 = \frac{4}{4 + 1} = \frac{4}{5}$$

$$a_5 = \frac{5}{5 + 1} = \frac{5}{6}$$

So the first five terms are $\dfrac{1}{2}, \dfrac{2}{3}, \dfrac{3}{4}, \dfrac{4}{5}, \dfrac{5}{6}$

3.   Again, letting n be successively 1 through 5, we get:

$$a_1 = (1 - 1)^2$$

$$a_2 = (2 - 1)^2$$

$$a_3 = (3 - 1)^2$$
$$a_4 = (4 - 1)^2$$
$$a_5 = (5 - 1)^2$$

So the first five terms are 0, 1, 4, 9, 16

5. $b_n = \left(1 + \dfrac{1}{n}\right)^n$

So, $b_1 = 2, b_2 = \dfrac{9}{4}, b_3 = \dfrac{64}{27}, b_4 = \dfrac{625}{256}, b_5 = \dfrac{7776}{3125}$

7. $u_n = (-1)^n$

So, $u_1 = -1, u_2 = 1, u_3 = -1, u_4 = 1, u_5 = -1$

9. $a_n = \dfrac{(-1)^{n+1}}{n!}$

So, $a_1 = 1, a_2 = -\dfrac{1}{2}, a_3 = \dfrac{1}{6}, a_4 = -\dfrac{1}{24}, a_5 = \dfrac{1}{120}$

11. $a_n = 3n$

So, $a_1 = 3, a_2 = 6, a_3 = 9, a_4 = 12, a_5 = 15$

13. $a_1 = 1$

$a_n = (1 + a_{n-1})^2 \quad n \geq 2$

So:

$$a_1 = 1$$
$$a_2 = (1 + a_1)^2 = 2^2 = 4$$
$$a_3 = (1 + a_2)^2 = 5^2 = 25$$
$$a_4 = (1 + a_3)^2 = 26^2 = 676$$
$$a_5 = (1 + a_4)^2 = 677^2 = 458,329$$

and the first five terms are 1, 4, 25, 676, 458329.

15. $a_1 = 2$

$a_2 = 2$

$a_n = a_{n-1}a_{n-2},$ for $n \geq 3$

So, $a_1 = 2, a_2 = 2, a_3 = 4, a_4 = 8, a_5 = 32.$

17. $a_1 = 1$

$a_{n+1} = na_n, n \geq 1$

So, $a_1 = 1, a_2 = 1, a_3 = 2, a_4 = 6, a_5 = 24$

19. $a_1 = 0$

   $a_n = 2^{a_{n-1}}, \quad n \geq 2$

   So, $a_1 = 0, a_2 = 1, a_3 = 2, a_4 = 4, a_5 = 16$

21. First, we compute the required values of a_n as shown in the table:

n	1	2	3	4
a_n	−1	1	−1	1

   Now graph these values:

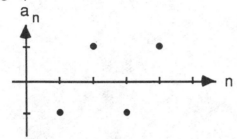

23. First, we compute the required values of a_n as shown in the table:

n	1	2	3	4
a_n	1	$\frac{1}{2}$	$\frac{1}{3}$	$\frac{1}{4}$

   Now graph these values:

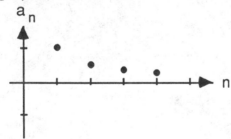

25. First, we compute the required values of a_n as shown in the table:

n	1	2	3
a_n	0	$\frac{1}{3}$	$\frac{1}{2}$

Now graph these values:

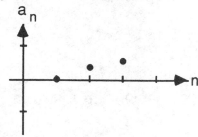

27. $a_n = 2^n$
So the sum is $2 + 4 + 8 + 16 + 32 = 62$

29. $a_n = n^2 - n$
So the sum is $0 + 2 + 6 + 12 + 20 = 40$

31. $a_n = \dfrac{(-1)^n}{n!}$
So the sum is $-1 + \dfrac{1}{2} - \dfrac{1}{6} + \dfrac{1}{24} - \dfrac{1}{120} = -\dfrac{19}{30}$

33. $a_1 = 1$
$a_2 = 2$
$a_n = a^2_{n-1} + a^2_{n-2} \quad n \geq 3$
So the sum is $1 + 2 + 5 + 29 + 866 = 903$

35. $a_1 = 2$
$a_n = (a_{n-1})^2 \quad n \geq 2$
So the sum is $2 + 4 + 16 + 256 = 278$

37. $\displaystyle\sum_{k=1}^{3} (k - 1) = 0 + 1 + 2 = 3$

39. $\displaystyle\sum_{k=4}^{5} k^2 = 16 + 25 = 41$

41. $\displaystyle\sum_{n=1}^{3} x^n = x + x^2 + x^3$

43. $\displaystyle\sum_{n=1}^{4} \frac{1}{n} = 1 + \frac{1}{2} + \frac{1}{3} + \frac{1}{4} = \frac{25}{12}$

45. $\displaystyle\sum_{j=1}^{9} \log_{10} \frac{j}{j+1} = \log_{10} \frac{1}{2} + \log_{10} \frac{2}{3} + \log_{10} \frac{3}{4} + \log_{10} \frac{4}{5} + \log_{10} \frac{5}{6}$

$$+ \log_{10} \frac{6}{7} + \log_{10} \frac{7}{8}, \ \log_{10} \frac{8}{9} + \log_{10} \frac{9}{10}$$

$$= \log_{10} \left(\frac{1}{2} \cdot \frac{2}{3} \cdot \frac{3}{4} \cdot \frac{4}{5} \cdot \frac{5}{6} \cdot \frac{6}{7} \cdot \frac{7}{8} \cdot \frac{8}{9} \cdot \frac{9}{10} \right)$$

$$= \log_{10} \frac{1}{10}$$

$$= -1$$

47. $\displaystyle\sum_{j=1}^{6} \left(\frac{1}{j} - \frac{1}{j+1} \right)$

$$= \left(1 - \frac{1}{2} \right) + \left(\frac{1}{2} - \frac{1}{3} \right) + \left(\frac{1}{3} - \frac{1}{4} \right) + \left(\frac{1}{4} - \frac{1}{5} \right) + \left(\frac{1}{5} - \frac{1}{6} \right) + \left(\frac{1}{6} - \frac{1}{7} \right)$$

$$= 1 - \frac{1}{7}$$

$$= \frac{6}{7}$$

49. $\displaystyle 5 + 5^2 + 5^3 + 5^4 = \sum_{j=1}^{4} 5^j$

51. $\displaystyle x + x^2 + x^3 + x^4 + x^5 + x^6 = \sum_{j=1}^{6} x^j$

53. $\displaystyle 1 + \frac{1}{2} + \frac{1}{3} + \ldots + \frac{1}{12} = \sum_{k=1}^{12} \frac{1}{k}$

55. $\displaystyle 2 - 2^2 + 2^3 - 2^4 + 2^5 = \sum_{j=1}^{5} (-1)^{j+1} 2^j$

57. $1 - 2 + 3 - 4 + 5 = \sum_{j=1}^{5} (-1)^{j+1} j$

59. (a) $F_1 = 1$
$F_2 = 1$
$F_{n+2} = F_n + F_{n+1} \quad n \geq 1$
Evaluating the first 10 terms, we obtain the table:

F_1	F_2	F_3	F_4	F_5	F_6	F_7	F_8	F_9	F_{10}
1	1	2	3	5	8	13	21	34	55

(b) We complete the chart:

n	$F_1 + F_2 + \ldots + F_n$	$F_{n+2} - 1$
1	1	1
2	2	2
3	4	4
4	7	7
5	12	12

(c) The chart completed in (b) shows the hypothesis to be true for $n = 1$.
Assuming:
$$F_1 + F_2 + \ldots + F_k = F_{k+2} - 1$$
Therefore:
$$\begin{aligned} F_1 + F_2 + \ldots + F_k + F_{k+1} &= F_{k+2} - 1 + F_{k+1} \\ &= F_{k+3} - 1 \\ &= F_{(k+1)+2} - 1 \end{aligned}$$
which completes the induction.

(d) From (a), $F_5 = 5 \geq 5$, so the hypothesis is true for $n = 5$. For some
$k \geq 5$, assume:
$$F_k \geq k$$
Then:
$$F_{k+1} = F_k + F_{k-1} \geq F_k + 1 \geq k + 1$$
and the induction is complete.

(e) Since $F_1{}^2 = 1^2 = 1 = F_1F_2 = 1(1) = 1$, then the hypothesis is true for $n = 1$. Assuming:

$$F_1{}^2 + F_2{}^2 + \ldots + F_k{}^2 = F_kF_{k+1}$$

Then:

$$
\begin{aligned}
F_1{}^2 + F_2{}^2 + \ldots + F_k{}^2 + F^2{}_{k+1} &= F_kF_{k+1} + F^2{}_{k+1} \\
&= F_{k+1}(F_k + F_{k+1}) \\
&= F_{k+1}(F_{k+2})
\end{aligned}
$$

and the induction is complete.

(f) Since $F_2{}^2 = 1^2 = 1 = F_1F_3 + (-1)^1 = 2 - 1 = 1$, the hypothesis is true for $n = 1$. Assume:

$$F^2{}_{k+1} = F_kF_{k+2} + (-1)^k$$

Then:

$$
\begin{aligned}
F_{k+1}F_{k+2} + F^2{}_{k+1} &= F_kF_{k+2} + F_{k+1}F_{k+2} + (-1)^k \\
F_{k+1}(F_{k+2} + F_{k+1}) &= F_{k+2}(F_k + F_{k+1}) + (-1)^k \\
F_{k+1}F_{k+3} &= F^2{}_{k+2} + (-1)^k \\
F^2{}_{k+2} &= F_{k+1}F_{k+3} + (-1)^{k+1}
\end{aligned}
$$

and the induction is complete.

(g) Since $\begin{pmatrix} 1 & 1 \\ 1 & 0 \end{pmatrix}^2 = \begin{pmatrix} 2 & 1 \\ 1 & 1 \end{pmatrix} = \begin{pmatrix} F_3 & F_2 \\ F_2 & F_1 \end{pmatrix}$ then the hypothesis is true for $n = 2$. Assuming:

$$\begin{pmatrix} 1 & 1 \\ 1 & 0 \end{pmatrix}^k = \begin{pmatrix} F_{k+1} & F_k \\ F_k & F_{k-1} \end{pmatrix}$$

Then:

$$
\begin{aligned}
\begin{pmatrix} 1 & 1 \\ 1 & 0 \end{pmatrix}^{k+1} &= \begin{pmatrix} 1 & 1 \\ 1 & 0 \end{pmatrix}\begin{pmatrix} F_{k+1} & F_k \\ F_k & F_{k-1} \end{pmatrix} \\
&= \begin{pmatrix} F_k + F_{k+1} & F_k + F_{k-1} \\ F_{k+1} & F_k \end{pmatrix} \\
&= \begin{pmatrix} F_{k+2} & F_{k+1} \\ F_{k+1} & F_k \end{pmatrix}
\end{aligned}
$$

and the induction is complete.

13.4 Arithmetic Sequences and Series

1. (a) To find the common difference, d, we simply subtract any term from the succeeding term.

Here, that can be:

$$3 - 1 = 2$$
$$\text{or} \quad 5 - 3 = 2$$
$$\text{or} \quad 7 - 5 = 2$$

2 is the required common difference.

(b)   Again we subtract terms:

$$6 - 10 = -4$$
$$2 - 6 = -4$$
$$-2 - 2 = -4$$

The common difference is -4. It is not necessary to try all three pairs, but this helps to verify that we have an arithmetic sequence.

(c) $1 - \dfrac{2}{3} = \dfrac{4}{3} - 1 = \dfrac{5}{3} - \dfrac{4}{3} = \dfrac{1}{3}$

So $\dfrac{1}{3}$ is the common difference.

(d) $1 + \sqrt{2} - 1 = \sqrt{2}$ or $(1 + 2\sqrt{2}) - (1 + \sqrt{2}) = \sqrt{2}$

Here, $\sqrt{2}$ is the common difference.

3.   Since $a = 10$ and $d = 11$, then using $a_n = a + (n - 1)d$ we find:

$$a_{12} = 10 + (12 - 1)11 = 131$$

5. $a_{100} = 6 + (100 - 1)(5) = 6 + 495 = 501$

7. $a_{1000} = -1 + (1000 - 1)(1) = 998$

9. $a_4 = -6$, $a_{10} = 5$, thus:

$$-6 = a + 3d$$
$$5 = a + 9d$$

Subtracting the second equation from the first yields:

$$-6d = -11$$
$$d = \dfrac{11}{6}$$

So:

$$a = 5 - 9 \left(\dfrac{11}{6} \right)$$

$$a = 5 - \dfrac{33}{2}$$

$$a = \dfrac{-23}{2}$$

11. $a_{60} = 105, d = 5$, so:
$$105 = a + 59(5)$$
$$105 = a + 295$$
$$a = -190$$

13. Since $a_{15} = a + 14d$ and $a_7 = a + 6d$, then:
$$a_{15} - a_7 = 8d$$
$$-1 = 8d$$
$$d = -\frac{1}{8}$$

15. Since $a = 1$ and $d = 1$, then:
$$S_{1000} = \frac{1000}{2}(2 + 999) = 500,500$$

17. For $\frac{\pi}{3} + \frac{2\pi}{3} + \pi + \frac{4\pi}{3} + \ldots + \frac{13\pi}{3}$, $a = \frac{\pi}{3}$, $d = \frac{\pi}{3}$, so the sum is:
$$S_{13} = \frac{13}{2}\left(\frac{2\pi}{3} + \frac{12\pi}{3}\right) = \frac{14(13)(\pi)}{6} = \frac{91\pi}{3}$$

19. Since $d = 5$ and $S_{38} = 3534$, then:
$$3534 = \frac{38}{2}\left(2a + 37(5)\right)$$
$$3534 = 38a + 3515$$
$$19 = 38a$$
$$a = \frac{1}{2}$$

21. Here $a = 4$, $a_{16} = -100$, therefore:
$$S_{16} = 16\left(\frac{4 - 100}{2}\right)$$
$$S_{16} = -7688$$
So we have:
$$-768 = \frac{16}{2}\left(2(4) + 15d\right)$$
$$-768 = 64 + 120d$$
$$-832 = 120d$$
$$d = \frac{-104}{15}$$

23. Since $a_8 = 5$ and $S_{10} = 20$, then:
$$5 = a + 7d$$
$$20 = 5(2a + 9d)$$
$$4 = 2a + 9d$$

We solve the system:
$$a + 7d = 5$$
$$2a + 9d = 4$$
Multiplying the first equation by -2 and adding to the second equation:
$$-2a - 14d = -10$$
$$\underline{2a + 9d = 4}$$
$$-5d = -6$$
$$d = \frac{6}{5}$$
So:
$$a = 5 - 7\left(\frac{6}{5}\right) = -\frac{17}{5}$$

25. $S = S_{20} = \displaystyle\sum_{k=1}^{20} (4k + 3)$ so $a = 7$ and $a_{20} = 83$, thus:

$$S = 20\left(\frac{7 + 83}{2}\right) = 900$$

27. Let x denote the middle term, so the three terms are x - d, x, x + d, and:
$$(x - d) + x + (x + d) = 30 \text{ while } x(x - d)(x + d) = 360$$
equivalently:
$$3x = 30, \text{ so } x = 10$$
$$x(x^2 - d^2) = 360$$
and:
$$100 - d^2 = 36$$
$$d = \pm 8$$
So the terms are 2, 10, 18 or 18, 10, 2

29. Using equations as in exercise #27:
$$3x = 6, \text{ so } x = 2$$
$$(x - d)^3 + x^3 + (x + d)^3 = 132$$
$$(2 - d)^3 + 8 + (2 + d)^3 = 132$$
$$(2 - d)^3 + (2 + d)^3 = 124$$
$$16 + 12d^2 = 124$$
$$d^2 = 9$$
$$d = \pm 3$$
So the terms are -1, 2, 5 or 5, 2, -1

31. (a) $a_2 - a_1 = -1 - \dfrac{1}{1 + \sqrt{2}}$

$\qquad\qquad = \dfrac{-2 - \sqrt{2}}{1 + \sqrt{2}}$

$\qquad\qquad = \dfrac{(1 - \sqrt{2})(-2 - \sqrt{2})}{-1}$

$\qquad\qquad = -\sqrt{2}$

$\qquad a_3 - a_2 = \dfrac{1}{1 - \sqrt{2}} + 1$

$\qquad\qquad = \dfrac{2 - \sqrt{2}}{1 - \sqrt{2}}$

$\qquad\qquad = \dfrac{(2 - \sqrt{2})(1 + \sqrt{2})}{-1}$

$\qquad\qquad = -\sqrt{2}$

hence $a_2 - a_1 = a_3 - a_2$

(b) $a = \dfrac{1}{1 + \sqrt{2}}$, from (a) $d = -\dfrac{2 + \sqrt{2}}{1 + \sqrt{2}}$

$\qquad$ So $S_6 = 3\left(\dfrac{2}{1 + \sqrt{2}} - \dfrac{10 + 5\sqrt{2}}{1 + \sqrt{2}}\right)$

$\qquad\qquad = 3\left(\dfrac{-8 - 5\sqrt{2}}{1 + \sqrt{2}}\right)$

$\qquad\qquad = -\dfrac{24 + 15\sqrt{2}}{1 + \sqrt{2}}$

$\qquad\qquad = (24 + 15\sqrt{2})(1 - \sqrt{2})$

$\qquad\qquad = 24 - 30 - 9\sqrt{2}$

$\qquad\qquad = -6 - 9\sqrt{2}$

33. $a = \dfrac{1}{1 + \sqrt{b}}$ while $d = \dfrac{1}{2}\left(\dfrac{1}{1 - \sqrt{b}} - \dfrac{1}{1 + \sqrt{b}}\right)$

$\qquad\qquad\qquad\qquad = \dfrac{1}{2}\left(\dfrac{2\sqrt{b}}{1 - b}\right)$

$\qquad\qquad\qquad\qquad = \dfrac{\sqrt{b}}{1 - b}$

Therefore:

$\qquad S_n = \dfrac{n}{2}\left(\dfrac{2}{1 + \sqrt{b}} + (n - 1)\dfrac{\sqrt{b}}{1 - b}\right)$

$\qquad\qquad = \dfrac{n}{2}\left(\dfrac{(2 - 2\sqrt{b}) + (n - 1)\sqrt{b}}{1 - b}\right)$

$$= \frac{n}{2(1-b)}\left(2 + (n-3)\sqrt{b}\right)$$

35.

$$\frac{n^2}{m^2} = \frac{S_n}{S_m} = \frac{\frac{n}{2}\left(2a + (n-1)d\right)}{\frac{m}{2}\left(2a + (m-1)d\right)}$$

$$\frac{2a + (n-1)d}{2a + (m-1)d} = \frac{n}{m}$$

$$m\left(2a + (n-1)d\right) = n\left(2a + (m-1)d\right)$$

$$2am + m(n-1)d = 2an + n(m-1)d$$

$$2a(m-n) = \left(n(m-1) - m(n-1)\right)d$$

$$d = \frac{2a(m-n)}{m-n}$$

$$d = 2a \text{ (assuming } m \neq n)$$

Consequently:

$$\frac{a_n}{a_m} = \frac{a + (n-1)(2a)}{a + (m-1)(2a)} = \frac{1 + 2n - 2}{1 + 2m - 2} = \frac{2n-1}{2m-1}$$

37. Let the three consecutive terms be: $x - d$, x, $x + d$, then because of the Pythagorean Theorem:

$$(x-d)^2 + x^2 = (x+d)^2$$

$$x^2 - 2xd + d^2 + x^2 = x^2 + 2xd + d^2$$

$$x^2 - 4xd = 0$$

$$x = 0 \text{ or } x = 4d$$

Since the side of a triangle cannot have zero length, then $x = 4d$ and the three terms are: $3d$, $4d$, $5d$, which is clearly similar to a 3 - 4 - 5 right triangle.

39. We have $\frac{1}{b} - \frac{1}{a} = \frac{1}{c} - \frac{1}{b}$, from which it follows that $b = \frac{2ac}{a+c}$. Therefore:

$$\ln(a+c) + \ln(a-2b+c) = \ln(a+c) + \ln\left(a - \frac{4ac}{a+c} + c\right)$$

$$= \ln(a+c) + \ln\left(\frac{a^2 + ac - 4ac + ac + c^2}{a+c}\right)$$

$$= \ln(a+c) + \ln\frac{(a-c)^2}{a+c}$$

$$= \ln(a-c)^2$$

$$= 2\ln(a-c), \text{ as required.}$$

13.5   Geometric Sequences and Series

1.   The first three terms have a common ratio, hence:
$\frac{x}{9} = \frac{4}{x}$, therefore $x^2 = 36$ and $x = \pm 6$
Since the ratio is positive, then the second term is 6.

3.   Letting the common ration be r, we have:
4, 4r, and $4r^2$ so $64r^3 = 8000$
Therefore, $r^3 = 125$, so $r = 5$, and the second and third terms are 20 and 100, respectively.

5. $a_1 = -1$, $r = -1$, so $a_{100} = -1(-1)^{99} = 1$

7. $a_1 = \frac{2}{3}$, $r = \frac{2}{3}$, so $a_8 = \frac{2}{3}\left(\frac{2}{3}\right)^7 = \frac{256}{6561}$

9. $4096 = a_7 = r^6$, so $r = \pm\sqrt[6]{4096} = \pm 4$

11. $S_{10} = \frac{7(1 - 2^{10})}{1 - 2} = -7(1 - 1024) = 7161$

13. $1 + \sqrt{2} + 2 + \ldots + 32 = S_{11}$
$$= \frac{1(1 - (\sqrt{2})^{11})}{1 - \sqrt{2}}$$
$$= \frac{1 - 32\sqrt{2}}{1 - \sqrt{2}}$$
$$= 63 + 31\sqrt{2}$$

15. $\displaystyle\sum_{k=1}^{6} \left(\frac{3}{2}\right)^k = S_6$
$$= \frac{\frac{3}{2}\left(1 - \left(\frac{3}{2}\right)^6\right)}{1 - \frac{3}{2}}$$
$$= -3\left(1 - \frac{729}{64}\right)$$
$$= \frac{1995}{64}$$

17. $\displaystyle\sum_{k=2}^{6} \left(\frac{1}{10}\right)^k = S_6 - a_1$

$$= \frac{\frac{1}{10}\left(1 - \left(\frac{1}{10}\right)^6\right)}{1 - \frac{1}{10}} - \frac{1}{10}$$

$$= \frac{1}{9}\left(1 - \frac{1}{1000000}\right) - \frac{1}{10}$$

$$= \frac{1}{9}\left(\frac{999999}{1000000}\right) - \frac{1}{10}$$

$$= \frac{111111}{1000000} - \frac{1}{10}$$

$$= \frac{11111}{1000000}$$

which is equivalent to 0.011111

19. $\displaystyle\frac{2}{3} - \frac{4}{9} + \frac{8}{27} - \cdots = \frac{\frac{2}{3}}{1 + \frac{2}{3}} = \frac{2}{5}$

21. $\displaystyle 1 + \frac{1}{1.01} + \frac{1}{(1.01)^2} + \cdots = \frac{1}{1 - \frac{1}{1.01}} = 101$

23. $\displaystyle .555\ldots = \frac{5}{10} + \frac{5}{100} + \cdots = \frac{\frac{5}{10}}{1 - \frac{1}{10}} = \frac{5}{9}$

25. $\displaystyle .12323\ldots = \frac{1}{10} + \frac{23}{1000} + \frac{23}{100000} + \cdots$

$$= \frac{1}{10} + \frac{\frac{23}{1000}}{1 - \frac{1}{100}}$$

$$= \frac{1}{10} + \frac{23}{990}$$

$$= \frac{122}{990}$$

$$= \frac{61}{495}$$

27. $.432\ldots = \frac{432}{1000} + \frac{432}{1000000} + \cdots$

$$= \frac{\dfrac{432}{1000}}{1 - \dfrac{1}{1000}}$$

$$= \frac{432}{999}$$

$$= \frac{16}{37}$$

29.   For $\dfrac{a}{r}$, a, ar we have:

$$\frac{a}{r}(a)(ar) = -1000$$

$$a^3 = -1000$$
$$a = -10$$

So we have:

$$\frac{a}{r} + a + ar = 15$$

$$\frac{-10}{r} - 10 - 10r = 15$$

$$2r^2 + 5r + 2 = 0$$
$$(2r + 1)(r + 2) = 0$$
$$r = -\frac{1}{2},\ -2$$

31. $\dfrac{\sqrt{3}}{\sqrt{3} + 1} + \dfrac{\sqrt{3}}{\sqrt{3} + 3} + \cdots = \dfrac{\dfrac{\sqrt{3}}{\sqrt{3} + 1}}{1 - \dfrac{\sqrt{3} + 1}{\sqrt{3} + 3}}$

$$= \frac{\dfrac{\sqrt{3}}{\sqrt{3} + 1}}{\dfrac{2}{\sqrt{3} + 3}}$$

$$= \frac{\sqrt{3}(\sqrt{3} + 3)}{(\sqrt{3} + 1)2}$$

$$= \frac{3 + 3\sqrt{3}}{2(1 + \sqrt{3})}$$

$$= \frac{3}{2}$$

33. For $a_1, a_2, \ldots$ a geometric sequence,

$$S = a_1 + a_2 + \ldots + a_n = \frac{a_1(1 - r^n)}{1 - r} \text{ where } r \text{ is the common ratio.}$$

Also, $T = \dfrac{1}{a_1} + \dfrac{1}{a_2} + \ldots + \dfrac{1}{a_n} = \dfrac{\dfrac{1}{a_1}\left(1 - \dfrac{1}{r^n}\right)}{1 - \dfrac{1}{r}}$

Therefore:

$$\frac{S}{T} = \frac{\dfrac{a_1(1 - r^n)}{1 - r}}{\dfrac{\dfrac{1}{a_1}\left(1 - \dfrac{1}{r^n}\right)}{\dfrac{r - 1}{r}}}$$

$$= \frac{a_1(1 - r^n)a_1(r - 1)r^n}{(1 - r)r(r^n - 1)}$$

$$= a_1{}^2 r^{n-1}$$

$$= a_1(a_1 r^{n-1})$$

$$= a_1 a_n$$

13.6   Permutations and Combinations

1.   There are 6 routes, 3(2) = 6

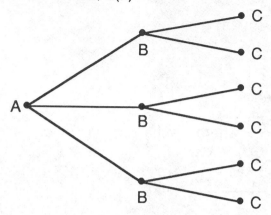

3.   There are 12 routes, 3(2)(2) = 12

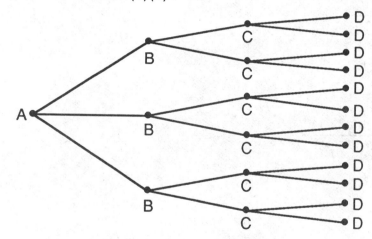

5.   P(4,2) = 4(3) = 12

7.   P(5,3) = 5(4)(3) = 60

9.   Using the multiplication rule:
         3(6)(6) = 108

11.   10(9)(8)(26)(25)(24) = 11,232,000 plates

13.   P(10,10) = 10! = 3,628,800 ways

15.   P(n,n) = 24, therefore n! = 24, so n = 4 letters

17. $P(8,1) = 8$

19. $P(6,3) = 6(5)(4) = 120$

21. $P(n,n-1) = n(n-1)(n-2) \ldots (n-(n-1)+1)$
$$= n(n-1)(n-2) \ldots (2)$$
$$= n!$$

23. $P(100,50) = 100(99)(98) \ldots (51)$
$P(101,51) = 101(100)(99) \ldots (51)$
$P(101,51) = 101(P(100,50))$
$P(101,51) > P(100,50)$

25. Following the solution of example 9:
$$2P(5,5) = 2(5!) = 240$$

27. As is example 9:
$$2P(3,3) = 2(3!) = 12$$

29. (a) $9(10)(10) = 900$
(b) $9(9)(8) = 648$

31. (a) $9(9)(9) = 729$
(b) $9(8)(7) = 504$
(c) $1(8)(7) = 56$
(d) $5(7)(4) = 140$

33. (a) $C(12,11) = \dfrac{12!}{11!1!} = 12$

(b) $C(12,1) = \dfrac{12!}{1!11!} = 12$

35. (a) $C(8,3) = \dfrac{8!}{3!5!} = \dfrac{8(7)(6)}{6} = 56$

(b) $C(8,5) = \dfrac{8!}{3!5!} = 56$

37. (a) $C(12,5) = \dfrac{12!}{5!7!} = \dfrac{12(11)(10)(9)(8)}{5(4)(3)(2)} = 792$

(b) $C(12,7) = 792$

39. $C(n, n-2) = \dfrac{n!}{(n-2)!(2!)} = \dfrac{n(n-1)}{2}$

41. $C(8,3) = \dfrac{8!}{3!5!} = \dfrac{8(7)(6)}{3(2)} = 56$

43. (a) $C(10,6) = \dfrac{10!}{4!6!} = \dfrac{10(9)(8)(7)}{4(3)(2)} = 210$

 (b) $[\,C(4,3)\,][\,C(6,3)\,] = \dfrac{4!}{3!1!} \cdot \dfrac{6!}{3!3!} = \dfrac{4(6)(5)(4)}{6} = 80$

45. Using the method of example 13;
$$C(6,2) - 6 = \dfrac{6!}{4!2!} - 6 = 15 - 6 = 9$$

47. $C(8,3) = \dfrac{8!}{5!3!} = \dfrac{8(7)(6)}{3(2)} = 56$

49. First, notice that no two different combinations of these coins can add up to the same sum. Then we simply add the number of ways of combining the four coins, one at a time, two at a time, three and four at a time, thus:
$$C(4,1) + C(4,2) + C(4,3) + C(4,4) = 4 + 6 + 4 + 1 = 15 \text{ sums}$$

51. (a) $[\,C(9,6)\,][\,C(8,2)\,] = \dfrac{9!}{3!6!} \cdot \dfrac{8!}{6!2!} = \dfrac{9(8)(7)(8)(7)}{3(2)(2)} = 2352 \text{ committees}$

 (b) $C(9,6)\,C(8,2) + C(9,7)\,C(8,1) + C(9,8)\,C(8,0)$
$$= \left(\dfrac{9(8)(7)}{3(2)} \cdot \dfrac{8(7)}{2} \right) + \left(\dfrac{9(8)}{2} \cdot \dfrac{8}{1} \right) + \dfrac{9}{1}$$
$$= 2352 + 288 + 9$$
$$= 2649 \text{ committees}$$

53. In a polygon with 10 vertices, first choose a particular vertex (there are 9 other vertices to which a line could be drawn.) If lines are drawn to the two adjacent vertices, the lines would become sides, not diagonals; thus, there are 7 diagonals from each vertex. Not wanting to count a diagonal from one vertex to another twice, we must divide by 2. Thus, there are $\dfrac{7 \times 10}{2} = 35$ diagonals.

13.7   Introduction to Probability

1. (a) {2,4,6}
    (b) {4,5,6}
    (c) {2,4,5,6}
    (d) {4,6}

3. (a) {1,3,5}
    (b) {1,2,3,4,5,6}
    (c) {1,2,3,4,5,6}
    (d) Ø

5. No, $A \cap B = \{4,6\}$

7. Yes, $C \cap D = \emptyset$

9. (a) 3
    (b) 3
    (c) 4

11. (a) 3
    (b) 6
    (c) 0

13. (a) $\dfrac{3}{6} = \dfrac{1}{2}$

    (b) $\dfrac{3}{6} = \dfrac{1}{2}$

15. (a) $\dfrac{3}{6} = \dfrac{1}{2}$

    (b) $\dfrac{6}{6} = 1$

17. (a) $\dfrac{4}{6} = \dfrac{2}{3}$

    (b) $\dfrac{3}{6} + \dfrac{3}{6} = 1$

19. (a) $\dfrac{5}{6}$

    (b) $\dfrac{3}{6} + \dfrac{3}{6} = 1$

21. $\dfrac{3}{8}$

23. $\dfrac{4}{8} = \dfrac{1}{2}$

25. $\dfrac{2}{8} = \dfrac{1}{4}$

27. $P(A \cup B)$ $= P(A) + P(B) - P(A \cap B)$
$= \dfrac{3}{8} + \dfrac{1}{4} - 0$
$= \dfrac{5}{8}$

29. $P(A \cup C)$ $= P(A) + P(C) - P(A \cap C)$
$= \dfrac{3}{8} + \dfrac{1}{2} - \dfrac{1}{8}$
$= \dfrac{6}{8}$
$= \dfrac{3}{4}$

31. $P(C \cup F)$ $= P(C) + P(F) - P(C \cap F)$
$= \dfrac{1}{2} + \dfrac{1}{2} - 0$
$= 1$

33. $P(E \cup F)$ $= P(E) + P(F) - P(E \cap F)$
$= \dfrac{1}{4} + \dfrac{1}{2} - \dfrac{1}{8}$
$= \dfrac{5}{8}$

35. $P(B \cup C)$ $= P(B) + P(C) - P(B \cap C)$
$= \dfrac{1}{4} + \dfrac{1}{2} - \dfrac{1}{4}$
$= \dfrac{1}{2}$

37. 0

39. $P(D \cup E) = P(D) + P(E) - P(D \cap E)$

$$= \frac{1}{8} + \frac{1}{4} - \frac{1}{8}$$

$$= \frac{1}{4}$$

41. $\dfrac{5}{C(6,2)} = \dfrac{5(4!)(2)}{6!} = \dfrac{5}{15} = \dfrac{1}{3}$

43. (a) $\dfrac{12}{14} = \dfrac{6}{7}$

(b) $\dfrac{12}{14} \cdot \dfrac{11}{13} \cdot \dfrac{10}{12} \cdot \dfrac{9}{11} \cdot \dfrac{8}{10} = \dfrac{72}{182} = \dfrac{36}{91}$

45. $\dfrac{1}{3} + \dfrac{1}{4} - 0 = \dfrac{7}{12}$

47. $\dfrac{7}{9} = \dfrac{5}{9} + \dfrac{4}{9} - P(A \cap B)$, so $P(A \cap B) = \dfrac{2}{9}$

49. (a) $\dfrac{6}{15} \cdot \dfrac{5}{15} = \dfrac{1}{8}$

(b) $\dfrac{10}{16} \cdot \dfrac{9}{15} = \dfrac{3}{8}$

(c) $\dfrac{1}{8} + \dfrac{3}{8} = \dfrac{1}{2}$

51. $P(A\ 1st\ or\ A\ 2nd) = P(A\ 1st) + P(A\ 2nd) - P(A\ both)$

$$= \frac{1}{2} + \frac{3}{10} - \frac{1}{10}$$

$$= \frac{7}{10}$$

53. $\dfrac{13}{52} \cdot \dfrac{12}{51} \cdot \dfrac{11}{50} \cdot \dfrac{10}{49} \cdot \dfrac{9}{48} = \dfrac{33}{66640}$

Chapter 13 Review Exercises

1.   When n = 1: $5 = \frac{5}{2}(1)(1 + 1) = 5$

    Assuming: $5 + 10 + \ldots + 5k = \frac{5}{2}k(k + 1)$

    Then: $5 + 10 + \ldots + 5k + 5(k + 1) = \frac{5}{2}k(k + 1) + 5(k + 1)$

$$= (k + 1)\left(\frac{5}{2}k + 5\right)$$

$$= \frac{5}{2}(k + 1)(k + 2)$$

which completes the induction.

3.   When n = 1: $1 \bullet 2 = 2 = \frac{1}{3}(1)(1 + 1)(1 + 2) = 2$

    Assuming: $1 \bullet 2 + 2 \bullet 3 + \ldots + k(k + 1) = \frac{1}{3}k(k + 1)(k + 2)$

    Then: $1 \bullet 2 + 2 \bullet 3 + \ldots + k(k + 1) + (k + 1)(k + 2)$

$$= \frac{1}{3}k(k + 1)(k + 2) + (k + 1)(k + 2)$$

$$= \left(\frac{1}{3}k + 1\right)(k + 1)(k + 2)$$

$$= \frac{1}{3}(k + 1)(k + 2)(k + 3)$$

which completes the induction.

5.   For n = 1: $1 = 3 + (2 - 3)2 = 3 - 2 = 1$
    Assuming: $1 + 3 \bullet 2 + 5 \bullet 2^2 + \ldots + (2k - 1) \bullet 2^{k-1} = 3 + (2k - 3) \bullet 2^k$
    Then: $1 + 3 \bullet 2 + \ldots + (2k - 1)2^{k-1} + (2k + 1)2^k$
$$= 3 + (2k - 3)2^k + (2k + 1)2^k$$
$$= 3 + (4k - 2)2^k$$
$$= 3 + (2k - 1)2^{k+1}$$
$$= 3 + (2(k + 1) - 3) \bullet 2^{k+1}$$
and the induction is complete.

7.   For n = 1: $1 = (1^2 - 2 + 3)2 - 3 = 1$
    Assuming:
$$1 + 2^2 \bullet 2 + 3^2 \bullet 2^2 + 4^2 \bullet 2^3 + \ldots + k^2 \bullet 2^{k-1} = (k^2 - 2k + 3)2^k - 3$$

Then:
$$1 + 2^2 \bullet 2 + \ldots + (k+1)^2 2^k = (k^2 - 2k + 3)2^k - 3 + (k+1)^2 2^k$$
$$= 2^k\left(k^2 - 2k + 3 + (k+1)^2\right) - 3$$
$$= 2^k(2k^2 + 4) - 3$$
$$= 2^{k+1}(k^2 + 2) - 3$$
$$= 2^{k+1}\left((k+1)^2 - 2k + 1\right) - 3$$
$$= 2^{k+1}\left((k+1)^2 - 2(k+1) + 3\right) - 3$$

and the induction is complete.

9.   For $n = 1$: $7^1 - 1 = 6 = 3(2)$
Assuming: $7^k - 1 = 3L$
Then: $7^{k+1} - 1 = 3L + 7^{k+1} - 7^k$
$$= 3L + 7^k(7 - 1)$$
$$= 3L + 6(7^k)$$
$$= 3(L + 2 \bullet 7^k)$$
and the induction is complete.

11. $(3a + b^2)^4$

$$= \binom{4}{0}(3a)^4 + \binom{4}{1}(3a)^3(b^2) + \binom{4}{2}(3a)^2(b^2)^2 + \binom{4}{3}(3a)(b^2)^3 + \binom{4}{4}(b^2)^4$$
$$= 81a^4 + 108a^3b^2 + 54a^2b^4 + 12ab^6 + b^8$$

13. $(x + \sqrt{x})^4 = \binom{4}{0}x^4 + \binom{4}{1}x^3(\sqrt{x}) + \binom{4}{2}x^2(\sqrt{x})^2 + \binom{4}{3}x(\sqrt{x})^3 + \binom{4}{4}(\sqrt{x})^4$

$$= x^4 + 4x^3\sqrt{x} + 6x^3 + 4x^2\sqrt{x} + x^2$$

15. $(x^2 - 2y^2)^5 = \binom{5}{0}(x^2)^5 - \binom{5}{1}(x^2)^4(2y^2) + \binom{5}{2}(x^2)^3(2y^2)^2 - \binom{5}{3}(x^2)^2(2y^2)^3$

$$+ \binom{5}{4}(x^2)(2y^2)^4 - \binom{5}{5}(2y^2)^5$$
$$= x^{10} - 10x^8y^2 + 40x^6y^4 - 80x^4y^6 + 80x^2y^8 - 32y^{10}$$

17. $\left(1 + \frac{1}{x}\right)^5 = \binom{5}{0} + \binom{5}{1}\frac{1}{x} + \binom{5}{2}\left(\frac{1}{x}\right)^2 + \binom{5}{3}\left(\frac{1}{x}\right)^3 + \binom{5}{4}\left(\frac{1}{x}\right)^4 + \binom{5}{5}\left(\frac{1}{x}\right)^5$

$$= 1 + \frac{5}{x} + \frac{10}{x^2} + \frac{10}{x^3} + \frac{5}{x^4} + \frac{1}{x^5}$$

19. $(a\sqrt{b} - b\sqrt{a})^4 = a^2b^2(\sqrt{a} - \sqrt{b})^4$

   $= a^2b^2\left((\sqrt{a})^4 - 4(\sqrt{a})^3\sqrt{b} + 6(\sqrt{a})^2(\sqrt{b})^2 - 4(\sqrt{a})(\sqrt{b})^3 + (\sqrt{b})^4\right)$

   $= a^2b^2(a^2 - 4a\sqrt{ab} + 6ab - 4b\sqrt{ab} + b^2)$

   $= a^4b^2 - 4a^3b^2\sqrt{ab} + 6a^3b^3 - 4a^2b^3\sqrt{ab} + a^2b^4$

21. $\binom{5}{5-1}(3x)(y^2)^4 = 5(3x)y^8 = 15xy^8$

23. Here $7 - r + 1 = 5$, so $r = 3$, and the coefficient of the third term is:

   $$\binom{7}{2}(2)^2 = (4)\frac{7!}{5!2!} = 84$$

25. $r - 1 = 6$, so $r = 7$, and the coefficient of the seventh term is:

   $$\binom{8}{6} = \frac{8(7)}{2} = 28$$

27. $\binom{2}{0}^2 + \binom{2}{1}^2 + \binom{2}{2}^2 = (1)^2 + (2)^2 + (1)^2 = 6$

   $\binom{4}{2} = \frac{4(3)}{2} = 6$

29. $\binom{4}{0}^2 + \binom{4}{1}^2 + \binom{4}{2}^2 + \binom{4}{3}^2 + \binom{4}{4}^2 = 1^2 + 4^2 + 6^2 + 4^2 + 1^2 = 70$

   $\binom{8}{4} = \frac{8(7)(6)(5)}{4(3)(2)} = 70$

31. $\binom{3}{0} + \binom{3}{1} + \binom{3}{2} + \binom{3}{3} = 1 + 3 + 3 + 1 = 8 = 2^3$

33. $a_1 = \dfrac{2}{1+1} = 1$

   $a_2 = \dfrac{4}{2+1} = \dfrac{4}{3}$

   $a_3 = \dfrac{6}{3+1} = \dfrac{3}{2}$

   $a_4 = \dfrac{8}{4+1} = \dfrac{8}{5}$

We graph these points:

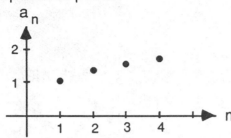

35. $a_1 = (-1)\left(1 - \frac{1}{2}\right) = -\frac{1}{2}$

   $a_2 = (1)\left(1 - \frac{1}{3}\right) = \frac{2}{3}$

   $a_3 = (-1)\left(1 - \frac{1}{4}\right) = -\frac{3}{4}$

   $a_4 = (1)\left(1 - \frac{1}{5}\right) = \frac{4}{5}$

We graph the points:

37. $a_0 = -3$
   $a_1 = -12$
   $a_2 = -48$
   $a_3 = -192,$
   The first four terms are -3, -12, -48, -192

39. (a) $\displaystyle\sum_{k=1}^{3} (-1)^k(2k + 1) = -3 + 5 - 7 = -5$

(b) $\displaystyle\sum_{k=0}^{8}\left(\frac{1}{k+1}-\frac{1}{k+2}\right)$

$$= \left(1-\frac{1}{2}\right)+\left(\frac{1}{2}-\frac{1}{3}\right)+\left(\frac{1}{3}-\frac{1}{4}\right)+\left(\frac{1}{4}-\frac{1}{5}\right)+\left(\frac{1}{5}-\frac{1}{6}\right)+\left(\frac{1}{6}-\frac{1}{7}\right)$$
$$+\left(\frac{1}{7}-\frac{1}{8}\right)+\left(\frac{1}{8}-\frac{1}{9}\right)+\left(\frac{1}{9}-\frac{1}{10}\right)$$
$$= 1-\frac{1}{10}$$
$$= \frac{9}{10}$$

41. $\displaystyle\sum_{k=1}^{5}\frac{5}{3^k}$

43. Here $a_n = 1 + 4n$, so $a_{18} = 1 + 4(18) = 73$

45. Here $a_n = \dfrac{10}{2^{n-1}}$, so $a_{12} = \dfrac{10}{2^{11}} = \dfrac{5}{1024}$

47. $S_{12} = (12)\left(\dfrac{8+\frac{43}{2}}{2}\right) = (6)\dfrac{59}{2} = 177$

49. By inspection:
$S_1 = 7$; $S_2 = 77$; ... ; so $S_{10} = 7{,}777{,}777{,}777$

51. $a_3 = 4$
$a_5 = 10$
$\dfrac{a_5}{a_3} = \dfrac{10}{4} = \dfrac{5}{2} = r^2$ and $r = \pm\sqrt{\dfrac{5}{2}}$

Since r is known to be negative, $r = -\sqrt{\dfrac{5}{2}}$ and $a_6 = -\sqrt{\dfrac{5}{2}}(10) = -5\sqrt{10}$

53. $S = \dfrac{\frac{3}{5}}{1-\frac{1}{5}} = \dfrac{3}{4}$

55. $S = \dfrac{\dfrac{1}{9}}{1 + \dfrac{1}{9}} = \dfrac{1}{10}$

57. $.45\ldots = .45 + .0045 + .000045 + \ldots$

This is a geometric sequence with $a = .45$, $r = \dfrac{1}{100}$, so:

$$.45\ldots = \dfrac{.45}{1 - \dfrac{1}{100}} = \dfrac{45}{99} = \dfrac{15}{33} = \dfrac{5}{11}$$

59. $\begin{aligned}
S_n &= \dfrac{n}{2}\big(2(1) + (n-1)1\big) \\[4pt]
&= \dfrac{n}{2}(2 + n - 1) \\[4pt]
&= \dfrac{n}{2}(1 + n) \\[4pt]
&= \dfrac{n^2}{2} + \dfrac{n}{2} \\[4pt]
&= n + \dfrac{n^2}{2} - \dfrac{n}{2} \\[4pt]
&= n + \dfrac{n(n-1)}{2}
\end{aligned}$

61. $\begin{aligned}
S_n &= \dfrac{n}{2}\big(2(1) + (n-1)3\big) \\[4pt]
&= \dfrac{n}{2}(2 + 3n - 3) \\[4pt]
&= \dfrac{n}{2}(3n - 1) \\[4pt]
&= \dfrac{3n^2}{2} - \dfrac{n}{2} \\[4pt]
&= n + \dfrac{3n^2}{2} - \dfrac{3n}{2} \\[4pt]
&= n + \dfrac{3n(n-1)}{2}
\end{aligned}$

63. (a) $1^2 + 2^2 + \ldots + 50^2 \approx \dfrac{\left(50 + \frac{1}{2}\right)^{2+1}}{2+1}$

$$= \dfrac{\left(\frac{101}{2}\right)^3}{3}$$

$$= \dfrac{1030301}{24}$$

$$\approx 42929$$

(b) $\dfrac{50(51)(101)}{6} = 42925$, exactly

Percent error $= 100 \bullet \dfrac{4}{42925} \approx 0.00932\ \%$

(c) $1^4 + 2^4 + \ldots + 200^4 \approx \dfrac{(200.5)^5}{5} \approx 6.48040 \times 10^{10}$

(d) $1^4 + 2^4 + \ldots + 200^4 = \dfrac{200(201)(401)(120599)}{30}$

$$\approx 6.48027 \times 10^{10}$$

Percent error $= 100 \bullet \dfrac{0.00013 \times 10^{10}}{6.48027 \times 10^{10}} = 2 \times 10^{-3}\ \%$

65. $4 \times 4 = 16$ different numbers (assumes repetition)

67. {abc, acb, bac, bca, cab, cba, abd, adb, bad, bda, dab, dba, acd, adc, cad, cda, dac, dca, bcd, bdc, cbd, cdb, dbc, dcb}
     $P(4,3) = 4(3)(2) = 24$

69. $P(12,8) = 12(11)(10)(9)(8)(7)(6)(5) = 19{,}958{,}400$

71. There are a total of 6! different arrangements, while 2(5!) have e, f next to one another, hence:
     $$6! - 2(5!) = 4(5!) = 4(120) = 480$$

73. $C(9,2) \bullet C(10,2) = \dfrac{9!}{7!2!} \bullet \dfrac{10!}{8!2!} = (36)(45) = 1620$ subcommittees

75. $\dfrac{9}{12} \bullet \dfrac{8}{11} = \dfrac{72}{132} = \dfrac{6}{11}$

77. (a) $\dfrac{5}{12} \cdot \dfrac{4}{11} = \dfrac{5}{33}$

(b) $\dfrac{7}{12} \cdot \dfrac{6}{11} = \dfrac{7}{22}$

(c) $\dfrac{5}{33} + \dfrac{7}{22} = \dfrac{31}{66}$

79. (1,2) or (2,1); hence $\dfrac{2}{36} = \dfrac{1}{18}$

81. (1,6), (6,1), (2,5), (5,2), (3,4), (4,3); hence $\dfrac{6}{36} = \dfrac{1}{6}$

83. (5,6), (6,5); and the 6 from exercise #81; so $\dfrac{8}{36} = \dfrac{2}{9}$

85. (4,6), (6,4), (5,5), (5,6), (6,5), (6,6); so $\dfrac{6}{36} = \dfrac{1}{6}$

87. There are six ways to get 7, and five ways to get 8; since there are 36 possible tosses, then there are:

$$36 - (6 + 5) = 36 - 11 = 25$$

ways to get a different sum than 7 or 8. The probability is $\dfrac{25}{36}$.

89. (a) $\dfrac{7}{15}$

(b) $\dfrac{8}{15}$

(c) $\dfrac{10}{15} = \dfrac{2}{3}$

(d) $\dfrac{10}{15} = \dfrac{2}{3}$

91. (a) Since there are 900 three-digit numbers and 648 with no repetition, then there are 900 - 648 = 252 with repetition.

(b) $\dfrac{252}{900} = \dfrac{7}{25}$

93. Call $b = ra$ and $c = r^2a$, so $a + ar + ar^2 = 70$. Since $4a$, $5b$, $4c$ are consecutive terms in an arithmetic sequence, then their common difference is the same. So:

$$
\begin{aligned}
5b - 4a &= 4c - 5b \\
10b &= 4a + 4c \\
5b &= 2a + 2c \\
5(ra) &= 2a + 2(r^2a) \\
5ra &= 2a + 2r^2a
\end{aligned}
$$

Since a is nonzero, we divide by a:

$$
\begin{aligned}
5r &= 2 + 2r^2 \\
2r^2 - 5r + 2 &= 0 \\
(2r - 1)(r - 2) &= 0 \\
r &= \frac{1}{2}, 2
\end{aligned}
$$

If $r = \frac{1}{2}$, we find a:

$$
\begin{aligned}
a + a \bullet \frac{1}{2} + a \bullet \frac{1}{4} &= 70 \\
7a &= 280 \\
a &= 40
\end{aligned}
$$

So the terms are 40, 20, 10
If $r = 2$, we find a:

$$
\begin{aligned}
a + 2a + 4a &= 70 \\
7a &= 70 \\
a &= 10
\end{aligned}
$$

So the terms are 10, 20, 40

95. We assume:

$$
\frac{1}{c + a} - \frac{1}{b + c} = \frac{1}{a + b} - \frac{1}{c + a}
$$

Our goal is to prove that:

$$
b^2 - a^2 = c^2 - b^2
$$

Multiply the first equation by $(c + a)(b + c)(a + b)$:

$$
\begin{aligned}
(b + c)(a + b) - (c + a)(a + b) &= (c + a)(b + c) - (b + c)(a + b) \\
(ab+ac+bc+b^2) - (ac+bc+ab+a^2) &= (bc+ab+ac+c^2) - (ab+ac+bc+b^2) \\
b^2 - a^2 &= c^2 - b^2
\end{aligned}
$$

This proves the desired result.

97. (a)   We must have $4 + x = r(3 + x)$ and $5 + x = r^2(3 + x)$,

so $r = \dfrac{4 + x}{3 + x}$. Substituting into the second equality:

$$5 + x = \left(\frac{4 + x}{3 + x}\right)^2 (3 + x)$$

$$5 + x = \frac{(4 + x)^2}{3 + x}$$

Multiplying each side by $3 + x$:

$$15 + 8x + x^2 = 16 + 8x + x^2$$

$$15 = 16$$

So no such value for x exists.

(b)   Here $b + x = r(a + x)$ and $c + x = r^2(a + x)$, so $r = \dfrac{b + x}{a + x}$.

Substituting:

$$c + x = \left(\frac{b + x}{a + x}\right)^2 (a + x)$$

$$(c + x)(a + x) = (b + x)^2$$

$$ac + (a + c)x + x^2 = b^2 + 2bx + x^2$$

$$(a + c - 2b)x = b^2 - ac$$

$$x = \frac{b^2 - ac}{a + c - 2b}$$

(Note that $a + c - 2b = 0$ for (a), explaining why no x could be found).

THE END